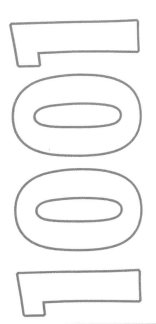

1001

GRE

FAMILY PUBS

GW00319541

Editorial: lifestyleguides@theAA.com

Directory generated by the AA Establishment Database, Information Research, AA Hotel Services

The contents of this publication are believed correct at the time of printing. Nevertheless, the Publisher cannot be held responsible for any errors or omissions or for changes in the details given in this guide or for the consequences of any reliance on the information provided by the same.

Assessments of AA inspected establishments are based on the experience of the Hotel and Restaurant Inspectors on the occasion(s) of their visit(s) and therefore descriptions given in this guide necessarily dictate an element of subjective opinion which may not reflect or dictate a reader's own opinion on another occasion. See **www.theAA.com** for a clear explanation of how, based on our Inspector's inspection experiences, establishments are graded. If the meal or meals experienced during an inspection fall between award levels the restaurant concerned may be awarded the lower of any award levels applicable.

Web Site addresses are included where they have been supplied and specified by the respective establishment. Such Web Sites are not under the control of The Automobile Association Developments Limited and as such The Automobile Association Developments Limited has no control over them and will not accept any responsibility or liability in respect of any and all matters whatsoever relating to such Web Sites including access, content, material and functionality. By including the addresses of third party Web Sites the AA does not intend to solicit business or offer any security to any person in any country, directly or indirectly.

Typeset by Jamie Wiltshire
Printed in Italy by G. Canale & C. S.p.A. - Borgaro T.se (Turin)

Front cover - all images are from AA World Travel Library, except for bc Photodisc: cl AA/T Locke; c AA/R Ireland; cr AA/C Jones; bl AA/W Voysey; br J Sparkes

p1 cl AA/T Locke; c AA/R Ireland; cr AA/C Jones; b J A Tims; p4-5 AA/T Mackie; p55 AA/A Tryner; p56-7 AA/P Sharpe; p110-11 AA/C Sawyer; p218-9 AA/J Wood; p309 AA/J Wood; p310-11 AA/A Hopkins; p332-3 AA/I Burgum

Every effort has been made to trace the copyright holders, and we apologise in advance for any accidental errors. We would be happy to apply the corrections in the following edition of this publication. Pub descriptions have been contibuted to by the following team of writers: Phil Bryant, Michael Buttler, Nick Channer, David Foster, David Halford, Julia Hynard, Denise Laing, Jenny White

A CIP catalogue record for this book is available from the British Library

ISBN-10: 0-7495-5308-1
ISBN-13: 978-0-7495-5308-1

Published by AA Publishing, which is a trading name of Automobile Association Developments Limited, whose registered office is: Fanum House, Basing View, Basingstoke, Hampshire RG21 4EA

www.theAA.com

Registered number 1878835

A03199

How to use the guide

① BURWARDSLEY

② **The Pheasant Inn** ★★ HL ◉ ♀ **③**

Nr Tattenhall CH3 9PF

④ ☎ 01829 770434 📠 01829 771097

Email: info@thepheasantinn.co.uk

Web: www.thepheasantinn.co.uk

⑤ **Dir:** *From Chester A41 to Whitchurch, after 4m left to Burwardsley. Follow signs 'Cheshire Workshops'*

⑥ This 300-year-old, sandstone, half-timbered, former farmhouse is set in beautiful surroundings, attracting walkers, golfers, anglers and visitors to the nearby Chester racecourse and Oulton Park racing circuit.

⑦ **Open:** 11-11 **Bar Meals:** L served all week 12-10 D

⑧ served all week 12-10 (Sun 12-8.30) Av main course £8.95 **Restaurant Meals:** L served all week D served

⑨ all week Av 3 course alc £20 **Brewery/Company:** Free

House 🍺: Weetwood Old Dog, Eastgate, Best, Hoegarden and guest Bitter ♀: 8 **Children's Facilities:** Licence Play area (Swings) Cutlery Highchair Food warming Baby

⑩ changing **Nearby:** Candle Factory, Cheshire Ice Cream

⑪ Farm, Sandstone Trail **Notes:** Garden: Ten tables, views of the Cheshire Plains **Parking:** 40

This guide is divided into regions. Within each region counties are listed alphabetically. To find a particular county refer to page opposite. Locations and pub names are listed alphabetically.

① **Town name**

② **Establishment name**

③ **AA Awards for accommodation, food and wine**

④ **Contact details:** Telephone, fax, e-mail and website

⑤ **Directions:** Where shown these have been provided by the pubs themselves. Please telephone for directions where these are not supplied.

⑥ **Description**

⑦ **Open:** Daily opening times, plus seasonal variations

⑧ **Bar meals:** Times for lunch and dinner, plus days meals served, variations & average price

⑨ **Restaurant Meals:** Times for lunch and dinner, plus days meals served, variations & average price

⑩ **Nearby:** Attractions or facilities close to the pub that are suitable for families

⑪ **Notes:** Info on dogs and gardens

ACCOMMODATION DESIGNATORS

All accommodation inspected under the new Common Standards is given one of 12 descriptive designators to help you choose the different types of accommodation available in Britain.

For more detailed information go to:

www.theAA.com/travel/

accommodation_restaurants_grading.html

(Please note that we do not list room or price information in this guide. If you need to know more about accommodation please contact the establishment directly)

B&B:	Private house managed by owner
GH:	Guest house, a larger B&B
GA:	Guest accommodation
INN:	Traditional inn with pub atmosphere
FH:	B&B on a working farm
HL:	Hotel
SHL:	Small hotel managed by owner
RR:	Restaurant with Rooms
THH:	Town House Hotel
CHH:	Country House Hotel
MH:	Metro Hotel
BUD:	Budget Hotel

Keys to symbols and abbreviations

Telephone	☎	Star (AA Award for accommodation - each star rating is followed by a designator which indicates the type of accommodation)	★
Fax Number	📠		
Rosette (AA Award for food)	◉		
Diamond (AA Award for guest accommodation)	♦	Wine Glass (Pubs who serve more than 6 wines by the glass)	♀
		Tankard (Principal Beers)	🍺
		No credit cards	💳

Contents

Central England

Heights of Abraham cable car, Peak District.

BOLLINGTON

The Church House Inn 🍷

Church Street SK10 5PY

☎ 01625 574014 📄 01625 562026

Email: info@the-church-house-inn.co.uk

Dir: *From A34 take A538 towards Macclesfield. Through Prestbury, then follow Bollington signs*

There's a homely feel to this stone-built village free house with its beams, log fires and agricultural decorations. The pub also features a small enclosed beer garden. The varied menu ranges from lunchtime baguettes, burgers and jacket potatoes to main meals like Barnsley lamb chop with red wine and cranberry sauce; and salmon fillet with cream and dill sauce. Vegetarian options feature on the daily specials board.

Open: 12-3 5.30-11 (Fri-Sun all day) **Bar Meals:** L served all week 12-2.30 D served all week 6.30-9.30 (Sun open all day) Av main course £6.45 **Restaurant Meals:** L served all week 12-2.30 D served all week 6-9.30 (Fri-Sun open all Day) Av 3 course alc £12.50 **Brewery/Company:** Free House 🍺: Greene King IPA, Black Sheep, Stella, Interbrew Boddington's 🍷: 18 **Children's Facilities:** Menu/Portions Cutlery Games Highchair Food warming Baby changing **Nearby:** Peak district walks, Trafford Centre (Man Utd.) **Parking:** 4

BROXTON

The Copper Mine

Nantwich Road CH3 9JH

☎ 01829 782293

Email: geoff@the-coppermine.freeserve.co.uk

Dir: *At Sainsbury's rdbt take Whitchurch A41, at next rdbt turn left onto Nantwich A534, 1m Copper Mine on right.*

A well known food venue, this pub is convenient for Cheshire Ice Cream Farm, Beeston Castle, and the Candle Factory at Cheshire Workshops. Sit in the conservatory to make the most of the beautiful views, or in summer, enjoy the patio and lawn with mature trees. Meals range from salads, sandwiches and omelettes through to main meals such as salmon and broccoli fish cakes with a pink Caesar dressing or home-made steak burger with chips.

Open: 12-3 6-11 **Bar Meals:** L served Tue-Sun 12-2.30 D served Tue-Sun 6.30-9.30 Av main course £7.95 **Restaurant Meals:** L served Tue-Sun 12-2.30 D served Tue-Sun 6.30-9.30 **Brewery/Company:** Free House 🍺: Marstons Cream Flow, Pedigree & Banks Real Ale **Children's Facilities:** Play area Menu/Portions Highchair Food warming **Nearby:** Cheshire Candle Factory, The Cheshire Ice Cream Farm, Zoo **Notes:** Garden: Large patio area with flower gardens & lawns **Parking:** 80

BURWARDSLEY

The Pheasant Inn ★★ HL 🏵 🍷

Nr Tattenhall CH3 9PF

☎ 01829 770434 📄 01829 771097

Email: info@thepheasantinn.co.uk

Web: www.thepheasantinn.co.uk

Dir: *From Chester A41 to Whitchurch, after 4m left to Burwardsley. Follow signs 'Cheshire Workshops'*

This 300-year-old, sandstone, half-timbered, former farmhouse is set in beautiful surroundings, attracting walkers, golfers, anglers and visitors to the nearby Chester racecourse and Oulton Park racing circuit.

Open: 11-11 **Bar Meals:** L served all week 12-10 D served all week 12-10 (Sun 12-8.30) Av main course £8.95 **Restaurant Meals:** L served all week D served all week Av 3 course alc £20 **Brewery/Company:** Free House 🍺: Weetwood Old Dog, Eastgate, Best, Hoegarden and guest Bitter 🍷: 8 **Children's Facilities:** Licence Play area (Swings) Cutlery Highchair Food warming Baby changing **Nearby:** Candle Factory, Cheshire Ice Cream Farm, Sandstone Trail **Notes:** Garden: Ten tables, views of the Cheshire Plains **Parking:** 40

CHOLMONDELEY
The Cholmondeley Arms ★★★ INN ♟
Malpas SY14 8HN
☎ 01829 720300 📠 01829 720123
Email: guy@cholmondeleyarms.co.uk
Web: www.cholmondeleyarms.co.uk
Dir: *On A49, between Whitchurch & Tarporley*
Where once village children got to grips with the three Rs, grown-ups now get to grips with pints. For until 1982 this elegant pub was the village school. The menu is varied and won't break the bank.
Open: 11-3 6-11 Closed: 25 Dec **Bar Meals:** L served all week 12-2.30 D served all week 6.30-10 Av main course £10 **Restaurant Meals:** L served all week 12-2.30 D served all week 6.30-10 Av 3 course alc £20 **Brewery/Company:** Free House 🍺: Marston's Pedigree,

Adnams Bitter, Banks's, Everards Tiger Best ♟: 7 **Children's Facilities:** Play area Menu/Portions Cutlery Highchair Food warming Baby changing **Nearby:** Cholmondelay Castle Gardens, Staircase locks at Birnburg & Hawkstone Park Follies **Notes:** Dogs allowed in bar, in garden, in bedrooms **Garden:** Large lawns **Parking:** 60

HAUGHTON MOSS
The Nags Head ♟
Long Lane Nr Tarporley CW6 9RN
☎ 01829 260265 📠 01829 261364
Email: rorykl@btinternet.com
Web: www.ournagshead.co.uk
Dir: *Turn off A49 S of Tarporley at Beeston/Haughton sign into Long Ln, continue for 1.75m*
A typical 16th-century Cheshire black and white building, once a smithy. Inside are low ceilings, crooked beams, exposed brickwork, real fires and the promise of service with a smile. A comprehensive set of menus offers starters like whitebait, and roast chicken and bacon tagliatelle, and mains such as duck with orange sauce, fillet of beef Rossini, and battered cod. Ask owner Debbie Keigan about the Cash Trap board game she devised.

Open: 12-12 **Bar Meals:** L served all week 12-10 D served all week 12-10 Av main course £9.50 **Restaurant Meals:** L served all week 12-10 D served all week 12-10 Av 3 course alc £19 🍺: Flowers IPA, Marstons Pedigree, Abbot Ale ♟: 20 **Children's Facilities:** Licence Play area (Activity run) Menu/Portions Cutlery Games Food warming **Nearby:** Beeston Castle, Candle Factory, Bunbury Water Mill **Notes:** Dogs allowed in garden, Water, **Garden:** Large garden & patio areas, bowling green **Parking:** 60

NANTWICH
The Thatch Inn ♟
Wrexham Road Faddiley CW5 8JE
☎ 01270 524223 📠 01270 524674
Email: thethatchinn@aol.com
Dir: *Follow signs for Wrexham from Nantwich, inn is 4m from Nantwich*
The black-and-white Thatch Inn is believed to be the oldest as well as one of the prettiest pubs in south Cheshire. It has a large garden, and inside you'll find oak beams, and open fires. The menu offers grills; traditional favourites; tastes from afar (nachos, lasagne, curry); and fish, summer salads, light bites and a children's menu.
Open: 11-11 (Sun 12-10.30) **Bar Meals:** L served all week 11-9.30 D served all week 11-9.30 (Sun 12-9.30) Av main course £7.95 **Restaurant Meals:** L served all

week 12-9.30 D served all week 12-9.30 **Brewery/Company:** Free House 🍺: Marston Pedigree, Timothy Taylor Landlord, Weetwoods, Archers, Northern Brewing ♟: 24 **Children's Facilities:** Fam room Play area (Climbing frame & Wendy House) Highchair Food warming Baby changing **Notes:** **Garden:** Landscaped garden with seating **Parking:** 60

PLUMLEY
The Golden Pheasant Hotel 🍷
Plumley Moor Road Knutsford WA16 9RX
☎ 01565 722261 📠 01565 722125
Web: www.thegoldenpheasanthotel.co.uk
Dir: *From M6 junct 19, take A556 signed Chester. 2m turn left at signs for Plumley/Peover. Through Plumley, after 1m pub opposite rail station.*
In the heart of rural Cheshire, the hotel has a large restaurant, bar area, public bar, children's play area and bowling green. The menu offers substantial choice, from bar snacks such as nachos or panninis, to a more elaborate restaurant menu, including pork medallions in apricot and tarragon reduction. Real ales are pulled from the attractive handpumps installed by J.W. Lees, one of the country's few remaining independent family breweries with its own cooperage.
Open: 11-11 (Sun 12-10.30) **Bar Meals:** L served all week 12-2.30 D served all week 6-9.30 (Sat 12-9.30, Sun 12-8.30) Av main course £6.95 **Restaurant Meals:** L served all week 12-2.30 D served all week 6-9.30 (Sat 12-9.30, Sun 12-8.30) Av 3 course alc £20 **Brewery/Company:** J W Lees 🍺: J W Lees Bitter, GB Mild & Moonraker 🍷: 10 **Children's Facilities:** Licence Play area (in large garden) Menu/Portions Games Highchair Food warming Baby changing **Nearby:** Tatton Park, Chester Zoo, Delamere Forest **Notes:** Dogs allowed in garden, Water **Garden:** Seating front and back of pub **Parking:** 80

PLUMLEY
The Smoker 🍷
Knutsford WA16 0TY
☎ 01565 722338 📠 01565 722093
Email: smoker@plumley.fsword.co.uk
Dir: *from M6 junct 19 take A556 W. Pub is 1.75m on left*
A 400-year-old coaching inn named after a white charger bred as a racehorse by the Prince Regent. The pub's striking wood-panelled interior provides a traditional, welcoming atmosphere, with its log fires, beams and assortment of horse brasses. There's an excellent choice of starters and a wide range of main courses, including lamb kebabs, Morecambe Bay shrimps, steak and ale pie, and seafood pancake.
Open: 10-3 6-11 (all day Sun) **Bar Meals:** L served all week 11.30-2.30 D served all week 6-9.15 (Sun 12-9) Av main course £8.50 **Restaurant Meals:** L served all week 11.30-2.30 D served all week 6.30-9.30 (Sun 12-9) Av 3 course alc £15.95 **Brewery/Company:** Frederic Robinson 🍺: Robinson's Best & Hatters Mild, Double Hop, Old Stockport, Robinsons Smooth 🍷: 10 **Children's Facilities:** Play area (Swing, slide, climbing frame) Menu/Portions Highchair Food warming **Notes:** Garden: Large lawned area, 15 large dining benches **Parking:** 100

SHOCKLACH
Bull Inn Country Bistro
Worthenbury Road Malpas SY14 7BL
☎ 01829 250239
Email: jaws@fsbdial.co.uk
This welcoming mid-19th-century pub is located in a quiet village 20 minutes from Chester. Exposed beams, many other original features, and often a cosy log fire greet visitors heading for a pint of Mansfield Cask, or a traditional pub meal. Popular are fish, chips and mushy peas, 'big and hearty' pies, curries, braised beef, pork loin with black pudding, grills, poached salmon, and vegetarian pancakes. For the kids there are burgers, pizzas and nuggets.
Open: 12-3 6.30-11 (Sun 7-10.30) **Bar Meals:** L served Fri-Sun 12-2.30 D served Tue-Sun 6.30-9 (Sun 7-9) Av main course £8.95 **Restaurant Meals:** L served Fri-Sun 12-2.30 D served Tue-Sun 6.30-9 (Sun 12-2.30, 7-9) 🍺: Mansfield Cask, Pedigree, Guinness **Children's Facilities:** Licence Cutlery Games Highchair Food warming **Notes:** Garden: Small area with picnic benches **Parking:** 30

SWETTENHAM
The Swettenham Arms 🍷
Swettenham Lane Congleton CW12 2LF
☎ 01477 571284 📄 01477 571284
Email: info@swettenhamarms.co.uk
Web: www.swettenhamarms.co.uk
Dir: *M6 junct 18 to Holmes Chapel, then A535 towards Jodrell Bank. 3m right (Forty Acre Lane) to Swettenham.*
In a tiny village, an idyllically situated, heavily beamed free house behind the 13th-century church. The pub goes back almost as far: it was probably a nunnery, linked to the church by an underground passage.
Open: 12-3 6.30-11 (open all day Sun) **Bar Meals:** L served all week 12-2.30 D served all week 7-9.30 (Sun 12-9.30) Av main course £10.95 **Restaurant Meals:** L served all week 12-2.30 D served all week 7-9.30 (Sun 12-9) Av 3 course alc £25 **Brewery/Company:** Free House 🍺: Landlord, Hydes, Beartown, Pride of Pendle, San Miguel lager & Guest Beers 🍷: 8 **Children's Facilities:** Menu/Portions Highchair Food warming Baby changing **Nearby:** Arboretum and nature reserve **Notes:** Garden: Picnic area, lavender & sunflower meadow **Parking:** 150

TUSHINGHAM CUM GRINDLEY
Blue Bell Inn
nr Witchurch SY13 4QS
☎ 01948 662172 📄 01948 662172
Web: www.surftech.co.uk/bell
Dir: *A41 4m N of Whitchurch, signed Bell O'the Hill.*
A lovely black-and-white building that oozes character with its abundance of beams, open fires and horse brasses. In what must be a unique tale from the annals of pub-haunting, it was once occupied by a duck whose spirit is reputedly sealed in a bottle buried in the bottom step of the cellar. Believe that or not, the Blue Bell remains a charming and characterful pub. Its oldest part dates to approximately 1550, and the main building was completed in 1667. It has all the features you'd expect of a timber-framed building of this date, including one of the largest working chimneys in Cheshire and a priest hole. Curios that have been discovered from within the wall structure are on show in the pub. The menu is based on traditional English fare, with specials prepared daily. Drink options include well-kept ales plus a selection of wines.
Open: 12-3 6-11 (Sun 12-3, 7-11) **Bar Meals:** L served Tue-Sun 12-2 D served Tue-Sun 6-9 **Restaurant Meals:** L served Tue-Sun 12-2 D served Tue-Sun 7-9 **Brewery/Company:** Free House 🍺: Carlins, Shropshire Gold, Golden Pippin, Thirst Quencher, Cheddar Valley Cider & Guest beers **Children's Facilities:** Fam room Menu/Portions Cutlery Games Food warming **Notes:** Dogs allowed in bar, in garden, Water Garden: Large open grass area with picnic benches **Parking:** 20

WRENBURY
The Dusty Miller 🍷
Nantwich CW5 8HG
☎ 01270 780537
Web: www.dustymiller-wrenbury.co.uk
A beautifully converted 16th-century mill building beside the Shropshire Union Canal. A black and white lift bridge, designed by Thomas Telford, completes the picture postcard setting. The menu, which tends to rely on ingredients from the region, offers light bites including filled rolls and a cheese platter alongside the more substantial baked hake with buttery mash and a white wine sauce.
Open: 11.30-3 6.30-11 (Fri/Sat 6.30-12) **Bar Meals:** L served Tue-Sun 12-2 D served all week 6.30-9.30 (Sun 12-2.30, 7-9) Av main course £10 **Restaurant Meals:** L served Tue-Sun 12-2 D served all week 6.30-9.30 **Brewery/Company:** Robinsons 🍺: Robinsons Best Bitter, Double Hop, Old Tom, Hatters Mild & Hartleys XB 🍷: 12 **Children's Facilities:** Menu/Portions Highchair Food warming **Nearby:** Cholmondeley Castle Garden, Snugbury's Ice Cream at Nantwich & Barn Books **Notes:** Dogs allowed in bar, in garden, Water & kennel Garden: Canalside garden accessible via footbridge **Parking:** 60

CHESHIRE

WYBUNBURY
The Swan ♟

Main Road Nr Nantwich CW5 7NA

☎ 01270 841280 📄 01270 841200

Email: bistrobonsamis@btconnect.com

Dir: *M6 junct 16 towards Chester & Nantwich. Turn left at lights in Wybunbury*

The Swan, a pub since 1580, is situated in the village centre next to the church. All the food is freshly prepared on the premises and includes glazed lamb shoulder, Cumberland sausage, basil-crusted cod fillet, crispy half roast duckling, and beef, mushroom and Jennings ale pie. The menu also features hot baps, thick-cut sandwiches and salads. Sit in the garden below the church tower.

Open: 12-11 **Bar Meals:** L served Tue-Sun 12-2 D served all week 6.30-9.30 (Sun & BHs 12-8) Av main course £10 **Restaurant Meals:** L served Tue-Sun 12-2 D served all week 6.30-9.30 (BHs 12-8) Av 3 course alc £20 **Brewery/Company:** Jennings Brothers Plc ☛: Jennings Bitter, Cumberland Ale, Guest beers, Abbot Ale & Townhouse Ales ♟: 9 **Children's Facilities:** Licence Menu/Portions Cutlery Highchair Food warming **Nearby:** Stapley Water Gardens **Notes:** Dogs allowed in bar Garden: Benches, tables on lawn next to church **Parking:** 50

ALFRETON
White Horse Inn ♟

Badger Lane Woolley Moor DE55 6FG

☎ 01246 590319 📄 01246 590319

Email: info@the-whitehorse-inn.co.uk

Web: www.the-whitehorse-inn.co.uk

Dir: *From A632 (Matlock/Chesterfield rd) take B6036. Pub 1m after Ashover. From A61 take B6036 to Woolley Moor*

Situated on an old toll road, close to Ogston Reservoir, this 18th-century inn has outstanding views over the Amber Valley. There is a bar food menu and a main menu. There is a good choice of real ales.

Open: 12-3 6-11 (Sun 12-10.30, all day summer wknds) **Bar Meals:** L served Tue-Sun 12-2 D served Tue-Sat 6-9 Av main course £7.50 **Restaurant Meals:** L served all week 12-2 D served Tue-Sat 6-9 (Sun 12-4) **Brewery/Company:** Free House ☛: Jennings Cumberland, Adnams Broadside, Blacksheep, 1744, Worthington Cask ♟: 8 **Children's Facilities:** Licence Play area (Adventure playground,football pitch,sand pit) Menu/Portions Games Highchair Food warming **Notes:** Garden: Large patio with picnic benches **Parking:** 50

ASHBOURNE
Dog & Partridge Country Inn ★★ HL ♟

Swinscoe DE6 2HS

☎ 01335 343183 📄 01335 342742

Email: dogpart@fsbdial.co.uk

Web: www.dogandpartridge.co.uk

This country free house was extended in 1966 to accommodate the Brazilian World Cup football team, who practised in a nearby field. Nowadays the pub scores highly for its extensive menus, offering a good selection of grills, fish, poultry and vegetarian dishes. Start, perhaps, with a wild mushroom feuilletté, followed by pan-fried liver with apple and cranberry; or local trout with stilton sauce. To finish, there's a wide choice of sweets, ice creams and cheeses.

Open: 11-11 **Bar Meals:** L/D served all week 11-11 **Restaurant Meals:** L served all week 11-11 D served all week **Brewery/Company:** Free House ☛: Greene King Old Speckled Hen & Ruddles County, Hartington Best, Wells Bombardier, Scottish Courage Courage Directors **Children's Facilities:** Fam room Play area (board games, sandpit, highchairs, change area) Menu/Portions Highchair Food warming Baby changing **Notes:** Dogs allowed in bar Garden: Good patio area with lovely views **Parking:** 50

BAKEWELL

The Monsal Head Hotel ★★ HL ♚

Monsal Head DE45 1NL

☎ 01629 640250 📄 01629 640815

Email: enquiries@monsalhead.com

Web: www.monsalhead.com

Dir: *A6 from Bakewell towards Buxton. 1.5m to Ashford. Follow Monsal Head signs, B6465 for 1m*

This distinctive, balconied hotel in the heart of the Peak District National Park enjoys lovely views over Monsal Dale. With its seven en suite bedrooms, the hotel complex is ideally located for walkers.

Open: 11.30-11 (Sun 12-10.30) Closed: 25 Dec **Bar Meals:** L served all week 12-9.30 D served all week (Sun 12-9) **Restaurant Meals:** L served all week 12-9.30 D served all week 7-9.30 (Sun 12-9)

Brewery/Company: Free House 🍺: Scottish Courage Theakston Old Peculier, Timothy Taylor Landlord, Whim Hartington IPA, Abbeydale Moonshine, Thornbridge Ales ♚: 15 **Children's Facilities:** Menu/Portions Highchair Food warming **Notes:** Dogs allowed in bar, in garden, in bedrooms, Water Garden: Enclosed, seats 100 **Parking:** 20

BAMFORD

Yorkshire Bridge Inn ★★ HL

Ashopton Road Hope Valley S33 0AZ

☎ 01433 651361 📄 01433 651361

Email: enquiries@ybridge.force9.co.uk

Web: www.yorkshire-bridge.co.uk

Dir: *A57 from M1, left onto A6013, pub 1m on right*

Dating from 1826, the Yorkshire Bridge Inn takes its name from an old packhorse bridge across the River Derwent on the road between Yorkshire and Cheshire. The bars are cosy and welcoming in winter, whilst in summer you can enjoy alfresco dining in the courtyard or spacious beer garden.

Open: 10-11 **Bar Meals:** L served all week 12-2 D served all week 6-9 (Sun 12-8.30) **Restaurant Meals:** L served all week 12-2 D served all week 6-9

Brewery/Company: Free House 🍺: Blacksheep, Old Peculier, Fullers London Pride, Copper Dragon IPA **Children's Facilities:** Play area Highchair Food warming Baby changing **Nearby:** Gullivers Kingdom, Chatsworth House & Farm, Donkey Sanctuary **Notes:** Dogs allowed in garden Garden: Walled courtyard, numerous seating areas **Parking:** 40

BARLOW

The Tickled Trout

33 Valley Road Dronfield S18 7SL

☎ 0114 2890893

A few miles outside Chesterfield, this quaint country pub is located at the gateway to the superb Peak District, renowned for its walking and splendid scenery. Within the pleasant, cosy atmosphere you can sample the inn's straightforward menu: among the fishy choices are fresh local trout with almond butter, beer-battered cod, and grilled monkfish with a tomato and basil sauce on a bed of cous-cous. The specials board should fill out the choices for those not inclined towards seafood.

Open: 12-3 6-11 (Sun 7-10.30) **Bar Meals:** L served all week 12-2.30 D served all week 6.30-9 (Sun 12-3) Av main course £6.50 **Restaurant Meals:** L served all week 12-2.30 D served all week 6.30-9

Brewery/Company: Free House 🍺: Marstons Pedigree, Mansfield Smooth, Marstons Finest Creamy & Guest **Children's Facilities:** Menu/Portions Cutlery Games Highchair Food warming **Nearby:** Chatworth House, Peak Village, Rowsley, Peak Railway, Gullivers Kingdom, Matlock Baty **Notes:** Dogs allowed in bar, in garden Garden: Patio with bench style tables **Parking:** 20

DERBYSHIRE

BRADWELL
The Bowling Green Inn ★★★★ INN ⚖
Smalldale S33 9JQ
☎ 01433 620450 📠 01433 620280
Web: www.bowlinggreeninn.co.uk
Dir: *Off A6187 onto B6049 towards Bradwell. Near bowling green*
A 16th-century coaching inn with impressive views over glorious countryside. Traditional country cooking and good value daily specials are supplemented by weekly changing ales.
Open: 12-11 **Bar Meals:** L served all week 12-2 D served all week 7-9 (Sun 12-3, 6-8) Av main course £7.95 **Restaurant Meals:** L served all week 12-2 D served all week 6-9 (Sun 12-3, 6-8) Av 3 course alc £16 **Brewery/Company:** Free House 🍺: Stones,

Timothy Taylor, Tetleys, Kelham Gold, Theakstons & Guest beers ⚖: 8 **Children's Facilities:** Licence Play area Menu/Portions Cutlery Games Highchair Food warming **Nearby:** Castleton Caverns, Chatsworth House Farm Yard, Heights of Abraham at Matlock **Notes:** Garden: Large patio area, spectacular views **Parking:** 80

CASTLETON
Ye Olde Nag's Head ⚖
Cross Street S33 8WH
☎ 01433 620248
Dir: *A57 from Sheffield to Bamford, through Hope Valley, turn right*
A traditional, family-run 17th-century coaching inn offering a warm welcome, a cosy bar with a real fire, and quality accommodation (antique four-poster beds and jacuzzis are available). Nearby are Chatsworth House, Haddon Hall and miles of wonderful walks. Food is served all day, starting with breakfasts and taking in everything from pies, tortilla wraps and burgers to sandwiches, afternoon teas and hearty, traditional evening meals.
Open: 9-11 **Bar Meals:** L served all week 12-6 D served all week 6-9 Av main course £8 **Restaurant Meals:** L served all week 12-6 D served all week 6-9 Av 3 course alc £15 **Brewery/Company:** Free House 🍺: Timothy Taylor Landlord, Black Sheep, Worthingtons, Guinness & local guest ale ⚖: 12 **Children's Facilities:** Menu/Portions Games Highchair Food warming **Notes:** Dogs allowed in bar **Parking:** 15

DOE LEA
Hardwick Inn ⚖
Hardwick Park Nr Chesterfield S44 5QJ
☎ 01246 850245 📠 01246 856365
Email: batty@hardwickinn.co.uk
Web: www.hardwickinn.co.uk
Dir: *M1 junct 29 take A6175. 0.5m L (signed Stainsby/Hardwick Hall). After Stainsby, 2m L at staggered junct. Follow brown tourist signs*
Pleasantly situated inn, dating from the 15th century, on the south gate of the National Trust's Hardwick Hall. It is built of locally quarried sandstone, and retains its historic atmosphere with open coal fires in winter.
Open: 11.30-11- **Bar Meals:** L/D served all week 11.30-9.30 (Sun 12-9) **Restaurant Meals:** L served Tue-Sun 12-2 D served Tue-Sat 7-9 (Sun 12-2) Av 3 course alc £13.6 **Brewery/Company:** Free House 🍺: Scottish Courage Theakston Old Peculier & XB, Greene King Old Speckled Hen & Ruddles County, Marston's Pedigree ⚖: 24 **Children's Facilities:** Licence Fam room Play area (Extensive garden & lawns) Menu /Portions Highchair Food warming **Nearby:** Hardwick Hall, park & lakes **Notes:** Garden: pond, picnic table

EYAM
Miners Arms
Water Lane Hope Valley S32 5RG
☎ 01433 630853 📠 01433 639050
Dir: *Off B6521, 5m N of Bakewell*
This welcoming 17th-century inn and restaurant in the famous plague village of Eyam gets its name from the local lead mines of Roman times. Choices from the seasonally changing menu might include rack of lamb with roast vegetables and rosemary cream sauce; or seared tuna steak with swede pûrée and a carrot and coriander jus. Standards such as sausage and mash with onion gravy and fish and chips are also served. Lighter bites include an interesting range of hot sandwiches on ciabatta bread.
Open: 12-11 **Bar Meals:** L served all week 12-2 D served Mon-Sat 6-9 (Mon 6-8, Sat 7-9, Sun 12-3) Av main course £9 **Restaurant Meals:** L served all week 12-3 D served Mon-Sat 6-9 Av 3 course alc £18
Brewery/Company: Free House 🍺: Interbrew Bass, Stones Bitter, Coors Worthington's Creamflow **Children's Facilities:** Menu/Portions Cutlery Games Food warming **Nearby:** Chatsworth House **Notes:** Dogs allowed in bar, in garden, in bedrooms, Water, food for overnight dogs Garden: 12 outdoor benches front & back **Parking:** 50

FENNY BENTLEY
Bentley Brook Inn ★★ HL
Ashbourne DE6 1LF
☎ 01335 350278 📠 01335 350422
Email: all@bentleybrookinn.co.uk
Web: www.bentleybrookinn.co.uk
Part of this charming, atmospheric old building was originally a thatched medieval farmhouse. The house became a restaurant in 1954, although it was the early 1970s before a full drinks licence was granted. Now open all day, the bar serves a selection of real ales and there is an award-winning restaurant, which overlooks the terrace and garden.
Open: 11-12 **Bar Meals:** L served all week 12-9 D served all week 12-9 (Sun 12-8) **Restaurant Meals:** L served all week 12-2.30 D served all week 7-9 Av 3 course alc £25.85 🍺: Leatherbritches Bespoke, Leatherbritches Hairy Helmet, Goldings, Marstons Pedigree **Children's Facilities:** Play area (Climbing frames) Menu/Portions Cutlery Highchair Food warming Baby changing **Nearby:** Gullivers Kingdom, Tissington Trail, Alton Towers **Notes:** Dogs allowed in bar Garden: Large terrace and lawn, fully fenced **Parking:** 100

FENNY BENTLEY
The Coach and Horses Inn 🍷
DE6 1LB
☎ 01335 350246 📠 01335 350178
Email: coachnhorses@aol.com
This award-winning, family-run, 17th-century coaching inn is beautifully located on the edge of the Peak District National Park. The cosy interior features stripped wood furniture and low beams. Expect real ales and good home cooking along the lines of sliced venison haunch with port and forest fruits; pan-fried tuna steak with vegetable pesto and salsa dressing; king prawns marinated in lime, chilli and coriander with mango couscous; or sea bass fillet on a herb, bacon and crouton salad.
Open: 11-11 **Bar Meals:** L served all week 12-9 D served all week 12-9 Av main course £9.2 **Restaurant Meals:** L served all week 12-9 D served all week 12-9
Brewery/Company: Free House 🍺: Marston's Pedigree, Timothy Taylor Landlord, Black Sheep Best, Oakham JHB, Thornbridge Hall Brewery ales 🍷: 6 **Children's Facilities:** Fam room Highchair Food warming **Nearby:** Chatsworth Farm, Alton Towers & Gulliver's Kingdom **Notes:** Garden: Gravelled area, seats 36 **Parking:** 24

DERBYSHIRE

HAYFIELD
The Royal Hotel 🍷
Market Street High Peak SK22 2EP
☎ 01663 742721 📠 01663 742997
Email: enquiries@royalhayfield.co.uk
Web: www.theroyalhayfield.co.uk
Dir: *Off A624*
A fine-looking, 1755-vintage building in a High Peak village that itself retains much of its old-fashioned charm. The oak-panelled Windsor Bar has log fires when you need them, and serves a constantly changing roster of real ales, bar snacks and selected dishes, while the dining room usually offers a traditional menu. Kinder Scout and the fells look impressive from the hotel patio.

Open: 11-11 **Bar Meals:** L served all week 12-2.15 D served all week 6-9.15 Av main course £7 **Restaurant Meals:** L served all week D served all week Av 3 course alc £16 **Brewery/Company:** Free House 🍺: Hydes, Tetleys, San Miguel 🍷: 8 **Children's Facilities:** Fam room Menu/Portions Cutlery Games Highchair Food warming Baby changing **Nearby:** Chestnut centre, swimming, playpark, skate park **Notes:** Garden: Patio, seats 80 **Parking:** 70

ROWSLEY
The Grouse & Claret ★★★ INN 🍷
Station Road Matlock DE4 2EB
☎ 01629 733233 📠 01629 735194
Dir: *On A6 between Matlock & Bakewell*
Named after a fishing fly, this establishment is a popular venue for local anglers. It's also handy for touring the Peak District, or the stately homes of Haddon Hall and Chatsworth House. The cosmopolitan menu offers something for everyone: a tuna melt sandwich, or crispy duck salad might fill the odd corner, whilst substantial dishes like meat and potato pie; chicken mango with spinach; and Cajun chicken penne will satisfy bigger appetites.
Open: 7.30-11 (Sun 7.30am-10.30pm) **Bar Meals:** L/D served all week 7.30am -9pm Av main course £7.50

Restaurant Meals: L served all week 7.30am-9pm D served all week 7.30am-9pm **Brewery/Company:** Wolverhampton & Dudley 🍺: Marston's Pedigree, Mansfield, Bank's Bitter 🍷: 12 **Children's Facilities:** Play area Highchair Food warming Baby changing **Nearby:** Chatsworth House, Bakewell & Matlock Bath **Notes:** Garden: Food served outside, great views **Parking:** 60

SHARDLOW
The Old Crown
Cavendish Bridge Nr Derby DE72 2HL
☎ 01332 792392
Email: bjohns5@aol.com
Web: www.oldcrown.batcave.net
Dir: *M1 junct 24 take A6 towards Derby. L before river, bridge into Shardlow*
Located on the southern side of the River Trent, The Old Crown was built as a coaching inn during the 17th century. Warmed by an open fire, the interior is traditional and atmospheric. Several hundred water jugs hang from the ceilings, while the walls display an abundance of brewery and railway memorabilia. Expect a good range of real ales, plus traditional food ranging from steak and ale pie to chicken tikka.

Open: 11-12 (Fri/Sat 11-1, Sun 10.30-12) **Bar Meals:** L served all week 12-2 D served Mon-Thu & Sat 5-8 (Sun 12-3) Av main course £6.50 🍺: Marston's Pedigree, Burtonwood Bitter, Camerons Strongarm & 4 Guest Ales **Children's Facilities:** Play area Menu/Portions Highchair Food warming **Nearby:** Shardlow Marina, Donington Race Track & American Adventure **Notes:** Dogs allowed in bar, Water Garden: Long with benches & children's play area **Parking:** 25

SOUTH WINGFIELD
The White Hart ♥
Moorwood Moor DE55 7NU
☎ 01629 534229 📠 01629 534229
Email: allanwhitehart@w32.co.uk
Web: www.whitehart-moorwood-moor.co.uk
Dir: *Near Wingfield Manor*
Classic award-winning country pub at the gateway to the Derbyshire Peak District, superbly situated for walkers and cyclists and offering wonderful views across to Wingfield Manor where Mary, Queen of Scots was held captive. A good reputation for locally-sourced food and home-grown ingredients guarantees everything from bread to truffles are made in the White Hart's kitchen. Expect chicken and locally-supplied black pudding roulade, natural-smoked haddock, Bakewell pudding, and a range of Derbyshire cheeses.
Open: 12-3 5-12 (Sat 12-11, Sun 12-10.30) **Bar Meals:** L served Sat-Sun 12-2 D served Mon-Sat 6-10 (Sun 12-6) Av main course £9.95 **Restaurant Meals:** L served Sat-Sun 12-2 D served Mon-Sat 5-10 (Sun 12-4) Av 3 course alc £15.95 🍺: Pedigree, Guinness, Bass, guest beer ♥: 10 **Children's Facilities:** Play area Menu/Portions Food warming Baby changing **Nearby:** Alton Towers, Gullivers Kingdom, Crich Tramway Museum **Notes:** Dogs allowed in bar, chew sticks behind bar Garden: Decking area with seating, lawned area **Parking:** 30

TIDESWELL
The George Hotel ♥
Commercial Road Buxton SK17 8NU
☎ 01298 871382 📠 01298 871382
Email: georgehoteltideswell@yahoo.co.uk
Web: www.george-hotel-tideswell.co.uk
Dir: *A619 to Baslow, A623 towards Chapel en le Frith, 0.25m*
A 17th-entury coaching inn in a quiet village conveniently placed for exploring the National Park and visiting Buxton, Chatsworth and the historic plague village of Eyam. Quality home-cooked food includes venison cooked in red wine sauce, roast pheasant with bacon, potatoes and mushrooms, seafood crumble, and whole rainbow trout with almonds.
Open: 12-3 6-11 (Open all day Sat-Sun) **Bar Meals:** L served all week 12-2 D served all week 6-9 (All day Sat-Sun (Summer)) Av main course £6 **Restaurant Meals:** L served all week 12-2 D served all week 6-9 (Summer Sat-Sun all day) Av 3 course alc £12
Brewery/Company: Hardy & Hansons Plc 🍺: Kimberley Cool, Olde Trip Bitter, Best Bitter ♥: 12 **Children's Facilities:** Play area (Enclosed garden) Menu/Portions Cutlery Highchair Food warming **Nearby:** Gullivers Kingdom, Alton Towers, Chatsworth **Notes:** Dogs allowed in bar, Water Garden: Enclosed with seating **Parking:** 25

WESSINGTON
The Three Horseshoes
The Green DE55 6DQ
☎ 01773 834854
Email: scott@3horseshoes-wessington.info
Web: www.3horseshoes-wessington.info
Dir: *A615 towards Matlock, 3m after Alfreton, 5m before Matlock*
A century ago horses were still being traded over the bar at this late-17th-century former coaching inn and associated blacksmith's forge, to both of which activities it no doubt owes its name. For a true taste of the Peak District try Derbyshire chicken with black pudding and apple; or braised lamb shank with celeriac purée. Several local walks start or end at the pub - why not order a picnic for refreshment, or even a hamper?
Open: 11.30-11 (Sun 12-10.30, Closed Mon in winter) **Bar Meals:** L served Tue-Sat, BHs 12-2 D served Tue-Thu, BHs 5.30-8.30 (Sun 12.30-4.45) **Restaurant Meals:** L served Sun in winter 12.30-3 D served Fri-Sat 7-9 (Sun 12.30-5) Av 3 course alc £21 🍺: Guinness, Hardys & Hansons Olde Trip, Carling H & H Cool & Monthly Guest Beer **Children's Facilities:** Play area (Frame, slide, swing & sandpit) Menu/Portions Cutlery Games Highchair Food warming Baby changing **Nearby:** Alton Towers, Gullivers World, Peak District National Park **Notes:** Dogs allowed in bar, Biscuits, Water Garden: Large gravelled area, seating, grassed area **Parking:** 18

DERBYSHIRE

HEREFORDSHIRE

ASTON CREWS
The Penny Farthing Inn
Ross-on-Wye HR9 7LW
☎ 01989 750366 📄 01989 750922
Dir: *5m E of Ross-on-Wye*
A whitewashed, 17th-century blacksmith's shop and later coaching inn high above the River Wye Valley. Inside, there are lots of nooks and crannies with oak beams, antiques, saddlery, and cheerful log fires. Debbie and Derek Royston took over in 2004 and soon became aware of ghostly goings-on, although they've never actually seen anything. Even so, glasses sometimes fall off the bar. There's nothing ethereal, however, about the extensive, frequently changing menu, which gives considerable prominence to fish.
Open: 12-3 6.30-11 (Open all day Fri-Sun (May-Sep))

Bar Meals: L served all week 12-2 D served all week 6-9 Av main course £10 **Restaurant Meals:** L served all week 12-2 D served all week 6-9 (Sun 12-2) Av 3 course alc £22.50 🍺: John Smiths, Abbott Ale, Wadworth 6X **Children's Facilities:** Menu/Portions Cutlery Highchair Food warming **Notes:** Dogs allowed in bar **Garden:** Large sloping garden, benches **Parking:** 50

BODENHAM
England's Gate Inn 🍷
HR1 3HU
☎ 01568 797286 📄 01568 797768
Dir: *Hereford A49, turn onto A417 at Bosey Dinmore hill, 2.5m on right*
A pretty black and white coaching inn dating from around 1540, with atmospheric beamed bars and blazing log fires in winter. A picturesque garden attracts a good summer following, and so does the food. The menu features such dishes as pan fried lamb steak with apricot and onion marmalade, roasted breast of duck with parsnip mash and spinach and wild rice cakes with peppers on a chilli and tomato salsa.
Open: 11-11 (Sunday 12-10.30) **Bar Meals:** L served all week 12-2.30 D served all week 6-9.30 Av main

course £8.95 **Restaurant Meals:** L served all week 12-2.30 D served all week 6-9.30 Av 3 course alc £16.95 **Brewery/Company:** Free House 🍺: Wye Valley Bitter, Butty Bach, Shropshire Lad, Guest Ales 🍷: 7 **Children's Facilities:** Menu/Portions Highchair Food warming **Notes:** Dogs allowed, Water **Garden:** Large sunken garden with large patio area **Parking:** 100

CANON PYON
The Nags Head Inn
HR4 8NY
☎ 01432 830252
Dir: *Telephone for directions*
More than four hundred years old, with flagstone floors, open fires and exposed beams to prove it. A comprehensive menu might entice you into starting with slices of smoked salmon drizzled with brandy, lemon and cracked pepper, then to follow with medallions of lamb in a sticky Cumberland sauce, breast of Gressingham duck in a rich morello cherry sauce, or butterflied sea bass on sauteed strips of carrot and chopped coriander. Vegetarian options include stuffed peppers and tagliatelle. Curry nights and Sunday carvery. The large garden features a children's adventure playground.

Open: 11-2.30 6-11 **Bar Meals:** L served Tue-Sun 12-2.30 D served all week 6.30-9.30 (Sun 12-9) Av main course £5.95 **Restaurant Meals:** L served Tue-Sun 12-2.30 D served all week 6.30-9.30 Sun 12-9 **Brewery/Company:** Free House 🍺: Fuller's London Pride, Boddingtons, Flowers, Nags Ale **Children's Facilities:** Play area (Adventure playground) Menu/Portions Cutlery Highchair Food warming **Notes:** **Garden:** Beer garden, patio, table seating for 60 **Parking:** 50

DORMINGTON

Yew Tree Inn

Len Gee's Restaurant Priors Frome HR1 4EH

☎ 01432 850467 📄 01432 850467

Email: len@lengees.info

Web: www.lengees.info

Dir: *A438 Hereford to Ledbury, turn at Dormington towards Mordiford, 0.5m on left.*

The panoramic views from this former hop-pickers' pub stretch right across Herefordshire towards Hay-on-Wye and the Black Mountains. There are plenty of walks in the surrounding countryside to help work up an appetite for one of Len Gee's home-cooked meals. The bar menu features light snacks and traditional pub favourites, whilst diners in the restaurant have options like monkfish in smoked bacon; rabbit and redcurrant pie; and ratatouille pancake with spinach cream sauce.

Open: 12-2 7-11 (Closed Tue Jan-Mar) **Bar Meals:** L served all week 12-2 D served all week 7-9 Av main course £6.99 **Restaurant Meals:** L served Wed-Mon 12-2 D served Wed-Mon 7-9 Av 3 course alc £18.50 **Brewery/Company:** Free House 🍺: Ruddles Best, Wye Valley, Greene King Old Speckled Hen, John Smiths & Spinning Dog Organic **Children's Facilities:** Menu/Portions Cutlery Games Highchair Food warming **Nearby:** Small Rare Breeds New Bridge Farm, Shortwood Family Farm & Organic Dairy **Notes:** Dogs allowed in bar, in garden, Waterbowls **Garden:** Terraced with views of Black Mountains **Parking:** 40

DORSTONE

The Pandy Inn

Golden Valley HR3 6AN

☎ 01981 550273 📄 01981 550277

Email: magdalena@pandyinn.wanadoo.co.uk

Web: www.pandyinn.co.uk

Dir: *Off B4348 W of Hereford*

Richard de Brito was one of the four Norman knights who killed Thomas à Becket in Canterbury Cathedral in 1170. After 15 years in the Holy Land he returned to England to build a chapel at Dorstone as an act of atonement. He is believed to have built The Pandy to house the workers, later adapting it to become an inn, which is now probably the oldest in the county. Later, during the Civil War in the 17th century, Oliver Cromwell is known to have taken refuge here. The ancient hostelry is located opposite the village green and part of it retains its original flagstone floors and beams. The large garden, which offers 19 tables and a children's playground, has views of Dorstone Hill. Food is freshly prepared daily and the seasonal menu includes Pandy pies and home-made puddings. Farmhouse ciders are served alongside local cask ales.

Open: 12-3 6-11 (Open all day May-Oct) **Bar Meals:** L served all week 12-3 D served all week 6-9.30 **Restaurant Meals:** L served all week 12-3 D served all week 6-11 **Brewery/Company:** Free House 🍺: Wye Valley Bitter & Butty Bach **Children's Facilities:** Licence Play area Menu/Portions Cutlery Highchair **Nearby:** Hay-on-Wye book fair, Horse Riding **Notes:** Dogs allowed in bar, in garden **Garden:** Large garden, views of Dorstone Hill **Parking:** 20

FOWNHOPE

The Green Man Inn ★★★ INN

HR1 4PE

☎ 01432 860243 📄 01432 860207

Email: info@thegreenmaninn.co.uk

Web: www.thegreenmaninn.co.uk

Dir: *From M50 take A449 then B4224 to Fownhope*

This white-painted 15th-century coaching inn has a host of beams inside and out. Set in an attractive garden close to the River Wye, it's an ideal base for walking, touring and salmon fishing. The extensive menu has something for everyone, with a range of filling sandwiches, jacket potatoes, burgers and ciabatta melts. Then there are hand-made pies, gourmet grills, and main course favourites like sausages and mash. All this, and sticky puddings too!

Open: 11-11 (Sun 11-10.30, Fri/Sat 11-12) **Bar Meals:** L/D served all week 12-9.30 Av main course £7.50 **Brewery/Company:** Free House 🍺: John Smith's Smooth, Samuel Smith **Children's Facilities:** Licence Fam room Highchair Food warming **Nearby:** Wye Leisure, Hereford Centre **Notes:** Dogs allowed in bar, in garden, in bedrooms **Garden:** Lawn area with seating overlooks countryside **Parking:** 80

HAMPTON BISHOP
The Bunch of Carrots 🍷
Hereford HR1 4JR
☎ 01432 870237 📠 01432 870237
Email: bunchofcarrotts@buccaneer.co.uk
Dir: *From Hereford take A4103, A438, then B4224*
Friendly pub with real fires, old beams and flagstones.
Its name comes from a rock formation in the River Wye
which runs alongside the pub. There is an extensive
menu plus a daily specials board, a carvery, salad buffet
and simple bar snacks. Check out the local Spinning
Dog beers.
Open: 11-3 6-11 **Bar Meals:** L served all week 12-2.30
D served all week 6-10 (Sun 9pm) Av main course £9
Restaurant Meals: L served all week 12-2 D served all
week 6-10 **Brewery/Company:** Free House 🍺:

Marstons Pedigree, Directors, Butcombe, Organic Bitter
& Local Beer 🍷: 11 **Children's Facilities:** Play area
Cutlery Highchair Food warming **Nearby:** Cathedral,
Brecon Mountains & River Wye **Notes:** Dogs allowed
Parking: 100

LEDBURY
The Verzon ★★ HL 🏵🏵 🍷
Trumpet HR8 2PZ
☎ 01531 670381 📠 01531 670830
Email: info@theverzon.co.uk
Web: www.theverzon.co.uk
Dir: *Situated 2.5m W of Ledbury on the A438 towards Hereford*
A former farmhouse, this Georgian country house hotel
stands in over four acres of countryside with views of the
Malvern Hills. Versatile facilities include a large function
room, a popular deck terrace and a comfortable lounge
with an open fire. The menu makes good reading with
classics like pan-fried rib-eye of Herefordshire beef with
grilled field mushrooms, roast plum tomatoes, sautéed
potatoes and sauce béarnaise, or steamed mussels
with white wine, cream and parsley.
Open: 8-11 **Bar Meals:** L served all week 12-2 D
served all week 7-9 (Sun 12-2.30) **Restaurant Meals:** L
served all week 12-2 D served all week 7-9 (Sun 12-
2.30) Av 3 course alc £25 🍺: Wye Valley Bitter, Butty
Bach, Tetley Smoothflow 🍷: 7 **Children's Facilities:**
Licence Menu/Portions Highchair Food warming Baby
changing **Nearby:** Shortwood Farm, Eastnor Castle,
Glazydays Pottery **Notes:** Garden: Large terrace and
lawn, views of Malvern Hill **Parking:** 80

LEOMINSTER
The Royal Oak Hotel ★★ HL
South Street HR6 8JA
☎ 01568 612610 📠 01568 612710
Email: reservations@theroyaloakhotel.net
Web: www.theroyaloakhotel.net
Dir: *Town centre, near A44/A49 junct*
Coaching inn dating from around 1733, with log fires,
antiques and a minstrels' gallery in the original ballroom.
The pub was once part of a now blocked-off tunnel
system that linked the Leominster Priory with other
buildings in the town. Good choice of wines by the glass
and major ales, and a hearty menu offering traditional
British food with a modern twist.
Open: 10-3 6-11 (Sat 10-11, Sun 12-10.30) **Bar
Meals:** L served all week 12-2.30 D served all week 7-
9 **Restaurant Meals:** L served Sun 12-2 D served all
week 7-9.30 Av 3 course alc £25 **Brewery/Company:**
Free House 🍺: Shepherd Neame Spitfire, Butty Bach by
Wye Valley **Children's Facilities:** Menu/Portions
Highchair Food warming **Notes:** Dogs allowed in bar, in
garden, in bedrooms, Water **Garden:** Decking, seats 20,
food served outside **Parking:** 15

MADLEY
The Comet Inn 🍷
Stoney Street HR2 9NJ
☎ 01981 250600
Email: stevewilson@thecometinn.co.uk
Web: www.thecometinn.co.uk
Dir: *approx 6m from Hereford on the B4352*
Located on a prominent corner position and set in two and a half acres, this black and white 19th-century inn was originally three cottages, and retains many original features and a roaring open fire. A simple, hearty menu includes steak and ale pie, shank of lamb, grilled gammon, chicken curry, cod in crispy batter, mushroom stroganoff, and a variety of steaks, baguettes, and jacket potatoes.
Open: 12-3 6-11 (Open all day Fri-Sun & BHs) **Bar**
Meals: L served all week 12-3 D served Mon-Sun 6-9 (All day Sat, Sun 12-4) Av main course £5 **Restaurant**
Meals: L served all week 12-2 D served Mon-Sat 7-9.30 Av 3 course alc £15 **Brewery/Company:** Free House 🍺: Hook Norton Best Bitter, Wye Valley Bitter, Tetley Smooth Flow, Carlsberg Tetley, Stowford Press 🍷: 22 **Children's Facilities:** Play area Menu/Portions Highchair Food warming **Notes:** Dogs allowed in bar, in garden, Bowl & outside tap **Garden:** Large garden with shrubs, seats 90 **Parking:** 50

MICHAELCHURCH ESCLEY
The Bridge Inn 🍷
HR2 0JW
☎ 01981 510646 🖨 01981 510646
Email: giss@yahoo.co.uk
Dir: *from Hereford take A465 towards Abergavenny, then B4348 towards Peterchurch. Turn left at Vowchurch for village*
By Escley Brook, at the foot of the Black Mountains and close to Offa's Dyke, there are 14th-century parts to this oak-beamed family pub: the dining room overlooks the garden, abundant with rose and begonias, and the river - an ideal area for walkers and nature lovers. Speciality dishes include steak and kidney with crispy dumplings.
Open: 12-3 6-11 (Sun 12-10.30) Closed: 25 Dec **Bar**
Meals: L served all week 12-3 D served all week 6-9
Restaurant Meals: L served all week 12-3 D served all week 6-9.30 **Brewery/Company:** Free House 🍺: Wye Valley Beers, John Smiths, Bridge Bitter 🍷: 20 **Children's Facilities:** Play area (Fenced, rope swing) Menu/Portions Cutlery Food warming **Notes:** Dogs allowed in bar, in garden, Water **Garden:** Large riverside patio, fenced garden, heaters **Parking:** 40

ORLETON
The Boot Inn
SY8 4HN
☎ 01568 780228 🖨 01568 780228
Email: thebootorleton@hotmail.com
Dir: *Follow the A49 S from Ludlow (approx 7m) to the B4362 (Woofferton), 1.5m off B4362 turn left. The Boot Inn is in the centre of the village*
Expect a relaxed and welcoming atmosphere in this black and white timbered inn, which dates from the 16th century. In winter a blazing inglenook fire warms the bar, where an selection of snacks, sandwiches and specials is offered alongside the regular menu. Specialities include a mixed grill and roast duck served with plum sauce.
Open: 12-3 6-11 **Bar Meals:** L served Tue-Sun 12-2 D served all week 7-9 Av main course £11 **Restaurant**
Meals: L served Tue-Sun D served all week 7-9 Av 3 course alc £18 **Brewery/Company:** Free House 🍺: Hobsons Best, Local Real Ales, Woods, Wye Valley **Children's Facilities:** Licence Play area (Children's play area) Menu/Portions Games Highchair Food warming **Notes:** Dogs allowed in bar, in garden, Water **Garden:** Lawn, BBQ area **Parking:** 20

HEREFORDSHIRE

SELLACK

The Lough Pool Inn ◉ ♀

Ross-on-Wye HR9 6LX

☎ 01989 730236 🖷 01989 730462

Dir: *A49 from Ross-on-Wye towards Hereford. Take road signed Sellack/Hoarwithy.*

First, the pronunciation - it's Luff Pool, although locals call it the Love Pool. In the 1870s this black and white, half-timbered pub doubled as beerhouse and butcher's shop, then in 1880, when it was granted inn status. People travel long distances to eat here.

Open: 11.30-2.30 6.30-11 (Sun 11-3, 6.30-10.30) Closed: 25 Dec **Bar Meals:** L served all week 12-2 D served all week 7-9.15 Av main course £12.50 **Restaurant Meals:** L served all week 12-2 D served all week 7-9.15 Av 3 course alc £22 **Brewery/Company:**

Free House 🍺: Wye Valley, Scottish Courage John Smiths, Best Bitter & Butty Bach plus guest ales 🍷: 10 **Children's Facilities:** Fam room Menu/Portions Highchair Food warming **Nearby:** Birds of Prey Centre, Goodrich Castle, Hampton Court **Notes:** Dogs allowed in bar, in garden, Water **Garden:** Lawn outside pub **Parking:** 40

SYMONDS YAT [EAST]

The Saracens Head Inn ★★★★ INN ♀

HR9 6JL

☎ 01600 890435 🖷 01600 890034

Email: contact@saracensheadinn.co.uk

Web: www.saracensheadinn.co.uk

Situated in an Area of Outstanding Natural Beauty on the east bank of the Wye where the river meets the Royal Forest of Dean, the Saracens Head has all-year-round appeal. The inn is very handy for exploring this unspoiled area. A wide choice of bar and restaurant fare.

Open: 11-11 **Bar Meals:** L served all week 12-2.30 D served all week 7-9.15 Av main course £8.50 **Restaurant Meals:** L served all week 12-2.30 D served all week 7-9.15 **Brewery/Company:** Free House 🍺: Scottish Courage Theakstons Best & Old Peculier, Old

Speckled Hen, Wye Valley Hereford Pale Ale, Wye Valley Butty Bach 🍷: 7 **Children's Facilities:** Menu/Portions Highchair Food warming Baby changing **Nearby:** Puzzle Wood, Jubilee Maze, Steam Railway **Notes:** Dogs allowed in bar, in garden, Bowls **Garden:** 2 riverside terraces **Parking:** 38

TILLINGTON

The Bell

HR4 8LE

☎ 01432 760395 🖷 01432 760580

Email: beltill@aol.com

Web: www.thebellinn.uk.com

Popular family-run pub whose features include an English oak floor in the lounge bar. The appetising menu features chicken fillet with sausage and thyme stuffing, salmon fillet and prawns in lemon and white wine, aromatic duck and oyster mushrooms in a plum sauce, and young rabbit braised with celeriac and fennel in creamy tarragon and lemon sauce. There's also a good lunchtime snack menu offering sandwiches, baguettes, soup and jackets.

Open: 11-3 6-11 (All day Sat-Sun) **Bar Meals:** L served all week 12-2.15 D served Mon-Sat 6-9.15 (Sun 12-

2.30) Av main course £9 **Restaurant Meals:** L served all week 12-2.15 D served Mon-Sat 6-9.15 Av 3 course alc £15 🍺: London Pride, Hereford Bitter, other local ales **Children's Facilities:** Play area (Tree-house, tunnell, swings, slide) Menu/Portions Cutlery Games Highchair Food warming **Nearby:** Mountain boarding, golf **Notes:** Dogs allowed in public bar **Garden:** Small paved area & large lawn with tables **Parking:** 60

ULLINGSWICK

Three Crowns Inn ☺ ♟

Hereford HR1 3JQ

☎ 01432 820279 📄 01432 820279

Email: info@threecrownsinn.com

Web: www.threecrownsinn.com

Dir: *From Burley Gate rdbt take A465 toward Bromyard, after 2m left to Ullingswick, left after 0.5m, pub 0.5m on right*

An unspoilt country pub in deepest rural Herefordshire, where food sources are so local their distance away is referred to in fields, rather than miles. A hand-written sign even offers to buy surplus garden fruit and veg from locals. Parterres in the garden give additional space for growing more varieties of herbs, fruit and vegetables that are not easy, or even possible, to buy commercially. The menus change daily, but there is always fish, such as line-caught poached monkfish and proscuito with celeriac mousse. Meat dishes have included braised belly of Berkshire pork and confit of Gressingham duck.

Open: 12-2.30 7-11 (May-Aug 12-3, 6-11) **Closed:** 2wks from Dec 25 **Bar Meals:** L served all week 12-2.30 D served all week 7-10 (Summer 6-10) **Restaurant Meals:** L served all week 12-2 D served all week 7-9.30 **Brewery/Company:** Free House 🍺: Hobsons Best, Wye Valley Butty Bach & Dorothy Goodbody's, guest beers ♟: 9 **Children's Facilities:** Play area (Mother & Baby changing facility) Menu/Portions Cutlery Games Highchair Food warming Baby changing **Notes:** Garden: Formal garden with patio, heaters **Parking:** 20

WALTERSTONE

Carpenters Arms ♟

HR2 0DX

☎ 01873 890353

Dir: *Off the A465 between Hereford & Abergavenny at Pandy*

There's plenty of character in this 300-year-old free house located on the edge of the Black Mountains where the owner, Mrs Watkins, was born. Here you'll find beams, antique settles and a leaded range with open fires that burn all winter. Popular food options include beef and Guinness pie; beef lasagna; and thick lamb cutlets. Ask about the vegetarian selection, and large selection of home-made desserts.

Open: 12-3 7-11 **Bar Meals:** L served all week 12-3 D served all week 7-9.30 **Restaurant Meals:** L served all week 12-3 D served all week 7-9.30 **Brewery/Company:** Free House 🍺: Wadworth 6X **Children's Facilities:** Fam room Play area **Parking:** 20

WELLINGTON

The Wellington

HR4 8AT

☎ 01432 830367

Email: thewellington@hotmail.com

Dir: *Turn off A49 between Hereford & Leominster into Wellington village centre. Pub approx 0.25m on left.*

The owners of this pub fled the London rat-race to live the dream of running a gastro-pub in rural Herefordshire. Staying true to their ideals and dedicated to the use of good local produce, they are now seeing the accolades rolling in. The bar menu offers the likes of scrambled eggs with oak smoked salmon while the restaurant showcases local produce like Herefordshire sirloin steak with fresh horseradish and chive cream and hand cut chips.

Open: 12-3 6-11 (Sun 12-3, 7-10.30) **Bar Meals:** L served Tue-Sun 12-2 D served Mon-Sat 7-9 Av main course £12.50 **Restaurant Meals:** L served Tue-Sun 12-2 D served Mon-Sat 7-9 Av 3 course alc £22 **Brewery/Company:** Free House 🍺: Hobsons, Wye Valley Butty Bach, Guest Real Ales **Children's Facilities:** Play area (Small play area in garden) Menu/Portions Cutlery Games Highchair Food warming **Nearby:** Hampton Court, Queenswood Country Park **Notes:** Dogs allowed in bar, in garden, Water Garden: Beer garden, play area, ample seating **Parking:** 20

WEOBLEY

The Salutation Inn ★★★★ INN ◉
Market Pitch HR4 8SJ
☎ 01544 318443 🖹 01544 318405
Email: salutationinn@btinternet.com
Web: www.thesalutationinn.co.uk
Dir: *On the A44, then A4112 (Leominster-Brecon road) 8m from Leominster*

A black and white timber-framed pub dating back more than 500 years and situated in a corner of the country renowned for its hops, cattle and apple orchards. The inn, sympathetically converted from an old ale house and adjoining cottage, is the perfect base for exploring the lovely Welsh Marches and enjoying a host of leisure activities, including fishing, horse riding, golf, walking, and clay shooting. The Salutation Inn's Oak Room Restaurant offers a range of award-winning dishes created with the use of locally sourced ingredients. Chef's specials are also served in the traditional lounge bar with its atmosphere and cosy inglenook fireplace.
Open: 11-11 (Sun 12-10.30) **Bar Meals:** L served all week 12-2.30 D served all week 6.30-9.30 (Sun 6.30-8) Av main course £10 **Restaurant Meals:** L served all week 12-2.30 D served Mon-Sat 7-9 Av 3 course alc £25 **Brewery/Company:** Free House 🍺: Hook Norton Best, Coors Worthington's Creamflow, Wye Valley Butty Bach, Flowers Best Bitter, Spinning Dog & Herefordshire Light Ale 🍷: 6 **Children's Facilities:** Licence Menu/Portions Games Food warming Baby changing **Nearby:** Go-carting, Horse riding, Cycling **Notes:** Garden: Courtyard, alfresco dining, screen & awning **Parking:** 14

WHITNEY-ON-WYE

Rhydspence Inn ★★ SHL
Hereford HR3 6EU
☎ 01497 831262 🖹 01497 831751
Email: info@rhydspence-inn.co.uk
Web: www.rhydspence-inn.co.uk
Dir: *N side of A438 1m W of Whitney-on-Wye*

The landlords of this former drovers' inn dish out a short history which dates its construction, probably as a hostelry, to 1380. The bar, elegant dining room and brasserie all have superb views over the largely unchanging Wye Valley. Food options include loin of venison, rack of Welsh lamb and vegetarian tortelloni.
Open: 11-2.30 7-11 **Bar Meals:** L served all week 11-1.45 D served all week 7-8.45 (Sun 12-2, 7-8.45) Av main course £7.50 **Restaurant Meals:** L served all week 11-1.45 D served all week 7-8.45 (Sun lunch 12-2, Dinner 7-8.45) Av 3 course alc £25 **Brewery/Company:** Free House 🍺: Robinsons Best, Interbrew Bass **Children's Facilities:** Fam room (Large grass area) Cutlery Highchair Food warming Baby changing **Notes:** Garden: 2/3 acres, mostly lawn **Parking:** 30

EAST LANGTON

The Bell Inn 🍷
Main Street Market Harborough LE16 7TW
☎ 01858 545278 🖹 01858 545748
Web: www.thebellinn.co.uk
Dir: *Leave Market Harborough on A6 N for Leicester, take 3rd right at rdbt 2m, follow signs for The Langtons on B6047 1.5m. Take 1st right signed East Langton.*

A creeper-clad, 16th-century listed building tucked away in a village with country walks all around. Peter Faye and Joy Jesson are enthusiastic owners, offering local meats, vegetables and cheeses as well as locally brewed ales.
Open: 12-2.30 7-11 Closed: Dec 25 **Bar Meals:** L served all week 12-2 D served Mon-Sat 7-9.30 (Sun 12-2.30) Av main course £10 **Restaurant Meals:** L served all week 12-2 D served Mon-Sat 7-9.30 Av 3 course alc £25 **Brewery/Company:** Free House 🍺: Greene King IPA & Abbot Ale, Langton Bowler Ale & Caudle Bitter 🍷: 7 **Children's Facilities:** Licence Menu/Portions Cutlery Highchair Food warming **Nearby:** Foxton Locks, National Space Centre & Rockingham Speedway **Notes:** Garden: Large, sunny, lawned with planted borders **Parking:** 20

FLECKNEY

The Old Crown 🍷

High Street LE8 8AJ

☎ 0116 2402223

Email: old-crown-inn@fleckney7.freeserve.co.uk

Web: www.theoldcrown.co.uk

Close to the Grand Union Canal and Saddington Tunnel, a traditional village pub that is especially welcoming to hiking groups and families. Noted for good real ales and generous opening times (evening meals from 5pm) offering a wide choice of popular food. The garden has lovely views of fields and the canal, as well as a pétanque court.

Open: 11-11 (Sun 12-10.30) **Bar Meals:** L served all week 12-2 D served Tue-Sat 5-9 Av main course £8 **Restaurant Meals:** L served all week 12-2 D served Tue-Sat 8-9 **Brewery/Company:** Everards Brewery **🍺:** Everards Tiger & Beacon, Scottish Courage Courage Directors, Adnams Bitter, Greene King Abbot Ale, Marston's Pedigree **Children's Facilities:** Fam room Play area (bouncy castle, playhouse) Menu/Portions Cutlery Games Highchair Food warming Baby changing **Notes:** Dogs allowed in bar, in garden, Water Garden: Very large, wonderful views **Parking:** 60

GRIMSTON

The Black Horse

3 Main Street Melton Mowbray LE14 3BZ

☎ 01664 812358 📠 01664 813138

Email: joe.blackhorsepub@virgin.net

Dir: *Telephone for directions*

A traditional 16th-century coaching inn displaying much cricketing memorabilia in a quiet village with views over the Vale of Belvoir. Plenty of opportunities for country walks, or perhaps a game of pétanque on the pub's floodlit pitch. Dishes include devilled whitebait with freshly twisted lemon and lime; local lamb cutlets with honey and mint sauce; five cheese and spinach canneloni; and giant Yorkshire pudding with mustard mash, Lincolnshire sausages and black pudding. Extensive sweet menu changes weekly.

Open: 12-3 6-11 **Bar Meals:** L served all week 12-2 D served Mon-Sat 6-9 Av main course £8.95 **Restaurant Meals:** L served all week 12-2 D served Mon-Sun 6-9 Av 3 course alc £15.15 **Brewery/Company:** Free House **🍺:** Adnams, Marstons Pedigree, Archers, guest ales **Children's Facilities:** Licence Fam room Play area Menu/Portions Games Highchair Food warming **Nearby:** Belvior Castle, Twin Lakes **Notes:** Dogs allowed in garden, Water Garden: Large beer garden, floodlights

---

HALLATON

The Bewicke Arms ★★★★ INN 🍷

1 Eastgate Market Harborough LE16 8UB

☎ 01858 555217 📠 01858 555598

Web: www.bewickearms.co.uk

Dir: *S of A47 between Leicester & junct of A47/A6003*

On Easter Monday 1770, a local chatelaine was saved from being gored by a raging bull when a hare ran across the bull's path. In gratitude, she arranged for two hare pies and a supply of ale to be given to the parish poor on each succeeding Easter Monday. The Bewicke Arms is now famous for its annual hare pie event.

Open: 12-3 6-11 (All day Sun, Winter months 7-11) Closed: Easter Monday **Bar Meals:** L served all week 12-2 D served Mon-Sat 7-9.30 (Food on Sun May-Oct) Av main course £8.95 **Restaurant Meals:** L served all week 12-2 D served Mon-Sat 7-9.30 Av 3 course alc £17.50 **Brewery/Company:** Free House **🍺:** Grain Store Brewery, Green King IPA, Grainstore Triple B, Guest beers 🍷: 18 **Children's Facilities:** Play area (Play area) Menu/Portions Cutlery Games Highchair Baby changing **Notes:** Garden: Patio with picnic benches, enclosed with pond **Parking:** 20

HATHERN

The Anchor Inn 🍷

Loughborough Road LE12 5JB

☎ 01509 842309

Email: stevejvincent@aol.com

Dir: *M1 junct 24, take A6 towards Leicester, 4.5m on left)*

Hathern's oldest pub, the Anchor was originally a coaching inn, with stables accessed through an archway off what is now the A6. It offers snacks galore, with vegetarian options, and a bar/restaurant menu presenting pasta, fish, and steaks, known here as Anchor Inn sizzlers. House specialities include supreme of chicken, and Barnsley lamb chop, pork chop and duck breast - all pan fried. Unquestionably family-friendly, with a fenced-off children's play area in the large garden.

Open: 12-11.30 **Bar Meals:** L served all week 12-3 D served all week 5-10 Av main course £6.50 **Restaurant Meals:** L served all week 12-9.30 D served all week 12-9.30 **Brewery/Company:** Scottish & Newcastle 🍺: John Smiths, Pedigree, Guest Beers, Four Cask Ales 🍷: 20 **Children's Facilities:** Licence Play area (Climbing frames, swings, baby changing room) Games Highchair Food warming **Notes:** Garden: Large garden, children's play area,french bowls **Parking:** 100

LONG CLAWSON

The Crown & Plough 🍷

East End LE14 4NG

☎ 01664 822322 📠 01664 822322

Email: crownandplough@btconnect.com

Web: www.crownandplough.co.uk

Newly re-opened under new ownership, following an extensive programme of refurbishment, the pub retains the atmosphere of a village local but with a contemporary flavour. It has a growing reputation for its food served from one menu throughout the bar, snug, restaurant and landscaped garden. There's a good choice of fish (pan-fried sea bass with home-made tagliatelle, mussels and clams), and the likes of whole roast partridge with gratin potatoes and Savoy cabbage.

Open: 11.30-2 5.30-11 (Fri-Sat 5.30pm-1am) **Bar Meals:** L served Tue-Sun 12-2 D served Tue-Sat 6.30-9.30 (Sun 12-3) Av main course £14 **Restaurant Meals:** L served Tue-Sun 12-2 D served Tue-Sat 6.30-9.30 (Sun 12-3) Av 3 course alc £26 🍺: Shepherd Neame, Spitfire, Lancaster Bomber, Marstons Pedigree, Adnams Explorer **Children's Facilities:** Menu/Portions Cutlery Games Highchair Food warming **Nearby:** Twinlakes, Belvoir Castle, Rutland Water **Notes:** Garden: Fully enclosed, landscaped, south facing **Parking:** 20

MEDBOURNE

The Nevill Arms

12 Waterfall Way LE16 8EE

☎ 01858 565288 📠 01858 565509

Email: nevillarms@hotmail.com

Dir: *A508 from Northampton to Market Harborough, then B664 for 5m. Left for Medbourne*

Warm golden stone and mullioned windows make this traditional old coaching inn, in its riverside setting by the village green, truly picturesque. The popular pub garden has its own dovecote and is a great attraction for children who like to feed the ducks. A choice of appetising home-made soups, spicy lamb with apricots, smoked haddock and spinach bake, and pork in apple cream and cider are typical examples of the varied menu.

Open: 12-2.30 6-11 (Sun 12-3, 7-10.30) **Bar Meals:** L served all week 12-2 D served all week 7-9.45 (Sun 7-9.30) Av main course £6.50 **Brewery/Company:** Free House 🍺: Fuller's London Pride, Adnams Bitter, Greene King Abbot Ale, Guest Beers **Children's Facilities:** Fam room Menu/Portions Games Highchair Food warming **Notes:** Garden: Edges the river bank, with picnic benches **Parking:** 30

REDMILE
Peacock Inn
Church Corner NG13 0GB
☎ 01949 842554 🖷 01949 843746
Email: info@thepeacockinnredmile.co.uk
Dir: *From A1 take A52 towards Nottingham*
The Peacock Inn is a 16th-century stone-built pub with a
lovely beamed interior and open fireplaces. Located in the
pretty village of Redmile, it sits beside the Grantham
Canal in the Vale of Belvoir, only two miles from the
picturesque castle. It has a local reputation for good
quality food, and offers a relaxed and informal setting for
wining, dining and socialising. The restaurant and bar
menus include dishes based on local seasonal produce.
Guest ales like Bombardier, Timothy Taylor Landlord and
Tetley Cask are on tap.

Open: 11-11 (Sun 12-10.30) **Bar Meals:** L served all
week 12-2.30 D served all week 7-9.30 Av main
course £12 **Restaurant Meals:** L served all week 12-
2.30 D served all week 7-9.30 **Brewery/Company:**
Traditional Free House Plc 🍺: Timothy Taylor Landlord,
Bombardier **Children's Facilities:** Play area (Mother &
baby room, highchairs) Baby changing **Parking:** 24

SOMERBY
Stilton Cheese Inn 🍷
High Street LE14 2QB
☎ 01664 454394
An attractive 17th-century village centre pub built of
mellow local sandstone. The same menus serve both bar
and restaurant, with a specials blackboard offering
further choice. On the carte expect grilled steaks; chicken
tikka masala; and deep-fried cod, while examples from
the specials board include monkfish and crayfish tails
thermidor; liver and bacon with bubble and squeak; pork
fillet in cider sauce; and butternut squash ravioli.
Open: 12-3 6-11 **Bar Meals:** L served all week 12-2
D served all week 6-9 (Sun 7-9) Av main course £7.50
Restaurant Meals: L served all week 12-2 D served all
week 6-9 (Sun 7-9) Av 3 course alc £14.50

Brewery/Company: Free House 🍺: Grainstore Ten Fifty,
Brewster's Hophead, Belvoir Star, Carlsberg-Tetley
Tetley's Cask, Marston's Pedigree 🍷: 10 **Children's
Facilities:** Fam room Menu/Portions Cutlery Highchair
Food warming **Nearby:** Twin Lakes, Borough Hill Iron
Age Hillfort, Melton Country Park **Notes:** Garden: Small
patio, seats around 20 **Parking:** 14

STATHERN
Red Lion Inn ⚘🍷
Red Lion Street LE14 4HS
☎ 01949 860868 🖷 01949 861579
Email: info@theredlioninn.co.uk
Web: www.theredlioninn.co.uk
Dir: *From A1 (Grantham), A607 towards Melton, turn
right in Waltham, right at next x-rds then left to Stathern*
The award-winning team at the Red Lion are passionate
about traditional pub values, aiming to serve excellent
food, beer and wine in an enjoyable atmosphere. You'll
find a traditional stone-floored bar and an informal
lounge. There's also an informal dining area and an
elegant dining room. Besides the hand-pumped local
beers, speciality beers and bottled ciders are also on
offer. Seasonal highlights include mulled wine and roast

chestnuts by the open fire in winter and Pimms cocktails
in the garden in summer. Produce from the best local
suppliers is used to create a daily-changing menu.
Open: 12-3 6-11 (Sat 12-11, Sun 12-5.30) **Closed:** 26
Dec, 1 Jan **Bar Meals:** L served all week 12-2 D
served Mon-Sat 7-9.30 (Sat 6-9.30 Sun 12-3) Av main
course £12.25 **Restaurant Meals:** L served all week
12-2 D served Mon-Sat 7-9.30 (Sun 12-3) Av 3 course
alc £24.25 **Brewery/Company:** Rutland Inn Company
Ltd 🍺: Grainstore Olive Oil, Brewster's VPA, Exmoor Gold.
London Pride, Leffe, Hoegaarden & Budvor 🍷: 8
Children's Facilities: Play area (Toys) Menu/Portions
Cutlery Games Highchair Food warming **Nearby:** Belvoir
Castle & Maze, Langar Karting & Twin Lakes **Notes:**
Dogs allowed in bar, in garden, Water **Garden:** Patio
garden, tables, chairs, heaters, BBQ **Parking:** 25

LEICESTERSHIRE

LINCOLNSHIRE

BOURNE
The Wishing Well Inn ♀
Main Street Dyke PE10 0AF
☎ 01778 422970 📠 01778 394508
Dir: *Take A15 towards Seaford, Inn in next village*
This village free house started life as a one-room pub
105 years ago, but the building itself is 300 years old.
Inside there's a wealth of old oak beams, as well as two
inglenook fireplaces in the bar and restaurant areas, the
smaller of which also houses a wishing well. Outside, an
attractive beer garden backs onto the children's play
area. Dine on pub favourites such as steak and ale pie or
a giant mixed grill.
Open: 9-11 (Winter 9-3, 5-11) **Bar Meals:** L served all
week 12-9 D served all week **Restaurant Meals:** L
served all week 12-2 D served all week 6.30-9

Brewery/Company: Free House 🍺: Greene King Abbot
Ale, Tiger Bitter, 3 Guest's ♀: 7 **Children's Facilities:**
Licence Play area Menu/Portions Cutlery Games
Highchair Food warming **Nearby:** Grimsthorpe Castle,
Rutland Water, Nene Valley Railway **Notes:** Garden:
Large garden with patio **Parking:** 100

BRIGG
The Jolly Miller
Brigg Road Wrawby DN20 8RH
☎ 01652 655658 📠 01652 657506
Web: www.jollymiller.co.uk
Dir: *1.5m E of Brigg on the A18, on left*
Popular country inn a few miles south of the Humber
Estuary. The pleasant bar and dining area are traditional
in style, and there's a large beer garden. The menu offers
a good range of food with most dishes under £5. Tuck
into a chip butty; vegetable burger bap; home-made
curry; or steak with onion rings. Puddings include hot
chocolate fudge cake and banana split. Play area and
children's menu.
Open: 12-11 (Tue 3-11) **Bar Meals:** L served all week
12-7.30 D served all week 12-7.30 (Sun 12-3) Av main
course £5 **Restaurant Meals:** L served 12-7.30
D served 5-7.30 (Sun 12-3) **Brewery/Company:**
Enterprise Inns 🍺: Guinness, Stella, Carling, Carling
Premier, John Smith Extra Smooth & 2 Guest Ales
Children's Facilities: Play area (Swing, slide, rdbt &
climbing frame) Menu/Portions Cutlery Games Highchair
Food warming Baby changing **Nearby:** Elsham Hall with
Zoo, Wrawby Postmill & Brigg Town **Notes:** Garden:
Patio, caravan park & animal farm **Parking:** 40

CONINGSBY
The Lea Gate Inn ♀
Leagate Road LN4 4RS
☎ 01526 342370 📠 01526 345468
Email: theleagateinn@hotmail.com
Web: www.the-leagate-inn.co.uk
Dir: *Off B1192 just outside Coningsby*
The oldest licensed premises in the county, dating from
1542, this was the last of the Fen Guide Houses that
provided shelter before the treacherous marshes were
drained. The oak-beamed pub has a priest's hole and a
very old inglenook fireplace among its features. The same
family have been running the pub for nearly 25 years.
Open: 11.30-2.30 6.30-11 (Sun 12-2.30, 6.30-10.30)
Bar Meals: L served all week 12-2 D served all week
6.30-9.30 **Restaurant Meals:** L served all week D

served all week 6.30-9.15 **Brewery/Company:** Free
House 🍺: Scottish Courage Theakstons XB, Marston's
Pedigree ♀: 7 **Children's Facilities:** Play area (Wooden
play area, bouncy castle in summer) Highchair Food
warming **Notes:** Garden: Large garden **Parking:** 60

EWERBY

The Finch Hatton Arms

43 Main Street Sleaford NG34 9PH

☎ 01529 460363 📠 01529 461703

Web: www.thefinchhattonarms.co.uk

Dir: *from A17 to Kirkby-la-Thorne, then 2m NE. Also 2m E of A153 between Sleaford & Anwick*

Originally known as the Angel Inn, this 19th-century pub was given the family name of Lord Winchelsea, who bought it in 1875. After a chequered history and a short period of closure, these days it offers pub, restaurant and hotel facilities. It offers an extensive and varied menu to suit all tastes and budgets, but with its traditional ale and regular customers it retains a 'local' atmosphere.
Open: 11.30-2.30 6.30-11 Closed: 25-26 Dec **Bar Meals:** L served all week 11.30-2 D served all week 6.30-10 Sun 6.30-9.30 Av main course £10
Restaurant Meals: L served all week 11.30-2 D served all week 6.30-10 (Sun 6.30-9.30) Av 3 course alc £18
Brewery/Company: Free House 🍺: Everards Tiger Best, Dixons Major, guest beer **Children's Facilities:** Licence Menu/Portions Cutlery Games Highchair Food warming Baby changing **Notes:** Garden: Tables outside
Parking: 60

FROGNALL

The Goat 🍷

155 Spalding Road Deeping St James PE6 8SA

☎ 01778 347629

Email: graysdebstokes@btconnect.com

Dir: *A1 to Peterborough, A15 to Market Deeping, old A16 to Spalding, pub about 1.5m from junct of A15 & A16*

Its 17th-century origins well concealed from the front, this cosy, friendly country pub has an open fire, large beer garden and plenty to amuse the children. Main courses include home-made prawn curry; trio of Grasmere sausages; or chef's pie of the day.
Open: 11-2.30 6-11 (Sun 12-3, 7-10.30) Closed: 25 Dec **Bar Meals:** L served all week 12-2 D served all week 6.30-9.30 (Sun 2.30-9) **Restaurant Meals:** L served all week 12-2 D served all week 6.30-9.30

Brewery/Company: Free House 🍺: 5 Guest Cask Ales change each week 🍷: 16 **Children's Facilities:** Fam room Play area (Action tree, adventure frame & swings) Menu/Portions Highchair Food warming **Nearby:** Ferry Meadows, Nene Valley Railway Park & Tallington Lakes
Notes: Garden: Covered patio, beer garden, seats approx 90 **Parking:** 50

GEDNEY DYKE

The Chequers 🍷

nr Spalding PE12 0AJ

☎ 01406 362666 📠 01406 362666

Dir: *From King's Lynn take A17, 1st rdbt after Long Sutton take B1359*

In a pretty village close to the Wash, this 18th-century country inn has a good selection of food. Local quails eggs with bacon; or bang bang chicken, and fish specials like marinaded loin of tuna with tomato salsa; or baked seabass with lobster fish cake are popular. Lincolnshire pork and leek sausages; and wild mushroom gateau crêpe with Parmesan shavings are non-fish options. Well-chosen ales, patio garden and outdoor eating in summer.
Open: 12-2 7-11 (Sun 12-2 7-10.30) Closed: 26 Dec
Bar Meals: L served Tue-Sun 12-2 D served Tue-Sun 7-9 (Sun 12-2.30) **Restaurant Meals:** L served Tue-Sun 12-2 D served Tue-Sun 7-9 (Sun 12-2.30, 7-9)
Brewery/Company: Free House 🍺: Adnams Best, Greene King Abbot Ale, Speckled Hen, IPA 🍷: 10
Children's Facilities: Menu/Portions Cutlery Highchair Food warming **Nearby:** Butterfly Park, Dinosaur Park
Notes: Garden: Beer garden, patio, food served outside
Parking: 25

LINCOLNSHIRE

LOUTH
Masons Arms
Cornmarket LN11 9PY
☎ 01507 609525 📠 0870 7066450
Email: info@themasons.co.uk
Web: www.themasons.co.uk
Located in the Cornmarket at the heart of Georgian Louth, this Grade II listed building dates back to 1725. In the days when it was known as the Bricklayers Arms, the local Masonic lodge met here. The downstairs Market Bar is for beer lovers, while the 'upstairs' restaurant offers an à la carte menu.
Open: 10-11 (Sat-Sun 10-12) **Bar Meals:** L served all week 12-2.30 D served Mon-Sat 6-9 (Sun 12-2) Av main course £5.95 **Restaurant Meals:** L served Sun 12-2 D served Sat 7-9.30 Av 3 course alc £18

Brewery/Company: Free House 🍺: Timothy Taylor Landlord, Marston's Pedigree, Batemans XB Bitter, XXXB & 2 Guest Beers **Children's Facilities:** Licence Menu/Portions Games Highchair Food warming **Nearby:** Pleasure Island Theme Park, Rand Farm Park & Fantasy Island Theme Park

SKEGNESS
The Vine Hotel ★★★ HL 🍷
Vine Road Seacroft PE25 3DB
☎ 01754 763018 & 610611 📠 01754 769845
Email: info@thevinehotel.com
Web: www.thevinehotel.com
Dir: *Hotel in Seacroft area of Skegness. S of the centre.*
Substantially unchanged since 1770, the Vine is the second oldest building in Skegness. The charming hostelry offers comfortable accommodation and a fine selection of Bateman's own ales. There is a varied bar menu.
Open: 11-11 (Sun 12-10.30) **Bar Meals:** L served all week 12-2.15 D served all week 6-9.15 (Sat-Sun all day) Av main course £7 **Restaurant Meals:** L served all week 12.30-2 D served all week 6.30-9.15 (Sun 12-

2.30) Av 3 course alc £20 **Brewery/Company:** Free House 🍺: Batemans XB & XXXB, Valiant & Blacksheep 🍷: 8 **Children's Facilities:** Licence Menu/Portions Highchair Food warming **Nearby:** Skegness Pier, Fantasy Island, Butlins **Notes:** Dogs allowed in bar, in garden, in bedrooms Garden: Secluded **Parking:** 50

SOUTH WITHAM
Blue Cow Inn & Brewery
High Street nr Grantham NG33 5QB
☎ 01572 768432 📠 01572 768432
Email: bookings@thebluecowinn.co.uk
Web: www.thebluecowinn.co.uk
Dir: *Between Stamford & Grantham on A1*
Just in Lincolnshire, with the Rutland border a few hundred yards away, this once-derelict, 13th-century inn stands close to the source of the River Witham. Part-timbered outside, the interior has a wealth of beamed ceilings and walls, stone floors and open log fires when the easterly winds whip across the Fens from Siberia. New owner Simon Crathorn is continuing in his predecessors' footsteps, brewing his own beers. The inn also has a patio beer garden for warm evenings.

Open: 12-11 **Bar Meals:** L served all week 12-2.30 D served all week 6-9.30 Av main course £8 **Restaurant Meals:** L served all week 12-2.30 D served all week 6-9.30 Av 3 course alc £15 **Brewery/Company:** Free House 🍺: Own beers **Children's Facilities:** Fam room Menu/Portions Cutlery Games Highchair Food warming **Nearby:** Burghley House, Horse events, Sacrewell Farm, Rutland Water, Water sports **Notes:** Dogs allowed in bar, Water Garden: Seating for 32 **Parking:** 45

STAMFORD

The George of Stamford ★★★ HL ◉ ♛
71 St Martins PE9 2LB
☎ 01780 750750 📠 01780 750701
Email: reservations@georgehotelofstamford.com
Web: www.georgehotelofstamford.com
Dir: *From Peterborough take A1 N. Onto B1081 for Stamford, down hill to lights. Hotel on left*

The two doors that greet customers entering The George - one marked 'London', the other 'York' - confirm the origins of this magnificent 16th-century coaching inn. Forty coaches a day once stopped here; twenty up, and twenty down, and beyond the doors lie the panelled waiting rooms originally used by passengers while the horses were changed in the hotel courtyard. Today's visitors will find welcoming log fires, oak-panelled restaurants, a walled monastery garden and a cobbled courtyard. The style of food is essentially traditional, utilising the freshest possible ingredients.
Open: 11-11 (Sun 12-11) **Bar Meals:** L served all week 11.30-2.30 Av main course £6.50 **Restaurant Meals:** L served all week 12.30-2.30 D served all week 7.30-10.30 Av 3 course alc £33 **Brewery/Company:** Free House ◼: Adnams Broadside, Fuller's London Pride, Greene King Ruddles Bitter ♛: 14 **Children's Facilities:** Menu/Portions Cutlery Games Highchair Food warming Baby changing **Nearby:** Nene Valley Railways, Rutland Water, Burghley Park & Stately Home **Notes:** Dogs allowed in bar, in garden, in bedrooms Dog pack, towel, blanket, feeding mat **Garden:** Sunken lawn, over 200 year-old Mulberry tree **Parking:** 120

WOOLSTHORPE

The Chequers Inn ★★★★ INN ◉ ♛
Main Street Grantham NG32 1LU
☎ 01476 870701
Email: justinnabar@yahoo.co.uk
Web: www.chequers-inn.net
Dir: *Approx 7m from Grantham town & main line railway. 3m from A607. Follow heritage signs to Belvoir Castle.*

Just a stone's throw from Belvoir Castle, The Chequers Inn mixes modern style with traditional features including five real fires. Drinkwise, there is an extensive range of continental lagers, real ales and fine wines plus fifty single malts. You can dine anywhere, from the traditional bar to the Bakehouse Restaurant (which contains an oven) or the more intimate Red Room. There is a strong emphasis on home cooking and quality ingredients, including locally sourced steaks and sausages. Outside, the pub has a cricket pitch, a pétanque pitch, and castle views from the mature garden.
Open: 12-3 5.30-11 **Bar Meals:** L served all week 12-2.30 D served all week 6-9.30 (No dinner Winter Sun, Sun 12-4) Av main course £13.50 **Restaurant Meals:** L served all week 12-2.30 D served all week 6-9.30 (No Dinner winter Sun, Sun 12-4) Av 3 course alc £25 **Brewery/Company:** Free House ◼: Staropramen, Hoegaarden, Stella Artois, Olde Trip & Marquis ♛: 25 **Children's Facilities:** Licence (Lounge with TVs showing cartoons & DVDs) Menu/Portions Cutlery Games Highchair Food warming **Nearby:** Belvoir Castle & Twin Lakes theme park **Notes:** Dogs allowed in bar, Hose & drinking bowls **Garden:** Mature, furniture, petanque pitch & views **Parking:** 35

ASHBY ST LEDGERS

The Olde Coach House Inn
Rugby CV23 8UN
☎ 01788 890349 📠 01788 891922
Email: oldcoachhouse@traditionalfreehouses.com
Dir: *M1 junct 18 follow A361/Daventry signs.Village on left*

A late 19th-century farmhouse and outbuildings, skilfully converted into a pub with dining areas, accommodation and meeting rooms, set in a village that dates way back to the Domesday Book of 1086. The village was home to Robert Catesby, one of the Gunpowder plotters. Beer is taken seriously here, with up to eight regularly changing real ales and legendary beer festivals. The pub also serves fresh, high quality food in comfortable surroundings, featuring game casserole, seafood linguine, massive mixed grills, Australian butterfish, grilled seabass, and summer barbecues.
Open: 12-11 (Sun 12-10.30) **Bar Meals:** L served all week 12-8.30 D served all week 12-8.30 Av main course £7 **Restaurant Meals:** L served all week D served all week Av 3 course alc £20 **Brewery/Company:** Free House ◼: Everards Original, Everards Tiger, Marstons Pedigree, guest beer **Children's Facilities:** Fam room Play area (Large wooden adventure playground) Menu/Portions Games Highchair Food warming Baby changing **Notes:** **Garden:** Landscaped garden, activity play area **Parking:** 50

BULWICK

The Queen's Head ♉
Main Street NN17 3DY
☎ 01780 450272
Dir: *Just off A43, between Corby and Stamford*
Overlooking the village church, this charming country pub is thought to have been a pub since the 17th century, although parts of the building date back to 1400. The name comes from the Portuguese wife of Charles II, Katherine of Braganza, who was well known for elaborate hair-dos. The cosy interior boasts open fireplaces and flagstone floors in a warren of small rooms. Relax with a pint of quality ale and some hearty pub food.
Open: 12-2.30 6-11 **Bar Meals:** L served Tue-Sun 12-2.30 D served Tue-Sat 6-9.30 (Sunday 12-3) Av main course £5.95 **Restaurant Meals:** L served Tue-Sun 12-2.30 D served Tue-Sat 6-9.30 (Sun 12-3) Av 3 course alc £25 **Brewery/Company:** Free House ♉: Shepherd Neame, Spitfire & Guest Ales, Rockingham Ales & Newby Wyke ♉: 9 **Children's Facilities:** Menu/Portions Cutlery Games Highchair Food warming **Nearby:** Rutland Water **Notes:** Dogs allowed in bar, Water Garden: Patio area **Parking:** 40

CLIPSTON

The Bulls Head ♉
Harborough Road Nr Market Harborough LE16 9RT
☎ 01858 525268
Dir: *On B4036 S of Market Harborough*
American airmen once pushed coins between the beams as a good luck charm before bombing raids, and the trend continues with foreign paper money pinned all over the inn. In addition to its good choice of real ales, the pub has an amazing collection of over 500 whiskies. The menu offered by the new tenants includes shark steaks, whole sea bass, hot toddy duck, and steak pie.
Open: 11.30-3 5.30-11 (Open Sat & Sun all day in summer) **Bar Meals:** L served all week 12-2.30 D served all week 6.30-9 Av main course £6.25 **Restaurant Meals:** L served all week 12-2.30 D served all week 6.30-9 Av 3 course alc £17.50
Brewery/Company: Free House ♉: Tiger, Beacon, Guest Beers & Seasonal ♉: 14 **Children's Facilities:** Licence Menu/Portions Highchair Food warming Baby changing **Nearby:** Foxton Locks **Notes:** Dogs allowed in bar, in garden, Water bowl **Garden:** Patio area with 10 tables **Parking:** 40

FARTHINGSTONE

The Kings Arms
Main Street nr Towcester NN12 8EZ
☎ 01327 361604 🖹 01327 361604
Email: paul@kingsarms.fsbusiness.co.uk
Dir: *from M1 take A45 W, at Weedon join A5 then right on road signed Farthingstone*
This cosy 18th-century, Grade II listed inn is tucked away in unspoilt countryside near Canons Ashby (NT), adorned with a collection of stone gargoyles. Excellent real ales can accompany the short menu, with its British cheese platters, sausage and mash, and Yorkshire pudding filled with steak and kidney or beef in Guinness. The landlord also sells cheeses and a variety of speciality regional foods including wild boar sausages, venison and Loch Fyne salmon.
Open: 12-2.30 7-11 (Lunchtime wknds only) **Bar Meals:** L served Sat-Sun 12-2 Av main course £6.60 **Brewery/Company:** Free House ♉: Oakham JHB, Jennings Bitter, Adnams, Brakspear Bitter, Youngs Bitter **Children's Facilities:** Fam room (Books, Puzzles, Games Room) Menu/Portions Games Food warming **Nearby:** Sulgrave Manor, Milton Keynes Snowdome, Billing Aquadrome **Notes:** Dogs allowed in bar, in garden, in bedrooms, Water **Garden:** Many plants, herb garden, **Parking:** 20

FOTHERINGHAY
The Falcon Inn ◉ ♟
Nr Oundle PE8 5HZ
☎ 01832 226254 🖹 01832 226046
Web: www.huntsbridge.com
Dir: *N of A605 between Peterborough & Oundle*
Fotheringhay is a perfect stone village with important historic connections. In 1452, in the now completely demolished Fotheringhay Castle, Richard III's life began, while in 1587 that of Mary, Queen of Scots ended. Overlooking the extraordinary church, which plays host to serious concerts, is the attractive 18th-century, stone-built Falcon, set within gardens redesigned by award-winning landscape architect, Bunny Guinness. It's a true local, with a Tap Bar regularly used by the Adnams-fuelled village darts team. The highly praised classic Italian food makes use of the latest season's olive oil and other fresh, seasonal ingredients. There are British classics too on the bar snack board, like Lancashire hotpot, potted shrimps and bangers and mash.
Open: 11.30-3 6-11 (Sun 12-3, 7-10.30, Sat 6-12 last orders 10pm) **Bar Meals:** L served all week 12-2.15 D served all week 7-9.30 Av main course £9.95
Restaurant Meals: L served all week 12-2.15 D served all week 6.15-9.30 Av 3 course alc £25
Brewery/Company: Free House 🍺: Adnams Bitter, Greene King IPA, Scottish Courage John Smith's, Nethergate ♟: 20 **Children's Facilities:** Play area (toys, highchairs) Menu/Portions Highchair Food warming
Nearby: Castle ruin & good walks available **Notes:** Garden: Good views over historic Fotheringhay Church
Parking: 30

MARSTON TRUSSELL
The Sun Inn ♟
Main Street Market Harborough LE16 9TY
☎ 01858 465531 🖹 01858 433155
This 17th-century coaching inn offers an original red brick bar, real coal winter fires, a friendly welcome, well-kept ales and a carefully chosen wine list. A typical menu includes starters of baked goats' cheese with fruit chutney, or garlic mushrooms with herb bread, followed by steak and ale pie, fish and chips or spinach and ricotta cannelloni.
Open: 11-3 6-11 **Bar Meals:** L served all week 12-2.30 D served all week 6-10 **Restaurant Meals:** L served all week 12-2.30 D served all week 6-10.30
🍺: Ruddles Best, Fosters, Marstons Pedigree, Charles Wells Bombardier & Everards Tiger ♟: 12 **Children's Facilities:** Licence Fam room Play area Menu/Portions Cutlery Games Highchair Food warming Baby changing
Nearby: Althorp, Jurassic Way & Foxton Locks **Notes:** Dogs allowed in bar **Parking:** 72

OUNDLE
The Montagu Arms ♟
Barnwell PE8 5PH
☎ 01832 273726 🖹 01832 275555
Email: ianmsimmons@aol.com
Web: www.themontaguarms.co.uk
Dir: *Off A605 opposite Oundle slip road*
One of Northamptonshire's oldest inns, the Montagu Arms was originally three cottages dating from 1601, housing the workmen building the nearby manor house. The inn has a large garden, well equipped for children's play, and overlooks the brook and village green of the royal village of Barnwell. An extensive menu serving the bar and restaurant ranges through snacks and sharing platters, and dishes such as Rutland sausages and mash, stuffed chicken, and crispy fish pie.
Open: 12-3 6-11 (Sat-Sun all day) **Bar Meals:** L served all week 12-2.30 D served all week 7-10 Av main course £8 **Restaurant Meals:** L served all week 12-2.30 D served all week 7-10 Av 3 course alc £15
Brewery/Company: Free House 🍺: Digfield Ales, Adnams Broadside, Hop Back Summer Lightning, Fullers London Pride, Oakham Ale, JHB ♟: 14 **Children's Facilities:** Play area (Swings, play area, log obstacle course) Menu/Portions Highchair Food warming Baby changing **Nearby:** Barnwell Country Park **Notes:** Garden: Large lawn, ample benches, petanque
Parking: 25

NORTHAMPTONSHIRE

NORTHAMPTONSHIRE

SIBBERTOFT
The Red Lion ♀
43 Welland Rise Nr Market Harborough Leicester
LE16 9UD
☎ 01858 880011 📠 01858 880011
Email: andrew@redlion880011.wanadoo.co.uk
Dir: *From Market Harborough take A4304, then A50.*
After 1m turn L

A friendly 300-year-old pub, the Red Lion has now been completely refurbished in a blend of contemporary and classic styles with oak beams and leather upholstery. The menu offers modern British cuisine and traditional pub favourites.

Open: 12-2 6-11 (Sun 7-10.30) **Bar Meals:** L served Wed-Sun 12-2 D served all week 6.30-9.45 (Sun 12-3) Av main course £7.50 **Restaurant Meals:** L served Wed-Sun 12-2 D served all week 6.30-9.45 (Sun 12-3) Av 3 course alc £18 **Brewery/Company:** Free House 🍺: Bass, Youngs, Boddingtons ♀: 20 **Children's Facilities:** Play area (Climbing frame) Menu/Portions Cutlery Games Highchair Food warming **Nearby:** Sibbertoft Gliding Club, Foxton Locks, Althrop Park **Notes:** Garden: Patio area, lawn **Parking:** 15

STOKE BRUERNE
The Boat Inn
Nr Towcester NN12 7SB
☎ 01604 862428 📠 01604 864314
Email: info@boatinn.co.uk
Web: www.boatinn.co.uk
Dir: *In village centre, just off A508 or A5*

Traditional thatched canalside inn run by the same family since 1877, located by a working lock and opposite a popular canal museum. Inside are cosy bars with open fires and flagstones. There's a traditional skittle alley next to the bar, and a restaurant that overlooks the busy lock, a bistro, and food available in the bar.

Open: 9-11 (closed 3-6 Mon-Thu in winter) **Bar Meals:** L/D served all week 9.30-9 Av main course £8 **Restaurant Meals:** L served Tue-Sun 12-2 D served all week 7-9 (Sun 6.30-8.30) **Brewery/Company:** Free House 🍺: Banks Bitter, Marstons Pedigree, Adnams Southwold, Frog Island Best, Marstons Old Empire **Children's Facilities:** Licence Menu/Portions Highchair Food warming **Nearby:** Boat trips on canal, canal museum **Notes:** Dogs allowed in bar, in garden, Water Garden: grass area by canal **Parking:** 50

WADENHOE
The King's Head ♀
Church Street Nr Oundle PE8 5ST
☎ 01832 720024
Email: burgessalex77@hotmail.com

Stone-built and partially thatched, this 16th-century inn stands by the River Nene in a pretty village setting. The interior is characterised by oak beams, quarry-tiled floors, a large inglenook fireplace and log fires, and there's a welcoming ambience throughout the bars and restaurant. A range of speciality beers is offered and a generous choice of wines by the glass. The riverside garden comprises a paddock, courtyard and patio with plenty of seating. The inn grows its own vegetables and herbs and other produce is locally sourced. Seafood and game in season are offered from the specials board, and typical dishes are fillets of red snapper simply grilled with butter and fresh parsley; and roast chicken with bread sauce. A game of Northamptonshire skittles is a pub feature.

Open: 11-3 5.30-11 (Sun 12-4, Closed Sun eve in winter) **Bar Meals:** L served all week 12-2.30 D served Mon-Sat 7-9.30 (Sun 12-3.30) Av main course £8.95 **Restaurant Meals:** L served all week 12-2.30 D served Mon-Sat 6.30-9.30 (Sun 12-3.30) **Brewery/Company:** Free House 🍺: Oakhams Bishops Farewell, London Pride & Oakham JHB ♀: 18 **Children's Facilities:** Play area (Large paddock, children must be supervised) Menu/Portions Cutlery Games Highchair Food warming **Nearby:** Nene Valley Railway, Ferry Meadows Country Park, Petersborough Cathedral **Notes:** Dogs allowed in bar, in garden, Water Garden: Large paddock, courtyard, patio, seating **Parking:** 20

KIMBERLEY
The Nelson & Railway Inn
12 Station Road Eastwood NG16 2NR
☎ 0115 938 2177 📄 0115 938 2179
Web: www.nelsonandrailway.co.uk
Dir: *1m N of M1 junct 26*
The landlord of 35 years gives this 17th-century pub its distinctive personality. Next door is the Hardy & Hanson brewery that supplies many of the beers, but the two nearby railway stations that once made it a railway inn are now sadly derelict. A hearty menu of pub favourites includes soup, ploughman's, and hot rolls, as well as grills and hot dishes like home-made steak and kidney pie; gammon steak; and mushroom stroganoff.
Open: 11-11 (Sun 12-10.30) **Bar Meals:** L served all week 12-2.30 D served all week 5.30-9 (Sun 12-6)

Restaurant Meals: L served all week 12-2.30 D served all week 5.30-9 (Sat 12-9, Sun 12-6)
Brewery/Company: Hardy & Hansons Plc 🍺: Hardys, Hansons Best Bitter, Classic, Cool & Dark, Olde Trip
Children's Facilities: Licence Fam room Highchair Food warming **Notes:** Dogs allowed in bar, Water provided Garden: Food served outdoors, patio/terrace **Parking:** 50

LAXTON
The Dovecote Inn 🍷
Moorhouse Road NG22 0NU
☎ 01777 871586
Email: dovecoteinn@yahoo.co.uk
Dir: *Exit A1 at Tuxford continue through Egmanton to Laxton.*
This rural 18th-century pub makes an ideal stopping point for walkers - and, as you can find out in the adjacent visitor centre, Laxton is one of the few places in Europe still farming by traditional methods. The comprehensive menu includes grills, salads and home-cooked short crust steak and Guinness pie. Daily specials might include sea bass stuffed with prawns; or pan-fried pork with cracked pepper and garlic, and vegetarians are well catered for.

Open: 11.30-3 6.30-11.30 (Fri-Sat 6-11.30) **Bar Meals:** L served all week 12-2 D served all week 6.30-9 Av main course £9.99 **Restaurant Meals:** L served all week 12-2 D served all week 6.30-9
Brewery/Company: Free House 🍺: Mansfield Smooth, Banks Smooth, Marston's Pedigree, Bombardier & Black Sheep 🍷: 10 **Children's Facilities:** Menu/Portions Cutlery Highchair Food warming **Nearby:** Medieval Farming Visitor Centre, Sherwood Forest, Rufford Country Park **Notes:** Dogs allowed in bar Garden: Table & chairs in front garden **Parking:** 45

NOTTINGHAM
Cock & Hoop 🍷
25 High Pavement NG1 1HE
☎ 0115 852 3231 📄 0115 852 3236
Email: drink@cockandhoop.co.uk
Web: www.cockandhoop.co.uk
Dir: *Follow tourist info signs for Galleries of Justice which are situated immediately opposite.*
Tasteful antiques, a real fire, a cellar bar and striking bespoke artwork characterize this traditional Victorian alehouse. It stands opposite the Galleries of Justice, where Lord Byron is said to have watched hangings from his lodgings above the pub. The imaginative menu could include haddock risotto; rump steak with béarnaise sauce; or a home-made burger with salad and fries.
Open: 12pm-1 (Open til 1am Fri-Sat) Closed: 25-26 Dec

Bar Meals: L/D served all week 12-7 Av main course £8.50 🍺: Deuchars IPA, Cock & Hoop, London Pride, Timothy Taylors Landlord, Old Speckled Hen 🍷: 7
Children's Facilities: Licence Fam room Menu/Portions Cutlery Highchair Food warming **Nearby:** Nottingham Castle, Galleries of Justice & Caves of Nottingham
Notes: Dogs allowed in bar, Water

THURGARTON
The Red Lion ♛

Southwell Road NG14 7GP

☎ 01636 830351

Web: www.redlionthurgarton.co.uk

Dir: *On A612 between Nottingham & Southwell*

This 16th-century inn was once a monks' alehouse. Pub food can be enjoyed in the bar, restaurant or garden. Main courses include beef and Guinness casserole, and chicken breast in garlic and mushroom sauce. For a lighter option, try a salad with roast ham or poached salmon and prawn; or the cheese platter.

Open: 11.30-2.30 6.30-11 (Open all day Sat-Sun & BHs)

Bar Meals: L served all week 12-2 D served all week 7-9.30 (Sat-Sun 12-9.30) Av main course £8.25

Restaurant Meals: L served all week 12-2 D served all week 7-10 **Brewery/Company:** Free House

🍺: Greene King Abbot Ale, Jenning Cumberland, Carlsberg-Tetley, Black Sheep, Mansfield Cask ♛: 7

Children's Facilities: Menu/Portions Cutlery Highchair Food warming **Nearby:** White Post Farm, Newark Castle, Nottingham City, Major Oak, Rufford Park **Notes:** Garden: Large spacious, well kept **Parking:** 40

CLIPSHAM
The Olive Branch ◉◉ ♛

Main Street LE15 7SH

☎ 01780 410355 ▤ 01780 410000

Email: info@theolivebranchpub.com

Web: www.theolivebranchpub.com

Dir: *2m off A1 at the B664 junct N of Stamford*

In 1999, three young men with the help of local villagers, friends and family saved the 19th-century Olive Branch from closure. The inn is now a highly successful business, and has expanded into a barn conversion 'party room' seating up to 28. The pub has an attractive front garden and terrace, and an interior full of locally made furniture including a rare 'nurdling chair', and artists' works (all for sale). The cooking is strongly based around local produce and seasonality, such as Lincolnshire sausages with English mustard.

Open: 12-3.30 6-11 (Sun 12-10.30 only, summer Sat 12-11) Closed: 26 Dec, 1 Jan **Bar Meals:** L served all week 12-2 D served all week 7-9.30 (Sun 12-3, 7-9)

Restaurant Meals: L served all week 12-2 D served all week 7-9.30 (Sun 12-3, 7-9) Av 3 course alc £23.75

Brewery/Company: Rutland Inn Company Ltd 🍺: Grainstore 1050 & Olive Oil, Fenland, Brewster's, VPA, Leffe, Hoegaarden & Budvor ♛: 15 **Children's Facilities:** Play area (Garden skittles) Menu/Portions Cutlery Games Highchair Food warming Baby changing **Nearby:** Twin lakes, Belvoir Castle Maze & Rutland Water **Notes:** Dogs allowed in bar, in garden Garden: Gravelled area, pergola, BBQ area, lawn **Parking:** 15

COTTESMORE
The Sun Inn ♛

25 Main Street LE15 7DH

☎ 01572 812321

Email: lindmann.london@btinternet.com

Web: www.thesun.cjb.net

Dir: *3m from Oakham*

Dating back to 1610, this whitewashed thatched pub boasts oak beams and a cosy fire in the bar. A well-priced menu supplemented by specials is on offer: chicken, leek and ham pie; grilled tuna steak with chilli dip; plus steaks and grills. Lunchtime snacks include baguettes; ham, eggs and chips; and ploughman's. Apparently the ghost of a young girl is sometimes seen behind the bar.

Open: 11.30-2.30 5-11 (Fri 11-3, Sat 11.30-11.30 & Sun 12-11) **Bar Meals:** L served Mon-Sun 12-2.15 D served Mon-Sun 6-9 (Fri-Sat 5.30-9.30, Sun 12-8.30) Av main course £7.95 **Restaurant Meals:** L served all week 12-2.15 D served all week 6-9 (Fri/Sat 5.30-9.30 & Sun 12-8.30) Av 3 course alc £15

Brewery/Company: Everards Brewery 🍺: Adnams Bitter, Everards Tiger, Marston's Pedigree, Scottish Courage Courage Directors, Greene King Abbot Ale & Guest Ales ♛: 9 **Children's Facilities:** Menu/Portions Cutlery Food warming **Nearby:** Rutland Water & Belvoir Castle **Notes:** Dogs allowed in bar, in garden Garden: Patio and Garden area **Parking:** 25

EMPINGHAM
White Horse Inn ★★ HL ♟
Main Street nr Oakham LE15 8PS
☎ 01780 460221 📠 01780 460521
Email: info@whitehorserutland.co.uk
Web: www.whitehorserutland.co.uk
Dir: *From A1 take A606 signed Oakham & Rutland Water*
A 17th-century former courthouse close to Rutland Water
that has lost none of its period charm. The comfortable,
atmosphere is complemented by a wide choice of hearty
meals and a well-stocked bar.
Open: 8-11pm **Bar Meals:** L served all week 12-2.15
D served all week 7-9.30 (Sun 12-9) Av main course £9
Restaurant Meals: L served all week 12-2.15 D served
all week 7-9.30 (Sun 12-9) Av 3 course alc £18
Brewery/Company: Enterprise Inns 🍺: John Smith's,
Grainstore Cooking, Ruddles Best, Abbot Ale, Adnams
Best Bitter ♟: 7 **Children's Facilities:** Menu/Portions
Games Highchair Food warming **Nearby:** Rutland Water,
Twin Lakes Adventure Park & Rockingham Race Track
Notes: Dogs allowed, Water Garden: Small sheltered
garden, seating **Parking:** 60

EXTON
Fox & Hounds ♟
19, The Green nr Oakham LE15 8AP
☎ 01572 812403 📠 01572 812403
Email: sandra@foxandhoundsrutland.co.uk
Web: www.foxandhoundsrutland.co.uk
Dir: *Take A606 from Oakham towards Stamford, at
Barnsdale turn left, after 1.5m turn right towards Exton.*
This imposing 17th-century pub is next to the village
green in the centre of the pretty village of Exton, with its
many thatched houses.
Open: 11-3 6-11 **Bar Meals:** L served all week 12-2 D
served Mon-Sat 6.30-9 Av main course £11
Restaurant Meals: L served all week 12-2 D served all
week 6.30-9 Av 3 course alc £19 **Brewery/Company:**
Free House 🍺: Greene King IPA, Grainstore Real Ales,
John Smiths Smooth ♟: 8 **Children's Facilities:**
Play area (Large garden, wooden play equipment)
Menu/Portions Games Highchair Food warming **Nearby:**
Rutland Water, Butterfly Farm, Burley Falconry Centre
Notes: Dogs allowed in bar, in garden, in bedrooms,
Water Garden: Large walled garden & patio area
Parking: 20

LYDDINGTON
Old White Hart ♟
51 Main St LE15 9LR
☎ 01572 821703 📠 01572 821965
Email: mail@oldwhitehart.co.uk
Web: www.oldwhitehart.co.uk
Dir: *From A6003 between Uppingham & Corby take
B672*
Set amongst the sandstone cottages of rural Lyddington,
this honey-coloured stone free house close to Rutland
Water has retained its original beamed ceilings, stone
walls and open fires, and is surrounded by well-stocked
gardens. Greene King and Timothy Taylor are amongst
the beers on offer, along with interesting, freshly
prepared food. The menu includes English mustard
toad in the hole, and there are fish and vegetarian
choices plus a selection of daily specials.
Open: 12-3 6.30-11 Closed: 25 Dec **Bar Meals:** L
served all week 12-2 D served Mon-Sat 6.30-9 (Sun
12-2.30) Av main course £10 **Restaurant Meals:** L
served all week 12-2 D served Mon-Sat 6.30-9 (Sun
12-2.30) Av 3 course alc £23 **Brewery/Company:** Free
House 🍺: Greene King IPA & Abbot Ale, Timothy Taylor
Landlord, Fullers London Pride ♟: 7 **Children's
Facilities:** Play area (Swing in garden etc) Menu/Portions
Games Highchair Food warming Baby changing **Nearby:**
Rutland Water, park in village, numerous walks **Notes:**
Garden: Beer garden, heated patio area, marquee
Parking: 50

RUTLAND

RUTLAND

OAKHAM

Barnsdale Lodge Hotel ★★★ HL ◉ ♈
The Avenue Rutland Water, North Shore LE15 8AH
☎ 01572 724678 🖹 01572 724961
Email: enquiries@barnsdalelodge.co.uk
Web: www.barnsdalelodge.co.uk
An Edwardian-style hotel overlooking Rutland Water in the heart of this picturesque little county. Its rural connections go back to its 17th-century origins as a farmhouse, but nowadays the Barnsdale Lodge offers modern comforts and hospitality. Real ales including local brews are served in the bar, with dishes such as half-roast chicken with chipolata and crispy bacon roasties, smoked haddock and baby spinach risotto or roasted Rutland Water trout.
Open: 7-11- **Bar Meals:** L served all week 12.15-2.15 D served all week 7-9.30 **Restaurant Meals:** L served all week 12.15-2.15 D served all week 7-9.45 Av 3 course alc £22.50 **Brewery/Company:** Free House 🍺: Rutland Grainstore, Courage Directors, John Smith's ♈: 8 **Children's Facilities:** Play area (Swings, slide, croquet, crazy golf) Highchair Food warming Baby changing **Notes:** Dogs allowed in bar, in garden, water, field for walks **Garden:** Courtyard, established garden with lawns **Parking:** 280

OAKHAM

The Blue Ball ♈
6 Cedar Street Braunston-in-Rutland LE15 8QS
☎ 01572 722135
Dir: *From A1 take A606 to Oakham. Village SW of Oakham. Pub next to church.*
A 17th-century thatched inn with open log fires and a cosy bar area, reputedly Rutland's oldest pub. There are five dining areas under low-beamed ceilings, where typical dishes include pork fillet served with a brandy, cream and peppercorn sauce with caramelised apples; chicken breast with a mushroom and tarragon sauce; and spinach and ricotta tortellini in a tomato sauce with shavings of gran padano cheese.
Open: 12-3 6-11 (Sat-Sun all day) **Bar Meals:** L served all week 12-2 D served Mon-Sat 6.30-9 (Sat-Sun 12-3) Av main course £14 **Restaurant Meals:** L served all week 12-2 D served Mon-Sat 6.30-9 (Sat-Sun 12-3) **Brewery/Company:** Free House 🍺: Kronenburg, London Pride, San Miguel, Greene King IPA, Fosters & Guinness ♈: 17 **Children's Facilities:** Licence Menu/Portions Games Highchair Food warming **Nearby:** Rutland Water **Notes:** Dogs allowed in bar, bones & water **Garden:** Decking with seating and awnings **Parking:** 5

OAKHAM

The Old Plough ♈
2 Church Street Braunston LE15 8QT
☎ 01572 722714 🖹 01572 770382
Email: info@oldploughrutland.com
Web: www.oldploughrutland.com
Dir: *From A1 to Stansford, A606 to Oakham, at 1st mini rdbt right onto High St until railway crossing. Left, 2nd turn on left signed Braunston.*
This is a genteel and very popular country village pub dating back to 1783. Handy for visiting Oakham. Expect speciality evenings an an enthusiasm for good food
Open: 11-11 (Fri-Sat 11-12) **Bar Meals:** L served all week 12-2.30 D served all week 6-9.30 (Sun 12-9) Av main course £9.95 **Restaurant Meals:** L served all week 12-2.30 D served all week 6-9.30 (Sun 12-9) Av 3 course alc £19 🍺: Boddingtons, Bass Cask, Greene King IPA, Grainstore, Cooting Triple B, Ten Fify, Grainstore Cooking, 10/50, Timothy Taylor Landlord & Guests ♈: 9 **Children's Facilities:** Play area Menu/Portions Cutlery Games Highchair Food warming **Nearby:** Twin Lakes, Rutland Water & Space Museum **Notes:** Dogs allowed in bar **Garden:** Large beer garden, patio **Parking:** 30

STRETTON
Ram Jam Inn 🍷
The Great North Road Oakham LE15 7QX
☎ 01780 410776 🖹 01780 410361
Dir: *On A1 n'bound carriageway past B1668, through service station into car park*
The inn is thought to have got its current name some time during the 18th century when the pub sign advertised 'Fine Ram Jam', though few people, if indeed anyone, are sure what that might have been. These days, the informal café-bar and bistro exude warmth. The patio overlooks the orchard and paddock, and in fine summer weather is set for alfresco dining from the comprehensive all-day menu.
Open: 7-11 **Bar Meals:** L/D served all week 12-9.30 Av main course £8.95 **Restaurant Meals:** L served all week 12-9.30 D served all week Av 3 course alc £16
Brewery/Company: Free House 🍺: Scottish Courage John Smith's Cask and Smooth, Marstons Pedigree, Greene King IPA 🍷: 8 **Children's Facilities:** Play area (Lrg outside area) Menu/Portions Cutlery Games Highchair Food warming Baby changing **Nearby:** Rutland Water, Burghley House, Belton House **Notes:** Garden: Patio set for open air dining **Parking:** 64

WING
Kings Arms ★★★★ INN ⊛ 🍷
Top Street LE15 8SE
☎ 01572 737634 🖹 01572 737255
Email: info@thekingsarms-wing.co.uk
Web: www.thekingsarms-wing.co.uk
Dir: *1m off B6003 between Uppingham & Oakham*
Located in the quaint village of Wing, The Kings Arms is an ideal base from which to explore the market towns of Oakham, Uppingham and Stamford. Imaginative cooking style underpinned by traditional and classic dishes.
Open: 12-3 6-11 (Summer, open all day wknds) **Bar Meals:** L served Tue-Sun 12-2 D served all week 6-9 Av main course £10 **Restaurant Meals:** L served Tue-Sun 12-2 D served all week 6.30-9 Av 3 course alc £20 **Brewery/Company:** Free House 🍺: Timothy Taylor Landlord, Marstons Pedigree, Grainstore Cooking and Guest beer 🍷: 20 **Children's Facilities:** Menu/Portions Cutlery Highchair Food warming **Nearby:** Rutland Nature Reserve, Rockingham Castle, Twinlakes Adventure Park & Rutland Water **Notes:** Garden: Outside dining area
Parking: 25

BISHOP'S CASTLE
Boars Head 🍷
Church Street SY9 5AE
☎ 01588 638521 🖹 01588 630126
Email: sales@boarsheadhotel.co.uk
Web: www.boarsheadhotel.co.uk
Dir: *In town centre*
One of Bishop's Castle's earliest surviving buildings, this former coaching inn was granted its first full licence in 1642. According to legend, it escaped being destroyed by fire during the Civil War because many of the Royalists were drinking here at the time. The integrity of the pub remains intact, with exposed beams, log fires and a chimney containing a priest hole. An appetising menu offers the likes of Spanish paella and chicken in cream and sherry sauce.
Open: 11.30-11 (Sun 12-10.30) **Bar Meals:** L served all week 12-3 D served all week 6.30-9 (Sun 12-9.30) Av main course £8 **Restaurant Meals:** L served all week 12-3 D served all week 6.30-9 Av 3 course alc £20 **Brewery/Company:** Free House 🍺: Scottish Courage Courage Best & Courage Directors & regular guests 🍷: 8 **Children's Facilities:** Licence (Highchairs, cot) Menu/Portions Games Highchair Food warming **Nearby:** Hoo Farm, Wonderland, Secret Hills **Parking:** 20

CLEOBURY MORTIMER
The Crown Inn 🍷
Hopton Wafers DY14 0NB
☎ 01299 270372 📄 01299 271127
Web: www.crownathopton.co.uk
Dir: *On A4117 8m E of Ludlow, 2m W of Cleobury Mortimer*
A quick glance at this 16th-century, one-time coaching inn suggests that it is constructed from Virginia creeper, so densely does its foliage cover every square inch of the façade, except the windows. Fresh local produce lies behind the seasonal menus featuring not just traditional dishes, but also more adventurous house specialities.
Open: 12-3 6-12 **Bar Meals:** L served all week 12-2.30 D served all week 6-9.30 (Sun 12-3, 7-9) Av main course £9.50 **Restaurant Meals:** L served all week 12-

2.30 D served all week 7-9.30 Av 3 course alc £25.50
Brewery/Company: Free House 🍺: Timothy Taylor Landlord, Hobsons Best + guest beers 🍷: 10 **Children's Facilities:** Play area (Large pondside garden) Menu/Portions Cutlery Highchair Food warming **Notes:** Garden: 3 large patios, nature garden with pond
Parking: 60

CLUN
The Sun Inn
10 High Street SY7 8JB
☎ 01588 640559 📄 01588 640277
Email: marieboul@hotmail.com
Web: www.thesunatclun.co.uk
A 15th-century inn of cruck frame construction set in a pretty Shropshire village. There are two bars, the stone-flagged snug and carpeted lounge furnished with settles and featuring a piece of 17th-century wallpaper. Freshly prepared home-cooked food is served, including a good choice of fish, such as whole grilled halibut with horse-radish sauce, and favourites like beef and Guinness pie. In fine weather food and drinks can be enjoyed outside on the patio area.
Open: 12-12 (Sat-Sun 12pm-1am) **Bar Meals:** L served

Thu-Tue 12-2 D served all week 6-9 Av main course £10.95 **Restaurant Meals:** L served all week 12-2 D served all week 6-9 (Sun 7-8.30) Av 3 course alc £17.50 🍺: Jennings Cockerhoop, Camerons Creamy Bitter, Banks Original & Monthly Guest Beers **Children's Facilities:** Licence Menu/Portions Games Highchair Food warming **Notes:** Dogs allowed in bar, no dogs in eating area Garden: Patio **Parking:** 6

CRAVEN ARMS
The Sun Inn 🍷
Corfton SY7 9DF
☎ 01584 861239 & 861503
Email: normanspride@aol.com
Web: www.thesuninncorfton.co.uk
Dir: *On the B4368 7m N of Ludlow*
First licensed in 1613, this historical pub in beautiful Corvedale is run by landlord Norman Pearce and his family. Norman brews his own Corvedale beers, using local borehole water, and sells them bottled and from the barrel. Landlady Teresa Pearce cooks all the meals, which might include lamb casserole; ocean pie; lamb rogan josh; and steak and chips. The pub puts on small beer festivals at Easter and August bank holidays.
Open: 12-2.30 6-12 (Fri/Sat 6pm-1am) **Bar Meals:** L

served all week 12-2 D served all week 6-9 (Sun 12-3, 7-9) Av main course £7.9 **Restaurant Meals:** L served all week 12-2 D served all week 6-9.30 (Sun 12-3, 7-9)
Brewery/Company: Free House 🍺: Corvedale Normans Pride, Secret Hop, Dark & Delicious, Julie's Ale, Katie's Pride 🍷: 14 **Children's Facilities:** Licence Play area (Swings) Menu/Portions Cutlery Games Highchair Food warming **Nearby:** Acton Scott Farm Museum, Ludlow Castle, Severn Valley Railway **Notes:** Dogs allowed in bar, Water Garden: 4 benches with tables, pretty views
Parking: 30

IRONBRIDGE
The Malthouse ♔
The Wharfage TF8 7NH
☎ 01952 433712 🗎 01952 433298
Email: enquiries@themalthouseironbridge.com
Web: www.themalthouseironbridge.com
Originally known as the Talbot, this building has been an inn since the 1800s. Ironbridge, a designated UNESCO World Heritage Site, is famous for its spectacular natural beauty and award-winning museums. Close by are river-side walks and stretches of peaceful woodland, while the towns of Bridgnorth and Ludlow are within easy reach. The Malthouse has twice been extensively refurbished and now offers six rooms above a popular jazz bar.
Open: 11-11 (Sun 12-3 6-10.30) **Bar Meals:** L served all week 12-2.30 D served all week 6-9.30 Av main course £8 **Restaurant Meals:** L served all week 12-2 D served all week 6.30-9.45 **Brewery/Company:** Punch Taverns 🍺: Flowers Original, Boddingtons, Tetley ♔: 10 **Children's Facilities:** Licence Menu/Portions Cutlery Games Highchair Food warming Baby changing **Nearby:** 10 historical museums **Parking:** 15

LUDLOW
The Cookhouse Cafe Bar ♦♦♦♦ ◉◉ ♔
Bromfield SY8 2JR
☎ 01584 856565 & 856665 🗎 01584 856661
Email: info@theclive.co.uk
Web: www.theclive.co.uk
Dir: *Located 2m N of Ludlow on A49 between Hereford and Shrewsbury*
The Cookhouse Café Bar is part of a complex, which includes the Clive Restaurant with rooms, and function facilities, in a former farmhouse and outbuildings.
Open: 11-11 (Sun 11-10) Closed: 25-26 Dec **Bar Meals:** L served all week 12-3 D served all week 6-10 (Sat-Sun 12-10) Av main course £8.95 **Restaurant Meals:** L served all week 12-3 D served all week 6-10 Av 3 course alc £25 **Brewery/Company:** Free House 🍺: Hobsons Best Bitter, Interbrew Worthington Cream Flow, Caffreys ♔: 8 **Children's Facilities:** Play area (Changing Room, Colouring Kits, Fish Pool) Menu/Portions Cutlery Games Highchair Food warming **Nearby:** Discovery Castle, Play barn at Craven Arms, Ludlow Castle **Notes:** Garden: Courtyard, beer lawn **Parking:** 100

MADELEY
The New Inn
Blists Hill Victorian Town Legges Way Telford TF7 5DU
☎ 01952 601018 🗎 01785 252247
Email: sales@jenkinsonscaterers.co.uk
Dir: *Between Telford & Broseley*
Here's something different - a Victorian pub that was moved brick by brick from the Black Country and re-erected at the Ironbridge Gorge Open Air Museum. The building remains basically as it was in 1890, and customers can buy traditionally brewed beer at five-pence farthing per pint - roughly £2.10 in today's terms - using pre-decimal currency bought from the bank. The mainly traditional menu includes home-made soup; steak and kidney pudding; and ham and leek pie.
Open: 11-4 Closed: 24-25 Dec, 1 Jan **Bar Meals:** L served all week 12-3 Av main course £7.50 **Restaurant Meals:** L served all week 12-3 **Brewery/Company:** Ironbridge Gorge Museums 🍺: Banks Bitter, Banks Original, Pedigree **Children's Facilities:** Fam room Play area Menu/Portions Highchair Food warming **Nearby:** Wonderland, Enginuity, **Parking:** 300

SHROPSHIRE

MUCH WENLOCK
Longville Arms
Longville in the Dale TF13 6DT
☎ 01694 771206 📄 01694 771742
Dir: *From Shrewsbury take A49 to Church Stretton, then B4371 to Longville*
Prettily situated in a scenic corner of Shropshire, ideally placed for walking and touring, this welcoming country inn has been carefully restored. Solid elm or cast-iron-framed tables, oak panelling and wood-burning stoves are among the features that help to generate a warm, friendly ambience. Favourite main courses on the bar menu and specials board include steak and ale pie, chicken wrapped in bacon and stuffed with pâté, smoked haddock, mixed fish platter, and a range of steaks.
Open: 12-3 7-11 **Bar Meals:** L served all week 12-2.30 D served all week 7-9.30 Av main course £9.95 **Restaurant Meals:** L served Sun 12-2.30 D served Fri-Sat 7-9.30 Av 3 course alc £22 **Brewery/Company:** Free House 🍺: Local guest beers **Children's Facilities:** Play area (swings, slides, Play house, trampolines) Menu/Portions Cutlery Highchair **Nearby:** Wenlock Edge, Secret Hills, Acton Scott Farm **Notes:** Dogs allowed in bar Garden: Patio area
Parking: 40

MUNSLOW
The Crown Country Inn ★★★★ INN ◉◉ 🍷
Nr Craven Arms SY7 9ET
☎ 01584 841205 📄 01584 841255
Email: info@crowncountryinn.co.uk
Web: www.crowncountryinn.co.uk
Dir: *On B4368 between Craven Arms & Much Wenlock*
The Crown is a three-storey Grade II listed Tudor inn with a lovely setting below the rolling hills of Wenlock Edge in the Vale of the River Corve.
Open: 12-2 6.30-11 Closed: 25 Dec **Bar Meals:** L served Tue-Sun 12-2 D served Tue-Sun 6.30-9 Av main course £10.50 **Restaurant Meals:** L served Tue-Sun 12-2 D served Tue-Sun 6.30-9 Av 3 course alc £22.50 **Brewery/Company:** Free House 🍺: Holden's Black Country Bitter, Black Country Mild, Holden's Golden Glow, Holden's Special Bitter & Three Tuns Brewery 3X 🍷: 7 **Children's Facilities:** Licence Play area Menu/Portions Cutlery Games Highchair Food warming **Nearby:** Ironbridge Victorian Village, Rats Farm Country Matters **Notes:** Garden: Large garden with grassed and patio areas **Parking:** 20

NORTON
The Hundred House Hotel ★★ HL ◉◉ 🍷
Bridgnorth Road nr Shifnal TF11 9EE
☎ 01952 730353 📄 01952 730355
Email: reservations@hundredhouse.co.uk
Web: www.hundredhouse.co.uk
Dir: *On A442, 6m N of Bridgnorth, 5m S of Telford centre*
The words 'Temperance Hall' on the Art Nouveau stained-glass doors set the tone here for an experience that is unique, sometimes witty and always delightful. The quirky charm extends to the bedrooms and gardens.
Open: 11-2.30 6-11 (Sun 11-10.30) Closed: 25-26 Dec Eve **Bar Meals:** L served Mon-Sat 12-2.15 D served Mon-Sun 6-9 (Sun 7-9) Av main course £8.95 **Restaurant Meals:** L served all week 12-2.15 D served Mon-Sat 6-9 **Brewery/Company:** Free House 🍺: Heritage Bitter, Highgate Saddlers Bitter, Highgate Dark Mild, Everards Tiger, Charles Wells & Bombardier 🍷: 16 **Children's Facilities:** Menu/Portions Highchair Food warming Baby changing **Nearby:** Ironbridge Gorge Museum, Enginuity at Ironbridge, Telford Park **Notes:** Garden: Extensive herb & large floral garden **Parking:** 40

SHREWSBURY
The Plume of Feathers ★★★ INN
Harley SY5 6LP

☎ 01952 727360 📠 01952 728542

Email: feathersatharley@aol.com

Nestled under Wenlock Edge, this 17th-century inn has stunning views across the valley. Look for the Charles I oak bedhead, full size cider press and inglenook fireplace. The bar and restaurant food reflects the seasons, and there is a changing fish menu.

Open: 12-3 5-11 (Sat 12-11.30, Sun 12-10.30) **Bar Meals:** L served all week 12-2 D served all week 6.30-9 (Sun 12-4, 6.30-8) Av main course £6.50 **Restaurant Meals:** L served all week 12-2 D served all week 6.30-9 (Sun 12-4, 6.30-9.30) Av 3 course alc £20

Brewery/Company: Free House 🍺: Worthingtons, Guinness, Directors, Carling & Guest beers **Children's Facilities:** Licence Play area (Football pitch & trampoline) Menu/Portions Cutlery Games Highchair Food warming **Nearby:** Ironbridge Gorge Museum, Telford Town Park, West Midlands Safari Park **Notes:** Garden: Lawn, tables, chairs, parasols & lovely views **Parking:** 70

UPPER AFFCOT
The Travellers Rest Inn 🍷
Church Stretton SY6 6RL

☎ 01694 781275 📠 01694 781555

Email: reception@travellersrestinn.co.uk

Web: www.travellersrestinn.co.uk

Dir: *Situated alongside A49 5m S of Church Stretton*

Customers travel some distance to enjoy the friendly atmosphere, great range of real ales and good pub meals at this traditional south Shropshire inn situated between Church Stretton and Craven Arms. Food (served until 9pm) could include cottage pie; traditional gammon; a choice of curries; and broccoli and cheese bake. Decadent desserts include a range of ice cream sundaes and traditional favourites such as hot chocolate fudge cake.

Open: 11-11 **Bar Meals:** L served all week 11.30-8.30 D served all week 11.30-8.30 (Sun 12-8.30) Av main course £7.50 🍺: Wood Shropshire Lad, Hobsons Best Bitter, Bass, Guinness, Travellers Best 🍷: 14 **Children's Facilities:** Licence Menu/Portions Highchair Baby changing **Nearby:** Shropshire Hills Discovery Centre, Ludlow Castle, Acton Scott Farm Museum **Notes:** Dogs on leads allowed in bar **Parking:** 50

WESTON HEATH
The Countess's Arms 🍷
nr Shifnal TF11 8RY

☎ 01952 691123 📠 01952 691660

Email: thecountesssarms@hotmail.com

Dir: *1.5m from Weston Park. Turn off A5 onto A51 towards Newport*

In the owners' own words, 'a large contemporary eatery in a refurbished traditional pub'; very popular particularly for jazz night on Fridays. Customers in the spacious gallery bar can look down on the blue glass mosaic-tiled bar below.

Open: 12-11 (Sun 12-10.30) **Bar Meals:** L served all week 12-6 D served all week 6-9.30 (Sun 12-8.30) Av main course £8.95 **Restaurant Meals:** L served all week 12-6 D served all week 6-9.30 (Sun 12-8.30)

Brewery/Company: Free House 🍺: Robinsons, St Austell Tribute, Woods Hopping Mad 🍷: 10 **Children's Facilities:** Play area (Trampoline, wendy house, goals) Menu/Portions Cutlery Games Highchair Food warming Baby changing **Nearby:** Weston Park, Cosford Air Museum, Bliss Hill Museum, Ironbridge **Notes:** Garden: Large grassed area with play area **Parking:** 100

SHROPSHIRE

WHITCHURCH
Willeymoor Lock Tavern ♀
Tarporley Road SY13 4HF
☎ 01948 663274
Dir: 2m N of Whitchurch on A49 (Warrington/Tarporley)
A former lock keeper's cottage idyllically situated beside the Llangollen Canal. Mrs Elsie Gilkes has been licensee here for some 25 years. Low-beamed rooms are hung with a novel teapot collection, there are open log fires and a range of real ales. Deep-fried fish and a choice of grills rub shoulders with traditional steak pie, chicken curry and vegetable chilli. Other options include salad platters, children's choices and gold rush pie for dessert.
Open: 12-11 (Sun 12-2.30 7-10.30) Closed: 25 Dec
Bar Meals: L served all week 12-2 D served all week 6-9 (7pm on Sun in winter) **Restaurant Meals:** L served

all week 12-2 D served all week 6-9
Brewery/Company: Free House ◀: Guest Ales, Abbeydale, Moonshine, Weetwood, Oakham JHB, Best & Eastgate, Timothy Taylor Landlord ♀: 8 **Children's Facilities:** Play area (Enclosed area, wooden adventure play ground) Cutlery Highchair Food warming **Notes:** Garden: Besides canal, enclosed play area **Parking:** 50

ALSAGERS BANK
The Gresley Arms
High Street ST7 8BQ
☎ 01782 720297 📄 01782 720297
A 200-year-old pub in a semi-rural location set between two country parks, making it a popular stopping off point for walkers and cyclists. It is a friendly local, with a traditional bar, separate lounge and large family room, serving real ale and real food at a reasonable price. The menu encompasses basket meals (chicken, scampi, beefburger), steaks with sauces, light bites, main meals and daily specials, such as braised lamb shank, and tagliatelle Niçoise.
Open: 12-3 6-11 (All day Fri-Sun) **Bar Meals:** L served all week 12-2.30 D served all week 6-9.30 (Sat-Sun 12-9.30) Av main course £6 **Restaurant Meals:** L

served all week 12-3 D served all week 6-9.30 (Sat-Sun 12-9.30) ◀: 6 guest beers **Children's Facilities:** Fam room (garden with play equipment) Menu/Portions Highchair Food warming **Nearby:** Alton Towers, Trentham Gardens, Waterworld **Notes:** Dogs allowed in bar Garden: Large garden, mountain views **Parking:** 30

ECCLESHALL
The George ♀
Castle Street ST21 6DF
☎ 01785 850300 📄 01785 851452
Email: information@thegeorgeinn.freeserve.co.uk
Web: www.thegeorgeinn.freeserve.co.uk
Dir: 6m from M6 junct 14
A family-run, 16th-century former coaching inn with its own micro-brewery, where the owners' son produces award-winning Slater's ales. Occasional beer festivals are held, and the menu features a wide variety of dishes, including spicy chilli tortillas; fish stew; roast salmon with hoi sin sauce, chive mash and stir-fry veg; and cod in Slater's ale batter. A selection of salads, baked potatoes and sandwiches is also available.
Open: 11-11 (Sun 12-10.30) Closed: 25 Dec **Bar**

Meals: L served all week 12-9.30 D served all week 6-9.30 (Sun 12-8.30) Av main course £9.50 **Restaurant Meals:** L served all week 12-2.30 D served all week 6-9.45 **Brewery/Company:** Free House ◀: Slaters Ales **Children's Facilities:** Menu/Portions Cutlery Highchair Food warming **Notes:** Dogs allowed in bar **Parking:** 30

LEEK

Three Horseshoes Inn ★★ HL ◉ ♟

Buxton Road Blackshaw Moor ST13 8TW

☎ 01538 300296 ◈ 01538 300320

Web: www.threeshoesinn.co.uk

There are great views from the attractive gardens of this sprawling, creeper-covered inn. Inside, the main bar features wood fires in the winter, with a good selection of real ales and guest beers. Visitors can choose from traditional décor and roast meats in the bar carvery, the relaxed atmosphere of the brasserie, and the more formal restaurant. Choices include eggs Benedict with smoked haddock and spinach; and roasted vegetable, rosemary and goats' cheese tarte Tatin.

Open: 12-3 6-11 **Bar Meals:** L served all week 12-2 D served all week 6.30-9 (Sun 12-3, 6-8.30 & all day in summer) Av main course £7.75 **Restaurant Meals:** L served Wed-Sun 12.30-1.30 D served all week 6.30-9 **Brewery/Company:** Free House ◧: Theakstons XB Courage Directors, Morland Old Speckled Hen, Kronenbourg 1664 ♟: 12 **Children's Facilities:** Play area Highchair Food warming Baby changing **Nearby:** Alton Towers, Peak Park, Churnel Valley Railway **Parking:** 100

NORBURY JUNCTION

The Junction Inn

Stafford ST20 0PN

☎ 01785 284288 ◈ 01785 284288

Dir: *From M6 take road for Eccleshall, left at Gt Bridgeford towards Woodseaves, left towards Newport, left for Norbury Junction*

Not a railway junction, but a beautiful stretch of waterway where the Shropshire Union Canal meets the disused Newport arm. The inn offers fabulous views and a great stop off point for canal walkers. Food ranges from baguettes, burgers and basket meals to grills and home-made pies. Popular options are sizzling chicken fajitas, giant battered cod and a gargantuan mixed grill. Caravans are welcome and canal boat hire is available.

Open: 11-11 **Bar Meals:** L served all week 11-9 D served all week 11-9 Av main course £6 **Restaurant Meals:** L served all week 12-9 D served all week 12-9 **Brewery/Company:** Free House ◧: Banks Mild, Banks Bitter, Junction Ale and guest ales **Children's Facilities:** Play area (Board games, football field) Menu/Portions Highchair Food warming Baby changing **Notes:** Dogs allowed in garden, Water **Garden:** Scenic garden with fabulous views **Parking:** 100

STAFFORD

The Moat House ★★★★ HL ◉◉ ♟

Lower Penkridge Road Acton Trussell ST17 0RJ

☎ 01785 712217 ◈ 01785 715344

Email: info@moathouse.co.uk

Web: www.moathouse.co.uk

Dir: *M6 J13 towards Stafford, 1st R to Acton Trussell*

Grade II listed mansion dating back to the 15th century and situated behind its original moat. Quality bedrooms, conference facilities and corporate events are big attractions, and with four honeymoon suites, the Moat House is a popular venue for weddings. Inside are oak beams and an inglenook fireplace, and the bar and food trade brings in both the hungry and the curious who like to savour the charm and atmosphere of the place. Major refurbishments have contributed a stylish lounge area serving brasserie-style food. Among the more popular dishes are rocket and goats' cheese soup or tuna spring roll, followed by braised shank of lamb with bubble and squeak and a rosemary jus.

Open: 10-11 Closed: 25-26 Dec, 1-2 Jan **Bar Meals:** L served Mon-Sat 12-2.15 D served Sun-Fri 6-9.30 Av main course £12.50 **Restaurant Meals:** L served all week 12-2 D served all week 7-9.30 Av 3 course alc £34.50 **Brewery/Company:** Free House ◧: Bank's Bitter, Marston's Pedigree, Murphys ♟: 13 **Children's Facilities:** Licence Fam room (Changing Room) Menu/Portions Highchair Food warming Baby changing **Nearby:** Alton Towers, Cadbury World, Shughborough Farm **Notes:** Garden: Adjoining the moated manor, overlooks moat **Parking:** 200

STAFFORDSHIRE

TATENHILL
Horseshoe Inn 🍷
Main Street Burton-on-Trent DE13 9SD
☎ 01283 564913 📠 01283 511314
Dir: *From A38 at Branston follow signs for Tatenhill*
Probably five to six hundred years old, this historic pub
retains much original character, including evidence of a
priest's hiding hole. In winter, log fires warm the bar and
family area. In addition to home-made snacks like chilli
con carne, and Horseshoe brunch, there are sizzling
rumps and sirloins, chicken curry, moussaka, battered
cod with chips and mushy peas, and a pasta dish of the
week. And specials too - beef bourguignon, or steak and
kidney pudding, for instance.
Open: 11-11 **Bar Meals:** L served all week 12-9.30 D
served all week 12-9.30 (Sun 12-9) Av main course
£7.50 **Restaurant Meals:** L served all week 12-9.30
D served all week 12-9.30 Av 3 course alc £14
Brewery/Company: Wolverhampton & Dudley
🍺: Marstons Pedigree 🍷: 14 **Children's Facilities:** Fam
room Play area (Play area, pets corner) Menu/Portions
Cutlery Games Highchair Food warming Baby changing
Nearby: Maize Maze, Byrkley Garden Centre **Notes:**
Dogs allowed in bar, Water **Garden:** Small enclosed
garden with fish pond **Parking:** 70

ALCESTER
The Throckmorton Arms ★★★★ INN 🍷
Coughton B49 5HX
☎ 01789 766366 📠 01789 762654
Email: info@thethrockmortonarms.co.uk
Web: www.thethrockmortonarms.co.uk
Dir: *A435 from Birmingham. Through Mappleborough
Green & Studley. 2m, pub on right.*
A charming traditional coaching inn steeped in history,
with oak beams and open fires harmonising easily with
modern comforts. Locally acclaimed food worth trying at
lunchtime includes Glastonbury lamb cooked in red wine;
and spicy vegetable chilli. Evening meals include cod and
salmon brochette; and oven-roasted chicken fillet. Daily
changing specials are likely to be steak, kidney and suet
pudding; homemade faggots; fillets of sea bream; and
vegetable lasagne.
Open: 12-11 (Sun 12-10.30) **Bar Meals:** L served all
week 12-2.30 D served Mon-Sat 6.30-9 (Sun 12-7,
Winter Sun 12-4) Av main course £9.95 **Restaurant
Meals:** L served all week 12-2.30 D served Mon-Sat
6.30-9 (Sun 12-7, Winter Sun 12-4) Av 3 course alc
£20 **Brewery/Company:** Free House 🍺: Tribute, Hook
Norton, Butty Bach, Pure Gold & The Usual 🍷: 10
Children's Facilities: Menu/Portions Games Highchair
Food warming Baby changing **Notes:** Dogs allowed in
bar **Garden:** Outside patio and dining area **Parking:** 45

ALDERMINSTER
The Bell ★★★★ INN 🍷
Stratford-upon-Avon CV37 8NY
☎ 01789 450414 📠 01789 450998
Email: info@thebellald.co.uk
Web: www.thebellald.co.uk
Dir: *On A3400 3.5m S of Stratford-upon-Avon*
Just a few miles from Stratford-upon-Avon in the heart of
Shakespeare country, The Bell at Alderminster is ideally
placed for exploring the Cotswolds. An 18th-century
coaching inn, its interior blends modern touches with
traditional charms. Noted for its quality food, welcoming
atmosphere and imaginative, constantly changing menu.
Open: 11.30-2.30 6.30-11 **Bar Meals:** L served all
week 12-2 D served all week 7-9.30 **Restaurant
Meals:** L served all week 12-2 D served all week 7-
9.30 **Brewery/Company:** Free House 🍺: Greene King
IPA, Abbot Ale, Hook Norton 🍷: 11 **Children's Facilities:**
Menu/Portions Cutlery Games Highchair Food warming
Nearby: Butterfly Farm, Warwick Castle,
Teddy Bear Museum **Notes:** Dogs allowed in bar, in
garden, in bedrooms, Water **Garden:** Enclosed courtyard
Parking: 70

BROOM

Broom Tavern 🍷

High Street Alcester B50 4HL

☎ 01789 773656 📄 01789 773656

Email: webmaster@broomtavern.co.uk

Dir: *N of B439 W of Stratford-upon-Avon*

A 16th-century brick and timber inn, now completely refurbished with new furniture and décor, and a large newly created beer garden where barbecues are held in summer. Very much at the heart of village life, it is home to the Broom Tavern Golf Society, and fun days, charity events and outings are a feature. Typical dishes are home-made pies, local faggots and meat or vegetable lasagne, followed by treacle sponge and custard.

Open: 12-3 6-11 (Fri-Sat 12-11, Sun 12-3) **Bar Meals:** L served all week 12-2 D served Mon-Sat 6-9 (Fri-Sat 6-9.30) Av main course £7.95 **Restaurant Meals:** L served all week 12-2 D served all week 6.30-9 (Fri-Sat 6-9.30) **Brewery/Company:** Punch Taverns 🍺: Green King IPA, Black Sheep & Timothy Taylors Landlord 🍷: 20 **Children's Facilities:** Cutlery Highchair Food warming **Notes:** Garden: Front and rear gardens with picnic tables **Parking:** 30

ETTINGTON

The Houndshill 🍷

Banbury Road Stratford-upon-Avon CV37 7NS

☎ 01789 740267 📄 01789 740075

Dir: *On A422 SE of Stratford-upon-Avon*

Family-run inn situated at the heart of England, making it a perfect base for exploring popular tourist attractions such as Oxford, Blenheim, Stratford and the Cotswolds. The pleasant tree-lined garden is especially popular with families. Typical dishes range from poached fillet of salmon, and faggots, mash and minted peas, to supreme of chicken and ham and mushroom tagliatelle.

Open: 12-3 6-11 (Sun 12-3, 7-10.30) Closed: Dec 25-28 **Bar Meals:** L served all week 12-2 D served all week 7-9.30 Av main course £8.50 **Restaurant Meals:** L served all week 12-2 D served all week 9.30 Av 3 course alc £16.50 **Brewery/Company:** Free House 🍺: Hook Norton Best, Spitfire 🍷: 7 **Children's Facilities:** Play area (Swing, climbing frame, slide) Menu/Portions Highchair Food warming **Nearby:** Warwick Castle, Srtatford Butterfly Farm, Hatton Country Park **Notes:** Dogs allowed Garden: Large lawn with benches, children's play area **Parking:** 50

FARNBOROUGH

The Inn at Farnborough ⊛🍷

Banbury OX17 1DZ

☎ 01295 690615 📄 01295 690032

Email: enquiries@innatfarnborough.co.uk

Web: www.innatfarnborough.co.uk

Formerly the butcher's house on the Farnborough Estate, once known as the Butcher's Arms, the inn is a Grade II listed free house in a picturesque village setting. Parts of the building date back 400 years, and include an original inglenook fireplace. A good range of real ales and 14 wines by the glass are served alongside dishes based on high-quality Heart of England produce. Typical dishes from the fixed price menu are Oxfordshire Cropredy Dexter meatballs with grain mustard sauce, and Dorset crab with salmon and scallop risotto and saffron sauce. Carte dishes include the likes of the Inn's salmon fish cakes with baby spinach and hollandaise sauce; and specials such as rocket and Kenyan bean salad and salsa verde. Families are welcome, with smaller portions for children available.

Open: 12-3 6-11 (all day Sat/Sun) **Bar Meals:** L served all week 12-3 D served all week 6-11 (All day Sat/Sun) Av main course £13.95 **Restaurant Meals:** L served all week 12-3 D served all week 6-11 (Sat-Sun all Day) Av 3 course alc £25 **Brewery/Company:** Free House 🍺: Budwar, Leffe, Old Speckled Hen, Greene King IPA, Guinness, Hook Nord & Best 🍷: 14 **Children's Facilities:** Licence Menu/Portions Games Highchair Food warming Baby changing **Notes:** Dogs allowed in bar, in garden, Dog bowls **Garden:** Sunny, terraced garden **Parking:** 40

WARWICKSHIRE

LAPWORTH

The Boot Inn

Old Warwick Road B94 6JU

☎ 01564 782464 📄 01564 784989

Email: the bootinn@lovelypubs.co.uk

Web: www.thebootatlapworth.com

Beside the Grand Union Canal in the unspoilt village of Lapworth, this lively and convivial 16th-century former coaching inn is well worth seeking out. Apart from its smartly refurbished interior, the attractive garden is a great place to relax on warm days, while a canopy and patio heaters makes it a comfortable place to sit even on cooler evenings. But the main draw is the modern brasserie-style food, with wide-ranging menus that deliver home-produced dishes. A selection from the menu includes prawn, smoked haddock and spring onion fishcake, served with lemon gremolata and herb aioli; haddock in tempura batter with pea purée, sauce gribiche and frites; and fillet steak with smoked roast garlic, spinach and mascarpone mash.

Open: 11-11 (Thu, Fri & Sat open until 12) Closed: Dec 25 **Bar Meals:** L served all week 12-2.30 D served all week 7-10 Av main course £9 **Restaurant Meals:** L served all week 12-2.30 D served all week 7-10 Av 3 course alc £16 **Brewery/Company:** Laurel Pub Partnerships ▣: Greene King Old Speckled Hen, Wadworth 6X, Scottish Courage John Smith's, Brew XI ⬥: 6 **Children's Facilities:** Menu/Portions Cutlery Games Highchair Food warming **Nearby:** Haton Country World, Parkwood House & Baddesley Clinton Hall **Notes:** Dogs on leads allowed in bar, Water **Garden:** Patio and grass with heaters & canopy **Parking:** 200

NAPTON-ON-THE-HILL

The Bridge at Napton

Southam Road CV47 8NQ

☎ 01926 812466

Email: info@thebridgeatnapton.co.uk

Web: www.thebridgeatnapton.co.uk

Dir: *At Bridge 111 on the Oxford Canal on A425 2m out of Southam and 1m from Napton-on-the-Hill*

With a restaurant, three bars and a large garden this is an ideal place to moor the narrow boat, park the car or lean the bike against a wall. Built as a stabling inn at bridge 111 on the Oxford canal, the pub even has its own turning point for barges. There are some excellent ales, and the menu offers everything from gammon, egg and chips, through to salmon in champagne and pink peppercorn sauce.

Open: 12-3 6-11 (Apr-Nov open all day Sat-Sun, Nov-Apr closed Sun eve, Mon lunch) **Bar Meals:** L served all week 12-2 Av main course £9 **Restaurant Meals:** L served all week 12-2 D served all week 6-9 Av 3 course alc £16.50 **Brewery/Company:** Punch Taverns ▣: Cask Marque acredited & 3 guest ales **Children's Facilities:** Fam room Play area (Swings, climbing frame & slide) Menu/Portions Cutlery Highchair Food warming **Nearby:** Oxford Canal, Warwick Castle **Notes:** Dogs allowed in bar, Water Bowls & Food **Garden:** 0.75acre on canal, lawns, seating **Parking:** 35

RUGBY

Golden Lion Inn ★★★ HL ⬥

Easenhall CV23 0JA

☎ 01788 832265 📄 01788 832878

Email: dawn@goldenlioninn.co.uk

Web: www.goldenlioninn.co.uk

Dir: *From Rugby take A426, follow signs for Nuneaton*

A charming 16th-century free house with oak-beamed ceilings and narrow doorways set in one of the county's best kept villages. Choose between home-cooked bar food and gourmet dining in the restaurant.

Open: 11-11 **Bar Meals:** L served all week 12-2 D served all week 6-9.30 (Sun carvery 12-3, bar menu 3-9) Av main course £10 **Restaurant Meals:** L served Mon-Sun 12-2 D served Mon-Sun 6-9.30 (Sun carvery 12-3, bar menu 12-8.45) Av 3 course alc £19

Brewery/Company: Free House ▣: Tetley's Original & Guest Ales ⬥: 7 **Children's Facilities:** Menu/Portions Cutlery Games Highchair Food warming Baby changing **Nearby:** Coombe Abbey Country Park, Warwick Castle, Kenilworth Castle **Notes:** **Garden:** Large garden, spacious terrace, good views **Parking:** 80

SHIPSTON ON STOUR

The Cherington Arms ♀
Cherington CV36 5HS
☎ 01608 686233
Email: thecheringtonarms@hooknorton.tablesir.com
Web: www.cheringtonarms.com
Dir: *12m from Stratford-upon-Avon. 14m from Leamington and Warwick. 10m from Woodstock*
An attractive 17th-century inn with exposed beams and Cotswold stone walls, stripped wood furniture and roaring log inglenook fire. The ever-changing chalkboard menus might announce crab fishcakes with mango and chilli salsa; home-made beef and Hooky (ie Hook Norton beer, as sold in the bar) pie; breast of chicken stuffed with sun-dried tomato and cream pesto; and risotto of char-grilled artichoke, asparagus and green beans. Outside are large riverside gardens with a mill race.
Open: 12-3 6.30-11.30 (Open all day at wknds in summer) **Bar Meals:** L served Tue-Sun 12-2 D served Tue-Sun 7-9 (Sun 12-3) Av main course £9.75
Restaurant Meals: L served Tue-Sun 12-2 D served Tue-Sat 7-9 (Fri/Sat 7-9.30, Sat 12-2.30, Sun 12-3) Av 3 course alc £18.75 **Brewery/Company:** Hook Norton Brewery ◑: Hook Norton Best Bitter, Hook Norton Generation, Hook Norton Old Hooky, guest ales ♀: 11
Children's Facilities: Menu/Portions Cutlery Games Highchair Food warming Baby changing **Nearby:** Cotswold Wildlife Park, Model Village, Birdland in Bourton-on-the-Water **Notes:** Dogs allowed in bar, in garden, Water bowls indoors & outdoors **Garden:** Unspoilt orchard and patio with mill race **Parking:** 40

SHIPSTON ON STOUR

The Red Lion ★★★★ INN ♀
Main Street Long Compton CV36 5JS
☎ 01608 684221 ▤ 01608 684221
Email: redlionhot@aol.com
Dir: *On A3400 between Shipston on Stour & Chipping Norton*
A Grade II listed, stone-built coaching inn dating from 1748, located in an Area of Outstanding Natural Beauty and ideally situated for such major attractions as Stratford-upon-Avon, Warwick, Oxford and the Cotswold Wildlife Park. The bar is full of atmosphere, and visitors can eat there or in the restaurant area.
Open: 11-2.30 6-11 (Fri-Sun 11-11) **Bar Meals:** L served all week 12-2.30 D served all week 6-9.30 (Fri-Sun 12-9.30) **Brewery/Company:** Free House ◑: Hook Norton Best, Adnams, Timothy Taylor ♀: 7 **Children's Facilities:** Play area (Large garden/play equipment) Menu/Portions Cutlery Games Highchair Food warming **Nearby:** Cotswold Wildlife Park, Blenheim Palace, Warwick Castle **Notes:** Dogs allowed in bar, in garden, in bedrooms **Garden:** Large garden with views **Parking:** 60

SHREWLEY

The Durham Ox Restaurant and Country Pub ♀
Shrewley Common Warwick CV35 7AY
☎ 01926 842283 ▤ 0121 705 9315
Email: hospitalityengineers@btinternet.com
Web: www.durham-ox.com
An award-winning pub/restaurant in a peaceful village four miles from Warwick and Leamington. Warm and inviting, its old beams, open fire and traditional hospitality combine with a city chic that give it a competitive edge. Success is in no small measure due to the restaurant, where Master Chef Simon Diprose prepares impressive, seasonally changing classic and contemporary dishes. A meal might consist of deep-fried Boursin with ratatouille and basil sorbet; roast fillet of five-spice salmon with sweet corn, pak choi and coriander dressing; and hot chocolate and Snickers fondant with vanilla ice cream. Children are offered penne pasta, and home-made fishcakes from their own menu. Extensive gardens incorporate a safe children's play area.
Open: 12-11 **Bar Meals:** L served all week 12-3 D served all week 6-10 (Sun 12-9) Av main course £13
Restaurant Meals: L served all week 12-3 D served all week 6-10 (Sun 12-9) Av 3 course alc £25
Brewery/Company: Greene King ◑: IPA, Old Speckled Hen, Guinness & Abbot Ale ♀: 12 **Children's Facilities:** Play area Menu/Portions Cutlery Games Highchair Food warming Baby changing **Nearby:** Hatton Country World and Farm, Warwick Castle, Kenilworth Castle **Notes:** **Garden:** Spacious gardens with log cabin, BBQ, seating **Parking:** 100

WARWICKSHIRE

TEMPLE GRAFTON
The Blue Boar Inn 🍷
Nr Alcester B49 6NR
☎ 01789 750010 📠 01789 750635
Email: blueboar@covlink.co.uk
Web: www.blueboarinn.co.uk
Dir: *Take left turn to Temple Grafton off A46 (from Stratford to Alcester). Pub at 1st x-rds*
An inn since the early 1600s, it features a glass-covered well from which water was formerly drawn for brewing. Not long before it first opened for business, William Shakespeare married Ann Hathaway in the village church. There's an extensive menu, open fires in winter, and good views of the Cotswolds from the patio garden year-round. **Open:** 11-12 **Bar Meals:** L served all week 12-3 D served all week 6-10 (Sat 12-10, Sun 12-9) **Restaurant**

Meals: L served all week 12-3 D served all week 6-10
Brewery/Company: Free House 🍺: Morland Old Speckled Hen, Best, Deuchars IPA, Guest beer 🍷: 20
Children's Facilities: Licence Menu/Portions Cutlery Highchair Food warming **Notes:** Garden: Terraced patio area, tables, benches **Parking:** 50

WELFORD-ON-AVON
The Four Alls 🍷
Binton Bridges CV37 8PW
☎ 01789 750228 📠 01789 750262
Web: www.fouralls.greatpubs.net
Dir: *B439 from Stratford then left*
Contemporary art and modern furnishings give a continental feel to the striking interior of this centuries-old inn, set in the heart of Shakespeare country. Outside, you'll find a riverside garden and patio as well as a front garden and play area. The menus also have a continental flavour: favourites include Mediterranean sea bass; and roasted peppered duck breast. **Open:** 11-3 6-11 (Open all day wk ends & BHs) **Bar Meals:** L served all week 12-2.30 D served all week 7-10 Av main course £8 **Restaurant Meals:** L served all

week 12-2 D served all week 7-10 Av 3 course alc £20
Brewery/Company: Enterprise Inns 🍺: Black Sheep, Wadworth 6X, Greene King IPA 🍷: 10 **Children's Facilities:** Licence Play area (Slide, mini obstacle course) Menu/Portions Cutlery Games Highchair Food warming **Notes:** Garden: Riverside patio & bench seating **Parking:** 60

WITHYBROOK
The Pheasant 🍷
Main Street Nr Coventry CV7 9LT
☎ 01455 220480 📠 01455 221296
Email: thepheasant01@hotmail.com
Dir: *7m from Coventry*
This charming 17th-century free house has been in the same ownership since 1981. The pub stands beside the brook where withies were once cut for fencing. An inglenook fireplace, farm implements and horse-racing photographs characterise the interior, where daily blackboard specials supplement an extensive menu. Typical options include braised pheasant in Madeira sauce; cheesy fisherman's pie; and broccoli and walnut lasagne. **Open:** 11-1am (Sun 12-11) Closed: 25-26 Dec **Bar Meals:** L served all week 12-2 D served all week

6.15-10 (Sun 12-9) **Brewery/Company:** Free House 🍺: Courage Directors, Theakstons Best, John Smiths Smooth 🍷: 9 **Children's Facilities:** Menu/Portions Highchair Food warming **Nearby:** Mega Bowl, Cinemas & Ricoh Stadium **Notes:** Dogs allowed In the garden at manager's discretion Garden: Tables alongside a brook with grassy banks **Parking:** 55

SEDGLEY
Beacon Hotel & Sarah Hughes Brewery ♟
129 Bilston Street Dudley DY3 1JE
☎ 01902 883380 📠 01902 884020
Email: andrew.brough@tiscali.co.uk
Little has changed in 150 years at this traditional brewery tap, which still retains its Victorian atmosphere. The rare snob-screened island bar serves a taproom, snug, large smoke-room and veranda. Proprietor John Hughes re-opened the adjoining Sarah Hughes Brewery in 1987, 66 years after his grandmother became the licensee. Flagship beers are Sarah Hughes Dark Ruby, Surprise and Pale Amber, with guest bitters also available.
Open: 12-2.30 5.30-10.45 (Fri 5.30-11, Sat 12-3 6-11, Sun 12-3 7-10.30) **Brewery/Company:** Sarah Hughes Brewery ◾: Sarah Hughes Dark Ruby, Surprise & Pale Amber, Selection of Guest Beers and seasonal products ♟: 8 **Children's Facilities:** Licence Fam room Play area (Roundabout, slide, climbing frame) Food warming Baby changing **Nearby:** Black Country Museum, Dudley Zoo, Baggeridge Country Park **Notes:** Dogs allowed in bar, Water **Garden:** Beer garden with benches, tables & play area **Parking:** 50

SOLIHULL
The Boat Inn ♟
222 Hampton Lane Catherine-de-Barnes B91 2TJ
☎ 0121 705 0474 📠 0121 704 0600
Email: steven-hickson@hotmail.com
Village pub with a small, enclosed garden located right next to the canal in Solihull. Real ales are taken seriously and there are two frequently changing guest ales in addition to the regulars. There is also a choice of 14 wines available by the glass. Fresh fish is a daily option, and other favourite fare includes chicken cropper, Wexford steak, and beef and ale pie.
Open: 11-11 (Sun 12-10.30) **Bar Meals:** L served all week 12-10 D served all week 12-10 Av main course £7.95 ◾: Bombardier, Greene King IPA, 2 guest ales ♟: 14 **Children's Facilities:** Licence Fam room Menu/Portions Cutlery Games Highchair Food warming Baby changing **Nearby:** Warwick Castle, Stratford-upon-Avon, NEC **Notes:** Dogs allowed **Garden:** Large enclosed garden - tables & chairs **Parking:** 90

WEST BROMWICH
The Vine
Roebuck Street B70 6RD
☎ 0121 553 2866 📠 0121 525 5450
Email: bharat@thevine.co.uk
Web: www.thevine.co.uk
Dir: *0.5m from junct 1 of M5. 2m from West Bromwich town centre*
Well-known, family-run business renowned for its good curries and cheap drinks. Since 1978 the typically Victorian alehouse has provided the setting for Suresh "Suki" Patel's eclectic menu. You can choose from a comprehensive range of Indian dishes (chicken tikka masala, goat curry, lamb saag), a BBQ menu and Thursday spit roast, offered alongside traditional pub meals like sausage and chips, chicken and ham pie, and toasted sandwiches. The Vine boasts the Midlands' only indoor BBQ.
Open: 11.30-2.30 5-11 (Fri-Sun all day) **Bar Meals:** L served all week 12-2 D served all week 5-10.30 (Sun 1-10.30) Av main course £4.25 **Restaurant Meals:** L served all week D served all week 5-10.30 (Sat-Sun 1-10.30) **Brewery/Company:** Free House ◾: Banks, Brew XI, John Smiths **Children's Facilities:** Fam room Play area (Indoor/Outdoor) Menu/Portions Games Food warming **Nearby:** West Bromwich Town Centre, West Bromwich Football Club, Sandwell Valley and Park **Notes:** **Garden:** Large beer garden, play area

WEST MIDLANDS

BRETFORTON

The Fleece Inn

The Cross Evesham WR11 7JE

01386 831173

Email: nigel@thefleeceinn.co.uk

Web: www.thefleeceinn.co.uk

Dir: *From Evesham follow signs for B4035 towards Chipping Campden. Through Badsey, follow road into Bretforton. Turn right at village hall continue past church, pub located in corner of open parking area.*

The Fleece, or The Ark as it is known locally, has been part of Cotswold history for the six centuries since it was built as a longhouse.

Open: 11-11 (Winter Mon to Fri 11-3, 6-11, Sat & Sun open all day) **Bar Meals:** L served all week 12-2.30 D served Mon-Sat 6.30-9 Av main course £6.50 : Hook Norton Best Bitter, Pigs Ear, Goff's White Knight, Slaters Supreme & Purity Ubu : 12 **Children's Facilities:** Licence Play area (Climbing frame & adventure playground) Menu/Portions Cutlery Highchair Food warming Baby changing **Nearby:** Twyford Country Park, Cotswold Wildlife Park & Strutford Butterfly Farm **Notes:** Garden: Large orchard garden

BROMSGROVE

Epic' Bar Brasserie

68 Hanbury Road Stoke Prior B60 4DN

01527 871929 01527 575647

Email: bromsgrove@epicbrasseries.co.uk

Web: www.epicbrasseries.com

Dir: *A38 from Bromsgrove towards Worcester, at x-rds take B4091 towards Hanbury, pub on right.*

Bar cum brasserie with a sleek contemporary look which accurately reflects the style of cooking. Produce is carefully sourced for excellence and ethical acceptability, and there's a predominantly organic menu for children. Otherwise, the cooking is thoroughly grown up, with a menu ranging through salads, pasta, risotto, meat and fish, including brodetta (Italian fish and shellfish stew), and slow-braised lamb shank. Outside there's a large patio and terrace area with an olive tree.

Open: 11-11 (Sun 12-10.30) **Bar Meals:** L served all week 12-3 D served Mon-Sat Av main course £13 **Restaurant Meals:** L served all week 12-2.30 D served Mon-Sat 6.30-9.30 (Sun 12.30-3.30, Fri-Sat 6.30-10) Av 3 course alc £27.50 : Changing guest ale, Boddingtons, Guinness : 9 **Children's Facilities:** Licence Fam room (Garden games in summer) Menu/Portions Cutlery Games Highchair Food warming Baby changing **Nearby:** Cadbury World, Sea Life Centre, Avoncroft Museum **Notes:** Garden: Large patio, terrace area **Parking:** 60

CLENT

The Bell & Cross

Holy Cross DY9 9QL

01562 730319 01562 731733

Web: www.bellandcrossclent.co.uk

At the foot of the Clent Hills, this award-winning pub/restaurant serves modern-style food in a traditional setting. The pub dates from the early 19th-century and today is owned by Roger Narbett, chef to the England football team. Several rooms make up the pub, and real ales are served along with an interesting wine list, twelve of which are available by the glass; in warmer weather the covered patio makes for pleasant alfresco dining. Light dishes available in the bar might include roasted red pepper and aubergine soup; or tart Tatin of spinach, roast tomatoes and mozzarella. The enterprising main menu could list navarin of Cotswold lamb; roast Cornish cod; or fillet of pork with Parma ham. Some tempting desserts might be sticky toffee and banana waffle; or white chocolate and rhubarb trifle. More dishes using fresh local produce appear on the blackboards.

Open: 12-3 6-11 Closed: 25 Dec **Bar Meals:** L served all week 12-2 D served all week 6.30-9.15 (Sun 12-2.30, 7-9) Av main course £6.95 **Restaurant Meals:** L served all week 12-2 D served all week 6.30-9.15 (Sun 12-2.30, 7-9) Av 3 course alc £21.50 **Brewery/Company:** Enterprise Inns : Pedigree, Mild, Bitter & Guest Beers : 14 **Children's Facilities:** Licence Menu/Portions Food warming **Nearby:** Kidderminster Safari Park, Clent Hills, Stuart Crystal Museum **Notes:** Dogs allowed in bar, Water Garden: Well kept, south facing, patio area **Parking:** 26

CLOWS TOP
The Colliers Arms
Tenbury Road DY14 9HA
☎ 01299 832242
Dir: *On A456, 4m from Bewdley, 7m from Kidderminster.*
Now refurbished, this popular pub-restaurant is family
owned and run. All the food is home cooked, and plenty
of fish is on offer, for example, smoked haddock and crab
tart; or monkfish in a light curry sauce. Among the more
traditional dishes might be home-made lasagne; liver and
bacon. Do not leave, however, without sampling one of
the delicious home-made puddings.
OPENTIMES **Bar Meals:** L served all week 12-2 D
served Mon-Sat 6.30-9 Av main course £9.95
Restaurant Meals: L served all week 12-2 D served all
week 6.30-9 Av 3 course alc £19.95 🍺: Hobsons Best,
Town Cider, Fosters, John Smith's & Guinness
Children's Facilities: Menu/Portions Cutlery Games
Highchair Food warming Baby changing **Notes:** Dogs
allowed in bar Garden: Fenced garden, flower borders,
furniture **Parking:** 50

DROITWICH
The Chequers 🍷
Cutnall Green WR9 0PJ
☎ 01299 851292 🖨 01299 851744
Web: www.chequerscutnallgreen.co.uk
The Chequers is a charming village pub five miles from
Droitwich, and home to the chef of the English football
team, Roger Narbett. You can see his display of football
memorabilia in the bar. The pub is traditional in style
with an open fire, panelled bar and richly coloured
furnishings, while sandblasted beams, a tiled and wooden
floor and comfortable sofas give the dining room a more
contemporary feel. There's a great choice of food, with
sandwiches, baguettes, paninis, light bites and salads
at lunchtime, supplemented by daily specials from the
board. The dinner menu offers a comprehensive
selection, starting perhaps with whisky cured Scottish
smoked salmon with quail eggs and horseradish cream.
Influences from an entirely different part of the world are
evident in a main course of slow-cooked lamb shank
with provençale bean cassoulet and rosemary pistou, or
escalope of veal schnitzel with spaghetti carbonara.
Open: 12-3 6-11 Closed: 25 Dec & 1 Jan **Bar Meals:** L
served all week 12-2 D served all week 6.30-9.15 (Sun
12-2.30, 7-9) **Restaurant Meals:** L served all week 12-
2 D served all week 6.30-9.15 (Sun 12-2.30, 7-9) Av 3
course alc £21.50 **Brewery/Company:** Enterprise Inns
🍺: Timothy Taylors, Banks Pedigree, Banks Bitter, Banks
Mild, Hook Norton, Ruddles 🍷: 11 **Children's Facilities:**
Licence Fam room Menu/Portions Highchair Food
warming **Notes:** Dogs allowed in garden Garden: Patio
& Garden with seating & flower borders **Parking:** 75

FLYFORD FLAVELL
The Boot Inn ★★★★ INN 🍷
Radford Road WR7 4BS
☎ 01386 462658 🖨 01386 462547
Email: enquiries@thebootinn.com
Web: www.thebootinn.com
Dir: *Take Evesham Rd, left at 2nd rdbt onto A422, Flyford
Flavell signed after 3m.*
A Georgian fronted country pub, dating in part back to
the 13th century. The heavily beamed and timbered bar
and restaurant have open fires, and you will find a good
selection of beers, malts and wines. There are gardens
front and back, with a heated patio and quality wooden
furniture. Offers home-cooked food.
Open: 12-12 **Bar Meals:** L served all week 12-2 D
served all week 6.30-10 (Sun 12-5.30, 7-9.30)
Restaurant Meals: L served all week 12-2 D served
all week 6.30-10 (Sat 6-10, Sun 12-5.30, 7-9.30)
🍺: Old Speckled Hen, Worthingtons, Greene King IPA,
London Pride & Adnams 🍷: 7 **Children's Facilities:**
Menu/Portions Cutlery Highchair Food warming Baby
changing **Notes:** Dogs allowed in bar, in garden
Parking: 30

KINGTON

The Red Hart 🍷

Stratford Road WR7 4DD

☎ 01386 792559 📠 01386 793748

Email: enquiries@redhart.co.uk

Web: www.redhart.co.uk

Dir: *Located on A422, Stratford Rd, Nr Flyford Flavell 4m from Worcester, junct 6 of M5, 6m from Redruth.*

It's hard to believe that until 2001 this beautiful, easy-going country pub and restaurant was a derelict shell. That year Jane and Barr Pritchard, and a team of local craftsmen, stripped the interior to reveal its original looks, while adding some stunning contemporary touches. **Open:** 12-3 5-11 (Fri/Sat 12-12, Sun 12-11) **Bar Meals:** L served all week 12-2.30 D served all week 6-10 (Sat/Sun 12-10) Av main course £9.50 **Restaurant Meals:** L served all week 12-2.30 D served all week 6-10 (Sun 12-10) Av 3 course alc £19 🍺: Banks, Pedigree, Kronenburg, Stella & Fosters 🍷: 10 **Children's Facilities:** Licence Menu/Portions Cutlery Games Highchair Food warming **Nearby:** Ragley Hall, Stratford Upon Avon & Spechley Gardens **Notes:** Dogs allowed in bar Garden: Decked area with log burners **Parking:** 35

MARTLEY

Admiral Rodney Inn ♦♦♦♦

Berrow Green WR6 6PL

☎ 01886 821375 📠 01886 822048

Email: rodney@admiral.fslife.co.uk

Web: www.admiral-rodney.co.uk

Dir: *From M5 junct 7, take A44 signed Leominster. After approx 7m at Knightwick turn right onto B4197. Inn 2m on left at Berrow Green.*

This early 17th-century farmhouse-cum-alehouse stands in the heart of the countryside on the Worcester Way footpath. It has a split-level restaurant housed in a barn. **Open:** 11-3 5-11 (Mon 5-11pm, all day Sat, Sun) **Bar Meals:** L served Tue-Sun 12-2 D served all week 6.30-9 (Sun 12-2.30, Sat 6.30-9.30) Av main course £8 **Restaurant Meals:** L served Sun 12-2.30 D served Mon-Sun 7-9 (Sat 7-9.30) Av 3 course alc £25 **Children's Facilities:** Licence Menu/Portions Highchair Food warming Baby changing **Nearby:** Quadbiking, Fishing, Swimming, River Teme and Country Walks **Notes:** Dogs allowed in bar, in garden, Water Garden: Covered terrace with lighting & heating lamps **Parking:** 40

OMBERSLEY

Crown & Sandys Arms 🍷

Main Road WR9 0EW

☎ 01905 620252 📠 01905 620769

Email: enquiries@crownandsandys.co.uk

Web: www.crownandsandys.co.uk

This classy establishment is run by Richard Everton who also owns the village deli and wine shop, so expect excellent wines as well as a good selection of real ales. Although the décor is as trendy and modern as they come, the original beams and fireplaces seem to have no trouble co-existing with it. Regular 'wine dinners' and theme evenings add to the appeal for regulars. The food is as modern as the décor. Sandwiches, paninis, baguettes and hot dishes are available at lunchtime, and daily specials could include lavender-infused confit duck leg with spiced red cabbage and soy and sesame dressing, followed by cod with sundried tomato and olive compote. The à la carte menu features a selection from the grill, such as five-spiced Gressingham duck with sweet potato, parsnips, cinnamon and cassis jus. **Open:** 11-3 5-11 **Bar Meals:** L all week 12-2.30 D all week 6-10 (Sun all day to 9) Av main course £10.95 **Restaurant Meals:** L served all week 12-2.30 D served all week 6-10 (Sun all Day to 9) Av 3 course alc £20 **Brewery/Company:** Free House 🍺: Sadlers Ale, Marstons, Banks Bitter, Burtons Bitter, Marstons Pedigree & Jennings 🍷: 10 **Children's Facilities:** Menu/Portions Games Highchair Food warming Baby changing **Nearby:** Worcester Cathedral, West Midlands Safari Park, Worcester Rugby Club **Notes:** Garden: Large beer garden, Japanese style terrace **Parking:** 100

POWICK
The Halfway House Inn
Bastonford WR2 4SL

☎ 01905 831098 📠 01905 831704

Dir: *From A15 junct 7 take A4440 then A449*

Situated on the A449 between Worcester and Malvern, this delightful pub is just a few minutes' drive from the picturesque spa town of Malvern, a popular centre for exploring the Malvern Hills. The menu choice ranges from Herefordshire fillet steak or roasted Gressingham duck breast to baked fillet of Scottish salmon and spinach, ricotta and beef tomato lasagne.

Open: 12-3 6-11 **Bar Meals:** L served all week 12-2 D served all week 6-9 Av main course £12.50 **Restaurant Meals:** L served all week 12-2 D served all week 6-9 **Brewery/Company:** Free House 🍺: Abbot Ale, St Georges Bitter, Fuller's London Pride, Timothy Taylor **Children's Facilities:** Play area (Enchanted tree play area in garden) Menu/Portions Games Highchair Food warming **Notes:** Garden: Lawn area **Parking:** 30

STONEHALL
The Fruiterer's Arms
Stonehall Common Norton WR5 3QG

☎ 01905 820462 📠 01905 820501

Email: thefruiterersarms@btopenworld.com

Web: www.thefruiterersarms.co.uk

Dir: *2m from M5 junct 7. Stonehall Common 1.5m from St Peters Garden Centre Norton*

Pub on Stonehall Common, once frequented by the area's fruit pickers. Four guest ales are rotated weekly, and there's a main menu, specials menu and Sunday menu offered in the bar, restaurant, garden pavilion and garden. Favourite dishes include Swiss chicken with Alpine cheese, fillet of lamb with Madeira and rosemary, and the fresh fish of the day. The garden is large and has a purpose-built play area for children.

Open: 12-3 6-11 (all day Sun & Sat in Summer) **Bar Meals:** L served all week 12-2 D served all week 6-9.15 Av main course £6.50 **Restaurant Meals:** L served all week 12-2.30 D served all week 6-9.15 (All Day Sun) Av 3 course alc £28 🍺: Bombardier, St Austell Tribute, Guest ales **Children's Facilities:** Licence Play area (Wood chipping base, 50mtr zip wire.) Menu/Portions Cutlery Games Highchair Food warming Baby changing **Nearby:** Worcester City & River Severn Boating **Notes:** Garden: 17 acres, 50-seat wooden pavilion, seats **Parking:** 35

TENBURY WELLS
Peacock Inn
Worcs WR15 8LL

☎ 01584 810506 📠 01584 811236

Email: thepeacockinn001@aol.com

Web: www.peacockvillageinn.com

Dir: *Exit M5 junct 3, follow A456 for 40m then A443 to Tenbury Wells, 0.75m on right*

A 14th-century coaching inn overlooking the River Teme, with a sympathetic extension and pleasant patio eating area. The relaxing bars and oak-panelled restaurant are enhanced by oak beams, dried hops and open log fires. Local market produce features on the menus.

Open: 11.30-3.30 5.30-12 **Bar Meals:** L served all week 12-2 D served all week 6.30-9 Av main course £10.50 **Restaurant Meals:** L served all week 12-2 D served all week 6.30-9 Av 3 course alc £17.50 **Brewery/Company:** Free House 🍺: Hobsons Best Bitter, Spitfire, Tetley Cask **Children's Facilities:** Licence Menu/Portions Highchair Food warming **Nearby:** Severn Valley Railway, West Midland Safari Park, Hoo Farm **Notes:** Dogs allowed in bar, in garden Garden: Garden with tables and benches **Parking:** 30

WORCESTERSHIRE

WORCESTERSHIRE

TENBURY WELLS
The Fountain Hotel ♟
Oldwood St Michaels WR15 8TB
☎ 01584 810701 📄 01584 819030
Email: enquiries@fountain-hotel.co.uk
Web: www.fountain-hotel.co.uk
Dir: *1m out of Tenbury Wells on the A4112 Leominster Road*

A fine example of the black and white timbered inns that are common in these parts, The Fountain is run by Russell Allen, a well-travelled big-game fisherman, and his chef wife, Michaela, and has been winning plaudits for its quality food and real ales.
Open: 9-11 **Bar Meals:** L served all week 9-9 D served all week 9-9 **Restaurant Meals:** L served all week 12-10 D served all week 12-10 **Brewery/Company:** Free House 🍺: Fountain Ale, Old Speckled Hen, Greene King IPA, Wye Valley Bitter, Butty Bach ♟: 20 **Children's Facilities:** Licence Fam room Play area (Swings, slides, assault course, trampoline) Menu/Portions Cutlery Highchair Food warming Baby changing **Notes:** Garden: Large, secluded Patio area with heaters **Parking:** 60

TIBBERTON
The Bridge Inn
Plough Road WR9 7NQ
☎ 01905 345874
Email: dlmagor@yahoo.com
Dir: *From Worcester M5 junct 6, cross rdbt towards Evesham, take 1st left to Crowle/Tibberton, through Tibberton until bridge/canal*

The pub dates from 1820, when the Worcester/Birmingham canal was cut through, and is situated beside it. It provides a popular watering hole for boaters, ramblers and walkers, and has a canal-side beer garden. One menu is served throughout.
Open: 11.30-3 5-11 (Open 11.30-11 in summer) **Bar Meals:** L served all week 12-2 D served all week 6-9 Av main course £6.50 **Restaurant Meals:** L served all week 12-2 D served all week 6-9 🍺: Banks Bitter, Banks Original, Pedigree, guest ale **Children's Facilities:** Licence Play area (Enclosed garden) Menu/Portions Cutlery Highchair Food warming Baby changing **Nearby:** Spetchley Park, Warwick Castle **Notes:** Dogs allowed in bar Garden: Canalside beer garden **Parking:** 30

Dovedale valleys, Peak District.

North England

Ullswater, Lake District.

BLENCOGO
The New Inn ♀
Wigton CA7 0BZ
☎ 016973 61091 🖹 016973 61091
Dir: *From Carlisle, take A596 towards Wigton, then B5302 towards Silloth. After 4m Blencogo signed on left*
This late Victorian sandstone pub has superb views of the north Cumbrian fells and Solway Plain. It is located in a farming hamlet, and the impressive menu makes good use of produce from the region – perhaps Cumbrian venison with blueberry and Drambuie sauce and whole-grain mustard mash or lamb from Dearham, chargrilled and topped with a mustard and herb crust and served with colcannon. A selection of malt whiskies is kept.
Open: 7-11 (Sun 12-3, 6.30-10.30) Closed: 1st 2 weeks in Jan **Bar Meals:** L served Sun 12-2 D served Thu-Sun 7-9 Av main course £12 **Restaurant Meals:** L served Sun 12-2 D served Thu-Sun 7-9 (Sun 12-2) **Brewery/Company:** Free House 🍺: Yates, Carlisle State Bitter, Hesketh New Market, Black Sheep ♀: 10 **Children's Facilities:** Menu/Portions Cutlery Games Highchair Food warming Baby changing **Parking:** 50

BOOT
Brook House Inn ★★★★ INN ♀
Eskdale CA19 1TG
☎ 019467 23288 🖹 019467 23160
Email: stay@brookhouseinn.co.uk
Web: www.brookhouseinn.co.uk
Family-run country inn located in the heart of Eskdale with glorious views and fabulous walking country all around. Five or six real ales are kept during the summer and three in winter, along with an extensive selection of malt whiskies. Home-made food is available all day in the restaurant, bar and snug.
Open: 11-11 (8-12 during high season) Closed: 25 Dec **Bar Meals:** L served all week 12-5.30 D served all week 5.30-8.30 Av main course £8.95 **Restaurant Meals:** L served all week pre-booked 12-4.30 D served all week 6-8.30 Av 3 course alc £20 **Brewery/Company:** Free House 🍺: Theakstons Best, Timothy Taylors Landlord + up to 4 guest ales ♀: 8 **Children's Facilities:** Licence Fam room Menu/Portions Cutlery Games Highchair Food warming Baby changing **Nearby:** Boot Corn Mill, Muncaster, Ravenglass-Eskdale Railway **Notes:** Garden: Terrace; views of valley **Parking:** 25

BOOT
The Boot Inn formerly The Burnmoor Inn ♀
Eskdale Valley CA19 1TG
☎ 019467 23224 🖹 019467 23337
Email: enquiries@bootinn.co.uk
Web: www.bootinn.co.uk
Dir: *Follow signs for Eskdale then Boot from the A595*
You can walk to Scafell Pike (England's highest mountain) and Wastwater (England's deepest lake) from this award-winning, traditional 16th-century free house. The whole family is welcome - and that includes the dog!
Open: 11-11 **Bar Meals:** L served all week 11-5 D served all week 6-9 (Sun 11-5, 6-8.30) Av main course £7.50 **Restaurant Meals:** L served all week 11-5 D served all week 6-9 (Sun 11-5, 6-8.30) Av 3 course alc £18 🍺: Hartleys XB, Old Stockport, Cumbria Way, Double Hop & Unicorn ♀: 8 **Children's Facilities:** Licence Fam room Play area (Swings, ropes, climbing frame, slide) Menu/Portions Cutlery Games Highchair Food warming Baby changing **Nearby:** Muncaster Owl Centre, Ravenglass & Boot Water Mill **Notes:** Dogs allowed in bar, in garden, in bedrooms Garden: Part paved and part grassed, seating 40 people **Parking:** 30

BOUTH

The White Hart Inn 🍷

Ulverston LA12 8JB

☎ 01229 861229 🖷 01229 861229

Email: nigelwhitehart@aol.com

Web: bed-and-breakfast-cumbria.co.uk

Dir: *1.5m from A590, 10m M6 junct 36*

Bouth today reposes quietly in the Lake District National Park, although once it had an occasionally noisy gunpowder factory. When this closed in 1928 villagers turned to woodland industries and farm labouring instead, and some of their tools now adorn this 17th-century coaching inn. Ever-changing specials are served in the upstairs restaurant that looks out over woods, fields and fells, or the horseshoe-shaped bar, with six real ales, including Cumbrian brews, 35 malts and real cider.

Open: 12-2 6-11 **Bar Meals:** L served Wed-Sun 12-2 D served Mon-Sun 6-8.45 (Closed Mon/Tues lunch except BHs) Av main course £9.75 **Restaurant Meals:** L served 12-2 D served Wed-Sun 6-8.45 Av 3 course alc £18 **Brewery/Company:** Free House 🍺: Black Sheep Best, Jennings Cumberland Ale, Tetley, Yates Bitter, Timothy Taylor Landlord 🍷: 7 **Children's Facilities:** Licence Fam room (Playground Opposite) Menu/Portions Games Highchair Food warming Baby changing **Nearby:** Dalton Zoo, Lakeside Aquarium & Haverthwaite Steam Trains **Notes:** Garden: West facing terrace **Parking:** 30

BOWLAND BRIDGE

Hare & Hounds Country Inn 🍷

Grange-over-Sands LA11 6NN

☎ 015395 68333 🖷 015395 68777

Dir: *M6 onto A591, left after 3m onto A590, right after 3m onto A5074, after 4m sharp left & next left after 1m*

This 17th-century coaching inn is set in the pretty little hamlet of Bowland Bridge, not far from Bowness. It is wonderfully located below Cartmel Fell and has the beautiful Winster Valley almost to itself. A traditional country pub atmosphere is fostered by the flagstone floors, exposed oak beams, ancient pews warmed by open fires, and cosy niches. The food at this pub is another good reason for a visit.

Open: 11-11 **Bar Meals:** L served all week 12-2.30 D served all week 6-9 **Restaurant Meals:** L served all week 12-2.30 D served all week 6-9 **Brewery/Company:** Free House 🍺: Black Sheep, Jennings, Boddingtons 🍷: 10 **Children's Facilities:** Fam room Play area (Swings, Tables, Grassed Area) Menu/Portions Cutlery Games Highchair Food warming Baby changing **Notes:** Garden: Orchard with tables and hard area with tables **Parking:** 80

BRAITHWAITE

Coledale Inn

nr Keswick CA12 5TN

☎ 017687 78272 🖷 017687 78272

Email: info@coledale-inn.co.uk

Web: www.coledale-inn.co.uk

Dir: *From M6 junct 50 take A66 towards Cockermouth for 18 miles. Turn to Braithwaite then on towards Whinlatter Pass, follow sign on left, over bridge to hotel*

Built as a woollen mill in about 1824, this traditional pub was converted for pencil making before becoming an inn. Peacefully set above Braithwaite village, it is full of attractive Victorian prints, furnishings and antiques, with a fine cellar that includes cask-conditioned local ales. Its terrace and garden are very popular with walkers. Expect the likes of chicken breast with stilton and leek sauce, red Thai curry, and grilled Borrowdale trout finished with toasted almonds.

Open: 11-11 **Bar Meals:** L served all week 12-2 D served all week 6-9 Av main course £8.605 **Restaurant Meals:** L served all week 12-2 D served all week 6-9 **Brewery/Company:** Free House 🍺: Yates, Theakstons, Jennings Best, John Smiths **Children's Facilities:** Play area Menu/Portions Highchair Food warming **Nearby:** Derwent Water, Trotters World of Animals **Notes:** Dogs allowed in bar, in garden, Water Garden: Lawn with benches **Parking:** 20

CUMBRIA

BRAMPTON
Blacksmiths Arms ★★★★ INN ☻

Talkin Village CA8 1LE

☎ 016977 3452 📄 016977 3396

Email: blacksmithsarmstalkin@yahoo.co.uk

Web: www.blacksmithstalkin.co.uk

Dir: *from M6 take A69 E, after 7m straight over rdbt, follow signs to Talkin Tarn then Talkin Village*

Originally the local smithy, this attractive village inn dates from 1700. It stands in the heart of scenic countryside; Talkin Tarn lake is half a mile away. The well-balanced menu is supplemented by daily-changing specials.
Open: 12-3 6-11 (Sun 12-3, 6-10.30) **Bar Meals:** L served all week 12-2 D served all week 6-9 Av main course £8 **Restaurant Meals:** L served all week 12-2 D served all week 6-9 Av 3 course alc £14

Brewery/Company: Free House ◀: Black Sheep Best, Yates, Jennings Cumberland, Scottish Courage John Smith's, Youngers Scottish Bitter ☻: 20 **Children's Facilities:** Menu/Portions Highchair Food warming **Nearby:** Hadrians Wall, Eden Ostrich World **Notes:** Garden: Tables in summer, lawn & paving **Parking:** 20

BROUGHTON-IN-FURNESS
Blacksmiths Arms ☻

Broughton Mills LA20 6AX

☎ 01229 716824

Email: blacksmithsarms@aol.com

Web: www.theblacksmithsarms.com

Dir: *A593 from Barrow-in-Furness towards Coniston, 1.5m take left signed Broughton Mills, pub 1m on left.*

The Blacksmiths Arms, set in a secluded Lakeland valley, dates back to 1577 and was originally a farmhouse called Broadstones. The interior is beautifully preserved, with the old farmhouse range, oak-panelled corridor, worn slate floors sourced from local quarries, and low beams. Gaslights in the dining room and bar still work when the electricity fails. The chef proprietor uses local suppliers who guarantee the quality produce, and serves beer from local micro-breweries. You will often find Herdwick lamb, which is reared in the Lickle Valley, on the menu, along with traditional steak pie in suet pastry made from local beef.
Open: 12-11 (Oct-May 12-2.30, 5-11) Closed: Dec 25 **Bar Meals:** L served Tue-Sun 12-2 D served Mon-Sun 6-9 Av main course £8.95 **Restaurant Meals:** L served Tue-Sun 12-2 D served Mon-Sun 6-9 Av 3 course alc £17 **Brewery/Company:** Free House ◀: Jennings Cumberland Ale, Dent Aviator, Barngates Tag Lag, Moorhouses Pride of Pendle, Hawkshead Bitter ☻: 7 **Children's Facilities:** Games Highchair Food warming **Nearby:** Fell walking & bird watching **Notes:** Dogs allowed in bar, in garden **Garden:** Patio area tables and chairs **Parking:** 20

BUTTERMERE
Bridge Hotel ★★★ HL ☻

Cockermouth CA13 9UZ

☎ 017687 70252 📄 017687 70215

Email: enquiries@bridge-hotel.com

Web: www.bridge-hotel.com

Dir: *Take B5289 from Keswick*

Spend a weekend at this 18th-century former coaching inn and enjoy its stunning location between Buttermere and Crummock Water. Main courses from the restaurant include braised venison with wild mushrooms and onions in an Old Peculiar jus; or pan-fried seabass with Mache salad. The bar menu offers Cumberland hotpot, Cumberland sausage, and a good range of vegetarian choices. For smaller appetites there's a good selection of salads, sandwiches and toasties.

Open: 9.30-12 (All day in summer) **Bar Meals:** L served all week 12-6 D served all week 6-9.30 Av main course £5 **Restaurant Meals:** L served Sun 12-2 D served all week 7-8.30 **Brewery/Company:** Free House ◀: Theakston's Old Peculiar, Black Sheep Best, Buttermere Bitter, Boddingtons ☻: 12 **Children's Facilities:** Licence Menu/Portions Cutlery Games Highchair Food warming Baby changing **Parking:** 60

CALDBECK
Oddfellows Arms

Wigton CA7 8EA

☎ 016974 78227 📄 016974 78056

This 17th-century former coaching inn is set in a scenic conservation village in the northern fells. Popular with coast-to-coast cyclists and walkers on the Cumbrian Way, the Oddfellows serves Jennings Bitter and Cumberland ale. Lunchtime snacks include jacket potatoes, sandwiches, or hot beef in a roll, whilst specials and vegetarian blackboards supplement the regular menu. Expect bacon chops with stilton; sirloin steaks; and local trout fillets. There's a daily curry, too.
Open: 11-12 **Bar Meals:** L served all week 12-2 D served all week 6-8.30 Av main course £7.50
Restaurant Meals: L served all week 12-2 D served all week 6.30-8.30 **Brewery/Company:** Jennings Brothers Plc 🍺: Jennings Bitter, Cumberland Ale **Children's Facilities:** Menu/Portions Highchair Food warming
Nearby: Waterfall walk **Notes:** Dogs allowed in bar, Water **Garden:** Beer garden **Parking:** 10

CARTMEL
The Cavendish Arms 🍷

LA11 6QA

☎ 015395 36240 📄 015395 35082

Email: food@thecavendisharms.co.uk
Web: www.thecavendisharms.co.uk
Dir: *M6 junct 36 take A590 signed for Barrow-in-Furness. Cartmel signed. In village take 1st right*
Situated within the village walls, this 450-year-old coaching inn is Cartmel's oldest hostelry. Many traces of its long history remain, from the mounting block outside the main door to the bar itself, which used to be the stables. Oak beams, uneven floors and an open fire create a traditional, cosy atmosphere, and outside there is a tree-lined garden overlooking a stream. Lunchtime sandwiches are served on locally-baked bread with a portion of chips, while hot options include home-made soup; and tiger prawn piri piri. An evening meal might begin with pressed game terrine with home-made apple and pistachio chutney, followed by oven-baked salmon with watercress sauce.
Open: 11.30-11 **Bar Meals:** L served all week 12-2 D served all week 6-9 (Sun 12-9) Av main course £10
Restaurant Meals: L served all week 12-2 D served all week 6-9 (Sun 12-9) **Brewery/Company:** Free House 🍺: Greene King IPA, Cumberland, Bombardier, Theakstons 🍷: 8 **Children's Facilities:** Menu/Portions Cutlery Games Highchair Food warming Baby changing
Nearby: Cartmel Priory, Newby Bridge Visitor Centre & Victorian Park, Beatrix Potter Museum **Notes:** Dogs allowed in bar, Water & food on request **Garden:** Tree lined adjoining & overlooking stream **Parking:** 25

COCKERMOUTH
The Trout Hotel ★★★ HL ◉ 🍷

Crown Street CA13 0EJ

☎ 01900 823591 📄 01900 827514

Email: enquiries@trouthotel.co.uk
Web: www.trouthotel.co.uk

Dating back to the late 17th century, the Trout became a hotel in the 1930s. Today, the pub is handy for a wide range of leisure pursuits, including horse riding, cycling, fell walking, climbing and fishing. The Terrace Bar and Bistro is just the place for comfort and relaxation, while the Derwent Restaurant offers traditional surroundings and a menu featuring fresh produce. Try seared peppered tuna steak, roast venison, whole Dover sole or smoked Cumberland sausage from the imaginative menu.
Open: 11-11 **Bar Meals:** L/D served all week 9.30-9.30
Restaurant Meals: L served Sat & Sun 12-2 D served all week 7-9.30 **Brewery/Company:** Free House 🍺: Jennings Cumberland Ale, Theakston Bitter, John Smiths, Marston's Pedigree, Courage Directors 🍷: 24
Children's Facilities: Menu/Portions Cutlery Games Highchair Food warming Baby changing **Nearby:** Maryport Aquarium, Sheep & Wool centre **Notes:** Garden: Riverside garden, food served outside
Parking: 50

CUMBRIA

CUMBRIA

CONISTON
The Black Bull Inn & Hotel 🍷
1 Yewdale Road LA21 8DU
☎ 015394 41335 🖷 015394 41168
Email: i.s.bradley@btinternet.com
Web: www.conistonbrewery.com
Dir: *23m from Kendal via Windermere and Ambleside from M6 junct 36 onto A590*

This family-run, 16th-century inn occupies an idyllic spot by Coniston Water at the foot of the 803mtr Old Man, whose big toe is said to be the large stone set into the lounge wall. Chalkboard regulars include grilled gammon, crispy local duckling, half shoulder of lamb, and Esthwaite trout fillets. Snacks and children's meals are also served. Prize winning ales from the small brewhouse behind the inn can be savoured in the bar.

Open: 11-11 (Sun 12-10.30) Closed: 25 Dec **Bar Meals:** L served all week 12-9.30 D served all week 12-9.30 Av main course £8.50 **Restaurant Meals:** D served all week 6-9 **Brewery/Company:** Free House ◀: Coniston Bluebird, Old Man Ale, Opium, Blacksmith & XB 🍷: 10 **Children's Facilities:** Licence Fam room Menu/Portions Cutlery Games Highchair Food warming Baby changing **Nearby:** Boat rides on the lake, Srizedale Park, Beatrix Potter's Home **Notes:** Dogs allowed in bar, in garden, in bedrooms Dog beds and meals **Garden:** Riverside patio outside **Parking:** 12

CROOK
The Sun Inn 🍷
Kendal LA8 8LA
☎ 01539 821351 🖷 01539 821351
Web: www.sun-inn-crook.co.uk
Dir: *Off the B5284*

A warmly welcoming inn dating from 1711, The Sun is steeped in tradition with winter fires and a summer terrace overlooking rolling countryside. The best local ingredients are used to create a variety of dishes, such as venison steak with wild mushroom sauce, game casserole, and fell-bred steaks. The bar snack and regular menus are supplemented by daily specials, and fresh fish is also featured.

Open: 12-2.30 6-11 (Sat 12-11, Sun 11.30-10.30) **Bar Meals:** L served all week 12-2.15 D served all week 6-8.45 (Sat & Sun all day) **Restaurant Meals:** L served all week 12-2.30 D served all week 6-9 ◀: Theakston, Scottish Courage John Smith's, Courage Directors, Wells Bombardier, Coniston Bluebird 🍷: 14 **Children's Facilities:** Menu/Portions Games Highchair Baby changing **Notes:** Dogs allowed in bar **Garden:** Terrace **Parking:** 20

ENNERDALE BRIDGE
The Shepherd's Arms Hotel
Lake District National Park CA23 3AR
☎ 01946 861249 🖷 01946 862472
Email: shepherdsarms@btconnect.com
Web: www.shepherdsarmshotel.co.uk
Dir: *A66 to Cockermouth (25m), A5086 to Egremont (5m) then follow signs to Ennerdale.*

Located on one of the most beautiful stretches of Wainwright's Coast to Coast footpath, this informal free house is a favourite with walkers. Bike hire and pony trekking can also be arranged. A nicely varied menu is served throughout.

Open: 11-2.30 5.30-11 (Apr-Oct open all day) **Bar Meals:** L served all week 12.15-1.45 D served all week 6.15-8.45 Av main course £7.50 **Restaurant Meals:** L served all week 12.15-1.45 D served all week 6.15-8.45 ◀: Jennings Bitter, Coniston Bluebird, Yates Fever Pitch, Shepherds Arms & Guest **Children's Facilities:** Licence Fam room Menu/Portions Cutlery Games Highchair Food warming Baby changing **Notes:** Dogs allowed in bar **Garden:** Patio area with tables, chairs, umbrellas **Parking:** 8

ESKDALE
King George IV Inn
nr Holmrook CA19 1TS
☎ 019467 23262 📠 019467 23334
Email: info@kinggeorge-eskdale.co.uk
Web: www.kinggeorge-eskdale.co.uk
Dir: *A590 to Greenodd, A5092 to Broughton-in-Furness then over Ulpha Fell towards Eskdale*
What we see today is a 17th-century coaching inn, although Roman origins are likely. It lies in one of Lakeland's finest hidden valleys, close to the narrow gauge Ravenglass & Eskdale steam railway, known affectionately as La'al Ratty. Inside are open fires, oak beams, low ceilings, flagged floors and antiques. Dishes include homemade steak and Old Peculier pie, curry, pan-fried liver and onions, ostrich fillet, and salmon in Martini, orange and ginger sauce. Vegetarian and small meals, pizzas and sandwiches.
Open: 11-11 **Bar Meals:** L served all week 12-8.30 D served all week 12-8.30 **Restaurant Meals:** L served all week 12-2 D served all week 6-9 **Brewery/Company:** Free House ■: Coniston Bluebird, Black Sheep Special, Jennings Cumberland Ales, Jennings Sneck Lifter & changing Cask Ales **Children's Facilities:** Highchair Food warming Baby changing **Notes:** Dogs allowed in bar, in garden, in bedrooms **Garden:** Beautiful views, ample tables **Parking:** 5

GOSFORTH
The Globe Hotel
CA20 1AL
☎ 01946 725235
Email: gosglobel@aol.com
Web: www.tp-inns.co.uk
Dir: *On the A595, 15m S of Whithaven*
Over a pint of Jennings Bitter in this friendly, traditionally furnished village pub, contemplate a walk round the shores of nearby Wast Water, England's deepest lake. Or, better still, walk first and get back here in time for that pint to accompany home-made fellman's steak, mushroom and brown ale pie with shortcrust pastry; grilled Cumberland sausages with pickled red cabbage and rich onion gravy; or deep-fried Whitby scampi with salad, chips and peas.
Open: 12-11 **Bar Meals:** L served Tue-Sun 12-2 D served Tue-Sun 6-9 Av main course £7 **Restaurant Meals:** L served Tue-Sun 12-2 D served Tue-Sun 6-9 Av 3 course alc £13 **Brewery/Company:** T & P Inns ■: Jennings Bitter, John Smiths Smooth, Stella, Cumberland Ale & Fosters ♟: 6 **Children's Facilities:** Licence Fam room Menu/Portions Games Highchair Food warming **Nearby:** Muncaster Castle, Sellafield Visitor Centre, La'al Ratty Steam Railway **Notes:** Dogs allowed in bar **Garden:** Tarmac area overlooking village square

GRASMERE
The Travellers Rest Inn ♟
Keswick Road LA22 9RR
☎ 015394 35604 📠 017687 72309
Email: stay@lakedistrictinns.co.uk
Web: www.lakedistrictinns.co.uk
Dir: *M6 to A591 to Grasmere, pub 0.5m N of Grasmere*
Located on the edge of picturesque Grasmere and handy for touring and exploring the ever-beautiful Lake District, the Travellers Rest has been a pub for more than 500 years. Inside a roaring log fire complements the welcoming atmosphere of the beamed and inglenooked bar area. An extensive menu of traditional home-cooked fare is offered, ranging from Westmorland terrine and eggs Benedict, to wild mushroom gratin and rump of Lakeland lamb.
Open: 12-11 (Sun 12-10.30) **Bar Meals:** L served all week 12-3 D served all week 6-9.30 (Mar-Oct, 12-9.30) Av main course £9.95 **Restaurant Meals:** L served all week 12-3 D served all week 6-9.30 (Mar-Oct, 12-9.30) Av 3 course alc £15 **Brewery/Company:** Free House ■: Jennings Bitter, Cumberland Ale, & Sneck Lifter, Jennings Cocker Hoop, Guest Ales ♟: 10 **Children's Facilities:** Fam room Menu/Portions Cutlery Games Highchair **Notes:** Dogs allowed in bar, in garden, in bedrooms, Water bowls **Garden:** Beer garden, stunning views, picnic tables **Parking:** 60

GREAT SALKELD
The Highland Drove Inn and Kyloes Restaurant 🍷
Penrith CA11 9NA
☎ 01768 898349 📠 01768 898708
Email: highlanddroveinn@btinternet.com
Web: www.highland-drove.co.uk
Dir: *Exit M6 junct 40, take A66 eastbound then A686 to Alston. After approx 4m, turn left onto B6412 for Great Salkeld and Lazonby.*
A 300-year-old country inn deep in the lovely Eden Valley, with a well-deserved reputation for high quality food.
Open: 12-3 6-11 (Sat 12-11) **Bar Meals:** L served Tue-Sun 12-2 D served all week 6.30-9 (Sun 12-2, 6-8.30) Av main course £7.95 **Restaurant Meals:** L served Tue-Sun 12-2 D served all week 6.30-9 (Sun 6.30-8.30) Av 3 course alc £24 🍺: Theakston Black Bull, John Smiths Cask, John Smiths Smooth, Youngers Scotch Bitter, Theakstons Mild & Guest Beer 🍷: 14 **Children's Facilities:** Licence Menu/Portions Cutlery Highchair Food warming **Nearby:** Eden Ostrich World, Eden Lacy Caves, Wetheriggs Pottery **Notes:** Dogs allowed in bar Garden: 'Flintstones' bedrock, with waterfall, pond **Parking:** 6

HAWKSHEAD
Kings Arms Hotel ★★★ INN
The Square LA22 0NZ
☎ 015394 36372 📠 015394 36006
Email: info@kingsarmshawkshead.co.uk
Web: www.kingsarmshawkshead.co.uk
Dir: *Exit M6 junct 36, follow A590 to Newby Bridge, turn right at 1st junct past rdbt, over bridge follow road for 8m to Hawkshead.*
Oak beams and an open fire complete the atmosphere of this charming 16th-century free house, which overlooks the main square that would have been familiar to William Wordsworth and Beatrix Potter. Mulled wine and local damson gin supplement the range of ales, whilst the lunchtime menu features an attractive selection of soups, sandwiches and hot meals. Dinner options include duck breast in plum sauce; and fellbred minted lamb with roasted winter vegetables.
Open: 10-12 **Bar Meals:** L served all week 12-2.30 D served all week 6-9.30 Av main course £8 **Restaurant Meals:** L served all week 12-2.30 D served all week 6-9.30 **Brewery/Company:** Free House 🍺: Carlsberg-Tetley Bitter, Black Sheep Best, Hawkshead Gold, Hawkshead Bitter, Coniston Bluebird & Guest ales **Children's Facilities:** Licence Menu/Portions Games Highchair Food warming Baby changing **Nearby:** Grisedale Forest Visitor Centre, Cruising on Lake Windermere **Notes:** Dogs allowed in bar, Water Garden: Walled area, picnic tables

HAWKSHEAD
Queens Head Hotel ★★ HL 🏅 🍷
Main Street LA22 0NS
☎ 015394 36271 📠 015394 36722
Email: enquiries@queensheadhotel.co.uk
Web: www.queensheadhotel.co.uk
Dir: *M6 junct 36, A590 to Newby Bridge, 1st right, 8m to Hawkshead*
This pub is in the centre of historic Hawkshead, the village where William Wordsworth attended school and Beatrix Potter created *Peter Rabbit*. The hotel regards the Lake District as its larder, with local trout, pheasant, traditionally cured hams and Cumberland sausage, and slow-maturing Herdwick lamb.
Open: 11-11 **Bar Meals:** L served all week 12-2.30 D served all week 6.15-9.30 (Sun 12-5) **Restaurant Meals:** L served all week 12-2.30 D served all week 6.15-9.30 (Sun 12-5) **Brewery/Company:** Frederic Robinson Ltd 🍺: Robinsons Unicorn, Hartleys Cumbria Way, Double Hop 🍷: 11 **Children's Facilities:** Licence Fam room Games Highchair Food warming **Nearby:** Beatrix Potter Hill Top & Gallery, Grizedale Forest **Notes:** Garden: Small gravel area with tables **Parking:** 14

HAWKSHEAD
The Sun Inn
Main Street LA22 0NT
☎ 015394 36747 📠 015394 36155
Email: rooms@suninn.co.uk
Web: www.suninn.co.uk
Dir: *N on M6 junct 36, take A591 to Ambleside, then B5286 to Hawkshead. S on M6 junct 40, take A66 to Keswick, A591 to Ambleside, then B5286 to Hawkshead.*
The Sun is a listed 17th-century coaching inn at the heart of the charming village where Wordsworth went to school. Inside are two resident ghosts - a giggling girl and a drunken landlord - and outside is a paved terrace with seating.
Open: 11-12 Bar Meals: L served all week 12-2.30 D served all week 6.15-9.30 (Sat-Sun all day) Restaurant

Meals: D served all week 6.30-9.30
Brewery/Company: Free House 🍺: Barn Gates Cracker, Jennings, Hesket & Newmarket plus two guest ales
Children's Facilities: Licence Fam room Menu/Portions Highchair Food warming Baby changing Nearby: Grizedale Forest, Aquarium of the Lakes, Go Ape Notes: Garden: Beer garden, paved terrace, seating

HESKET NEWMARKET
The Old Crown
CA7 8JG
☎ 016974 78288
Email: louhogg@daisybroadband.co.uk
Web: www.theoldcrownpub.co.uk
Dir: *From M6 take B5305, left after 6m towards Hesket Newmarket*
Both the pub and its associated micro-brewery are owned by co-operatives of local people and other supporters, so regulars know that their favourite pints will always be waiting for them. Aside from the real ales, there are seven Indian curries to choose from on the menu, including chicken korma, lamb Madras, and pork in a rich lentil sauce. Other meals include wild mushroom strudel with brandy sauce; Doris's steak

and ale pie; and ham, egg and chips.
Open: 12-3 5.30-11 Bar Meals: L served Wed-Sun 12-2 D served Wed-Sun Restaurant Meals: L served Wed-Sun 12-2 D served Wed-Sat 6.30-8.30
Brewery/Company: Free House 🍺: Doris, Skiddaw, Blencathra, Helvellyn Gold, Catbells, Great Cockup
Children's Facilities: Menu/Portions Cutlery Games Highchair Food warming Notes: Dogs allowed in bar

HEVERSHAM
Blue Bell Hotel
Princes Way LA7 7EE
☎ 015395 62018 📠 015395 62455
Email: stay@bluebellhotel.co.uk
Web: www.bluebellhotel.co.uk
Dir: *On A6 between Kendal & Milnthorpe*
Originally a vicarage for the old village, this hotel dates back as far as 1460. Heversham is an ideal base for touring the scenic Lake District and Yorkshire Dales, but pleasant country scenery can also be viewed from the hotel's well-equipped bedrooms. The charming lounge bar, with its old beams, is the perfect place to relax with a drink or enjoy one of the meals available on the menu, including potted shrimps, sirloin steak, Cumbrian game pie and Isle of Man crab.

Open: 11-11 Bar Meals: L served all week 12-9 D served all week 6-8.30 (Sat 12-3, 6-9) Av main course £7.95 Restaurant Meals: L served all week 11-9 D served all week 7-9 (Sun 11-8) Av 3 course alc £15
Brewery/Company: Samuel Smith 🍺: Samuel Smith Old Brewery Bitter Children's Facilities: Fam room (Changing room, Childrens Menu) Menu/Portions Cutlery Games Highchair Food warming Baby changing Nearby: Wildlife Oasis, Lake District National Park Notes: Dogs allowed in bar, in bedrooms Garden: Quiet garden, decoratively furnished Parking: 100

CUMBRIA

CUMBRIA

KENDAL
Gateway Inn 🍷
Crook Road LA8 8LX
☎ 01539 720605 & 724187 📠 01539 720581
Dir: *From M6 junct 36 take A590/A591, follow signs for Windermere, pub on left after 9m*
Located within the Lake District National Park, this Victorian country inn offers delightful views, attractive gardens and welcoming log fires. A good range of appetising dishes includes chicken casserole with red wine and herb dumplings, grilled fillets of sea bass with ratatouille and mussels, and roasted butternut squash filled with leeks and Stilton. Traditional English favourites of liver and onions or rabbit pie are also a feature.
Open: 11-11 **Bar Meals:** L/D served all week 12-9 Av main course £9 **Brewery/Company:** Daniel Thwaites Plc

🍺: Thwaites Bitter, Thwaites Smooth & Cask Ales 🍷: 11
Children's Facilities: Play area (Swings, slides & play house) Highchair Baby changing **Notes:** Dogs allowed in bar, Water & dog food **Garden:** Terrace, food served outside **Parking:** 50

KENDAL
The Gilpin Bridge Inn ★★★ INN
Bridge End Levens LA8 8EP
☎ 015395 52206 📠 015395 52444
Email: info@gilpinbridgeinn.co.uk
Web: www.gilpinbridgeinn.co.uk
Dir: *M6 junct 36, follow A590 towards Barrow*
Good food is the chief attraction at this popular pub which takes its name from a Norman knight who resided here after fighting the crusades.
Open: 11.30-2.30 5.30-11 (Open all day Summer, BHs)
Bar Meals: L served all week 11.30-2 D served all week 5.30-9 (Sun 12-9) Av main course £6.50
Restaurant Meals: L served all week 11.30-2 D served all week 5.30-9 (Sun 12-9) Av 3 course alc £12.50
🍺: Unicorn, Cumbria Way, Hartleys XB & Guest ales

Children's Facilities: Licence Fam room Play area (Wooden play equipment) Menu/Portions Cutlery Games Highchair Food warming **Nearby:** Grange-over-Sands Resort, World of Beatrice Potter **Notes:** Dogs allowed in bar, in garden **Garden:** Patio area adjacent to pub
Parking: 60

KESWICK
The Farmers
Portinscale CA12 5RN
☎ 01768 773442
Web: www.tp-inns.co.uk
Dir: *Exit M6 at junct 40 (Penrith) and follow A66 pass Keswick B5289 junct, left to Portinscale*
Revitalised as one of Keswick's foremost food-led pubs, everything from stocks, soups and breads to the after-dinner mints is freshly prepared. A typical starter might be mushroom risotto with charred asparagus and parmesan crisps, followed by roast chicken thighs stuffed with haggis on bubble and squeak, or a more traditional combination like grilled lemon sole with lemon and coriander butter.
Open: 12-11 **Bar Meals:** L served all week 12-2 D

served all week 6-9 Av main course £8.50 **Restaurant Meals:** L served all week 12-2 D served all week 6-9 Av 3 course alc £17.50 **Brewery/Company:** T & P Inns
🍺: Jennings Bitter, Jennings Cumberland Ale, Jennings Cumberland Cream **Children's Facilities:** Licence (Toy box and colouring materials) Menu/Portions Cutlery Games Highchair Food warming **Notes:** **Garden:** Raised gravel beer garden overlooking fells

KESWICK
The Horse & Farrier Inn ♀
Threlkeld Village CA12 4SQ
☎ 017687 79688 📄 017687 79823
Email: info@horseandfarrier.com
Web: www.horseandfarrier.com
Dir: *From junct 4 off M6, turn W signed Keswick (A66), after 12m, turn right signed Threlkeld. Located in centre of village.*

Renowned for its food and hospitality, this old stone inn has been part of the picturesque village of Threlkeld for over 300 years. It is ideally suited for visits to Keswick, Castlerigg stone circle, Greystoke castle and Ullswater.
Open: 8-12 **Bar Meals:** L served all week 12-2 D served all week 6-9 Av main course £8 **Restaurant Meals:** L served all week 12-2 D served all week 6-9

Av 3 course alc £22 🍺: Jennings Bitter, Cocker Hoop, Sneck Lifter, Cumberland Ale & Guest Ale ♀: 15
Children's Facilities: Licence Fam room Menu/Portions Cutlery Games Highchair Food warming **Nearby:** Cars of the Stars & Regheed Visitor Centre **Notes:** Dogs allowed in bar **Garden:** Long garden **Parking:** 60

KESWICK
The Kings Head ♀
Thirlspot CA12 4TN
☎ 017687 72393 📄 017687 72309
Email: stay@lakedistrictinns.co.uk
Web: www.lakedistrictinns.co.uk
Dir: *From M6 take A66 to Keswick then A591, pub 4m S of Keswick*

The view surrounding this 17th-century former coaching inn is truly sublime. On warm days and in summer, the garden is the best place to enjoy a meal or drink. Inside, old beams and inglenook fireplaces are traditional features of the bar, while a separate games room offers pool, snooker and darts. In the elegant restaurant try choosing between spicy citrus-crusted pork roast; stuffed roast poussin; and oven-baked sea bass, which might be preceded by filo wrapped prawns, or mushroom and thyme soup. On the bar menu you'll find Cumberland chargrill, beef stroganoff, wild mushroom gratin, Borrowdale trout stuffed with prawns, and Waberthwaite sausages, and there are sandwiches and salads.
Open: 12-11 (12-10.30 Sundays) **Bar Meals:** L served all week 12-3 D served all week 6-9.30 Av main course £9.95 **Restaurant Meals:** L served all week 12-3 D served all week 7-9 Av 3 course alc £15
Brewery/Company: Free House 🍺: Scottish Courage Theakston Best Bitter & Old Peculier, Jennings Bitter, Bluebird Bitter, Greene King Abbot Ale ♀: 10 **Children's Facilities:** Fam room Menu/Portions Games Highchair Food warming Baby changing **Notes:** Dogs allowed in bar, in garden, in bedrooms, Water **Garden:** Delightful, spectacular views of fells **Parking:** 60

KIRKBY LONSDALE
The Whoop Hall ★★ HL 👍♀
Skipton Road Carnforth LA6 2HP
☎ 015242 71284 📄 015242 72154
Email: info@whoophall.co.uk
Web: www.whoophall.co.uk
Dir: *From M6 take A65. Pub 1m SE of Kirkby Lonsdale*

16th-century converted coaching inn, once the kennels for local foxhounds. In an imaginatively converted barn you can relax and enjoy Yorkshire ales and a good range of dishes based on local produce. Oven baked fillet of sea bass with tagliatelle verde and tiger prawns, and stir-fried honey roast duck with vegetables and water chestnuts are among the popular favourites. The bar offers traditional hand-pulled ales and roaring log fires, while outside is a terrace and children's area.

Open: 7-11 **Bar Meals:** L served all week 12-6 D served all week 6-10 Av main course £5 **Restaurant Meals:** L served all week 12-2.30 D served all week 5-10 Av 3 course alc £15 **Brewery/Company:** Free House 🍺: Black Sheep, Greene King IPA, Tetley Smooth, Caffreys ♀: 14 **Children's Facilities:** Licence Fam room Play area (Adventure playground. Changing facilities) **Notes:** Dogs allowed in garden, in bedrooms, Water provided **Garden:** Terrace & lawn areas with good views **Parking:** 120

CUMBRIA

LITTLE LANGDALE
Three Shires Inn ★★ HL
Ambleside LA22 9NZ
☎ 015394 37215 📠 015394 37127
Email: enquiries@threeshiresinn.co.uk
Web: www.threeshiresinn.co.uk
Dir: *Turn off A593, 2.3m from Ambleside at 2nd junct signed for The Langdales. 1st left 0.5m. Hotel 1m up lane.*
This 19th-century hotel, five miles West of Ambleside, stands in the beautiful valley of Little Langdale near the meeting points of the three county shires of Westmorland, Cumberland and Lancashire.
Open: 11-11 (Dec-Jan 12-3, 8-10.30) **Closed:** Dec-25
Bar Meals: L served all week 12-2 D served all week 6-8.45 (Ltd evening meals Dec-Jan) Av main course £9.95
Restaurant Meals: D served all week 6-8.30 Av 3 course alc £20 **Brewery/Company:** Free House 🍺: Jennings Best & Cumberland, Coniston Old Man, Hawkshead Bitter **Children's Facilities:** Licence Games Highchair Baby changing **Nearby:** Boat Trips, Beatrix Potter & Go Ape **Notes:** Garden: Terrace and gardens next to stream **Parking:** 20

LOWESWATER
Kirkstile Inn ★★★★ INN 🍷
Cockermouth CA13 0RU
☎ 01900 85219 📠 01900 85239
Email: info@kirkstile.com
Web: www.kirkstile.com
For some 400 years, the Kirkstile Inn between Loweswater and Crummock Water has offered shelter and hospitality amidst the stunning Cumbrian fells. Set in the shadow of Melbreak, this is an ideal base for walking, climbing, boating and fishing, or just relaxing over a beer from a choice of local breweries.
Open: 11-11 **Closed:** 25 Dec **Bar Meals:** L served all week 12-2 D served all week 6-9 Av main course £8.50 **Restaurant Meals:** D served all week 6-9 Av 3 course alc £16 🍺: Rannerdale, Coniston Bluebird, Yates Bitter, Melbreak, Grasmoor Ales 🍷: 10 **Children's Facilities:** Licence Fam room (Toys & books) Menu/Portions Games Highchair Food warming Baby changing **Nearby:** Trotters World of Animals, Muncaster Castle **Notes:** Dogs allowed in bar, in garden, Water, allowed in some bedrooms, no dogs 6-10 Garden: Away from road with river adjacent **Parking:** 40

MELMERBY
The Shepherds Inn 🍷
Penrith CA10 1HF
☎ 01768 881919
Email: theshepherdsinn@btopenworld.com
Dir: *On A686 NE of Penrith*
Well-known in the North Pennines, this unpretentious sandstone pub looks across the village green towards remote moorland country, close to miles of spectacular walks. An interesting mix of well-kept real ales is constantly rotated, with regulars like Jennings Cumberland Ale, Black Sheep Best, and Courage Directors.
Open: 11-3 6-11 (Sun 12-3, 7-10.30) **Closed:** 25 Dec
Bar Meals: L served all week 11.30-2 D served all week 6-9 Av main course £8.50
Restaurant Meals: L served all week 11.30-2 D served all week 6-9 **Brewery/Company:** Enterprise Inns 🍺: Jennings Cumberland Ale, Black Sheep Best, Courage Directors 🍷: 8 **Children's Facilities:** Licence Menu/Portions Highchair Food warming **Notes:** Dogs allowed in bar **Parking:** 20

NEAR SAWREY
Tower Bank Arms

Hawkshead LA22 0LF

☎ 015394 36334

Email: towerbankarms@aol.com

Web: www.towerbankarms.com

Dir: *On B5285 SW of Windermere*

Next door to Hill Top, Beatrix Potter's former home, this 17th-century country inn was immortalised in *The Tales of Jemima Puddleduck*. It's still an ideal base for exploring the Lake District. The celebrity wall displays portraits of famous people, many of them patrons of the inn. A choice of cold and hot dishes ranges from salads, potted shrimps and cheese flan to game pie, Cumberland sausage and Barnsley chop.

Open: 11-11 (Winter Dec/Jan 11-3, 5.30-11)

Bar Meals: L served all week 12-2 D served all week 5.30-9 **Restaurant Meals:** L served all week 12-2 D served all week 5.30-9 **Brewery/Company:** Free House 🍺: Theakston Best & Old Peculier, Barngates Tag Lag, Hawkshead **Children's Facilities:** Licence Games Highchair Food warming **Nearby:** Beatrix Potter's House, Aquarium of the Lakes, Go Ape **Notes:** Dogs allowed in bar, in garden, in bedrooms **Garden:** 5 tables, 30 seats **Parking:** 8

NETHER WASDALE
The Screes Inn

Seascale CA20 1ET

☎ 019467 26262 📄 019467 26262

Email: info@thescreesinnwasdale.com

Web: www.thescreesinnwasdale.com

Dir: *To Gosforth on A595. Through Gosforth for 3m, then turn right signed Nether Wasdale. The Screes Inn is in the village on the left.*

Nestling in the scenic Wasdale Valley and close to Wastwater, this welcoming 300-year-old inn, with its cosy log fire, choice of real ales and large selection of malt whiskies makes an excellent base for walking, mountain biking or diving. The menu offers Woodall's Cumberland sausage with apple sauce, Gill Unsworth's home-baked steak and kidney pie, and tagliatelle with a creamy mushroom pesto sauce. There is a good choice of sandwiches at lunchtime.

Open: 12-11 Closed: Dec 25, Jan 1 **Bar Meals:** L served all week 12-3 D served all week 6-9 Av main course £8 **Restaurant Meals:** L served all week 12-3 D served all week 6-9 Av 3 course alc £13 **Brewery/Company:** Free House 🍺: Black Sheep Best, Yates Bitter, Coniston Bluebird, Derwent **Children's Facilities:** Licence Menu/Portions Games Highchair Food warming Baby changing **Nearby:** Seafield Visitors' Centre, Minature Railway, Muncaster Castle **Notes:** Dogs allowed in bar, in garden, in bedrooms, Water **Garden:** Seating area to front & side of pub, BBQ area **Parking:** 30

OUTGATE
Outgate Inn

nr Hawkshead Ambleside LA22 0NQ

☎ 015394 36413

Email: outgate@outgate.wanadoo.co.uk

Web: www.theoutgateinn.co.uk

Dir: *Exit M6 junct 36, by-passing Kendal, A591 towards Ambleside. At Clappersgate take B593 to Hawkshead then Outgate*

A 16th-century Lakeland inn only a mile down the road from where Wordsworth went to school. Without doubt he was inspired by the glorious walks and magnificent scenery surrounding this former tollhouse, which retains many original features. Winter fires and weekly jazz evenings help create an inviting atmosphere. An extensive and varied menu offers Lancashire hot pot, braised shoulder of lamb in mint gravy, Thai green chicken curry, and pan-fried escalope of corn-fed chicken.

Open: 11-3 6-11 (Sat 11-11 Sun 12-10.30) **Bar Meals:** L served all week 12-2 D served all week 6-9 (Sun 12-9) Av main course £8.95 **Restaurant Meals:** L served all week 12-2 D served all week 6-9 (Sun 12-9) **Brewery/Company:** Frederic Robinson Ltd 🍺: Hartleys XB, Old Stockport Bitter, Robinsons Smooth **Children's Facilities:** Licence Fam room Food warming **Nearby:** Beatrix Potters House Hill Top, Brockhole Park, Datton Animal Park **Notes:** Dogs allowed in bar, in garden, in bedrooms, Water **Garden:** Beer garden at the rear **Parking:** 30

RAVENSTONEDALE
Black Swan Hotel
Kirkby Stephen CA17 4NG
☎ 015396 23204
Email: enquiries@blackswanhotel.com
Web: www.blackswanhotel.com
Dir: *M6 junct 38 take A685 E towards Brough*
Ravenstonedale is a peaceful, unspoilt village in the
upper Eden Valley in Cumbria, lying between the Lake
District and Yorkshire Dales National Parks. The hotel is
a grand, solid-looking, Lakeland stone affair built around
1899. Meals are served in the lounge or the popular
restaurant. A sample menu includes local Cumberland
sausage, colcannon mash and rich onion gravy; local
Bessy Beck trout or salmon fishcakes with homemade
tartar sauce and pommes frites; fresh haddock in home-
made Black Sheep beer batter, chips and mushy peas; or
Moroccan lamb tagine with apricots and sweet potato
served with couscous. Panninis, toasties, jacket potatoes
and sandwiches are also available. Local beers include
Tirril, brewed at Brougham Hall. The pub's garden leads
across a bridge over a beck to a natural riverside glade.
Open: 8-12 (Fri-Sat 8-1) **Bar Meals:** L served all week
12-2 D served all week 6-9 Av main course £7.95
Restaurant Meals: L served all week 12-2 D served all
week 6-9 Av 3 course alc £16 **Brewery/Company:**
Free House 🍺: Black Sheep, John Smith's, Dent, Tirril
Brewery, Hawkshead Brewery, Lancaster Brewery 🍷: 6
Children's Facilities: Menu/Portions Games Highchair
Food warming **Nearby:** Otter Sanctuary **Notes:** Dogs
allowed in bar, in garden, in bedrooms **Garden:** River &
garden **Parking:** 25

RAVENSTONEDALE
King's Head Hotel ★★★ INN 🍷
Kirkby Stephen CA17 4NH
☎ 015396 23284
Email: enquiries@kings-head.net
Web: www.kings-head.net
Dir: *7 m from junct 38 Tebay on A685*
One of the oldest buildings in Ravenstonedale, this 17th-
century Cumbrian inn offers everyone a warm welcome.
Pool, darts, dominoes, bar skittles and shove ha'penny in
the games room.
Open: 11-3 6-11 (Fri-Sat Open all day Spring &
Summer) **Bar Meals:** L served all week 12-2 D served
all week 6-9 Av main course £10.50 **Restaurant
Meals:** L served all week 12-2 D served all week 6-9
Av 3 course alc £18.50 **Brewery/Company:** Free House
🍺: Black Sheep, Dent, Carlsberg-Tetley Tetley's Imperial,
Over 100 Guest Ales 🍷: 6 **Children's Facilities:**
Licence Fam room (Games room) Menu/Portions
Highchair Food warming Baby changing **Notes:** Dogs
allowed in bar, in garden, **Garden:** By river, offset from
building, tree canopy **Parking:** 10

RAVENSTONEDALE
The Fat Lamb Country Inn ★★ HL
Crossbank Kirkby Stephen CA17 4LL
☎ 015396 23242 📠 015396 23285
Email: fatlamb@cumbria.com
Web: www.fatlamb.co.uk
Dir: *On A683 between Sedbergh & Kirkby Stephen*
Paul Bonsall has owned the Fat Lamb since the early
Seventies, earning accolade after accolade. He serves no
ready-made meals, not even the bar snacks. The small
bar has an open fire in an old Yorkshire range, hand-
pulled local ales and a wide selection of malt whiskies.
Open: 11-2 6-11 **Bar Meals:** L served all week 12-2 D
served all week 6-9 Av main course £9 **Restaurant
Meals:** L served all week 12-2 D served all week 6-9
Av 3 course alc £17 **Brewery/Company:** Free House
🍺: Cask Condition Tetley's Bitter **Children's Facilities:**
Licence Play area (Garden with sandpit & playhouse)
Menu/Portions Cutlery Highchair Food warming Baby
changing **Nearby:** Otter trust, Ostrich World &
Wetheriggs Pottery **Notes:** Dogs allowed in bar, in gar-
den, in bedrooms **Garden:** Open grassed area
surrounded by shrubs **Parking:** 60

SEATHWAITE
The Newfield Inn ☒
Duddon Valley Broughton-in-Furness LA20 6ED

☎ 01229 716208

Email: paul@seathwaite.freeserve.co.uk

Web: www.newfieldinn.co.uk

Dir: *From Broughton-in-Furness take A595 for 0.5m, turn right before traffic lights at Duddon Bridge and follow 6m signed for Seathwaite.*

The sheltered garden of this early 17th-century free house enjoys stunning views of the surrounding fells. Located in Wordsworth's favourite Duddon Valley, the building was formerly a farm and a post office; it still boasts a real fire, oak beams and a wonderful slate floor. The menu encompasses home-made dishes like short-crust steak pie; and spicy bean casserole. There's also an ever-changing specials board and a list of delicious sweets.

Open: 11-11 **Bar Meals:** L served all week 12-9 D served all week 12-9 Av main course £6.50 **Restaurant Meals:** L served all week 12-9 D served all week 12-9 **Brewery/Company:** Free House ☒: Scottish Courage Theakston Old Peculier, Jennings Cumberland Ale, Caledonian Deuchars IPA ☒: 6 **Children's Facilities:** Play area (Large enclosed grass area) Menu/Portions Cutlery Games Highchair Food warming **Nearby:** Dalton Wildlife Park, Barrow Dock Museum, Raven Glass Railway **Notes:** Dogs allowed in bar, Water Garden: Sheltered, seating for 40, stunning views **Parking:** 30

SEDBERGH
The Dalesman Country Inn ☒
Main Street LA10 5BN

☎ 015396 21183 ☒ 015396 21311

Email: info@thedalesman.co.uk

Web: www.thedalesman.co.uk

Dir: *M6 junct 37, follow signs to Sedbergh, 1st pub in town on left*

Restored 16th-century coaching inn, handy for a choice of glorious walks along the River Dee or up to the Howgill Fells. The menu changes every fortnight. Popular patio and garden, and a good wine selection.

Open: 11-11 (Sun 12-10.30) **Bar Meals:** L served all week 12-2.30 D served all week 6-9.30 (Sat-Sun 12-9) **Restaurant Meals:** L served all week 12-2.30 D served all week 6-9.30 (Sat-Sun 12-9) **Brewery/Company:**

Free House ☒: Carlsberg-Tetley, Theakston Best Bitter, Black Sheep ☒: 9 **Children's Facilities:** Licence Fam room Menu/Portions Games Highchair Food warming **Nearby:** Farfield Mill, Garsdale Fun Factory, Bowness Boat Trips **Notes:** Garden: Wooden benches & tables at pub's front **Parking:** 8

SHAP
Greyhound Hotel ☒
Main Street Penrith CA10 3PW

☎ 01931 716474 ☒ 01931 716305

Email: postmaster@greyhoundshap.demon.co.uk

Dir: *Telephone for directions*

Built as a coaching inn in 1684, the Greyhound is a welcoming sight for travellers after crossing Shap Fell. It offers a choice of real ales and a good selection of wines. All meats are locally sourced. Good choice of children's dishes; snack menu at lunchtime.

Open: 11-11 (Sun 12-10.30) **Bar Meals:** L served all week 12-2 D served all week 6-9 Av main course £8.50 **Restaurant Meals:** L served all week 12-2 D served all week 6-9 Av 3 course alc £16 **Brewery/Company:** Free House ☒: Carlsberg-Tetley

Bitter, Young's Bitter, Greene King Old Speckled Hen, Jennings Bitter plus Guest Ales ☒: 10 **Children's Facilities:** Licence Menu/Portions Cutlery Highchair Food warming Baby changing **Nearby:** Reged Visitors' Centre, Shap Swimming pool, Shap Abbey **Notes:** Dogs allowed in bar Garden: Food served outside, Patio **Parking:** 30

TROUTBECK
Queens Head Hotel ★★★★ INN ♀

Townhead Windermere LA23 1PW

☎ 015394 32174 📄 015394 31938

Email: enquiries@queensheadhotel.com

Web: www.queensheadhotel.com

Dir: *M6 junct 36, A590/591, W towards Windermere, right at mini-rdbt onto A592 signed Penrith/Ullswater. Pub 2m on right.*

True to its roots, this smart 17th-century coaching inn offers sustenance and comfortable accommodation. Accomplished cooking is the watchword here, with hearty but innovative fare.

Open: 11-11 (Sun 12-10.30) Closed: 25 Dec **Bar Meals:** L served all week 12-2 D served all week 6.30-9 Av main course £12.95 **Restaurant Meals:** L served all week 12-2 D served all week 6.30-9 Av 3 course alc £24 **Brewery/Company:** Free House 🍺: Interbrew Boddingtons Bitter, Coniston Bluebird, Old Man Bitter, Jennings Cumberland Ale **Children's Facilities:** Licence Highchair Food warming Baby changing **Nearby:** Brockhole National Park Visitor Centre & World of Beatrix Potter **Parking:** 100

ULVERSTON
Farmers Arms ♀

Market Place LA12 7BA

☎ 01229 584469 📄 01229 582188

Email: roger@farmersulufreeserve.com

Web: www.farmersrestaurant-thelakes.co.uk

Dir: *In town centre*

A warm welcome is extended at this lively 16th-century inn located at the centre of the attractive, historic market town. The visitor will find a comfortable and relaxing beamed front bar with an open fire in winter. Landlord Roger Chattaway takes pride in serving quality food; his Sunday lunches are famous, and at other times there's a varied and tempting specials menu, and lunchtime choice of hot and cold sandwiches, baguettes or ciabatta, and various salads.

Open: 10-11 **Bar Meals:** L served all week 11-3 D served all week 5.30-8.30 Av main course £8.95 **Restaurant Meals:** L served all week 11-3 D served all week 5.30-8.30 Av 3 course alc £14.95 **Brewery/Company:** Free House 🍺: Hawkshead Best Bitter, Hoegarden, John Smiths ♀: 12 **Children's Facilities:** Licence Highchair Food warming **Nearby:** Wildlife Park, Glass Works, Swathmoor Hall **Notes:** Garden: Sunny patio garden, outdoor heaters & canopy

ULVERSTON
The Devonshire Arms ♀

Victoria Road LA12 0DH

☎ 01229 582537 & 480287 📄 01229 480287

Located on the outskirts of the bustling market town of Ulverston, this popular pub is home to a wide range of cask beers and guest ales, as well as two dart teams. The menu focuses on classic pub grub, with plenty in the way of light bites: baguettes, burgers, jackets and the like, as well as some more filling mains. These range from home-made mince and onion pie to vegetable korma curry.

Open: 11-2.30 5.30-11 (Autumn-Winter 6-11) **Bar Meals:** L served Thu-Tue 12-2 D served Thu-Tue 6-8.30 (Sun 12-2, 6-8.30) Av main course £6.95 🍺: Tetley Smooth, Jennings Cumberland, Carling Lager & Tetley Dark Mild ♀: 8 **Children's Facilities:** Licence Menu/Portions Cutlery Games Highchair Food warming Baby changing **Nearby:** Dalton-in-Furness Animal Park, Stan Laurel Museum, Aquarium of Life Lakeside **Notes:** Garden: Patio area, sun trap **Parking:** 6

CUMBRIA

WATERMILLOCK

Brackenrigg Inn ★★★★ INN ♟

Lake Ullswater Penrith CA11 0LP

☎ 017684 86206 📠 017684 86945

Email: enquiries@brackenrigginn.co.uk

Web: www.brackenrigginn.co.uk

Dir: *M6 junct 40 take the A66 (signed Keswick). Then take A592 signed Ullswater. 6m from M6 and Penrith*

A white-painted roadside inn, dating from the 18th century in a breathtakingly beautiful position with sweeping views over Ullswater and Helvellyn. Traditional menus using fresh local produce.

Open: 12-11 (Nov-Mar, Mon-Fri closed 3-5pm) **Bar Meals:** L served all week 12-2.30 D served all week 6.30-9 Av main course £9 **Restaurant Meals:** L served all week 12-2.30 D served all week 6.30-9 Av 3 course alc £27 🍺: Theakstons Best, Jennings Cumberland, Black Sheep Special, Coniston Bluebird, Jennings Cocker Hoop ♟: 12 **Children's Facilities:** Licence Menu/Portions Highchair Food warming **Nearby:** Alpaca Centre, Ullswater Steamers, Wetheriggs Pottery **Notes:** Dogs allowed in bar, Water **Garden:** Views of Lake Ullswater, Llewellyn & Valley **Parking:** 40

WHITEHAVEN

The Waterfront ♟

West Strand CA28 7LR

☎ 01946 691130 📠 01946 695987

Email: thewaterfront@aol.com

Web: www.tp-inns.co.uk

Dir: *From M6 follow A66 towards Workington. Take A595 towards Whitehaven then A5094, located in the town centre on the harbourside.*

The Waterfront lives up to its name with lovely views from its large Georgian windows across old Whitehaven harbour, which was once the third busiest port in the country. There's a cosy modern feel to the interior, and the friendly, knowledgeable staff are eager to make you feel at home. Expect local lamb shank on celeriac mash; wild mushroom risotto with parmesan shavings; and salmon with saffron mussel sauce and Moroccan cous cous.

Open: 12-11 **Bar Meals:** L served all week 12-2 D served all week 6-9.30 Av main course £10 **Restaurant Meals:** L served all week 12-2 D served all week 6-9.30 Av 3 course alc £16 **Brewery/Company:** T & P Inns 🍺: Jennings Bitter, Cumberland Ale, Cocker Hoop, Fosters & Stella ♟: 11 **Children's Facilities:** Licence Cutlery Games Highchair Food warming **Nearby:** Whitehaven Beacon, Rum Story & Noah's Ark **Notes:**

WINDERMERE

Eagle & Child Inn ★★★ INN ♟

Kendal Road Staveley Kendal LA8 9LP

☎ 01539 821320

Email: info@eaglechildinn.co.uk

Web: www.eaglechildinn.co.uk

Dir: *Exit M6 junct 36 then A590 towards Kendal join A591 towards Windermere. Staveley approx 2m*

This pub's riverside gardens are delightful, and it's surrounded by excellent walking, cycling and fishing country. Meat and fresh bread come from the village, game from nearby estates. Dishes include home-made hummus and black olive salad, followed by beef and Black Sheep ale pie.

Open: 11-11 **Bar Meals:** L served Mon-Fri 12-2.30 D served Mon-Fri 6-9 **Restaurant Meals:** L served Mon-Fri 12-2.30 D served Mon-Fri 6-9 🍺: Black Sheep Best Bitter, Coniston Bluebird Bitter, Dent Ales, Yates Bitter, Tirril Brewery ♟: 8 **Children's Facilities:** Play area (Safe garden) Games Highchair Food warming **Nearby:** Play park, Beatrix Potter Exhibition **Notes:** Dogs allowed in bar, in garden **Garden:** Riverside location, secluded rear terrace **Parking:** 16

CUMBRIA

WORKINGTON
The Old Ginn House
Great Clifton CA14 1TS

☎ 01900 64616 🖷 01900 873384

Email: enquiries@oldginnhouse.co.uk

Web: www.oldginnhouse.co.uk

Dir: *3 miles from Workington, 4 miles from Cockermouth, just off the A66*

Successfully converted from a 17th-century farm, where wool was once treated by 'ginning' in what is today's rounded main bar. The butter yellows, bright check curtains and terracotta tiles of the dining areas exude a warm Mediterranean glow, while outside is an attractive courtyard. An extensive menu of mostly traditional bar food is supplemented by dishes such as braised shoulder of lamb, salmon fillet with lobster and prawn sauce, and stilton and vegetable crumble.

Open: 11-12 Closed: 24-26 Dec, 1 Jan **Bar Meals:** L served all week 12-2 D served all week 6-9.30 Av main course £6.95 **Restaurant Meals:** L served all week 12-2 D served all week 6-9.30 Av 3 course alc £15 🍺: Jennings Bitter, John Smiths Bitter, Murphys, Stella and 4X **Children's Facilities:** Licence Menu/Portions Cutlery Games Highchair Food warming Baby changing **Nearby:** Maryport Aquarium, Ravenglass & Eskdale Minature Railway, Trotters World of Animals **Notes:** Garden: Courtyard **Parking:** 40

YANWATH
The Yanwath Gate Inn 🍷
Penrith CA10 2LF

☎ 01768 862386 🖷 01768 899892

Email: enquiries@yanwathgate.com

Web: www.yanwathgate.com

The Yanwath Gate Inn has been offering hospitality in the North Lakes since 1683. Today the ethos of owner Matt Edwards is to offer good quality informal dining based on produce which is usually local and organic if possible. Fish is delivered fresh every morning so there are always fish and seafood specials on the à la carte menu.

Open: 11-11 **Bar Meals:** L served all week 12-2.30 D served all week 6-9.30 Av main course £15

Restaurant Meals: L served all week 12-2.30 D served all week 6-9.30 Av 3 course alc £30

Brewery/Company: Free House 🍺: Jennings Bitter Smooth, Hesket Brewery, Doris 90th Birthday Ale, Tirril Bewshers Bitter & Budvar 🍷: 9 **Children's Facilities:** Licence Menu/Portions Highchair Food warming **Nearby:** Wetheriggs Pottery, Rheged Centre **Notes:** Dogs allowed in bar Garden: Secluded terrace, lawns, landscaped garden **Parking:** 40

AYCLIFFE
The County 🍷
13 The Green Darlington DL5 6LX

☎ 01325 312273 🖷 01325 308780

Web: www.the-county.co.uk

Dir: *Off the A167 into Aycliffe*

Overlooking an award-winning village green, here is a pub/bistro that serves food from daily blackboards offering aromatic spiced mackerel, tomato and vegetable ragout; slow-roast pork belly; and Provençale vegetable and goats' cheese lasagne. Owner Andrew Brown was the first Raymond Blanc scholarship winner in 1995, since when his career rise has been meteoric. Not only has The County featured on the BBC's *Food and Drink* programme, but Tony Blair has famously dined here with Jacques Chirac.

Open: 12-3 5.30-11 Closed: 25-26 Dec, 1 Jan **Bar Meals:** L served Mon-Sat 12-2 D served Mon-Sat 6-7 Av main course £8.95 **Restaurant Meals:** L served Mon-Sat 12-2 D served Mon-Sat 6-9.30 Av 3 course alc £25 **Brewery/Company:** Free House 🍺: Scottish Courage , Wells Bombardier, Jennings Cumberland Ale, Castle Eden & Camerons, Changing Ales, Theakstons Best 🍷: 9 **Children's Facilities:** Menu/Portions Highchair Food warming **Parking:** 30

CO DURHAM

BARNARD CASTLE
The Morritt Arms Hotel ★★★ HL 🍷
Greta Bridge DL12 9SE
☎ 01833 627232 📠 01833 627392
Email: relax@themorritt.co.uk
Web: www.themorritt.co.uk
Dir: *At Scotch Corner take A66 towards Penrith, after 9m turn at Greta Bridge. Hotel over bridge on left.*
Situated in rural Teesdale, The Morritt Arms has been an inn for two centuries. The present building began life in the 17th century as a farmhouse, although buried underneath are the remains of a Roman settlement. In its busy coaching days The Morritt and other Greta Bridge inns were important overnight stops for the London-Carlisle service. Charles Dickens researched *Nicholas Nicklelby* here in 1839, his stay commemorated by the Dickens Bar, with a famous mural by John Gilroy. The artist, in turn, is remembered in Gilroy's Restaurant, the more formal dining area.
Open: 11-11 **Bar Meals:** L served all week 12-3 D served all week 6-9.30 (Sun 6-9) Av main course £9 **Restaurant Meals:** L served all week 12-3 D served all week 7-9 (Sun 7-9) Av 3 course alc £30
Brewery/Company: Free House 🍺: John Smith's, Timothy Taylor Landlord, Black Sheep Best, Cumberland Ale 🍷: 20 **Children's Facilities:** Fam room Play area (Swings, slide, grass area) Menu/Portions Games Highchair Food warming Baby changing **Nearby:** Otter Trust, Raby Castle, Timothy Hackworth Railway Museum **Notes:** Dogs allowed in bar, in garden, in bedrooms, Water on request **Garden:** Terraced, traditional garden, picnic benches **Parking:** 100

FIR TREE
Duke of York ★★★★ INN
Crook DL15 8DG
☎ 01388 762848 📠 01388 767055
Email: suggett@firtree-crook.fsnet.co.uk
Web: www.english-inns.co.uk
Dir: *on A68 to Scotland, 12m W of Durham City*
Former drovers' and coaching inn, dating from 1749, on the tourist route to Scotland, midway between York and Edinburgh. An old world atmosphere with 'mouseman' Robert Thompson's furniture, and the proprietor's collection of African memorabilia and Stone Age flints.
Open: 11-2.30 6.30-10.30 **Bar Meals:** L served all week 12-2 D served all week 6.30-9 Av main course £8.50 **Restaurant Meals:** L served all week 12-2 D served all week 6.30-9 Av 3 course alc £27
Brewery/Company: Free House 🍺: Black Sheep, Worthington **Children's Facilities:** Licence Play area Menu/Portions Cutlery Highchair Food warming **Nearby:** Hamsterley Forest, Beamish Museum, Harpeley POW Camp **Notes:** Garden: Garden at rear of pub, patio area outside **Parking:** 65

MIDDLESTONE
Ship Inn
Low Road Bishop Auckland DL14 8AB
☎ 01388 810904
Email: graham@snaithg.freeserve.co.uk
Dir: *On B6287, Kirk Merrington to Coundon road*
Beer drinkers will appreciate the string of CAMRA accolades received by this family-run pub on the village green. In the last five years regulars could have sampled well over 800 different beers. Ask about the pub's challenge for regulars to send postcards from every country in the world. Home-cooked food in the bar and restaurant. The rooftop patio has spectacular views over the Tees Valley and Cleveland Hills.
Open: 4-11 (Thu-Sat 12-11, Sun 12-10) **Bar Meals:** L served Fri-Sun 12-2.30 D served Mon, Wed-Sat 5-9 (Sun 12-2) **Restaurant Meals:** L served Fri-Sun 12-2.30 D served Mon, Wed-Sat 5-9 (Sun 12-2)
Brewery/Company: Free House 🍺: Timothy Taylor Landlord & 5 Guest Ales **Children's Facilities:** Fam room Play area Games Highchair Food warming **Notes:** Dogs allowed in bar, in garden, Water **Garden:** Patio with panoramic views **Parking:** 6

MIDDLETON-IN-TEESDALE

The Teesdale Hotel ★★ HL

Market Square Nr Barnard Castle DL12 0QG

☎ 01833 640264 🖹 01833 640651

Email: enquiries@teesdalehotel.com

Web: www.teesdalehotel.com

The hotel lies just off the Pennine Way, close to some of Northern England's loveliest scenery. Tastefully modernised, this family-run coaching inn is noted for its striking 18th-century stone exterior. Inside, the friendly atmosphere and cosy log fires simply add to the charm. Look out for poached salmon with spring onion, dill and white wine sauce; steak and kidney pie; or breast of chicken topped with asparagus and cheese sauce. Vegetarian options are available.

Open: 11-11 **Bar Meals:** L served all week 12-2 D served all week 7-9 Av main course £8 **Restaurant Meals:** L served Sun 12-2.30 D served all week 7-9 Av 3 course alc £20 **Brewery/Company:** Free House 🍺: Guinness, Tetley Smooth, Jennings Cumberland Ale, Jennings Red Breast & Carlsberg **Children's Facilities:** Menu/Portions Cutlery Highchair Food warming **Notes:** Dogs allowed in bar **Parking:** 20

NEWTON AYCLIFFE

Blacksmiths Arms ☗

Preston le Skerne (off Ricknall Lane) DL5 6JH

☎ 01325 314873

As its name suggests, this traditional pub was originally a blacksmith's shop dating from the 1700s. Set in isolated farmland, it enjoys an excellent reputation locally as a good dining pub. Fish dishes range from honey glazed ginger salmon, baked sea bass with lime, and tuna steak with king prawn and tarragon. Chef's specialities include game pie, navarin of lamb, and spicy parsnip soup.

Open: 12-3 6-11 (Sun-10.30) Closed: 1 Jan **Bar Meals:** L served Tue-Sun 11.30-2 D served Tue-Sun 6-9.30 (Sun 12-10.30) Av main course £10

Brewery/Company: Free House 🍺: Ever changing selection of real ales ☗: 10 **Children's Facilities:** Play area (Toys, Swings & Climbing Frames) Menu/Portions Highchair Food warming Baby changing **Notes:** Garden: Fully enclosed, rural setting, 0.75 acre **Parking:** 25

ROMALDKIRK

Rose and Crown ★★ HL ◉◉ ☗

Barnard Castle DL12 9EB

☎ 01833 650213 🖹 01833 650828

Email: hotel@rose-and-crown.co.uk

Web: www.rose-and-crown.co.uk

Dir: *6m NW from Barnard Castle on B6277.*

Dating back to 1733, the award-winning inn stands in the middle of three greens, still bearing the ancient stocks and water pump. Step inside the inn to discover polished panelling, old beams, gleaming brasses, fresh flowers and maybe the odd creaking stair.

Open: 11.30-3 5.30-11 Closed: Dec 23-27 **Bar Meals:** L served all week 12-1.30 D served all week 6.30-9.30 Av main course £10.50 **Restaurant Meals:** L served Sun only 12-1.30 D served all week 7.30-9 Av 3 course alc £17.25 **Brewery/Company:** Free House 🍺: Theakston Best, Black Sheep Best ☗: 10 **Children's Facilities:** Licence (Games & books) Menu/Portions Games Highchair Food warming Baby changing **Nearby:** High Force Waterfall, Raby Castle **Notes:** Dogs allowed in bar, in garden, in bedrooms Garden: Tables at front **Parking:** 24

TRIMDON
The Bird in Hand
Salters Lane TS29 6JQ
☎ 01429 880391
Village pub nine miles west of Hartlepool with fine views over surrounding countryside from an elevated position. There's a cosy bar and games room, a good choice of cask ales and guest beers, a spacious lounge and large conservatory restaurant. Traditional Sunday lunch goes down well, as does breaded plaice and other favourites. In summer you can sit outside in the garden, which has a roofed area for climbing plants.
Open: 12-11 (Sun 12-10.30) **Bar Meals:** L served Mon-Sat 12-2.30 D served Mon-Sat 5-9 Av main course £3.50 🍺: **Children's Facilities:** Fam room (Eating) Menu/Portions Cutlery Games Highchair Food warming

Notes: Dogs allowed in bar Garden: Enclosed area with gazebo roof **Parking:** 30

LITTLEBOROUGH
The White House 🍷
Blackstone Edge Halifax Road OL15 0LG
☎ 01706 378456
Old coaching house, built in 1671, standing high on the Pennines 1,300 feet above sea level, with panoramic views of the moors and Hollingworth Lake far below. The pub is on the Pennine Way, attracting walkers and cyclists who sup on Theakston's and regular guest ales. Fresh fish is a feature of the blackboard specials: cheddar topped grilled haddock, lobster thermidor and chargrilled tuna with balsamic glaze. Alternatives include steaks or lamb Henry.
Open: 12-3 6-11 Closed: 25 Dec **Bar Meals:** L served all week 12-2 D served all week 6.30-9 (Sun 12-9) Av main course £6.50 **Brewery/Company:** Free House 🍺:

Timothy Taylor Landlord, Theakstons Bitter, Exmoor Gold, Blacksheep, Phoenix **Children's Facilities:** Menu/Portions Highchair Food warming **Parking:** 44

OLDHAM
The Roebuck Inn 🍷
Strinesdale OL4 3RB
☎ 0161 624 7819 📠 0161 624 7819
Email: smhowarth1@aol.com
Dir: *From Oldham Humps Bridge take Huddersfield Road, turn right at 2nd lights onto Ripponden Road, after 1m turn right at lights onto Turfpit Lane, follow road for 1m.*
Historic inn located on the edge of Saddleworth Moor in the rugged Pennines, 1000 feet above sea level. Part of the pub was once a Sunday School, while the upstairs lounge served as a morgue. This may explain the presence of the ghost of a girl who drowned in the local reservoir. The menu offers an extensive choice from vegetarian dishes and steaks to fish dishes and mains like lambs' liver and onions or meat and potato pie.

Open: 12-2.30 5-12 (Sun all day) **Bar Meals:** L served all week 12-2.15 D served all week 5-9.30 (Sun 12-8.15) Av main course £10 **Restaurant Meals:** L served all week 12-2.15 D served all week 5-9.30 (Sun 12-8.15) Av 3 course alc £20 **Brewery/Company:** Free House 🍺: Tetleys, guest beer 🍷: 8 **Children's Facilities:** Play area (Play area) Menu/Portions Cutlery Games Highchair Food warming Baby changing **Notes:** Dogs allowed **Parking:** 40

WIGAN
Bird I'th Hand
Gathurst Road Orell WN5 0LH

☎ 01942 212006

Handy for Aintree races, this lively pub may well have once been the home of Dr Beecham of 'powders' fame. Home-made food, freshly prepared from market produce, characterises the imaginatively designed menu which offers the likes of stuffed chicken breast, beef Stroganoff, Great Grimsby fish pie, Bird special farmhouse stew, liver and onions, and Brixham plaice. Extensive range of starters.

Open: 12-11 (Fri-Sat 12pm-3am) **Bar Meals:** L served all week 12-9 D served all week 12-9 Av main course £7.95 **Restaurant Meals:** L served all week 12-9 D served all week 12-9 (Sun 12-8) Av 3 course alc £14.95

🍺: John Smiths, Directors Bitter, Foster Chesnut Mild, Guest beer **Children's Facilities:** Play area (Bouncy castles) Menu/Portions Cutlery Games Highchair Food warming Baby changing **Notes:** Garden: Large, BBQ, patio & pets corner **Parking:** 35

PORT ERIN
Falcon's Nest Hotel ★★ HL
The Promenade Station Road IM9 6AF

☎ 01624 834077 📠 01624 835370

Email: falconsnest@enterprise.net
Web: www.falconsnesthotel.co.uk

A popular local hotel, established in 1845, occupying a prime position overlooking Port Erin Bay, with spectacular views, particularly from the non-smoking conservatory dining room. The lounge and saloon bars serve local real ales, over 150 whiskies, meals and snacks. There is also a carte menu in the hotel restaurant and a carvery option. Theme nights offer a variety of cuisines like curry, Italian, Mexican and steaks.

Open: 10.30-12 **Bar Meals:** L served all week 12-9 D served all week 12-9 (Sun 12-2, 6-9) Av main course £7.50 **Restaurant Meals:** L served all week 12-2 D served all week 6-9 (Sun 12-2, 6-9) Av 3 course alc £20 **Brewery/Company:** Free House 🍺: Manx Guest Ale, Guinness, Carling & John Smith **Children's Facilities:** Licence Fam room Menu/Portions Cutlery Games Highchair **Nearby:** Beach **Notes:** Dogs allowed in garden, in bedrooms **Parking:** 100

BILSBORROW
Owd Nell's Tavern 🍷
Guy's Thatched Hamlet Canal Side Nr Garstang PR3 0RS

☎ 01995 640010 📠 01995 640141

Email: info@guysthatchedhamlet.com
Web: www.guysthatchedhamlet.com
Dir: *Telephone for directions*

Owd Nell's is part of Guy's Thatched Hamlet, a popular spot offering eating, drinking, craft shopping, cricket, dancing and accommodation all in a thatched complex.

Open: 9-3 Closed: 25 Dec **Bar Meals:** L served all week 11-9 D served all week 11-9 Av main course £6 **Restaurant Meals:** L served all week 12-2.30 D served all week 5.30-10.30 (Sat 12pm-1am, Sun 12pm-10.30pm) 🍺: Boddingtons Bitter, Jennings Bitter, Copper Dragon, Black Sheep, Owd Nells Bitter, Moorhouses Bitter

🍷: 40 **Children's Facilities:** Fam room Play area (Tunnels, swings, see-saw) Menu/Portions Games Highchair Food warming Baby changing **Nearby:** Blackpool Pleasure Beach, Farmer Parr's, Sandcastle Waterworld & Boar Park **Notes:** Dogs allowed in bar, in garden, Water **Garden:** Patio areas by the Lancaster Canal, 200 seats **Parking:** 300

BISPHAM GREEN
The Eagle & Child ♉

Maltkiln Lane Nr Ormskirk L40 3SG

☎ 01257 462297 🖨 01257 464718

Web: www.ainscoughs.co.uk

Dir: *3m from M6 junct 27. Over Parbold Hill, follow signs for Bispham Green on right*

This pub maintains its traditional atmosphere and offers five regularly changing guest ales and a beer festival every May. All the food is made on the premises with ingredients from local suppliers, and there is a good choice of dishes.

Open: 12-3 5.30-11 (Sun 12-10.30) **Bar Meals:** L served all week 12-2 D served all week 6-8.30 (Sun 12-8.30, Fri-Sat 6-9) Av main course £20 **Restaurant Meals:** L served all week 12-2 D served all week 6-8.30 (Fri-Sat 6-9, Sun 12-8.30) 🛢: Moorhouses Black Cat, Thwaites Bitter, 5 guest beers ♉: 6 **Children's Facilities:** Fam room Menu/Portions Highchair Food warming **Nearby:** Cedar Farm, Camelot, Martin Mere **Notes:** Dogs allowed in bar, Water bowls Garden: Large patio, wooden benches, bowling green **Parking:** 50

BLACKO
Moorcock Inn

Gisburn Road Nelson BB9 6NG

☎ 01282 614186 🖨 01282 614186

Email: boo@patterson1047.freeserve.co.uk

Dir: *M65 junct 13, take A682 to Blacko*

Family-run country inn with traditional log fires and good views towards the Pendle Way, ideally placed for non-motorway travel to the Lakes and the Yorkshire Dales. Home-cooked meals are a speciality, with a wide choice including salads and sandwiches, and vegetarian and children's meals. Tasty starters like cheesy mushrooms, and garlic prawns are followed by lasagne, various steak choices, pork in orange and cider, and trout grilled with lemon and herb butter.

Open: 12-2 6-9 (All day Sat, Sun close at 8) **Bar Meals:** L served all week 12-2 D served Tue-Sun 6-9.30 (Sun 12-7.30) **Restaurant Meals:** L served all week 12-2.30 D served Tue-Sun 6-9 (Sun 12-6) **Brewery/Company:** Daniel Thwaites Plc 🛢: Thwaites, Best Bitter, Smooth, Warfsteiner **Children's Facilities:** Menu/Portions Games Highchair **Notes:** Garden: Picnic benches, beautiful views **Parking:** 80

CARNFORTH
Old Station Inn ♉

Station Lane Burton LA6 1HR

☎ 01524 781225 🖨 01524 782662

Web: www.oldstationinnburton.co.uk

Dir: *from M6 take A6 signed Milnthorpe (Kendal), 3m before Milnthorpe turn right signed Burton/Holme*

Built in 1860 to serve the nearby mainline railway, this Victorian free house was formerly the Station Hotel. Here you'll find Boddington's and Black Sheep ales, as well as a regular guest beer and a decent choice of wines by the glass. Seafood is a speciality, and a single menu is served in the bar and non-smoking restaurant. Choices include grilled mackerel with garlic butter; and seared marlin with saffron rice and chargrilled peppers.

Open: 10-11 **Bar Meals:** L/D served all week 12-9.30 Av main course £8 **Restaurant Meals:** L served all week 12-9 D served all week Av 3 course alc £16 **Brewery/Company:** Free House 🛢: Jennings, Tillings Lancaster Brewery & 5 Guest Ales ♉: 29 **Children's Facilities:** Fam room Play area (inside and out) Menu/Portions Cutlery Games Highchair Food warming Baby changing **Nearby:** South Lakes Wildlife Oasis, Brewery Art Centre, Lake District **Notes:** Dogs allowed in bar, in garden, Water Garden: Lawned area with adventure playground **Parking:** 60

LANCASHIRE

CHIPPING
Dog & Partridge
Hesketh Lane Preston PR3 2TH
☎ 01995 61201 📄 01995 61446
Dating back to 1515, this pleasantly modernised rural pub in the Ribble Valley benefits from delightful views of the surrounding fells. The barn has been transformed into a welcoming dining area, where the emphasis is on home-made food using locally-sourced produce. The bar snack menu is comprehensive, while the à la carte menu includes braised pork chops, roast local duckling, and leek and mushroom crumble. Good range of vegetarian dishes.
Open: 11.45-3 6.45-11 (Sun 11.45-10.30) **Bar Meals:** L served all week 12-1.45 **Restaurant Meals:** L served all week 12-1.30 D served all week 7-9 (Sun lunch 12-3, carte menu 3.30-8.30) Av 3 course alc £20
Brewery/Company: Free House 🍺: Carlsberg-Tetley
Children's Facilities: Menu/Portions Highchair Food warming **Nearby:** Bowland Wild Boar Park **Parking:** 30

CLITHEROE
The Assheton Arms 🍷
Downham BB7 4BJ
☎ 01200 441227 📄 01200 440581
Email: asshetonarms@aol.com
Web: www.assheton-arms.co.uk
Dir: *From A59 to Chatburn, then follow Downham signs*
Better known to fans of the BBC's drama series *Born and Bred* as the Signalman's Arms, the inn is named after Lord Clitheroe's family, which owns the whole village. Present-day visitors will find the single bar and sectioned rooms furnished with solid oak tables, wingback settees, the original stone fireplace, and a large blackboard listing the range of daily dishes on offer. The pub is well placed for a moorland walk up Pendle Hill.
Open: 12-3 7-11 (Summer Sun open all day) **Bar Meals:** L served all week 12-2 D served all week 7-10 Av main course £9 **Brewery/Company:** Free House 🍺: Marstons Pedigree, Marston Bitter, Mansfield Bitter 🍷: 18 **Children's Facilities:** Menu/Portions Games Highchair Food warming Baby changing **Nearby:** Clitheroe Castle, Trough of Bowland & Downham Ducks
Notes: Dogs allowed in bar, Water **Parking:** 12

CLITHEROE
The Shireburn Arms ★★★ HL 🍷
Whalley Road Hurst Green BB7 9QJ
☎ 01254 826518 📄 01254 826208
Email: sales@shireburnarmshotel.com
Web: www.shireburnarmshotel.com
Dir: *Telephone for directions*
A privately run, 17th-century inn with super views, in the heart of the Ribble Valley. *Lord of the Rings* author J R R Tolkien used to drink here when visiting his son at Stonyhurst College nearby.
Open: 11-11 **Bar Meals:** L served all week 12-2 D served all week 5.30-9.30 (Sun 12-9) Av main course £8.50 **Restaurant Meals:** L served all week 12-2 D served all week 5.30-9.30 Av 3 course alc £18.50
🍺: Scottish Courage Theakstons Best Bitter, Mild & Guest Cask Ales 🍷: 10 **Children's Facilities:** Fam room Play area (Small Play area in garden, toys) Menu/Portions Cutlery Games Highchair Food warming Baby changing
Nearby: Tolkein trail, Stonyhurst College & Blackpool Pleasure Beach **Notes:** Dogs allowed in bar, in garden, in bedrooms **Garden:** Patio garden, seating for 60 people
Parking: 100

FORTON

The Bay Horse Inn ♿
LA2 0HR
☎ 01524 791204 📄 01524 791204
Email: bayhorseinfo@aol.com
Web: www.bayhorseinn.com
Dir: *1m S off Junct 33 of M6*
Due to a quirk of history, and the need for a railway station where no settlement actually existed, the area surrounding The Bay Horse Inn is also known as Bay Horse, which makes it an interesting as well as a rather beautiful place. The inn is traditional in style with a warm welcome, real cask beers and a good selection of malt whiskies; it also specialises in simple, fresh and imaginative dishes from an award-winning chef who is wholly self-taught. There is an excellent choice of fresh fish and seafood: warm Morecambe Bay shrimps with brandy butter; fillet of Lytham sea bass with potato purée. Local produce also features in other options, such as Lancashire lamb shank braised in Lancaster Bomber ale, and fillet of Bowland beef with real chips, rocket, and a peppercorn and Madeira cream.
Open: 12-3 6.30-11 **Bar Meals:** L served Tue-Sun 12-1.45 D served Tue-Sat 7-9.15 (Sun 12-7.30) Av main course £14 **Restaurant Meals:** L served Tue-Sun 12-1.45 D served Tue-Sat 7-9.15 (Sun 12-7.30) Av 3 course alc £25 🍺: Thwaites Lancaster Bomber, Moorhouses Pendle Witch, Masham Brewery & Black Sheep ♿: 11 **Children's Facilities:** Menu/Portions Cutlery Highchair Food warming Baby changing **Nearby:** Bowland Forest, Canal Towpath Walks & Butterfly House
Notes: Garden: Large rustic garden **Parking:** 30

GOOSNARGH

The Bushell's Arms ♿
Church Lane Preston PR3 2BH
☎ 01772 865235 📄 01772 865235
Dir: *Take A6 N to Garstang, right onto Whittingham Lane, after 3m left into Church Lane. Pub is by village green*
Dr Bushell was a philanthropic Georgian who built his villagers not just a hospital but this pub too. It seems that patients at the hospital were entitled to a daily pint of beer at the pub. A collection of main courses may include chicken breast filled with smoked Lancashire cheese and spinach and wrapped in bacon; oven roasted ham hock on a Bramley apple fritter, The Bushell's Pie of the day, or spinach and ricotta cheese cannelloni. Ideal walking country.
Open: 12-2 5-11 (All day Sun) **Bar Meals:** L served Tue-Sun 12-2 D served Tue-Sun 6-9 (Sun 12-8) Av main course £8.95 **Restaurant Meals:** L served Tue-Sun 12-2 D served Tue-Sun 6-9 (Sun 12-8) Av 3 course alc £15 **Brewery/Company:** Enterprise Inns 🍺: Timothy Taylor Landlord, Abbot Ale, Old Speckled Hen, Black Sheep, Adnams Broadside, Guest Beer ♿: 25 **Children's Facilities:** Menu/Portions Highchair Food warming Baby changing **Nearby:** Beacon Fell Country Park, Chingle Hall, Forest of Bowland **Notes:** Dogs allowed in bar, Water & Toys Garden: Secluded garden with lawns & flower beds **Parking:** 10

HASLINGDEN

Farmers Glory
Roundhill Road Rossendale BB4 5TU
☎ 01706 215748 📄 01706 215748
Dir: *On A667 8 miles equidistant from Blackburn, Burnley and Bury, 1.5m from M66*
Stone-built 300-year-old pub situated high above Haslingden on the edge of the Pennines. Formerly a coaching inn on the ancient route to Whalley Abbey, it now offers locals and modern A667 travellers a wide-ranging traditional pub menu of steaks, roasts, seafood, pizzas, pasta, curries and sandwiches.
Open: 12-3 7-11.30 **Bar Meals:** L served all week 12-2.30 D served all week 6.30-9.30 Av main course £6.95 **Restaurant Meals:** L served all week 12-2.30 D served all week 7-9.30 Av 3 course alc £13
Brewery/Company: Pubmaster 🍺: Carlsberg-Tetley Tetley Bitter, Marston's Pedigree, Greene King IPA, Jennings **Children's Facilities:** Menu/Portions Cutlery Games Highchair Food warming Baby changing **Nearby:** Camelot, Winfields, Rossendale Ski Slope **Notes:** Garden: 0.5 acre, fixed seating, ornamental fish pond **Parking:** 60

LANCASTER
The Stork Inn
Conder Green LA2 0AN
☎ 01524 751234 📠 01524 752660
Email: the.stork@virgin.net
Web: www.mortal-man-inns.co.uk
Dir: *M6 junct 33 take A6 north. Left at Galgate & next left to Conder Green*
White-painted coaching inn spread along the banks of the Conder Estuary, with a colourful 300-year-history that includes several name changes. The quaint sea port of Glasson Dock is a short walk along the Lancashire Coastal Way, and the Lake District is easily accessible. Seasonal specialities join home-cooked food like steak pie, locally-smoked haddock, salmon fillet with bonne femme sauce, and Cumberland sausage with onion gravy and mashed potatoes.
Open: 11-11 (Sun 12-10.30) **Bar Meals:** L served all week 12-3 D served all week 6-9 Av main course £6.95 **Restaurant Meals:** L served all week 12-2.30 D served all week 6-9 **Brewery/Company:** Free House
🍺: Boddingtons, Pedigree, Black Sheep, guest ales
Children's Facilities: Play area (Swings, slide climbing frame) **Notes:** Dogs allowed in bar, in garden, Water Garden: Large seating area with wishing well
Parking: 35

PRESTON
Cartford Country Inn & Hotel 🍷
Little Eccleston PR3 0YP
☎ 01995 670166 📠 01995 671785
Email: cartfordhotel@tiscali.co.uk
A former farmhouse, definitely three and possibly even four-hundred-years old. Today it is a pleasantly rambling, three-storey inn standing sentinel by the 40p toll bridge over the tidal River Wyre, a few miles from its meeting with the Irish Sea. The pub's own Hart Brewery out the back produces up to 30 different real ales, depending on the season. There's an all-embracing bar/restaurant menu, including sandwiches and hot meals. Eat outside overlooking the river, along 1.5 miles of which the Cartford owns exclusive fishing rights here.
Open: 12-3 6.30-11 Closed: Dec 25 **Bar Meals:** L served Mon-Sat 12-2 D served all week 6.30-9.30 Av main course £5.50 **Restaurant Meals:** L served 12-2 D served 6.30-9.30 **Brewery/Company:** Free House
🍺: Hart Beers, Fullers London Pride, Moorhouse, Guest ales **Children's Facilities:** Fam room Play area (Climbing frame, slide) Highchair Food warming **Notes:** Dogs allowed in bar **Parking:** 60

RIBCHESTER
The White Bull 🍷
Church Street Preston PR3 3XP
☎ 01254 878303
Email: wbribchester@btinternet.com
Web: www.whitebullribchester.co.uk
Dir: *Exit M6 junct 29 onto A59 towards Clitheroe, turn left at lights onto B6245, 2nd left on entering Ribchester.*
Grade II listed courthouse in the Roman town of Ribchester, built in 1707 using four Roman columns as front porch pillars. The former Roman bathhouse can be seen from the beer garden. Cask beers in the lounge and bars accompany a comprehensive selection of traditional pub food supplemented by regularly changing specials, such as fillet steak Rossini, and supreme of chicken filled with chorizo sausage and candied apricot.
Open: 12-11 **Bar Meals:** L served all week 12-9 D served all week 12-9 (Sun 12-8) Av main course £9.50 **Restaurant Meals:** L served all week 12-9 D served all week 12-9 (Sun 12-8) Av 3 course alc £15
Brewery/Company: Enterprise Inns 🍺: Taylors Landlord, Boddingtons Bitter, Black Sheep Best, Abbots Ale, Hoegarden 🍷: 10 **Children's Facilities:** Menu/Portions Cutlery Games Highchair Food warming **Nearby:** Roman Museum and Ruins, Ribble Way & Bowland Wild Boar Park **Notes:** Garden: Seating for 40 overlooking Roman ruins **Parking:** 14

SLAIDBURN
Hark to Bounty Inn
Townend nr Clitheroe BB7 3EP
☎ 01200 446246 📠 01200 446361
Email: manager@hark-to-bounty.co.uk
Web: www.hark-to-bounty.co.uk
Dir: *From M6 junct 31 take A59 to Clitheroe then B6478, through Waddington, Newton, onto Slaidburn*
A family-run, 13th-century inn known as The Dog until 1875 when Bounty, the local squire's hound, disturbed a post-hunt drinking session with its baying. The squire's vocal response obviously made a lasting impact.
Open: 11-11 **Bar Meals:** L served all week 12-2 D served all week 6-9 (Sun 12-8) Av main course £8.50
Restaurant Meals: L served Tue-Sun 12-2 D served Tue-Sat 6-9 (Sun all Day) Av 3 course alc £16.95

Brewery/Company: Scottish Courage 🍺: Theakston Old Peculier, Theakstons Bitter, Marstons Pedigree & 1 guest ale (changed monthly) **Children's Facilities:** Licence (Highchairs, table games) Menu/Portions Highchair Food warming Baby changing **Notes:** Dogs allowed in bar except during food service, in garden, in bedrooms Garden: Large enclosed area **Parking:** 25

WHALLEY
The Three Fishes 🍷
Mitton Road Mitton BB7 9PQ
☎ 01254 826888 📠 01254 826026
Email: kaye@northcotemanor.com
Web: www.thethreefishes.com
Dir: *3m from Whalley, signed to Stonyhurst.*
The Three Fishes prides itself on its 21st-century feel while it continues to embrace the values of a traditional English pub, with real beer, real food and real people. The menu is designed to include regional cookery and British classics using produce from the inn's acknowledged local food heroes. Children are made welcome and have their own menu of proper food in smaller portions.
Open: 12-11 Closed: Dec 25 **Bar Meals:** L served all week 12-2 D served all week 6-9 (Fri-Sat 6-9.30, Sun 12-8.30) Av main course £9 🍺: Thwaites Traditional, Thwaites Bomber, Moorhouse's Black Cat Mild & guest beer every month 🍷: 8 **Children's Facilities:** Licence Menu/Portions Cutlery Games Highchair Food warming Baby changing **Nearby:** The Tolkein Trail & Clitheroe Castle **Notes:** Dogs allowed in bar Garden: Fabulous views of The Ribble Valley **Parking:** 55

YEALAND CONYERS
The New Inn
40 Yealand Road Carnforth LA5 9SJ
☎ 01524 732938
Email: charlottepinder@hotmail.com
Web: www.the-newinn.com
Dir: *M6 junct 35, follow signs for Kendal (A6) approx 3m, past Holmere Hall, next junct on left, up hill turn left at T-junct. Pub is on left.*
A creeper-clad, traditional 17th-century village inn with a beamed bar and large stone fireplace as its centrepiece. A full range of bar food and restaurant food is served.
Open: 11.30-11 (Sun 12-10.30) **Bar Meals:** L served all week 11.30-9.30 D served all week 11.30-9.30 (Sun 12-9.30) **Restaurant Meals:** L served all week 11.30-9.30 D served all week 11.30-9.30 (Sun 12-9.30)

Brewery/Company: Frederic Robinson Ltd 🍺: Hartleys XB, Robinson's Seasonal Bitter, Old Tom **Children's Facilities:** Menu/Portions Highchair Food warming **Nearby:** Oasis Wildlife Park, Leighton Hall, Leighton Moss **Notes:** Dogs allowed in bar, in garden, Water Garden: quiet and private **Parking:** 50

LANCASHIRE

MERSEYSIDE / NORTHUMBERLAND

BARNSTON
Fox & Hounds 🍷
Barnston Road CH61 1BW
☎ 0151 6487685
Email: ralphleech@hotmail.com
Dir: *From M53 junct 4 take A5137 to Heswell. Right to Barnston on B5138*
Dating from 1911, this pub is in a conservation area and its Edwardian character has been preserved in the pitch pine woodwork and leaded windows. Collections of 1920s/30s memorabilia also feature. Six real ales, five lagers, sixty whiskies and twelve wines by the glass are served alongside a range of bar snacks, notably a variety of platters.
Open: 11-11 **Bar Meals:** L served all week 12-2 Av main course £6.95 **Brewery/Company:** Free House

🍺: Websters Yorkshire Bitter, Theakston, Best & Old Peculier, Marston Pedigree & two guest beers. 🍷: 12
Children's Facilities: Family room **Notes:** Dogs allowed in bar Garden: Lots of flowers, baskets and tubs
Parking: 60

ALNWICK
Masons Arms
Stamford Nr Rennington NE66 3RX
☎ 01665 577275
Email: bookings@masonsarms.net
Web: www.masonsarms.net
Dir: *NE of Alnwick on B1340, 0.5m past Ronnington*
A modernised 200-year-old coaching inn, known by the local community as Stamford Cott. It is a useful staging post for visitors to Hadrian's Wall, Lindisfarne and the nearby golf courses. The substantial home-cooked food is available in the bar and the restaurant.
Open: 12-2 6.30-11 (Sun 12-2 7-10.30) **Bar Meals:** L served all week 12-2 D served all week 6-9 (Winter 6.30-8.30) Av main course £7.50 **Restaurant Meals:** L served all week 12-2 D served all week 6-9 (Winter

6.30-8.30) Av 3 course alc £15 🍺: Scottish Courage John Smith's, Theakston Best, Secret Kingdom, Gladiator
Children's Facilities: Licence Fam room Menu/Portions Cutlery Highchair Food warming **Nearby:** Alnwick Gardens, Bamburgh Castle, Steam Railway **Notes:** Dogs allowed Garden: Grassed area with fountain and seating
Parking: 50

BELFORD
Blue Bell Hotel ★★ HL
Market Place NE70 7NE
☎ 01668 213543 📠 01668 213787
Email: bluebell@globalnet.co.uk
Web: www.bluebellhotel.com
Dir: *Off A1 25m from Berwick, 15m from Alnwick*
Richard Burton and Elizabeth Taylor are among a host of illustrious movie stars and television celebrities who have stayed at this 17th-century coaching inn on the A1 London to Edinburgh route. Choices from the restaurant menu may include chicken liver pâté with oatcakes as a starter, followed by grilled sirloin steak on roast asparagus with a stilton crust; and gingered rhubarb crumble with English custard to round off.
Open: 11-2.30 6.30-11 **Bar Meals:** L served all week

11-2 D served all week 6.30-9 **Restaurant Meals:** L served all week 12-2 D served all week 7-9
Brewery/Company: Free House 🍺: Interbrew Boddingtons Bitter, Northumbrian Smoothe, Calders, Tetleys Smooth **Children's Facilities:** Fam room Menu/Portions Cutlery Games Highchair Food warming
Notes: Garden: 3 acres **Parking:** 17

CARTERWAY HEADS

The Manor House Inn ♀

Shotley Bridge Consett DH8 9LX

☎ 01207 255268

Dir: *A69 W from Newcastle, left onto A68 then S for 8m. Inn on right.*

Newly refurbished after a fire and looking better than ever, this small family-run free house enjoys spectacular views across open moorland and the Derwent Reservoir from its lonely position high on the A68. The cosy stone-walled bar, with its log fires, low-beamed ceiling and massive timber support, offers a good range of well-kept real ales and around 70 malt whiskies.

Open: 11-11 **Bar Meals:** L/D served all week 12-9.30 (Sun 12-9) Av main course £11 **Restaurant Meals:** L served all week 12-2.30 D served all week 7-9.30 (Sun 7-9) **Brewery/Company:** Free House 🍺: Theakstons Best, Mordue Workie Ticket, Greene King Ruddles County, Scottish Courage Courage Directors, Bombardier ♀: 12 **Children's Facilities:** Licence Menu/Portions Highchair Food warming **Nearby:** Beamish Open Air Museum, Hadrian's Wall **Notes:** Dogs allowed in bar Garden: Small picnic area **Parking:** 60

CHATTON

The Percy Arms Hotel ♀

Main Road Alnwick NE66 5PS

☎ 01668 215244 📠 01668 215277

Web: www.percyarmshotel.co.uk

Dir: *From Alnwick take A1 N, then B6348 to Chatton*

Traditional 19th-century forming coaching inn, situated in the heart of rural Northumberland. Expect a warm, traditional pub welcome, as well as a selection of fine beers, wines and tempting food. Bar menu includes Aberdeen Angus steaks, deep-fried haddock, steak and kidney pie and a wide selection of fish and seafood dishes. Bar games include snooker, pool and darts.

Open: 11-11 (Sun 12-10.30) **Bar Meals:** L served all week 12-2 D served all week 6.30-9 **Restaurant Meals:** L served all week 12-1.30 D served all week 6.30-8.30 **Brewery/Company:** Jennings Brothers Plc 🍺: Jennings Cumberland Cream, guest beers ♀: 7 **Children's Facilities:** Licence Menu/Portions Cutlery Games Highchair Food warming Baby changing **Nearby:** Pot a Doodle Do, Chillingham Castle, Bamburgh Castle & Beach, Heatherslow Steam Railway **Notes:** Garden: patio/terrace, front beer garden, seats 20 **Parking:** 30

CRASTER

Cottage Inn ♀

Dunstan Village NE66 2UD

☎ 01665 576658 📠 01665 576788

Email: enquiries@cottageinnhotel.co.uk

Web: www.cottageinnhotel.co.uk

Dir: *NW of Howick to Embleton road*

Set in six acres of woodland, in an Area of Outstanding Natural Beauty, this 18th-century inn lies in a hamlet close to the coast. Nearby is Dunstanburgh Castle, one of Northumberland's great historic landmarks. Inside is a beamed bar, together with a restaurant, conservatory and patio. One menu serves all and includes the ever-popular Craster kippers, steak and game pie, venison sausages, and vegetable risotto. Local ingredients are used wherever possible.

Open: 11-12 **Bar Meals:** L served all week 12-2.30 D served all week 6-9.30 Av main course £8.50 **Restaurant Meals:** L served all week 12-2.30 D served all week 6-9.30 Av 3 course alc £19 **Brewery/Company:** Free House 🍺: Mordue, Tetley's, Farne Island, Black Sheep & Landlord ♀: 7 **Children's Facilities:** Play area (Outside play area, adventure play ground) Menu/Portions Games Highchair Food warming **Nearby:** Beach, Castle Mania **Notes:** Garden: Patio area with 6 acres of lawn & woodland **Parking:** 60

NORTHUMBERLAND

EGLINGHAM
Tankerville Arms
Alnwick NE66 2TX
☎ 01665 578444 📄 01665 578444
Dir: *B6346 from Alnwick*
The Tankerville Arms nestles in idyllic countryside about seven miles from Alnwick. Inside it is welcoming, and the pub attracts everyone from grandparents with children to families and young people. Fresh local produce is given careful but innovative handling and the results appear on the same menu throughout the pub.
Open: 12-2 7-11 (Times may vary, ring for details)
Closed: 25 Dec **Bar Meals:** L served all week 12-2 D served all week 6-9 Av main course £9.75 **Restaurant Meals:** L served all week 12-2 D served all week 6-9 Av 3 course alc £18 🍺: Greene King Ruddles Best,
Scottish Courage Courage Directors, Black Sheep Best, Mordue Workie Ticket, Timothy Taylor Landlord, Fiane Island **Children's Facilities:** Play area Menu/Portions Cutlery Games Highchair Food warming Baby changing **Nearby:** Alnwick Castle, Alnwick Tree House, Craigside Gardens **Notes:** Garden: Country garden, seating for 25, good views **Parking:** 15

ETAL
Black Bull
Cornhill upon Tweed TD12 4TL
☎ 01890 820200 📄 07092 367 733
Email: blackbulletal@aol.com
Web: www.blackbulletal.com
Dir: *10m N of Wooler right off A697, left at junction for 1m then left into Etal.*
The only thatched pub in Northumberland, the Black Bull stands by the ruins of Etal Castle, not far from the River Till, with the grand walking country of the Cheviots on the doorstep. Traditional pub food includes light bites such as sandwiches and hot baguettes, and hearty main courses including chicken, leek and Stilton pie; Cumberland sausage and mash; and steak and ale casserole with cheesy dumplings.
Open: 11-3.30 5.30-11 (Open all day summer, Closed Mon in winter) **Bar Meals:** L served all week 12-2 D served all week 6-9 (All day in summer) **Restaurant Meals:** L served all week 11.30-2.30 D served all week 6-9.30 (All Day in summer) **Brewery/Company:** Pubmaster 🍺: Jennings, Deuchers, John Smith Smooth, Fosters, Kronenburg **Children's Facilities:** Licence Menu/Portions Games Highchair Food warming **Notes:** Garden: Grass area with tables, chairs, gazebo, BBQ **Parking:** 10

FALSTONE
The Blackcock Inn ★★★ INN
nr Kielder NE48 1AA
☎ 01434 240200 📄 01434 240200
Email: dbdelboy@yahoo.co.uk
Web: www.theblackcockinnfalstone.co.uk
Dir: *Exit A1 junct 43 to Hexham and follow A6079 to Bellingham, brown signs to Kielder & Falstone*
Stone walls, log fires and original beams reflect the 18th-century origins of this traditional family-run free house. Nestling close to Kielder Water, the Blackcock makes an ideal base for walking, boating and fishing; the inn is also handy for the Rievers cycle route. The menu includes grills and pub favourites, as well as dishes like lamb shank in red wine and rosemary; and mushroom, brie, rocket and redcurrant filo bundle.
Open: 12-2 7-11 (Longer hrs in summer) **Bar Meals:** L served Wed-Sun 12-2 D served all week 7-8.30 (Sun 12-2, 7-8.30) **Restaurant Meals:** L served Wed-Sun 12-2 D served all week 7-8.30 **Brewery/Company:** Free House 🍺: Blackcock Ale, John Smiths, Cumberland & Guest beer **Children's Facilities:** Licence Fam room Play area (Swings & climbing frame) Menu/Portions Cutlery Games Highchair Food warming **Nearby:** Kielder Castle, Birds of Prey Centre, Tower Knowe **Notes:** Dogs allowed in bar, in garden, in bedrooms Feeding bowls Garden: Lawn, flower beds, picnic benches **Parking:** 20

FALSTONE

The Pheasant Inn ★★★★ INN

Stannersburn NE48 1DD

☎ 01434 240382 🖹 01434 240382

Email: enquiries@thepheasantinn.com

Web: www.thepheasantinn.com

Dir: *From A68 onto B6320, or from A69, B6079, B6320, follow signs 'Kielder Water'*

Enjoy the traditional warmth and friendly atmosphere of this cosy stone-walled pub. The bar menu changes daily.
Open: 11-3 6-11 (Opening times vary, ring for details)
Closed: Dec 25-26 **Bar Meals:** L served all week 12-2.30 D served all week 7-9 Av main course £7.50
Restaurant Meals: L served all week 12-2.30 D served all week 7-9 (Sun 12-2) Av 3 course alc £19 🍺:
Theakston Best, Marstons Pedigree, Timothy Taylor

Landlord, Greene King Old Speckled Hen, Wylam Gold
Children's Facilities: Fam room Play area Menu/Portions Cutlery Games Highchair Food warming Baby changing
Nearby: Kielder Water Leisure Park, Hadrians Wall, Newcastle Centre for Life **Notes:** Dogs allowed in garden, by arrangement only Garden: Grassed courtyard, stream running through **Parking:** 30

HAYDON BRIDGE

The General Havelock Inn 🍷

Ratcliffe Road Hexham NE47 6ER

☎ 01434 684376 🖹 01434 684283

Email: generalhavelock@aol.com

Web: www.northumberlandretaurants.co.uk

Dir: *On A69, 7m west of Hexham*

Built from Northumbrian stone in 1766, the inn was named after the Indian mutiny hero General Havelock. The restaurant in a converted barn overlooks the River Tyne, as does the tranquil south-facing patio. Locally sourced ingredients inspire fresh, modern dishes like pan-fried guinea fowl on cabbage and butternut squash.
Open: 12-2.30 7-11 **Bar Meals:** L served Tue-Sun 12-2 D served Tue-Sat 7-9 (Sun 12-2, 8-11) Av main course £11 **Restaurant Meals:** L served Tue-Sun 12-2

D served Tue-Sat 7-9 (Sun 12-2, 8-11) Av 3 course alc £22.75 **Brewery/Company:** Free House 🍺: Hesket Newmarket, Wylam Magic, Helvellyn Gold, Mordue Al Wheat Pet, Durham Brewery Magus 🍷: 9 **Children's Facilities:** Licence Menu/Portions Games Highchair Food warming **Notes:** Dogs allowed in bar Garden: Patio area on river bank, lots of plants

HEXHAM

Battlesteads Hotel & Restaurant

Wark NE48 3LS

☎ 01434 230209 🖹 01434 230039

Email: info@battlesteads.com

Web: www.battlesteads.com

Dir: *10m N of Hexham on B6320 Kielder Rd*

Built as a farmstead in 1747, this is a stone-built hostelry close to Hadrian's wall. There's a cosy fire in the bar, where a wide range of cask and bottle-conditioned beers from local micro breweries is on sale. Freshly cooked meals are based on home-grown lamb and local beef, with the menu offering Louisiana chicken, mushroom and haloumi stack, steak and ale pie, and roasted chunky cod. There's also a set menu.
Open: 11-11 **Bar Meals:** L served all week 12-3 D served all week 6.30-9.30 Av main course £10
Restaurant Meals: L served all week 12-3 D served all week 6.30-9.30 Av 3 course alc £18.50
Brewery/Company: Free House 🍺: Wylam Gold Tankard, Black Sheep Special, Durham White Velvet, Theakstons Black Bull, Durham Magus **Children's Facilities:** Licence Menu/Portions Cutlery Highchair Food warming **Nearby:** Hadrian's Wall, Kielder Water & Forest, Northumberland National Park **Notes:** Dogs allowed in bar Garden: Large, walled garden, tables & benches
Parking: 30

NORTHUMBERLAND

HEXHAM

Miners Arms Inn ♟

Main Street Acomb NE46 4PW

☎ 01434 603909

Dir: *17m W of Newcastle on A69, 2m W of Hexham.*
Close to Hadrian's Wall in a peaceful village, this
charming 18th-century pub has stone walls, beamed
ceilings and open fires. Real ales are a speciality, as is
good home-cooked food. Good setting for cyclists and
walkers, and the garden has an aviary.
Open: 5-11 (Etr, Sum, Xmas Hols 12-11 all wk) **Bar
Meals:** L served Sat-Sun 12-2.30 D served all week
6-8.30 (Sun 12-3.30) Av main course £6 **Restaurant
Meals:** L served Sat-Sun & Holidays12-2.30 D served
all week 6-8.30 (Sun 12-3.30) **Brewery/Company:**
Free House ⬛: Black Sheep Bitter, Yates, Durham White

Velvet, Boddingtons, Jennings Old Smoothy ♟: 7
Children's Facilities: Licence Fam room Menu/Portions
Cutlery Games Highchair Food warming **Nearby:**
Hadrian's Wall, Sele Park with play area **Notes:** Dogs
allowed in bar, in garden, Water and biscuits **Garden:**
Sun trap, BBQ, resident birds of prey

LONGFRAMLINGTON

The Anglers Arms

Weldon Bridge Morpeth NE65 8AX

☎ 01665 570271 & 570655 📄 01665 570041

Email: johnyoung@anglersarms.fsnet.co.uk

Web: www.anglersarms.com

Dir: *9m S of Alnwick right at signs for Weldon Bridge.
From S, A1 to by-pass Morpeth, left onto A697 for Wooler
& Coldstream. Travel 7m & left to Weldon Bridge.*
As you might expect from the name, the 18th-century
Anglers Arms is located by the Coquet river, next to
Weldon Bridge. Enjoy a meal in the unusual setting of an
old Pullman railway carriage
Open: 11-11 (Sun 12-11) **Bar Meals:** L served all week
12-9.30 D served all week 12-9.30 (Sun 12-9) Av main
course £10 **Restaurant Meals:** L served all week

12-2 D served all week 7-9 Av 3 course alc £29
⬛: Worthington, Boddingtons & 3 Guest **Children's
Facilities:** Licence Fam room Play area (in garden,
climbing frame) Menu/Portions Highchair Food warming
Baby changing **Nearby:** Alnwich Gardens, Craggside &
Bamburgh Castle **Notes:** Dogs allowed in garden
Garden: Well-tended 05 acre **Parking:** 30

LONGHORSLEY

Linden Tree ★★★★ HL ◉◉

Linden Hall Morpeth NE65 8XF

☎ 01670 500033 📄 01670 500001

Email: lindenhall@macdonald-hotels.co.uk

Web: www.macdonald-hotels.co.uk/lindenhall

Dir: *Off A1 on A697, 1m N of Longhorsley*
Originally two large cattle byres, this popular bar takes its
name from the linden trees in the grounds of Linden Hall
Hotel, an impressive Georgian mansion. Straightforward
meals range from aubergine and broccoli bake, braised
lamb shank, or medallions of pork, to grilled salmon, or
poached smoked cod fillets.
Open: 11-11 (Sun 12-10.30) **Bar Meals:** L/D served all
week 8am-9.30pm (Sun 12-4,6-9) Av main course £10
Restaurant Meals: L served all week 8am-9.30pm (Sun

12-4, 6-9) Av 3 course alc £20 **Brewery/Company:**
Free House ⬛: Worthington 1744, Greene King IPA,
Cafereys **Children's Facilities:** Licence Menu/Portions
Games Highchair Food warming Baby changing **Notes:**
Garden: Large open court yard **Parking:** 200

NEWTON ON THE MOOR
Cook and Barker Inn 🍷

Felton Morpeth NE65 9JY

☎ 01665 575234 📄 01665 575234

Web: www.cookandbarkerinn.co.uk

Dir: *0.5m from A1 S of Alnwick*

Traditional Northumbrian inn located in a picturesque village with views of the coast and the Cheviot Hills. Good quality fare and a welcoming atmosphere make this a popular dining destination. Real ales and wines by the glass are offered alongside an extensive menu. Seafood figures strongly; also grills, roasts and oriental dishes. **Open:** 11-3 6-11 **Bar Meals:** L served all week 12-2 D served all week 6-9 Av main course £7.95 **Restaurant Meals:** L served all week 12-2 D served all week 7-9 Av 3 course alc £28 🍺: Timothy Taylor Landlord, Theakstons Best Bitter, Fuller's London Pride, Batemans XXXB, Scottish Courage Courage Directors, Greene King Ruddles County 🍷: 12 **Children's Facilities:** Fam room Menu/Portions Cutlery Highchair Food warming **Nearby:** Alnwick Gardens, Alnwick Castle, Druridge Bay **Notes:** Garden: Pretty area with lots of space for children **Parking:** 60

ROWFOOT
The Wallace Arms

Featherstone Haltwhistle NE49 0JF

☎ 01434 321872 📄 01434 321872

Email: www.thewallacearms@btconnect.com

Web: www.thewallacearmshotel.com

The pub was rebuilt in 1850 as the Railway Hotel at Featherstone Park station, when the now long-closed Haltwhistle-Alston line (today's South Tyne Trail) was engineered. It changed to the Wallace Arms in 1885. Sample menu includes modestly-priced haddock fillet in beer batter, salmon fillet in lemon and tarragon sauce, steak and ale pie, grilled sirloin steak, and smoked haddock and prawn pasta. There are light snacks, burgers and sandwiches, if you prefer. **Open:** 11-3 4-12 (Opening times vary, ring for details) **Bar Meals:** L served all week 12-2.30 D served all week 6-9 **Restaurant Meals:** L served all week 12-2.30 D served all week 6-9 **Brewery/Company:** Free House 🍺: Hook Norton Old Hooky, Young's Special, Greene King IPA, Greene King Abbot Ale, Jennings Cumberland Ale **Children's Facilities:** Menu/Portions Highchair Food warming **Notes:** Garden: Large lawn surrounded by stone wall **Parking:** 30

WARDEN
The Boatside Inn 🍷

Hexham NE46 4SQ

☎ 01434 602233 601061

Dir: *Just off A69 west of Hexham, follow signs to Warden Newborough & Fourstones*

Attractive stone-built inn situated where the North and South Tyne rivers meet, beneath Warden Hill Iron Age fort. The name refers to the rowing boat that ferried people across the river before the bridge was built. It is a popular destination for walkers, promising real ale and good food cooked from local produce. Dishes include seafood stew, battered haddock, and slow roast lamb shoulder. There is also a garden with a lawn area and barbecue. **Open:** 11-11 **Bar Meals:** L served all week D served all week Av main course £8 **Restaurant Meals:** L served all week D served all week Av 3 course alc £25 **Brewery/Company:** Free House 🍺: Black Sheep 🍷: 15 **Children's Facilities:** Licence Menu/Portions Highchair Food warming **Notes:** Dogs allowed in bar, in garden, Water Garden: Paved patio with lawn area, hanging baskets **Parking:** 70

NORTH SHIELDS
Magnesia Bank 🍷
1 Camden Street NE30 1NH
☎ 0191 257 4831 📠 0191 258 6847
Email: info@magnesiabank.com
Web: www.magnesiabank.com
Dir: *2m E of Tyne Tunnel (N entrance)*
Set high up on the banks of the River Tyne above North Shields fish quay is this lively pub located in a converted bank. Its reputation for real ales is based on a local micro brewery's produce, with seven cask ales always on tap. The menu takes in starters of grilled field mushrooms topped with houmous, garlic and chilli tapenade, and mains of fish pie with salad and crusty bread. Several themed evenings are a special feature here.
Open: 11-11.30 (Fri 11-12, Sat 10-12, Sun 11-11) **Bar**

Meals: L served all week 11-9.45 D served all week 11-9.45 (Sun 11.30-8.45) Av main course £10
Restaurant Meals: L served all week 12-9.45 D served all week 12-9.45 (Sun 11.30-8.45) Av 3 course alc £18.50 **Brewery/Company:** Free House 🍺: Durham Brewery Magus, Mordue Brewery Workie Ticket, Black Sheep Bitter, Mordue 5 Bridges, Boddingtons, Old Speckled Hen 🍷: 7 **Children's Facilities:** Licence Menu/Portions Highchair Food warming **Nearby:** Wet & Wild swimming pool, Sea Life Centre, Tynemouth Castle

TYNEMOUTH
Copperfields ★★★ HL
Grand Hotel Hotspur Street NE30 4ER
☎ 0191 293 6666 📠 0191 293 6665
Email: info@grandhotel-uk.com
Web: www.grandhotel-uk.com
Dir: *On NE coast, 10m from Newcastle-upon-Tyne*
Copperfields bar is part of the Grand Hotel at Tynemouth, and is set on a cliff top commanding some of the most stunning views of natural coastline in the country. It was a frequent haunt of local boy Stan Laurel of Laurel and Hardy fame. Traditional home-cooked meals served in the bar include North Shields cod and chips, steak and mushroom pie and popular roast dinners.
Open: 12-11 (Sun 12-10.30) **Bar Meals:** L served all week 12-3 D served all week 3-8 **Restaurant Meals:** L served all week 12-3 D served Mon-Sat 6.30-9.45 🍺: Durham Magus, Bass '9', London Pride, Black Sheep, John Smiths **Children's Facilities:** Licence Menu/Portions Cutlery Games Highchair Food warming Baby changing **Nearby:** Beamish Museum, Hadrian's Wall, Centre for Life **Parking:** 16

WHITLEY BAY
The Waterford Arms
Collywell Bay Road Seaton Sluice NE26 4QZ
☎ 0191 237 0450 📠 0191 237 7760
Web: www.waterfordarms.co.uk
Dir: *From A1 N of Newcastle take A19 at Seaton Burn then follow signs for A190 to Seaton Sluice*
The building dates back to 1899 and is located close to the small local fishing harbour, overlooking the North Sea. Splendid beaches and sand dunes are within easy reach, and the pub is very popular with walkers. Seafood dishes are the speciality, including a jumbo cod, seared swordfish, lemon sole, halibut, and crab-stuffed plaice.
Open: 12-11 (Sun 12-10.30) **Bar Meals:** L served all week 12-4 D served all week (Sun 12-4) Av main course £5.95 **Restaurant Meals:** L served all week 12-9 D served all week (Sun 12-4) Av 3 course alc £7.25
Brewery/Company: Pubmaster 🍺: Tetleys, John Smiths, Scotch, Carling **Children's Facilities:** Cutlery Highchair Food warming **Nearby:** Whitley Bay coast and amusements **Notes:** Garden: Food served outside **Parking:** 10

HUGGATE
The Wolds Inn ★★★ GA
YO42 1YH
☎ 01377 288217
Email: huggate@woldsinn.freeserve.co.uk
Dir: *S off A166 between York & Driffield*
Probably the highest inn on the Yorkshire Wolds, 16th century in origin, with tiled roofs and white-painted chimneys, and a wood-panelled interior with open fires and gleaming brassware. Its elevation explains why the Wolds Topper, 'the mixed grill to remember', is so named; other main courses include steaks with a variety of sauces, rack of lamb, loin of pork, roast duckling, and Scottish salmon fillet, while vegetarians may consult their own blackboard.
Open: 12-2 6.30-11 (May-Sep open Sun at 6) **Bar**

Meals: L served Tue-Thu, Sat, Sun 12-2 D served Tue-Sun 6.30-9 (Sun 6-9 May-Sep) Av main course £6
Restaurant Meals: L served Tue-Thu, Sat & Sun12-2 D served Tue-Sun 6.30-9 (May-Sep Sun 6-9) Av 3 course alc £17 **Brewery/Company:** Free House 🍺: Carlsberg-Tetley Tetley Bitter, Timothy Taylor Landlord, Black Sheep **Children's Facilities:** Menu/Portions Cutlery Highchair Food warming **Notes:** Garden: Large & contained **Parking:** 50

LOW CATTON
The Gold Cup Inn 🍷
Stamford Bridge YO41 1EA
☎ 01759 371354 📠 01759 373833
Dir: *1m S of A166 or 1m N of A1079, E of York*
This family-run, 300-year-old country inn incorporates a two-part restaurant: one is small and intimate, with solid wood pews and tables reputedly made from a single oak; the other is larger and lighter with a vaulted ceiling. Bar areas are comfortable and relaxed, with an open fire and a cast-iron stove at opposite ends. Locally sourced ingredients are used as much as possible for dishes such as grilled salmon fillet topped with sautéed prawns, and chargrilled chicken breast.
Open: 12-3 6-11 (Sat 12-11, Sun 12-10.30) **Bar Meals:** L served Sun, Tue-Sat 12-2 D served all week 6-9 (12-9.30 wknds) Av main course £7 **Restaurant Meals:** L served Sun 12-5.30 D served all week 6-9 Av 3 course alc £18 **Brewery/Company:** Free House 🍺: John Smiths, Black Sheep 🍷: 10 **Children's Facilities:** Menu/Portions Cutlery Highchair Food warming **Nearby:** York Mining Museum, Castle Howard, Water World **Notes:** Garden: Large grassed area with flower beds, trees **Parking:** 60

SOUTH CAVE
The Fox and Coney Inn 🍷
52 Market Place Brough HU15 2AT
☎ 01430 422275 📠 01430 421552
Email: foxandconey@aol.com
Web: www.foxandconey.com
Dir: *4m E of M62 on A63. 4m N of Brough main railway.*
Right in the heart of South Cave, this family-run pub dates from 1739 and is probably the oldest building in the village. The inn, which is handy for walkers on the nearby Wolds Way, was known simply as The Fox until William Goodlad added the Coney (rabbit) in 1788. Jacket potatoes, salads and baguettes supplement varied hot dishes like steak in ale pie, chicken curry, seafood platter and mushroom Stroganoff.
Open: 11.30-2.30 4.30-11 **Bar Meals:** L served all week 11.30-2 D served all week 5.30-9.30 (Sun 12-3.30, 5.30-9) Av main course £7.95 **Restaurant Meals:** L served all week 11.30-2 D served all week 5.30-9.30 (Sun 12-9) Av 3 course alc £13.50 **Brewery/Company:** Enterprise Inns 🍺: Timothy Taylors Landlord, Scottish Courage John Smith's & Theakston Cool Cask, Deuchers IPA, Guest Beers 🍷: 15 **Children's Facilities:** Fam room Menu/Portions Cutlery Highchair Food warming Baby changing **Notes:** Garden: Seats approx 30 **Parking:** 22

NORTH YORKSHIRE

APPLETREEWICK
The Craven Arms ♥
Nr Skipton BD23 6DA
☎ 01756 720270
Email: thecravenarms@ukonline.co.uk
Dir: *From Skipton take A59 towards Harrogate, B6160 N. Village signed on right. Pub just outside village.*
Built as a farm by Sir William Craven (a Lord Mayor of London) in the mid-16th century, and later used as a weaving shed and courthouse, this ancient building retains its original beams, flagstone floors and magnificent Dales fireplace. The village stocks are still outside, with spectacular views of the River Wharfe and Simon's Seat. New owners have restored the interior, and plan a barn restaurant and extension to the beer garden.
Open: 11.30-3 6.30-11 (Closed Mon Thu eve winter)

Bar Meals: L served all week 12-2 D served Wed-Mon 6.30-9 (Sun 12-2, 6.30-8.30) **Brewery/Company:** Free House 🍺: Tetley, Folly Ale, Timothy Taylors Landlord & Golden Best ♥: 8 **Children's Facilities:** Menu/Portions Cutlery Games Highchair Food warming **Nearby:** Embsay & Bolton Abbey Steam Railway, Stump Cross Caverns, Bolton Abbey **Notes:** Dogs allowed in bar, in garden, Water bowls **Garden:** Walled grass beer garden, hill views **Parking:** 35

ASKRIGG
Kings Arms ♥
Market Place Wensleydale DL8 3HQ
☎ 01969 650817 📠 01969 650856
Email: kingsarms@askrigg.fsnet.co.uk
Dir: *N off A684 between Hawes & Leyburn*
At the heart of the Yorkshire Dales, Askrigg's pub was known as The Drovers in the TV series *All Creatures Great and Small*. Built in 1762 as racing stables and converted to a pub in 1860, today it boasts a good range of real ales and an extensive menu and wine list. Favourites are roasted rack of Dales lamb with a mustard and herb crust, beer-battered haddock fillet with chips, chicken breast with linguini, roasted seabass on Mediterranean vegetables or grilled gammon steak with eggs or pineapple rings. Spectacular inglenook fireplace in the main bar.
Open: 11-3 6-11 (Sat 11-11, Sun 12-10.30) **Bar Meals:** L served all week 12-2 D served all week 6.30-9 Av main course £10 **Restaurant Meals:** L served 12-2 D served all week 7-9 Av 3 course alc £20
Brewery/Company: Free House 🍺: Scottish Courage John Smiths, Black Sheep, Theakstons Best Bitter, Theakstons Old Peculier, McEwans 80 Shilling ♥: 6
Children's Facilities: Menu/Portions Highchair Food warming **Notes:** Dogs allowed in bar, Water provided **Garden:** paved courtyard

AUSTWICK
The Game Cock Inn
The Green nr Settle LA2 8BB
☎ 015242 51226
Email: richardlord495@hotmail.com
Richard and Trish Lord offer a warm welcome to this award-winning pub, set in the limestone village of Austwick. There's a large garden and children's play area, with winter log fires in the cosy bar. Expect real ale, a range of malt whiskies, and an imaginative menu. Typical dishes include giant ham shank with mash and pickled red cabbage, whilst one of the regular French evenings might feature fresh Toulouse sausage on provençale couscous.
Open: 11.30-3 6-1am (All day Sun) **Bar Meals:** L served all week 11.30-2 D served all week 6-9 (Sun 12-9) Av main course £6 **Restaurant Meals:** L served all week 11.30-2 D served all week 6-9 (Sun 12-9) Av 3 course alc £10 **Brewery/Company:** Thwaites 🍺: Thwaites Best Bitter & Smooth, Warfsteiner
Children's Facilities: Fam room Play area (Play area and bird avairy in garden) Menu/Portions Highchair Food warming **Nearby:** Falconry Centre, Ingleton Waterfalls, Caves at Clapham **Notes:** Garden: large beer garden **Parking:** 6

BOROUGHBRIDGE
The Black Bull Inn 🍷

6 St James Square Nr York YO51 9AR

☎ 01423 322413 📄 01423 323915

Dir: *From A1(M) junct 48 take B6265 E for 1m*

The picturesque Black Bull has been an inn since 1258 when it was one of the main stops for coaches on what is now the A1, and in those days it had stables and a black-smith's shop attached. Following a fire in 2004, much of the inn has been restored, and the food is as good as ever.

Open: 11-11 (Sun 12-10.30) **Bar Meals:** L served all week 12-2 D served all week 6-9 (Fri/Sat 6-9.30 Sun 12-2.30, 6-9) Av main course £6 **Restaurant Meals:** L served all week 12-2 D served all week 6-9 (Fri/Sat 6-9.30 Sun 12-2.30, 6-9) Av 3 course alc £20

Brewery/Company: Free House 🍺: Black Sheep, Scottish Courage John Smiths, Timothy Taylor Landlord, Cottage Brewing, Charles Wells Bombardier Premium Bitter, guest 🍷: 10 **Children's Facilities:** Menu/Portions Highchair Food warming **Nearby:** Lightwater Vallet, Knaresborough & Newby Hall **Notes:** Dogs allowed in bar, in bedrooms, Water, Toys **Parking:** 4

BROUGHTON
The Bull 🍷

nr Skipton BD23 3AE

☎ 01756 792065

Email: janeneil@thebullatbroughton.co.uk

Web: www.thebullatbroughton.co.uk

Dir: *On A59 3m from Skipton on A59*

Like the village itself, the pub is part of the 3,000-acre Broughton Hall estate, owned by the Tempest family for 900 years. Chef-cum-manager Neil Butterworth's compact, thoughtful menu offer Goosnargh duck breast with spring onion and coriander mash, chargrilled fillet steak, and goats' cheese on toast. The locally brewed Bull Bitter and guest ales are features, and twice a month a mystery meal is held on Guinea Pig Night.

Open: 12-3 5.30-11 (Sun 12-8) **Bar Meals:** L served all week 12-2 D served Mon-Sat 6-9 (Sun 12-6) **Restaurant Meals:** L served all week 12-2 D served Mon-Sat 6-9 (Sun & BHs 12-6) **Brewery/Company:** Free House 🍺: Scottish Courage, John Smith's Smooth, Bull Bitter (Local), Guest Ales, Copper Dragon 🍷: 6 **Children's Facilities:** Fam room Games Highchair Food warming **Nearby:** Embsay Steam Railway, Skipton Castle **Notes:** Dogs allowed in bar, in garden, Water & biscuits **Garden:** Large stone patio, heaters, seating **Parking:** 60

BURNSALL
The Red Lion ★★ HL 🌐🍷

By the Bridge Skipton BD23 6BU

☎ 01756 720204 📄 01756 720292

Email: redlion@daelnet.co.uk

Web: www.redlion.co.uk

Dir: *From Skipton take A59 E, take B6160 towards Bolton Abbey, Burnsall 7m.*

An old ferryman's inn with large gardens, standing by a five-arched bridge on the banks of the River Wharfe. Hospitality has been dispensed from here for centuries.

Open: 8-11.30- **Bar Meals:** L served all week 12-2.30 D served all week 6-9.30 Av main course £11 **Restaurant Meals:** L served all week 12-2.30 D served all week 7-9.30 Av 3 course alc £26.95 🍺: Theakston Black Bull, Greene King Old Speckled Hen, Timothy Taylor Landlord, Scottish Courage John Smith's 🍷: 14 **Children's Facilities:** Fam room Menu/Portions Highchair Food warming Baby changing **Nearby:** Lightwater Valley, Hesketh Farm Park & Newby Hall **Notes:** Dogs allowed in bar, in garden, in bedrooms **Garden:** Large garden, bordering the River Wharf **Parking:** 70

NORTH YORKSHIRE

CLAPHAM
New Inn 🍷
nr Settle LA2 8HH
☎ 01524 251203 📄 01524 251496
Email: info@newinn-clapham.co.uk
Web: www.newinn-clapham.co.uk
Dir: *On A65 in Yorkshire Dale National Park*
There's a warm and friendly welcome at this 18th-century free house, nestling beneath the famous summit of Ingleborough. Outdoor enthusiasts Keith and Barbara Mannion serve honest, wholesome food in their dining room.
Open: 11-11 **Bar Meals:** L served all week 12-2 D served all week 6.30-8.30 (Sun 6.30-8) Av main course £8.95 **Restaurant Meals:** L served all week 12-2 D served all week 6.30-8.30 (Sun 6.30-8) Av 3 course alc

£22 **Brewery/Company:** Free House 🍺: Black Sheep Best, Tetley Bitter, Copper Dragon Pippin, Thwaites Best & Thwaites Bomber 🍷: 18 **Children's Facilities:** Licence (Baby changing facilities) Menu/Portions Cutlery Highchair Food warming Baby changing **Nearby:** Falconry Centre & Ingleborough Cave **Notes:** Dogs allowed in bar, in garden, Garden: Seats, beer garden **Parking:** 35

CROPTON
The New Inn 🍷
Nr. Pickering YO18 8HH
☎ 01751 417330 📄 01751 417582
Email: info@croptonbrewery.co.uk
Web: www.croptonbrewery.com
Home of the award-winning Cropton micro-brewery, this family-run free house on the edge of the North York Moors National Park is popular with locals and visitors alike. Meals are served in the restored village bar and in the elegant Victorian restaurant: choices could include Whitby cod with mushy peas and home-made chips; and three cheese and roasted vegetable frittata.
Open: 11-11 **Bar Meals:** L served all week 12-2 D served all week 6-9 Av main course £9 **Restaurant Meals:** L served all week 12-2 D served all week 6-9

Av 3 course alc £16 🍺: Cropton Two Pints, Monkmans Slaughter, Yorkshire Moors Bitter, Honey Gold Bitter & Theakstons Best Bitter 🍷: 7 **Children's Facilities:** Fam room Play area Menu/Portions Games Highchair Food warming **Nearby:** Flamingo Land- Zoo and Fun Park, Eden Camp, Sea Life Centre **Notes:** Dogs allowed in bar, in garden, Garden: Beer garden **Parking:** 50

EGTON
The Wheatsheaf Inn
YO21 1TZ
☎ 01947 895271 📄 01947 895391
Dir: *Off A169 NW of Grosmont*
This unassuming old pub sits back from the wide main road, so be careful not to miss it. The main bar is cosy and traditional, with low beams, dark green walls and comfy settles. There's a locals' bar too, but it only holds about twelve, so get there early. The pub is very popular with fishermen, as the River Esk runs along at the foot of the hill, and is a big draw for fly-fishers in particular. A warming menu of hearty grub includes a good choice of fresh fish dishes such as mussel and garlic soup; fish stew; fresh crab thermidor; and cullen skink. Other choices include chicken and bacon puff pie; lamb shank

braised with redcurrant and Madeira gravy; fillet steak with Béarnaise sauce; and fish stew with smoked cod, salmon, clams, mussels, and white prawns in saffron sauce.
Open: 11.30-3 5.30-11.30 **Bar Meals:** L served Tue-Sun 12-2 D served Tue-Sat 6-9 Av main course £11 **Restaurant Meals:** L served Tue-Sun 12-2 D served Tue-Sat 6-9 **Brewery/Company:** Free House 🍺: Black Sheep Bitter, Black Sheep Special, John Smith, Adnams, Rigwelter **Children's Facilities:** Menu/Portions Cutlery Games Highchair Food warming **Nearby:** Beach, Steam Railway (featured in Harry Potter films) **Notes:** Dogs allowed in bar Garden: Lawned area with garden tables **Parking:** 30

EGTON BRIDGE
Horseshoe Hotel ♛
Whitby YO21 1XE
☎ 01947 895245
Dir: *From Whitby take A171 towards Middlesborough. Village signed in 5m.*
An 18th-century country inn by the River Esk, handy for visiting the North Yorkshire Moors Railway. Inside are oak settles and tables, local artists' paintings and, depending on the weather, an open fire. The main menu includes starters like crab cakes with a sweet chilli dip, and mains like lasagne, scampi, or pie of the day.
Open: 11.30-3 6.30-11 (All day Sat, Sun & BH's in Summer) Closed: 25-Dec **Bar Meals:** L served all week 12-2 D served all week 7-9 **Restaurant Meals:** L served all week 12-2 D served all week 7-9

Brewery/Company: Free House ◨: Copper Dragon & John Smiths, Durham, Black Sheep & Archers ♛: 7 **Children's Facilities:** Fam room Menu/Portions Cutlery Games Highchair Food warming Baby changing **Nearby:** Grosmont Steam Railway **Notes:** Dogs allowed in bar, in garden, Water **Garden:** Beautiful garden on banks of River Esk **Parking:** 25

ESCRICK
Black Bull Inn ♛
Main Street York YO19 6JP
☎ 01904 728245 ▤ 01904 728154
Email: bookings@yorkblackbullinn.com
Web: www.yorkblackbullinn.co.uk
Dir: *From York follow the A19 for 5m, enter Escrick, take 2nd left up main street, located on left*
Traditional cottage-style inn located in the pretty village of Escrick just south of the City of York. Locally supplied ingredients are used to prepare classic pub dishes such as haddock and chips, steak and ale pie, vegetable or meat lasagne, and steak with onion rings. Specials include lobster thermidor and beef Wellington. Sandwiches and panninis are also served at lunchtime.
Open: 12-3 5-11 (Sun all day) Closed: 24-26 Dec **Bar**

Meals: L served all week 12-2.30 D served all week 6-9.30 Av main course £7 **Restaurant Meals:** L served all week 12-2.30 D served all week 6-9.30 Av 3 course alc £18 **Brewery/Company:** Enterprise Inns ◨: John Smiths, Fosters, Stella, Theakstons, Guest beers ♛: 7 **Children's Facilities:** Fam room Cutlery Games Highchair Food warming **Parking:** 10

GREAT AYTON
The Royal Oak Hotel ★★★ INN ♛
123 High Street TS9 6BW
☎ 01642 722361 ▤ 01642 724047
Email: info@royaloak-hotel.co.uk
Web: www.royaloak-hotel.co.uk
Real fires and a relaxed atmosphere are part of the attraction at this traditional corner pub, run by the Monaghan family since 1978. A range of robust starters like pigeon, duck and foie gras terrine, Anglesea charcuterie platter, and butternut squash and goats' curd risotto might be followed by slow-cooked belly of pork, Brittany 'Cotriade' fish stew, pot-roast stuffed saddle of lamb, and toasted sea bass with saffron potatoes.
Open: 10.30-11 (Sun 12-10.30) Closed: Dec 25 **Bar Meals:** L served all week 12-2 D served all week 6.30-

9.30 Av main course £9 **Restaurant Meals:** L served all week 12-2 D served all week 6.30-9.30 **Brewery/Company:** Scottish & Newcastle Brewery ◨: Theakstons, John Smiths Smooth, Directors ♛: 10 **Children's Facilities:** Licence (crayons) Menu/Portions Cutlery Games Highchair Food warming Baby changing

GREAT OUSEBURN
The Crown Inn 🍷
Main Street York YO26 9RF
☎ 01423 330430 📄 01423 331095

The Crown remembers the days when regular visitors were cattle drovers and large parties of fishermen on coach outings from the coast. Barrett's Great Canadian Circus would winter in the village; the circus band was under the direction of Ambrose Tiller who went on to found the world-renowned dancing troupe the 'Tiller Girls'. The Crown prides itself on offering a wide choice of imaginative dishes prepared from the finest, mostly local fish, seafood, meat and game.
Open: 12-2 5-11 (Sat-Sun 12-11, BHs all day) Closed: 25 Dec **Bar Meals:** L served Thurs/Fri 12-2 D served Mon-Fri 5-9 (Sat 12-5, Sun 12-9) Av main course £6

Restaurant Meals: L served Sun 12-9 D served Mon-Sat 5-9 (Sat 12-9.30, Sun 12-9) **Brewery/Company:** Free House 🍺: Black Sheep Best, Scottish Courage, John Smith's, Hambeltons Best Bitter, Marstons Pedigree 🍷: 10 **Children's Facilities:** Play area Highchair Food warming Baby changing **Notes:** Garden: Paved, walled area **Parking:** 60

GREEN HAMMERTON
The Bay Horse Inn
York Road YO26 8BN
☎ 01423 330338 📄 01423 331279
Email: info@bayhorseinn.uk.com
Web: www.bayhorseinn.uk.com

A 200-year-old coaching inn located in a small village near the A1 and close to both York and Harrogate. Food is served in the bar and restaurant, and there is further seating outside, sheltered by the boundary hedge. Dishes might include bangers and mash, fish and chips, chicken and stilton, and a home-made pie of the day. Various steaks and grills are also a key feature of the menu.
Open: 12-3 6-12 (Summer 12-12) **Bar Meals:** L served Mon-Sun 12-2 D served Mon-Sat 6-9 (Fri/Sat 12-2.30, Sun 12-3) Av main course £8.25 **Restaurant Meals:** L served Tue-Sun D served all week 6.30-9 (Sun 12-3) 🍺: Worthington, Timothy Taylor, Black Sheep & John Smiths **Children's Facilities:** Menu/Portions Highchair Food warming **Notes:** Dogs allowed in garden, in bedrooms Garden: Seating for 30, sheltered by boundary hedge **Parking:** 40

HARROGATE
The Boars Head Hotel ★★★ HL ⍟⍟ 🍷
Ripley Castle Estate HG3 3AY
☎ 01423 771888 📄 01423 771509
Email: reservations@boarsheadripley.co.uk
Web: www.boarsheadripley.co.uk
Dir: *On A61 (Harrogate/Ripon rd). Hotel in village centre*

Sir Thomas and Lady Ingilby's luxurious furnishings have transformed this delightful old coaching inn into an impressive hotel, right at the heart of the Ripley Castle Estate. Originally known as the Star Inn, this was once the breakfast stop for the crowded charabancs that linked Leeds with Edinburgh. Sir William Ingilby closed all three of Ripley's inns when he inherited the estate soon after the First World War, and Ripley remained dry until the Star was reopened as the Boar's Head Hotel in 1990. The bistro menu ranges from substantial sandwiches and jacket potatoes to a selection of hot dishes. Diners in the elegant restaurant can look forward to dishes like watercress velouté and Chartreuse of wood pigeon or pan-fried sea bream with saffron mirepoix and bouillabaisse sauce.
Open: 11-11 (Winter 12-3, 5-10.30) **Bar Meals:** L served all week 12-2.30 D served all week 6.30-9.30 (Winter lunch 12-2, dinner Sun-Wed 6.30-9) Av main course £13 **Restaurant Meals:** L served all week 12-2 D served all week 7-9 **Brewery/Company:** Free House 🍺: Theakston Best & Old Peculier, Daleside Crackshot, Hambleton White Boar, Black Sheep Best 🍷: 10 **Children's Facilities:** Menu/Portions Cutlery Games Highchair Food warming Baby changing **Nearby:** Ripley Castle, Fountains Abbey, Mother Shipman's Cave **Notes:** Garden: Courtyard area **Parking:** 45

HAWES
The Moorcock Inn
Garsdale Head Sedburgh LA10 5PU
☎ 01969 667488
Email: admin@moorcockinn.com
Web: www.moorcockinn.com
Dir: *On the A684 5m from Hawes, 15m from Sedbergh on junct for Kirkby Stephen (10m). Garsdale Station 1m.*
New owners have decorated this welcoming free house with flair - a blend of original stonework and bright colours, furnished with comfy sofas and traditional wooden chairs. In winter, locals savour the pub's home-brewed ales around the wood-burning stove, whilst on warmer days there are spectacular views from the garden. Typical fare ranges from soup or a hot baguette to Lancashire hotpot; pan-fried tuna with garlic, lime and chilli; and brie, courgette and almond crumble.
Open: 10-11 **Bar Meals:** L served all week 12-3 D served all week 6.30-9 Av main course £7.50
Brewery/Company: Free House ⬛: Moorcock Ale, Black Sheep, Moorcock Brewery - OPA, Porter & Garsdale, Timothy Taylor Landlord & Guest Ales ♟: 7 **Children's Facilities:** Fam room Menu/Portions Cutlery Games Highchair Food warming **Nearby:** Forbidden Corner, White Scar Caves & Dales Countryside Museum **Notes:** Dogs allowed in bar, Water bowls Garden: Beer Garden, picnic benches, beautiful views **Parking:** 40

HOVINGHAM
The Worsley Arms Hotel ★★★ HL ◉ ♟
Main Street YO62 4LA
☎ 01653 628234 ▤ 01653 628130
Email: worsleyarms@aol.com
Web: www.worsleyarms.com
Dir: *Located on B1257 between Malton & Helmsley*
In 1841 Sir William Worsley thought he would turn the village of Worsley into a spa to rival Bath, and built a spa house and a hotel. However, he reckoned without the delicate nature of his guests who disliked the muddy track between the two. Inevitably the spa failed, but the hotel survived and, together with the separate pub, forms part of the Worsley family's historic Hovingham Hall estate, birthplace of the Duchess of Kent, and currently home to her nephew. You can eat in the restaurant or the Cricketer's Bar (the local team has played on the village green for over 150 years). Hambleton Stallion beer from nearby Thirsk is on tap, and food choices include speciality ciabatta sandwiches, and dishes such as trio of local sausages with creamy leek mash and sweet shallot gravy, and pan-fried sea bass with Whitby crab risotto and bloody Mary dressing.
Open: 12-2.30 7-11 **Bar Meals:** L served all week 12-2 D served all week 7-10 **Restaurant Meals:** L served Sun 12-2 D served all week 7-10 Av 3 course alc £27.50 **Brewery/Company:** Free House ⬛: Scottish Courage John Smith's, Hambleton Stallion ♟: 20 **Children's Facilities:** Menu/Portions Games Highchair **Nearby:** Jorvik **Notes:** Dogs allowed in bar, in garden, in bedrooms Garden: Formal and open gardens, mahogany furniture **Parking:** 30

KILBURN
The Forresters Arms Hotel ★★ INN
YO61 4AH
☎ 01347 868386 & 868550 ▤ 01347 868386
Email: paulcussons@forrestersarms.fsnet.co.uk
Web: www.forrestersarms.fsnet.co.uk
Dir: *6m from Thirsk*
Sturdy stone former-coaching inn still offering ten comfortable rooms for travellers passing close by the famous White Horse of Kilburn on the North York Moors. The cosy lower bar has some of the earliest oak furniture by Robert Thompson, with his distinctive mouse symbol on every piece. Evidence of the inn's former stables can be seen in the upper bar. Steak and ale pie, pheasant casserole, homemade lasagne and lamb chops are popular dishes.
Open: 11-11 **Bar Meals:** L served all week 12-2.30 D served all week 6.30-9 Av main course £8 **Restaurant Meals:** L served all week 12-2.30 D served all week 6.30-9 **Brewery/Company:** Free House ⬛: Scottish Courage John Smiths, Carlsberg-Tetley Tetley's, Hambleton **Children's Facilities:** Menu/Portions Highchair Food warming **Nearby:** Monk Park Farm, James Herriot Centre **Notes:** Dogs allowed in bar, in garden, in bedrooms Dog bowl, biscuits **Parking:** 40

NORTH YORKSHIRE

NORTH YORKSHIRE

KIRBY HILL
The Shoulder of Mutton Inn
nr Richmond DL11 7JH
☎ 01748 822772 📠 01325 718936
Email: info@shoulderofmutton.net
Web: www.shoulderofmutton.net
Dir: *4m N of Richmond, 6m from A1 A66 junct at Scotch Corner*
A traditional 18th-century inn with magnificent views over Holmedale and beyond. Open log fires burn in the bar area and dining room, where stone walls and original beams provide just the right kind of backdrop for renowned daily-changing home-cooked dishes such as pan-fried kidney, mushroom and bacon salad; and parma ham tutti frutti as starters; and millefeuille of crab and king prawn; and breast of chicken roquefort as mains.

Open: 6-11 **Bar Meals:** L served Sat-Sun 12-2 D served Wed-Sun 7-9 Av main course £12 **Restaurant Meals:** L served Sat-Sun 12-2 D served Wed-Sun 7-9 Av 3 course alc £22.50 **Brewery/Company:** Free House 🍺: Scottish Courage John Smiths, Jennings Cumberland Ale, Black Sheep Best **Children's Facilities:** Menu/Portions Cutlery Food warming **Notes:** Dogs allowed in bar, in garden, in bedrooms **Garden:** Paved **Parking:** 22

KIRKHAM
Stone Trough Inn 🏵 🍷
Kirkham Abbey YO60 7JS
☎ 01653 618713 📠 01653 618819
Email: info@stonetroughinn.co.uk
Web: www.stonetroughinn.co.uk
Dir: *1.5m off A64, between York & Malton*
Set high above Kirkham Priory and the River Derwent, this country inn was converted to licensed premises in the 1980s from Stone Trough Cottage. The inn has a great reputation for friendliness, fine food and real ales.
Open: 12-2.30 6-11 (Sat 12-11, Sun 11.45-10.30)
Closed: 25 Dec **Bar Meals:** L served Tue-Sun 12-2 D served Tue-Sun 6.30-8.30 Av main course £11.45
Restaurant Meals: L served Sun 12-2.15 D served Tue-Sat 6.45-9.30 Av 3 course alc £24

Brewery/Company: Free House 🍺: Tetley Cask, Timothy Taylor Landlord, Black Sheep Best, Malton Brewery Golden Chance, Guest ales 🍷: 11 **Children's Facilities:** Play area (Patio and lawn) Menu/Portions Cutlery Games Highchair Food warming **Nearby:** Castle Howard, Eden Camp & Kirkham Abbey **Notes:** Garden: Grassed area, patio, tables & good views **Parking:** 100

KNARESBOROUGH
The General Tarleton Inn 🏵🏵 🍷
Boroughbridge Road Ferrensby HG5 0PZ
☎ 01423 340284 📠 01423 340288
Email: gti@generaltarleton.co.uk
Web: www.generaltarleton.co.uk
Dir: *From A1 junct 48 take A605 to Knaresborough 4m. Pub on right.*
This traditional 18th-century coaching inn is surrounded by glorious North Yorkshire countryside. The low-beamed bar area is warm and welcoming, while the restaurant is ideal for an intimate dinner or small party. In contrast, the covered courtyard is a light, modern setting. Real ales and an extensive wine list support an all-pleasing menu.
Open: 12-3 6-11 **Bar Meals:** L served all week 12-2.15 D served all week 6-9.30 (Sun 6-8.30) Av main course £12.50 **Restaurant Meals:** L served Sun 12-1.45 D served Mon-Sat 6-9.30 **Brewery/Company:** Free House 🍺: Black Sheep Best, Timothy Taylors Landlord, Tetleys Smoothflow, guest beer 🍷: 10 **Children's Facilities:** Menu/Portions Games Highchair Food warming **Nearby:** Newby Hall, Fountains Abbey & Lightwater Valley **Parking:** 40

LEYBURN
Sandpiper Inn ♀

Market Place DL8 5AT

☎ 01969 622206 📄 01969 625367

Email: hsandpiper@aol.com

Web: www.sandpiperinn.co.uk

Dir: *From A1 take A684 to Leyburn*

Although it has been a pub for only 30 years, the building that houses the Sandpiper Inn in is the oldest in Leyburn, dating back to around 1640. It has a beautiful garden and, inside, a bar, snug and dining room serving a varied and exciting mix of traditional and more unusual dishes. **Open:** 11.30-3 6.30-11 (Sun 12-3, 6.30-10.30) **Bar Meals:** L served Tue-Sun 12-2.30 D served Tue-Sun 6.30-9 (Fri-Sat 6.30-9.30, Sun 7-9) **Restaurant Meals:** L served Tue-Sun 12-2.30 D served Tue-Sun 6.30-9 (Fri-Sat 6.30-9.30, Sun 12-2, 7-9) 🍺: Black Sheep Best, Black Sheep Special, Daleside, Copperdragon, Archers ♀: 8 **Children's Facilities:** Fam room Menu/Portions Cutlery Games Highchair Food warming **Nearby:** Wensleydale Railway, Forbidden Corner, Leyburn Model Village **Notes:** Dogs allowed in bar, In 'snug area' Garden: Terrace area to front

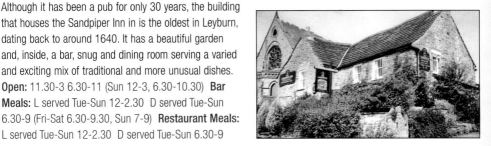

LINTON
The Fountaine Inn ♀

Skipton BD23 5HJ

☎ 01756 752210 📄 01756 753717

Email: fountaineinn1@tiscali.co.uk

Dir: *10m from Skipton take B6265. Right after Quarry*

Within the magnificent Yorkshire Dales National Park, in a sleepy hamlet beside the River Beck, this 16th-century inn is named after a local man who made his fortune in the Great Plague of London in 1665 - burying the bodies! On a more cheerful note, the menu offers grilled king scallops with pumpkin seeds, chilli and coriander sauce; smoked fish platter; or Irish stew and baby vegetables, though new owners may have made changes. **Open:** 11-11 (Sun 12-10.30) **Bar Meals:** L served all week 12-9 D served all week 12-9 Av main course £7 **Restaurant Meals:** L served Mon-Sun 12-3 D served Mon-Sun 6-9 Av 3 course alc £16 **Brewery/Company:** Free House 🍺: Black Sheep Best, Carlsberg-Tetley Tetley Bitter, Scottish Courage John Smith's ♀: 10 **Children's Facilities:** Fam room (High Chairs) Menu/Portions Games Highchair Food warming **Nearby:** Countryside **Notes:** Dogs allowed in bar, Water bowl Garden: Village green **Parking:** 20

LONG PRESTON
Maypole Inn ♀

Maypole Green Skipton BD23 4PH

☎ 01729 840219 📄 01729 840727

Email: landlord@maypole.co.uk

Web: www.maypole.co.uk

Dir: *On A65 between Settle and Skipton*

This inn has been welcoming visitors since 1695. Hand-pumped ales and traditional home cooking underpin the operation. Located at the edge of the Yorkshire Dales National Park, it's a good base for walking and cycling. Relax in the beamed dining room or cosy bar over a pint and a simple snack, sandwich, steak or salad; or try a 'special' like beef in ale pie or braised shoulder of lamb. **Open:** 11-3 6-11 (Sun 12-10.30, Sat 11-11) **Bar Meals:** L served all week 12-2 D served all week 6.30-9 (Sun 12-11) Av main course £8.50 **Restaurant Meals:** L served all week 12-2 D served all week 6.30-9 (Sun 12-9, Sat 12-9.30) 🍺: Timothy Taylor Landlord, Moorhouses Premier, Jennings, Cumberland, Bombaier & Guest ♀: 10 **Children's Facilities:** Cutlery Games Highchair Food warming **Notes:** Dogs allowed in bar, in garden, in bedrooms, Water Garden: Patio **Parking:** 30

NORTH YORKSHIRE

NORTH YORKSHIRE

MASHAM
Kings Head Hotel ★★ HL ♟
Market Place HG4 4EF
☎ 01765 689295 📠 01765 689070
Web: www.kingsheadmasham.com
Dir: *B6267 towards Masham*
Overlooking Masham's large market square with its cross and maypole, this tastefully renovated Georgian inn boasts open fires in the public rooms and a pleasant terrace for summer dining. Unwind over a pint of Theakston's in the bar, or sample a range of traditional and contemporary dishes in the wood panelled restaurant. Options might include minted lamb shoulder with creamy mash; chicken with thyme dumplings and Savoy cabbage; and smoked salmon penne pasta.
Open: 10.30-1 **Bar Meals:** L served all week 12-2.45 D served all week 6-9.45 Av main course £8.95 **Restaurant Meals:** L served all week 12-2.45 D served all week 6-9.45 **Brewery/Company:** Spirit Group ◖: Theakstons Best Bitter, Black Bull & Old Peculier, Theakstons XB, Black Sheep ♟: 14 **Children's Facilities:** Menu/Portions Games Highchair Food warming Baby changing **Nearby:** Lightwater Valley Theme Park, Middleham Castle, Leyburn Railway **Notes:** Garden: Georgian patio style

MIDDLEHAM
Black Swan Hotel ♟
Market Place DL8 4NP
☎ 01969 622221 📠 01969 622221
Email: blackswanmiddleham@breathe.com
Web: www.blackswan-middleham.co.uk
Dating back to the 17th-century and backing onto Middleham Castle, home of Richard III, this historic pub is at the heart of Yorkshire's racing country. Horses can be seen passing outside every morning on their way to the gallops. The emphasis here is on good food, with an appealing choice including Black Swan grill, chicken curry, bangers and mash, lasagne, and Kilnsey trout roasted with parsley and thyme dressing. There's also a good vegetarian choice.
Open: 10-3.30 6-12 (Sun 12-11.30) **Bar Meals:** L served all week 12-2 D served all week 6.30-9 **Restaurant Meals:** L served all week 12-2 D served all week 6.30-9 Av 3 course alc £21 **Brewery/Company:** Free House ◖: Scottish Courage John Smiths, Theakstons Best Bitter, Black Bull, Old Peculier & Guest Beers ♟: 7 **Children's Facilities:** Fam room Cutlery Games Highchair Food warming Baby changing **Nearby:** Forbidden Corner, Middleham Castle, Racing Stable **Notes:** Dogs allowed in bar, in bedrooms Dogs by appointment overnight Garden: Secluded and pretty Patio/Lawn

MIDDLESMOOR
Crown Hotel ♟
Pately Bridge HG3 5ST
☎ 01423 755204
Dir: *Telephone for directions*
The original building dates back to the 17th century; today it offers the chance to enjoy a good pint of local beer by a cosy, roaring log fire, or in a sunny pub garden. Stands on a breezy 900ft hilltop with good views towards Gouthwaite Reservoir. Ideal for those potholing or following the popular Nidderdale Way.
Open: 12-3 7-11 **Bar Meals:** L served Mon-Sun 12-2 D served Mon-Sat 7-8.30 (Closed Mon Lunch Winter, BHs) **Restaurant Meals:** L served all week 12-2 D served all week 7-8.30 **Brewery/Company:** Free House ◖: Black Sheep Best, Worthingtons Smooth, Interbrew Boddingtons Cream Flow ♟: 20 **Children's Facilities:** Menu/Portions Highchair Food warming **Notes:** Dogs allowed in bar, in garden, in bedrooms, Water **Parking:** 10

MUKER

The Farmers Arms ♛

Richmond DL11 6QG

☎ 01748 886297 🖹 01748 886375

Dir: *From Richmond take A6108 towards Leyburn, turn right onto B6270*

The last remaining pub - of three - in this old lead-mining village at the head of beautiful Swaledale, and a popular resting place for walkers on the Pennine Way and Coast-to-Coast route. With several miles under the belt, refuel with home-made steak pie; chicken alla Romana; deep-fried cod; liver and onions; or vegetable tandoori masala, aided and abetted by a pint of Castle Eden's Nimmos XXXX. Children's and smaller meals are also available. **Open:** 11-11Sun 12-10.30 **Bar Meals:** L served all week 12-2.30 D served all week 7-8.50 Av main course £7 **Brewery/Company:** Free House 🍺: Theakston Best & Old Peculier, John Smith's, Black Sheep, Guest Ales ♛: 10 **Children's Facilities:** Menu/Portions Cutlery Highchair Food warming **Nearby:** Richmond Castle, Wensleydale Cheese Visitors' Centre **Notes:** Dogs allowed in bar, Water provided **Garden:** Cobbled area with flower beds **Parking:** 6

OSMOTHERLEY

Queen Catherine Hotel ★★ INN

7 West End DL6 3AG

☎ 01609 883209

Email: queencatherine@yahoo.co.uk

Web: www.queencatherinehotel.co.uk

Named after Henry VIII's wife, Catherine of Aragon, who left her horse and carriage here while sheltering from her husband with nearby monks. There is no sense of menace around this friendly hotel nowadays, believed to be the only one in Britain bearing its name, and visitors can enjoy a well-cooked meal: monkfish tails, crab-stuffed chicken breast, lamb shank with minted gravy, Icelandic cod, and Whitby breaded scampi are all on the menu. **Open:** 12-11 **Bar Meals:** L served all week 12-2 D served all week 6-9 (Sun 12-9) **Restaurant Meals:** L served all week 12-2 D served all week 6-9 🍺: Hambleton Ales-Stud, Stallion, Bitter, Goldfield,Teeleys, Tetleys Smooth & Extra Cold **Children's Facilities:** Menu/Portions Cutlery Food warming **Notes:** Dogs allowed in bar, Water

PICKERING

Fox & Hounds Country Inn ★★ HL 🏵 ♛

Sinnington YO62 6SQ

☎ 01751 431577 🖹 01751 432791

Email: foxhoundsinn@easynet.co.uk

Web: www.thefoxandhoundsinn.co.uk

Dir: *3m W of town, off A170*

A by-pass built in the late 1930s leaves the village of Sinnington, midway between the market towns of Kirkbymoorside and Pickering, a peaceful, unspoilt backwater. The village green has a maypole and the attractive little River Seven supports a thriving duck population. **Open:** 12-2 6-11 (Sun 6-10.30) **Bar Meals:** L served all week 12-2 D served all week 6.30-9 (Sun 6.30-8.30) Av main course £10.85 **Restaurant Meals:** L served all week 12-2 D served all week 6.30-9 (Sun 6.30-8.30) Av 3 course alc £22 **Brewery/Company:** Free House 🍺: Theakston Best, Black Sheep Special, Worthingtons Creamflow ♛: 7 **Children's Facilities:** Menu/Portions Cutlery Highchair Food warming Baby changing **Nearby:** Flamingo Land, North York Moors Steam Railway & Ryedale Folk Museum **Notes:** Dogs allowed in bar, in garden, **Garden:** Lawn with tree feature **Parking:** 35

NORTH YORKSHIRE

PICKERING
The White Swan Inn ★★★ HL ⊛ ♈
Market Place Ryedale YO18 7AA
☎ 01751 472288 🖷 01751 475554
Email: welcome@white-swan.co.uk
Web: www.white-swan.co.uk
Dir: *From N: take A19 or A1 to Thirsk, A170 to Pickering, left at lights and 1st right onto Market Place, halfway up on left. From S: A1 or A1(M) to A64 to Malton rdbt A169 to Pickering.*
Blending traditional simplicity with understated style and luxury, this welcoming inn stands right in the centre of Pickering. It was built as a four-room cottage in 1532 and extended to become a coaching inn on the York to Whitby road. These days there are comfy sofas to relax in and the restaurant has stone flagged floors and a roaring winter fire. The owners and staff take great pride in their service, with careful attention to every detail, and dishes are prepared from the best Yorkshire ingredients. There are sandwiches and daily specials at lunchtime, whilst the dinner menu could feature smoked haddock and free range egg pie or wild mushroom risotto.
Open: 10-3 6-11 **Bar Meals:** L served all week 12-2 D served all week 7-9 **Restaurant Meals:** L served all week 12-2 D served all week 7-9 **Brewery/Company:** Free House ◼: Black Sheep Best & Special, Yorkshire Moors Cropton Brewery, Timothy Taylors Landord ♈: 10 **Children's Facilities:** Fam room (Lounge, boardgames) Menu/Portions Games Highchair Food warming **Nearby:** Eden Camp, Flamingo Land, North Yorkshire Moors Railway **Notes:** Dogs allowed in bar, in garden **Garden:** Terrace **Parking:** 35

REETH
Charles Bathurst Inn ★★★★ INN ♈
Arkengarthdale Richmond DL11 6EN
☎ 01748 884567 🖷 01748 884599
Email: info@cbinn.co.uk
Web: www.cbinn.co.uk
An 18th-century inn popular with walkers - it's about halfway along the coast-to-coast walk and real ales and real food. Located in remote Arkengarthdale, the CB (as regulars call it) was a bunkhouse for lead miners. The menu, based on fresh and largely locally sourced ingredients, is written up daily on an imposing mirror.
Open: 11-11 Closed: Dec 25 **Bar Meals:** L served all week 12-2 D served all week 6.30-9 Av main course £9 **Restaurant Meals:** L served all week 12-2 D served all week 6.30-9 Av 3 course alc £20 ◼: Theakstons, John Smiths Bitter & John Smiths Smooth, Black Sheep Best & Riggwelter ♈: 8 **Children's Facilities:** Play area (Swings, Climbing Frame & Seesaw) Menu/Portions Cutlery Games Highchair Food warming **Nearby:** Model Village, Hazel Brow Farm & Forbidden Corner **Notes:** Dogs allowed in bar **Garden:** Patio & play area **Parking:** 50

ROSEDALE ABBEY
The Milburn Arms Hotel ★★ HL ♈
Nr Pickering YO18 8RA
☎ 01751 417312 🖷 01751 417541
Email: info@millburnarms.co.uk
Web: www.milburnarms.co.uk
Dir: *A170 W from Pickering 3m, right at sign to Rosedale then 7m N*
This charming country house hotel is in the heart of the Yorkshire Moors in the picturesque village of Rosedale Abbey. Family-run, it is a perfect rural retreat.
Open: 11.30-3 6-11 Closed: 25 Dec **Bar Meals:** L served all week 12-2.15 D served all week 6-9 (Sun 12-3) Av main course £15 **Restaurant Meals:** L served Sun 12-2.30 D served all week 6-9.15 Av 3 course alc £22.50 ◼: Black Sheep Best, Carlsberg-Tetley Tetely Bitter, John Smith's, Stella, Theakstons, Timothy Taylors ♈: 8 **Children's Facilities:** Play area (Gardens and 7-acre field) Menu/Portions Cutlery Games Highchair Food warming Baby changing **Nearby:** Flamingoland, Pickering Steam Railway, Scarborough seaside **Notes:** Dogs allowed in 4 bedrooms, Water **Garden:** Large grassed lawn area to side and front **Parking:** 60

SCAWTON
The Hare Inn 🍷
Nr Thrisk YO7 2HG
☎ 01845 597524
Web: www.hareinn.co.uk
Mentioned in the Domesday Book, and once frequented by the abbots and monks of Rievaulx Abbey. In the 17th century ale was brewed here for local iron workers. Inside, as you might expect, low-beamed ceilings and flagstone floors, a wood-burning stove providing a warm welcome in the bar, and an old-fashioned kitchen range in the dining area. Diners may find baked Whitby haddock with a minted pea crust, Aberdeen Angus sirloin steak and caramelized red onion sandwich, crab and king scallop thermidor with a crunchy parmesan topping, tagliatelle in crab and salmon cream sauce, and poached lemon sole with crisp pancetta and pimientos.
Open: 12-3 6.30-11 (Sun 12-3.30, 6.30-11, summer varies) **Bar Meals:** L served Tue-Sun 12-2.30 D served Tue-Sat 6.30-8.45 (Sun 12-3) **Restaurant Meals:** L served Tue-Sun 12-2.30 D served Tue-Sat 6.30-8.45 **Brewery/Company:** Free House 🍺: Black Sheep, Scottish Courage John Smiths, Guest Beers 🍷: 14 **Children's Facilities:** Menu/Portions Highchair Food warming **Nearby:** Monkpark Farm, Eden Camp, Yorkshire Air Museum **Notes:** Garden: Small area at front, large seated area behind **Parking:** 18

SETTLE
Golden Lion Hotel ★★★★ INN 🍷
Duke Street BD24 9DU
☎ 01729 822203 🖨 01729 824103
Email: info@goldenlion.yorks.net
Web: www.yorkshirenet.co.uk/stayat/goldenlion
This traditional Dales' coaching inn has been the silent witness to incalculable comings and goings in Settle's market place since around 1640. Its cosy bars, open fire, commodious restaurant and comfy bedrooms often meet the needs of travellers on the spectacular Settle-Carlisle railway line. There is a good choice of beers and a strong emphasis on food prepared from fresh ingredients, with specials such as moules marinière, Moroccan lamb curry and vegetable stirfry.
Open: 11-11 **Bar Meals:** L served all week 12-2.30 D served all week 6-10 Av main course £7.50 **Restaurant Meals:** L served all week 12-2.30 D served all week 6-10 Av 3 course alc £18 **Brewery/Company:** Daniel Thwaites Plc 🍺: Thwaites Bitter, Bomber, Thoroughbred, Smooth & Guest beers 🍷: 9 **Children's Facilities:** Licence Menu/Portions Highchair Food warming **Nearby:** Falconry Centre & The Playbarn **Notes:** Garden: Patio with picnic benches & umbrellas **Parking:** 14

SKIPTON
Devonshire Arms 🍷
Grassington Road Cracoe BD23 6LA
☎ 01756 730237 🖨 01756 730142
A convivial 17th-century inn convenient for the Three Peaks, and original setting for the Rhylstone Ladies WI calendar. There are excellent views of Rhylstone Fell. A wide range of cask ales plus extensive wine list will wash down a menu that includes steak and mushroom pie cooked in Jennings Snecklifter ale, lamb Jennings, chicken Diane, and haddock and chips.
Open: 12-3 6-midnight (Sat 12-1am, Sun noon-midnight) **Bar Meals:** L served all week 12-2 D served all week 6.30-9 (Fri-Sat 6.30-9, Sun 12-4) **Restaurant Meals:** L served all week 12-2 D served all week 6.30-8.30 (Fri-Sat 6.30-9, Sun 12-4) **Brewery/Company:** Wolverhampton & Dudley 🍺: Jennings, Jennings Cumberland, Snecklifter, Tetley's 🍷: 7 **Children's Facilities:** Menu/Portions Cutlery Games Highchair Food warming **Notes:** Garden: Food served outside **Parking:** 80

NORTH YORKSHIRE

THIRSK
The Carpenters Arms 🍷
YO7 2DP
☎ 01845 537369 🖷 01845 537889
Web: www.carpentersarmfelixkirk.co.uk
Dir: *2m outside Thirsk on the A170*
An 18th-century inn in the pretty hamlet of Felixkirk, just outside the market town of Thirsk, where popular writer and vet, 'James Herriott' (Alf Wight), practised. Here you can expect a varied menu, with dishes like home-made fisherman's pie; Indonesian clay-baked chicken; or locally made bangers with mustard mash.
Open: 11.30-3 6.30-11 (Sun 12-8) Closed: 1wk in Jan or Feb, 25 Dec **Bar Meals:** L served Tue-Sun 12-2 D served Tue-Sat 7-9 Av main course £10.7 **Restaurant Meals:** L served Tue-Sun 12-2 D served Tue-Sat 7-9 Av

3 course alc £25 **Brewery/Company:** Free House
🍺: Black Sheep Bitter, Timothy Taylor Landlord, Greene King Old Speckled Hen, John Smiths Cask, guest ale
🍷: 12 **Children's Facilities:** Menu/Portions Cutlery Highchair Food warming Baby changing **Nearby:** Monk Park (Animal Farm), Lightwater Valley, Flamingo Land **Parking:** 50

THORNTON WATLASS
The Buck Inn ★★★ INN 🍷
Ripon HG4 4AH
☎ 01677 422461 🖷 01677 422447
Email: inwatlass1@btconnect.com
Web: www.buckwatlass.co.uk
Dir: *From A1 at Leeming Bar take A684 to Bedale, then B6268 towards Masham. Village 2m on right, hotel by cricket green*
The picturesque village of Thornton Watlass is where Wensleydale begins. The menu ranges from traditional, freshly prepared pub fare to exciting modern cuisine.
Open: 11-11 Closed: 25 Dec eve **Bar Meals:** L served all week 12-2 D served all week 6-9.30 (Sun 12-3, 6.30-9.30) **Restaurant Meals:** L served all week 12-2 D served all week 6.30-9.30 (Sun 12-3, 6.30-9.30) Av

3 course alc £17.50 🍺: Theakston Best, Black Sheep Best, John Smith's & Guest beers 🍷: 7 **Children's Facilities:** Play area (Outdoor swings, slide, climbing frame) Menu/Portions Cutlery Games Highchair Food warming Baby changing **Nearby:** Lightwater Valley, Forbidden Corner, Wensleydale Railway **Notes:** Dogs allowed **Garden:** Food served outside **Parking:** 40

WASS
Wombwell Arms 🍷
York YO61 4BE
☎ 01347 868280
Email: wykes@wombwellarms.wanadoo.co.uk
Web: www.thewombwellarms.co.uk
Dir: *From A1 take A168 to A19 junct. Take York exit, then left after 2.5m, left at Coxwold to Ampleforth. Wass 2m*
The building was constructed around 1620 as a granary, probably using stone from nearby Byland Abbey, and it became an ale house in about 1645. Stylishly decorated rooms provide the setting for bistro-style cooking.
Open: 11-3 6.15-11 (Closed Sun pm in low season)
Bar Meals: L served all week 12-2.30 D served all week (Sun 12-3) Av main course £12 **Restaurant Meals:** L served all week 12-2.30 D served all week

6.30-8.30 (Sun 12-3) Av 3 course alc £20
Brewery/Company: Free House 🍺: Black Sheep Best, Timothy Taylor Landlord, Tetley Extra Smooth 🍷: 7
Children's Facilities: Licence Menu/Portions Cutlery Highchair Food warming **Nearby:** Byland Abbey, Lightwater Theme Park, Flamingo Land **Notes:** Garden: Courtyard with Six Pin and benches **Parking:** 16

WEST BURTON
Fox & Hounds
Leyburn DL8 4JY

☎ 01969 663111 🖹 01969 663279

Email: foxandhounds.westburton@virgin.net

Dir: *A468 between Hawes & Leyburn, 0.5m E of Aysgarth*

Overlooking the village green in the unspoilt village of West Burton, this inn offers log fires and home cooking. Hand-pulled ales on offer at the bar include Black Sheep and Copper Dragon. Traditional pub food is provided to accompany your pint: dishes such as steak and kidney pie, curry, and lasagne will fortify you for country walks or visits to nearby waterfalls, castles or cheese-tasting at the Wensleydale Creamery.

Open: 11-12 **Bar Meals:** L served all week 12-2 D served all week 6-8.30 Av main course £6.95

Restaurant Meals: L served all week 12-2 D served all week 6-8.30 Av 3 course alc £15 **Brewery/Company:** Free House 🍺: Black Sheep, John Smiths, Tetleys, Copper Dragon **Children's Facilities:** Fam room Menu/Portions Cutlery Games Highchair Food warming Baby changing **Nearby:** Bolton Castle, Model Village, Flamingo Land **Notes:** Dogs allowed in bar **Parking:** 6

WIGGLESWORTH
The Plough Inn ♈
Skipton BD23 4RJ

☎ 01729 840243 🖹 01729 840638

Email: sue@ploughinn.info

Web: www.ploughinn.info

Dir: *From A65 between Skipton & Long Preston take B6478 to Wigglesworth*

Dating back to 1720, the bar of this traditional country free house features oak beams and an open fire. There are very fine views of the surrounding hills from the conservatory restaurant,

Open: 11-3 6-11 Closed: 8-24 Jan & Mons Nov-Mar

Bar Meals: L served all week 12-2 D served all week 6.30-9 (From 6 at busy times) Av main course £9

Restaurant Meals: L served all week 12-2 D served all week 7-9 Av 3 course alc £21.50 **Brewery/Company:** Free House 🍺: Carlsberg-Tetley Tetley Bitter, Black Sheep Best ♈: 6 **Children's Facilities:** Fam room Menu/Portions Cutlery Games Highchair Food warming **Nearby:** Horses health farm, Falconry Centre & Swimming pool **Notes:** Garden: Large area with views over Yorkshire Dales **Parking:** 70

YORK
Lysander Arms ♈
Manor Lane Shipton Road YO30 5TZ

☎ 01904 640845 🖹 01904 624422

Web: www.thelysanderarms.co.uk

The Lysander Arms is a newly constructed pub built on the site of an old RAF airfield. The contemporary feel of the pub's interior includes a long, fully air-conditioned bar with modern furnishings, brick-built fireplace and large-screen TV. The lunch menu features a choice of ciabatta, melted bloomer and poppy bagel sandwiches; specialities such as blackened Cajun chicken with char-grilled peppers; and in the evening, beef from the char grill, accompanied by thick chips.

Open: 11-11 (Sat 11-12.30, Sun 12-10.30) **Bar Meals:** L served Tue-Sun 12-2 D served Tue-Sat 5.30-9 (Sun 12-3) Av main course £7.50 **Restaurant Meals:** L served Tue-Sun 12-2 D served Tue-Sat 5.30-9 (Sun 12-3) Av 3 course alc £15 🍺: John Smiths Cask, Deuchars IPA, Fosters, Kronenbourg, John Smiths Smooth, Bombardier ♈: 18 **Children's Facilities:** Play area Menu/Portions Highchair Food warming Baby changing **Nearby:** Ten Pin Bowling, 10 screen cinema, Railway Museum **Notes:** Dogs allowed in bar Garden: Enclosed beer garden **Parking:** 35

SOUTH YORKSHIRE

BRADFIELD
The Strines Inn
Bradfield Dale Sheffield S6 6JE
☎ 0114 2851247
Web: www.thestrinesinn.freeserve.co.uk
Dir: *Off A57 between Sheffield toward Manchester*
A world away from nearby Sheffield, this popular Peak District free house nestles in breathtaking scenery opposite Strines Reservoir. Originally built for the Worrall family in 1275, most of the present building is 16th century; two of the three bars all have open winter fires. Traditional home-made fare ranges from sandwiches, salads and daily fresh fish to substantial Yorkshire puddings with a choice of beef, pork or vegetarian fillings.
Open: 10.30-3 5.30-11 (all day Mar-Sep, wkds open all day) Closed: Dec-25 **Bar Meals:** L served all week 12-2.30 D served all week 5.30-9 (all day weekends) Av main course £7.25 **Brewery/Company:** Free House ◀: Marston's Pedigree, Kelham Island, Mansfield Cask, Bradfield Bitter & Old Speckled Hen **Children's Facilities:** Play area (swings, rescued animals, play area) Menu/Portions Cutlery Food warming **Nearby:** Ladybower Resevoir, Chatsworth House, Castleton Mines **Notes:** Dogs allowed in bar, water, meat on Sundays Garden: Large, Children's play area & roaming peacocks **Parking:** 50

CADEBY
Cadeby Inn ♟
Main Street Doncaster DN5 7SW
☎ 01709 864009
Email: cadebyinn@bpcmail.co.uk
Web: www.cadebyinn.co.uk
Formerly a working farm before being converted into a pub, the Cadeby Inn is convenient for Conisbrough Castle, the Doncaster racecourse and the Earth Centre. The pub has added the Old Granary conference suite, an attractive venue with stone walls, mellow wood flooring and a rustic vaulted ceiling. John Smith's Cask and Black Sheep Bitter are mainstays at the bar, supported by Guinness, lagers and six wines served by the glass. The large front garden is enclosed by sandstone walls, with a patio area and a small back garden. Lunchtime brings an appealing range of sandwiches, as well as starters and light bites such as home-made soup or barbecued chicken wings. Larger appetites might consider butternut squash bake with sweet potato fries and vegetable jus; or pork and leek sausages with cheddar mash and apple gravy.
Open: 11-11 **Bar Meals:** L served all week 12-5 D served all week 6.30-9 Av main course £21 **Restaurant Meals:** L served all week 12-5 D served all week 6.30-9 Av 3 course alc £30 ◀: John Smiths Cask, Black Sheep Best Bitter, Guinness, Fosters, Kronenbourg Blanc ♟: 6 **Children's Facilities:** Licence Menu/Portions Cutlery Games Highchair Food warming **Nearby:** Doncaster Racecourse, Conisbrough Castle, The Earth Centre **Notes:** Garden: Large enclosed by walls **Parking:** 30

DONCASTER
Waterfront Inn ♟
Canal Lane West Stockwith DN10 4ET
☎ 01427 891223
Web: www.thewaterfrontinn.co.uk
Built in the 1830s overlooking the Trent Canal basin and the canal towpath, the pub is now popular with walkers and visitors to the nearby marina. Real ales and good value food are the order of the day, including pasta with home-made ratatouille, broccoli and cheese bake, deep fried scampi, half honey-roasted chicken, and home-made lasagne.
Open: 11.30-11 **Bar Meals:** L served all week 12-2 D served all week 6.30-8.30 (Sun 12-3) **Restaurant Meals:** L served all week 12-2 D served all week 6.30-8.30 (Sun 12-3) **Brewery/Company:** Enterprise Inns ◀: Scottish Courage John Smith Cask, Timothy Taylors, Greene King Old Speckled Hen, Deuchars IPA ♟: 9 **Children's Facilities:** Play area Menu/Portions Cutlery Highchair Food warming **Notes:** Dogs allowed, Water provided **Parking:** 30

PENISTONE
Cubley Hall 🍷
Mortimer Road Cubley S36 9DF
☎ 01226 766086 🖹 01226 767335
Email: cubley.hall@ukonline.co.uk
Web: www.cubleyhall.co.uk
Dir: *M1 junct 37 A628 towards Stalybridge. Hall just S of Penistone.*
A pub since 1983, Cubley Hall has a varied history as a moorland farm, gentleman's residence and children's home. Imaginative cuisine and all day Sunday carvery in the renowned restaurant; also a straightforward bar menu, children's menu, and daily blackboard specials.
Open: 11-11 **Bar Meals:** L served all week 12-9.30 D served all week 12-9.30 **Restaurant Meals:** L served Sun 12-9.30 D served Wknds **Brewery/Company:** Free

House 🍺: Carlsberg-Tetley Tetley Bitter, Burton Ale, Greene King Abbot Ale, Young's Special 🍷: 7 **Children's Facilities:** Fam room Play area (3 acres of ground and enclosed play area) Cutlery Games Highchair Food warming Baby changing **Nearby:** Magna, Cannon Hall Open Farm, Moor Walks **Notes:** Garden: Large lawns, seating areas and tables **Parking:** 100

CLIFTON
Black Horse Inn ◉ 🍷
Brighouse HD6 4HJ
☎ 01484 713862 🖹 01484 400582
Email: mail@blackhorseclifton.co.uk
Web: www.blackhorseclifton.co.uk
Dir: *1m from Bridgehouse town centre. 0.5m from M62 junct 25*
The loom-wrecking Luddites used to meet at this 17th-century coaching inn, which later became a variety club that played host to Roy Orbison, Showaddywaddy and Shirley Bassey. Serves good, home-cooked food.
Open: 11-12 **Bar Meals:** L served all week 12-5.30 D served all week 5.30-9.30 (Sun 12-8.30) Av main course £13.50 **Restaurant Meals:** L served all week 12-2.30 D served all week 5.30-9.30 (Sun 12.00-8.30) Av 3

course alc £25 **Brewery/Company:** Enterprise Inns 🍺: Black Sheep, Timothy Taylor Landlord, Old Speckled Hen, 🍷: 18 **Children's Facilities:** Menu/Portions Cutlery Highchair Food warming Baby changing **Nearby:** National Mining Museum, Eureka, Museum of Film & Photography **Notes:** Dogs allowed in garden Garden: Courtyard on two levels, hanging baskets **Parking:** 50

DEWSBURY
West Riding Licensed Refreshment Rooms
Dewsbury Railway Station Wellington Road WF13 1HF
☎ 01924 459193 🖹 01924 450404
Web: www.wrlrr.co.uk
A converted Grade II listed railway station built in 1848 and located on the Trans-Pennine route between Leeds and Manchester. The pub supports northern micro-breweries and is linked to an Anglo-Dutch brewery in Dewsbury, providing guests with a regular choice of guest ales. A daily-changing menu offers such dishes as steak and kidney pie, stewed steak with horseradish dumplings and sausage with bacon parcels and roast tomatoes.
Open: 11-11 (Sun-Mon 12-11, Fri-Sat 11-11:30) Closed: 25 Dec **Bar Meals:** L served Mon-Fri 12-3 D served Tues-Wed6-9 Av main course £4.50

Brewery/Company: Free House 🍺: Timothy Taylor Dark Mild & Landlord, Black Sheep Best, Anglo Dutch **Children's Facilities:** Fam room Menu/Portions Cutlery Highchair Food warming **Notes:** Dogs allowed in bar, in garden Garden: Food served outside, 8 wooden benches/tables **Parking:** 600

WEST YORKSHIRE

HALIFAX
Shibden Mill Inn ★★★★ INN ◉ ♀

Shibden Mill Fold HX3 7UL

☎ 01422 365840 🖹 01422 362971

Email: shibdenmillinn@zoom.co.uk

Web: www.shibdenmillinn.com

This 17th-century free house has been both a mill and a farm, and there was even once a boating lake where the top car park is. Sympathetic renovations have retained its original charm and character, especially in the cosy, friendly bar with its oak beams, rafters and open fires, and the intimate candlelit restaurant. The Sunday lunch menu is a feast in itself, offering starters, roasts, fish dishes, grills, traditional dishes like bubble and squeak, chicken pie or smoked salmon and sour cream. The main menu follows a similar format, featuring dishes like Gloucester Old Spot pork chop with sage mash and shallot sauce; or Round Green Farm venison burger with redcurrant compote and chunky chips. Desserts might include treacle and cinnamon tart with rhubarb ice-cream, or try the fantastic local cheese selection. **Open:** 12-2.30 5.30-11 **Bar Meals:** L served Mon-Sun 12-2 D served Mon-Sun 6-9.30 (Sun 12-7.30) Av main course £9.95 **Restaurant Meals:** L served all week 12-2 D served all week 6-9.30 (Sun 12-7.30) Av 3 course alc £27 **Brewery/Company:** Free House ▄: John Smiths, Theakston XB, Shibden Mill & 2 Guest Beers ♀: 14 **Children's Facilities:** Menu/Portions Cutlery Games Highchair Food warming Baby changing **Nearby:** Eureka, Shibden Park **Notes:** Garden: Stone flagged, raised beds, furniture **Parking:** 120

HALIFAX
The Rock Inn Hotel

Holywell Green HX4 9BS

☎ 01422 379721 🖹 01422 379110

Email: reservations@rockinnhotel.com

Web: www.rockinnhotel.com

Dir: *From M62 junct 24 follow Blackley signs, left at x-rds, approx 0.5m on left*

Substantial modern extensions have transformed this attractive 17th-century wayside inn into a thriving hotel and conference venue in the scenic valley of Holywell Green. All-day dining in the brasserie-style conservatory is truly cosmopolitan; kick off with freshly prepared parsnip and apple soup or crispy duck and seaweed, followed by liver and bacon, Thai-style steamed halibut, chicken piri piri or vegetables jalfrezi.
Open: 12-11 **Bar Meals:** L served all week 12-2.30 D served all week 5-9 Av main course £6 **Restaurant Meals:** L served all week 12-2.30 D served all week 5-9 **Brewery/Company:** Free House ▄: Black Sheep, Taylor Landlord, John Smiths **Children's Facilities:** Play area (special childrens menu) Menu/Portions Cutlery Games Highchair Food warming Baby changing **Nearby:** Eureka Children's Museum, Photograph Museum **Notes:** Dogs allowed in bar, Water Garden: Garden terrace surrounded by fields **Parking:** 120

MYTHOLMROYD
Shoulder of Mutton ♀

New Road Halifax HX7 5DZ

☎ 01422 883165

Dir: *A646 Halifax to Todmorden, in Mytholmroyd on B6138, opposite train station.*

Award-winning Pennines pub situated in the village where Poet Laureate Ted Hughes was born. Popular with walkers, young families and visitors to the area, the pub's reputation for real ales and hearty fare using locally sourced ingredients remains intact after 30 years of ownership. The menu ranges from snacks and sandwiches to vegetarian quiche; filled giant Yorkshire pudding; Cumberland sausages; and beef in ale.
Open: 11.30-3 7-11 (Sat 11.30-11, Sun 12-10.30) **Bar Meals:** L served Wed-Mon 11.30-2 D served Wed-Mon 7-8.15 (Sun 12-10.30) Av main course £3.99 **Restaurant Meals:** L served Wed-Mon 11.30-2 D served Wed-Mon 7-8.15 **Brewery/Company:** Enterprise Inns ▄: Black Sheep, Boddingtons, Greene King IPA, Taylor Landlord, Castle Eden ♀: 10 **Children's Facilities:** Fam room Play area Menu/Portions Highchair Food warming **Nearby:** Jerusalem Farm, Eureka, Hardcastle Crags **Notes:** Dogs allowed in bar, in garden, Water, Treats Garden: Riverside garden with floral display, seating **Parking:** 25

NEWALL
The Spite Inn ♟
nr Otley LS21 2EY

☎ 01943 463063

'There's nowt but malice and spite at these pubs', said a local who one day did the unthinkable - drank in both village hostelries, renowned for their feuding landlords. The Traveller's Rest, which became The Malice, is long closed, but the Roebuck has survived as The Spite. Salmon mornay, haddock, scampi, steak and ale pie, ostrich fillet and speciality sausages are likely to be on offer.

Open: 12-3 6-11 (Thu-Sat 12-11, Sun 12-10.30) **Bar Meals:** L served all week 12-2 D served Tue-Thu 6-8.30, Fri-Sat 6-9 6-9 Av main course £7 **Restaurant Meals:** L served all week 11.30-2 D served Tue-Thu 6-8.30, Sat 6-9 (Sun 12-5) **Brewery/Company:** Unique Pub Co Ltd ◀: John Smiths Smooth, Tetleys, Copper Dragon, plus guest ales ♟: 110 **Children's Facilities:** Menu/Portions Cutlery Highchair Food warming **Notes:** Dogs allowed in bar, in garden, Water provided **Garden:** Food served outside, lawned area **Parking:** 50

THORNTON
Ring O'Bells ♟
212 Hilltop Road Bradford BD13 3QL

☎ 01274 832296 📠 01274 831707

Email: enquiries@theringobells.com

Web: www.theringobells.com

Dir: *From M62 take A58 for 5m, right onto A644. 4.5m follow Denholme signs, onto Well Head Rd into Hilltop Rd.* From here there are dramatic moorland views stretching up to 30 miles on a clear day. The pub is a conversion of a Wesleyan chapel, and the restaurant was formerly two mill workers' cottages. Traditional and creative food is served in a warm and welcoming atmosphere.

Open: 11.30-3.30 5.30-11 (Sun 12-4.30, 6.15-10.30) Closed: 25 Dec **Bar Meals:** L served all week 12-2 D served all week 5.30-9.30 (Sat-Sun 6.15-9.30) Av main course £11.95 **Restaurant Meals:** L served all week 12-2 D served all week 7-9.30 (Sun 6.15-8.45) Av 3 course alc £22 ◀: Scottish Courage John Smiths & Courage Directors, Black Sheep & Black Sheep Special ♟: 10 **Children's Facilities:** Menu/Portions Highchair Food warming Baby changing **Nearby:** Howarth - Home of Brontë Family, Eureka **Parking:** 25

South & East England

Waterloo Bridge and the South Bank

BEDFORD

The Three Tuns

57 Main Road Biddenham MK40 4BD

☎ 01234 354847

Email: thethreetuns@btinternet.com

Web: www.threetonsbiddenham.com

A thatched village pub with a large garden, play area and dovecote. It has a friendly atmosphere, and is popular for its wide-ranging bar menu. Choose from sandwiches and snacks or popular main courses like burgers, seafood platter, and steaks with fries. There's also a range of home-made dishes such as steak and kidney pie, curry of the day, seafood platter, steak in red wine, and peppered pork. Children's meals are also available.

Open: 11-2.30 6-11 (Sun 12-3, 7-10.30) **Bar Meals:** L served all week 12-2 D served Mon-Sat 6-9 Av main course £7.50 **Restaurant Meals:** L served all week 12-2 D served Mon-Sat 6-9 **Brewery/Company:** Greene King : Greene King IPA, Abbot Ale **Children's Facilities:** Fam room Play area (swings, climbing frame) Menu/Portions Food warming **Notes:** Dogs allowed in garden, Water Garden: Large decking area/lawn with heaters **Parking:** 30

BLETSOE

The Falcon 🍷

Rushden Road MK44 1QN

☎ 01234 781222 📠 01234 781222

Email: info@thefalconbletsoe.co.uk

Web: www.thefalconbletsoe.co.uk

With its winter log fires and a beautiful beer garden for alfresco summer dining, this 17th-century coaching inn is a great place to visit at any time of the year. The Falcon is set in the rolling hills of north Bedfordshire with easy access from the A6, making it a popular destination for customers from far and wide. Step inside and you'll find the relaxed ambience of a traditional country inn.

Open: 12-3 6-11 (Sat 12-11, Sun 12-10.30) **Bar Meals:** L served all week 12-2.15 D served all week 6-9.15 Av main course £10 **Restaurant Meals:** L served all week 12-2.15 D served all week 6.30-9.15 Av 3 course alc £18.50 **Brewery/Company:** Charles Wells : Charles Wells Bombardier, Charles Wells Eagle, Fosters, Red Stripe 🍷: 7 **Children's Facilities:** Menu/Portions Cutlery Games Highchair Food warming **Nearby:** Thurleigh Farm **Notes:** Garden: Lawn, dining terrace overlooking garden **Parking:** 40

BOLNHURST

The Plough at Bolnhurst 🍷

Kimbolton Road MK44 2EX

☎ 01234 376274

Email: theplough@bolnhurst.com

Web: www.bolnhurst.com

Dir: *On B660 N of Bedford*

Fresh from running two successful pubs in Cambridgeshire, the Lees took over the Plough in 2005. Martin Lee trained with Raymond Blanc, Paul Heathcote and Marc Veyrat, so he knows his way around the kitchen, and he and his team offer modern British food made with quality ingredients including fish from Devon and venison from Suffolk. The veg is from local growers and the bread is made on site using the pub's own cultivated yeast. The Plough itself is thought to date from the late 15th century, and became a pub in 1830. Samples from the menu include roast corn-fed Goosnargh chicken with cauliflower purée, potato hash, pancetta and shallots; grilled Aberdeen Angus steaks with roast mushrooms, chips and béarnaise; or grilled plaice fillet with capers, parsley, spinach and sautéed potatoes.

Open: 12-3 6.30-12 (Closed Sun eve) Closed: New Year & 2wks Jan **Bar Meals:** L served Tue-Sun 12-2 D served Tue-Sat 6.30-9.30 (Sun 12-2.30) **Restaurant Meals:** L served Tue-Sun 12-2 D served Tue-Sat 6.30-9.30 (Sun 12-2.30) Av 3 course alc £25 **Brewery/Company:** Free House : Adnams Broadside, Nethergate Azzanewt 🍷: 12 **Children's Facilities:** Licence Menu/Portions Cutlery Games Highchair Food warming **Notes:** Dogs allowed **Parking:** 48

BROOM
The Cock
23 High Street SG18 9NA
☎ 01767 314411 📠 01767 314284
Dir: *Off B658 SW of Biggleswade*

Unspoilt to this day with its intimate quarry-tiled rooms with latched doors and panelled walls, this 17th-century establishment is known as 'The Pub with no Bar'. Real ales are served straight from casks racked by the cellar steps. A straightforward pub grub menu includes jumbo cod, roast chicken, gammon steak, breaded lobster, and breast of Cajun chicken. There is a camping and caravan site at the rear of the pub.
Open: 12-3 6-11 (Sat 12-4, Sun 12-4) **Bar Meals:** L served all week 12-2.30 D served Mon-Sat 7-9
Restaurant Meals: L served all week 12-2.30 D served

Mon-Sat 7-9.30 **Brewery/Company:** Greene King
🍺: Greene King Abbot Ale, IPA & Ruddles County
Children's Facilities: Fam room Play area (Outside) Highchair Food warming **Notes:** Dogs allowed in bar Garden: 12 tables on patio, lawn area **Parking:** 30

KEYSOE
The Chequers
Pertenhall Rd Brook End MK44 2HR
☎ 01234 708678 📠 01234 708678
Email: Chequers.keysoe@tesco.net
Dir: *On B660 N of Bedford*

A quiet 15th-century country pub in the same safe hands for over 25 years. No games machines, pool tables or jukeboxes disturb the simple pleasures of drinking well-kept real ales or eating tasty home-made food. Expect nothing fancy, with mainly pub stalwarts such as garlic mushrooms on toast and prawn cocktail as starters, steaks, chilli con carne, and fried scampi as mains, and enough children's favourites to keep them happy too.
Open: 11.30-2.30 6.30-11 **Bar Meals:** L served Wed-Mon 12-2 D served Wed-Mon 7-9.45

Brewery/Company: Free House 🍺: Hook Norton Best, Fuller's London Pride **Children's Facilities:** Fam room Play area (Play tree in garden) Menu/Portions Cutlery Highchair Food warming **Nearby:** Beds Butterfly Park, Grafham Water **Notes:** Garden: Patio & grassed area fenced off from car park **Parking:** 50

LINSLADE
The Globe Inn 🍷
Globe Lane Old Linslade Leighton Buzzard LU7 2TA
☎ 01525 373338 📠 01525 850551
Dir: *A5 S to Dunstable, follow signs to Leighton Buzzard (A4146)*

Standing on the banks of the Grand Union Canal, this friendly inn was first licensed in 1830 to serve passing canal boats. Pub favourites range from traditional fish and chips to steak and kidney pudding, whilst restaurant diners can expect mushroom ravioli; moules marinière; and slow-roast lamb shank.
Open: 11-11 (Sun 11-10.30) **Bar Meals:** L served all week 12-9 D served all week 12-9 (Sun 11-8) Av main course £8 **Restaurant Meals:** L served all week 12-3 D served all week 6-9 (Sun 12-9) Av 3 course alc £20

🍺: Greene King Abbott Ale, Old Speckled Hen, IPA & Ruddles County Ale, Hook Norton 🍷: 16 **Children's Facilities:** Play area (Swings, slides, Wendy house, fenced-off area) Menu/Portions Games Highchair
Nearby: Woburn Safari Park, Whipsnade Animal Park
Notes: Dogs allowed in bar, in garden, Water Garden: Large, seats approx 200 **Parking:** 150

NORTHILL
The Crown ♀
2 Ickwell Road nr Biggleswade SG18 9AA
☎ 01767 627337 📄 01767 627279
Dir: *Telephone for directions*
This delightful 16th-century pub, in its three-acre garden, lies between Northill church and the village duck pond. This is a popular area with walkers, and the Shuttleworth Collection of vintage aircraft at the Old Warden Air Museum is just down the road. Freshly prepared meals include lasagne, cottage pie, and salmon supreme, as well as main course salads and chargrilled steaks.
Open: 11.30-3 6-11.30 (Summer all day Sat-Sun) Closed: 25 Dec (eve) **Bar Meals:** L served all week 12-2.30 D served Mon-Sat 7-9.30 Av main course £8.20 **Restaurant Meals:** L served all week 12-2.30 D

served all week 7-9.30 Av 3 course alc £22
Brewery/Company: Greene King ◗: Greene King IPA, Abbot Ale, plus guest ales ♀: 7 **Children's Facilities:** Play area (Play equipment) **Notes:** Dogs allowed in bar, in garden, Water **Garden:** Very large **Parking:** 30

SOUTHILL
The White Horse ♀
High Street Biggleswade SG18 9LD
☎ 01462 813364
Email: jack@ravenathexton.f9.co.uk
Web: www.whitehorsesouthill.co.uk
A village pub retaining traditional values, yet happily accommodating the needs of non-smokers, children and those who like sitting outside on cool days (the patio has heaters). Locally renowned for its chargrilled steaks from the Duke of Buccleuch's Scottish estate. Other main courses include Cajun chicken, chargrilled pork loin steaks and Whitby Bay scampi. Old Warden Park and its Shuttleworth Collection of old planes is nearby.
Open: 11-3 6-11 (Sun 12-10.30, all day BHs) **Bar Meals:** L served all week 12-2 D served all week 6-9

(Sun 12-9, Wed-Sat 6-10) Av main course £7.50
◗: Greene King IPA, London Pride, Speckled Hen, Flowers ♀: 22 **Children's Facilities:** Play area (Climbing frame with swings and slides) Cutlery Games Highchair Food warming Baby changing **Nearby:** Woburn, Gullivers Land **Notes:** Garden: Large grassed area with trees & seating **Parking:** 60

STANBRIDGE
The Five Bells ♀
Station Road Stanbridge Leighton Buzzard LU7 9JF
☎ 01525 210224 📄 01525 211164
Dir: *Off A505 E of Leighton Buzzard*
A stylish and relaxing setting for a drink or a meal is offered by this white-painted 400-year-old village inn, which has been delightfully renovated and revived. The bar features lots of bare wood as well as comfortable armchairs and polished, rug-strewn floors. The modern decor extends to the bright, airy 75-cover dining room. There's also a spacious garden with patio and lawns. The inn, now headed up by new owners who took over in February 2006, offers bar meals, set menus and a carte choice for diners. The bar menu typically includes dishes such as smoked chicken, sun-dried tomato and pine nut

salad; battered fish, chips and mushy peas; baked courgettes stuffed with goat's cheese and mint with a mixed salad; rib eye steak with fries; and chicken, ham, leek and mushroom pie.
Open: 12-9.30 (Sun 12-9) **Bar Meals:** L/D served all week 12-9.30 Av main course £7.50 **Brewery/Company:** Traditional Free House Plc ◗: Greene King IPA, Timothy Taylors Landlord, London Pride ♀: 8 **Children's Facilities:** Play area (Slide, climbing wall, swing etc) Games Highchair **Nearby:** Leighton Buzzard Narrow Gorge Railway, Whipsnade Zoo **Notes:** Dogs allowed **Garden:** Large, traditional, Patio area **Parking:** 100

TILSWORTH
The Anchor Inn 🍷
1 Dunstable Road LU7 9PU
☎ 01525 210289 📠 01525 211578
Email: tonyanchorinn@aol.com
The only pub in a Saxon village, the Anchor dates from 1878. The restaurant is a recent addition to the side of the pub, and the whole building has recently been refurbished. The licensees pride themselves on their fresh food and well-kept ales. Hand-cut steaks are particularly popular (they buy the meat at Smithfield, butcher it and hang it themselves). An acre of garden includes patio seating, an adventure playground and a barbecue.
Open: 12-11 **Bar Meals:** L served all week 12-2.30 D served Mon-Sat 6-10 (Sun 12-7) Av main course £9
Restaurant Meals: L served all week 12-2.30 D served Mon-Sat 6-10 (Sun 12-7) Av 3 course alc £25
Brewery/Company: Greene King 🍺: Greene King IPA, Abbot Ale, Wadworth 6X, Guest Beers 🍷: 12 **Children's Facilities:** Fam room Play area (Adventure playground) Menu/Portions Cutlery Games Highchair Food warming **Nearby:** Mead Open Farm, Woburn Safari Park, Whipsnade Zoo **Notes:** Garden: 1acre+ of garden, seats, BBQ, patio **Parking:** 30

ASHMORE GREEN
The Sun in the Wood 🍷
Stoney Lane Newbury RG18 9HF
☎ 01635 42377 📠 01635 528392
Email: suninthewood@aol.com
Web: www.suninthewood.co.uk
Dir: *A34 Robin Hood rndbt, left to Shaw, at mini rndbt right then 7th left into Stoney Lane, 1.5m, pub on left*
This popular, extensively refurbished pub occupies a delightful woodland setting and yet is only a stone's throw from the centre of Newbury. Stone floors, plenty of wood panelling and various prints by Renoir and Monet add to the appeal. Sample a pint of Henry's Original IPA or a glass of wine from the ample choice on offer while perusing the menu. The extensive range of food includes shoulder of English lamb, classic beef bourguignon and pan-roasted medallions of pork fillet; Thursday night is steak night, with a choice of cuts and sauces. Children are made especially welcome. The children's menu not only aims to please, it's also a healthy option featuring burgers from the local butcher and home-made chicken breast nuggets.
Open: 12-2.30 6-11 **Bar Meals:** L served Tue-Sun 12-2 D served Tue-Sat 6-9.30 Av main course £7.95
Restaurant Meals: L served Tue-Sun 12-2 D served Tue-Sat 6-9.30 **Brewery/Company:** Wadworth 🍺: Wadworth 6X & Henrys Original IPA, Badger Tanglefoot 🍷: 15 **Children's Facilities:** Play area (Swings, slides, climbing frame & crazy golf) Menu/Portions Games Highchair Food warming Baby changing **Notes:** Garden: Lovely country garden among national woodland **Parking:** 70

CHIEVELEY
The Crab at Chieveley 🍷
North Heath Wantage Road Newbury RG20 8UE
☎ 01635 247550 📠 01635 247440
Email: info@crabatchieveley.com
Web: www.crabatchieveley.com
Dir: *Off B4494 N of Newbury*
Break that tedious M4 journey with a pit-stop at this old thatched dining pub. Specialising in mouth-watering fish dishes, with fresh deliveries daily, the Fish Bar offers, for example, hot Irish oysters with chorizo as a starter, and Cornish fish curry with coconut and cardamom-scented rice as a main. In the elegant, maritime-themed restaurant, saltmarsh lamb confit is accompanied by goat's cheese and shallot tart.
Open: 11-11 (Sun 12-10.30) **Bar Meals:** L served all week 12-2.30 D served all week 6-10 **Restaurant Meals:** L served all week 12-2.30 D served all week 6-10 Av 3 course alc £32.50 **Brewery/Company:** Free House 🍺: Fullers London Pride, Boddingtons, West Berkshire, Black Sheep, Timothy Taylors Landlord 🍷: 14 **Children's Facilities:** Play area (2 garden areas, patio, terrace) Menu/Portions Cutlery Games Highchair Food warming **Notes:** Dogs allowed in bar, in garden Garden: Seating and terrace with BBQ & marquee **Parking:** 80

BEDFORDSHIRE / BERKSHIRE

BERKSHIRE

CRAZIES HILL
The Horns 🍷
Nr Wargrave RG10 8LY
☎ 0118 9401416 📄 0118 9404849
Email: reservations@thehornspub.com
Web: www.thehornspub.com
Dir: *Off A321 NE of Wargrave*
At the end of the 19th century there were only 15 houses in Crazies Hill, the hamlet in which The Horns occupies a central position. Since then it has expanded rapidly and, incredibly, at one time supported six pubs. This beautifully restored, 16th-century pub has three interconnecting terracotta-coloured, oak-beamed rooms full of old pine tables, with stripped wooden floors, open fires and rugby memorabilia. It started life in Tudor times as a hunting lodge, to which a barn (now the dining area) was added some 200 years ago. Today's peaceful atmosphere is untroubled by music or electronic games. Dishes on offer include coq au vin with spring onion mash; pork tenderloin with black pudding and light Dijon mustard gravy; and salmon and haddock fishcakes with prawn and smoked salmon sauce. Freshly-filled baguettes and home-made desserts are also available.
Open: 11-11 **Bar Meals:** L served all week 12-3 D served all week 7-9.30 **Restaurant Meals:** L served all week 12-3 D served Mon-Sun 7-9.30
Brewery/Company: Brakspear 🍺: Brakspear Bitter
Children's Facilities: Fam room Play area (Climbing frame, swings) Menu/Portions Cutlery Games Highchair Food warming Baby changing **Nearby:** Henley Regatta
Notes: Dogs allowed in garden only
Garden: Large garden with lawn **Parking:** 45

CURRIDGE
The Bunk Inn 🍷
Nr Hermitage Thatcham RG18 9DS
☎ 01635 200400 📄 01635 200336
Web: www.thebunkinn.co.uk
Dir: *M4 junct 13, A34 N towards Oxford. Take 1st slip rd then right for 1m. right at T-junct, 1st right signed Curridge.*
Not that long ago local workmen used to bunk off to this now smart, revitalised country pub in wooded country-side, once the haunt of D H Lawrence who lived locally. Real ales and a log fire enhance the welcoming atmosphere, while food is freshly bought and prepared.
Open: 11-11 **Bar Meals:** L served all week 12-2.30 D served all week 6-9.30 **Restaurant Meals:** L served all week 12-2.30 D served all week 6-9.30
Brewery/Company: Free House 🍺: Arkells 3B, Wadworth 6X, Fuller's London Pride, plus guest ale
🍷: 9 **Children's Facilities:** Play area Menu/Portions Cutlery Games Highchair Food warming Baby changing
Nearby: The Living Rainforest, Bucklebury Farm Park
Notes: Dogs allowed in bar, in garden **Parking:** 38

HERMITAGE
The White Horse of Hermitage 🍷
Newbury Road Thatcham RG18 9TB
☎ 01635 200325
Email: info@whitehorsehermitage.com
Web: www.whitehorsehermitage.com
Equally ideal for morning coffee and a danish, a full breakfast or a leisurely lunch, this refurbished village pub lies close to the former home of writer D H Lawrence who regularly explored much of the area on foot. Inside is a photograph of the White Horse as it was about 50 years ago. A comprehensive menu offers the likes of bangers and mash, spaghetti with home-made tomato sauce, leg of confit duck, White Horse burger, and steak sandwich.
Open: 12-2.30 6-11 (Summer 12-11) **Bar Meals:** L served all week 12-2.30 D served all week 7-9.30 (Sun 12-3) Av main course £7 **Restaurant Meals:** L served all week 12-2.30 D served all week 7-9.30 (Sun 12-5) Av 3 course alc £15.50 **Brewery/Company:** Greene King 🍺: Abbot Ale, Greene King IPA, Budvar, Guinness & Kronenbourg 🍷: 9 **Children's Facilities:** Menu/Portions Cutlery Highchair Food warming Baby changing **Nearby:** The Living Rainforest, Theale Park, Didcot Railway Centre
Notes: Dogs allowed in bar, Tie-up area, drinking bowls
Garden: South facing, level, rural views **Parking:** 12

HUNGERFORD

The Crown & Garter ★★★★ GH ♀

Inkpen Common RG17 9QR

☎ 01488 668325

Email: gill.hern@btopenworld.com

Web: www.crownandgarter.com

Dir: *From A4 turn left to Kintbury and Inkpen. At village store turn left onto Inkpen Rd, stay on road to Inkpen.* Quiet lanes and cottages draped in honeysuckle mark the approach to this traditional 17th-century inn which was reputedly visited by James I on his way to see his mistress. The bar area has an inglenook fireplace and crisscrossed beams.

Open: 12-3 5.30-11 (Sun 7-10.30) **Bar Meals:** L served Wed-Sun 12-2 D served Mon-Sat 6.30-9.30 (Sun 12-2.30) Av main course £10 **Restaurant Meals:** L served Wed-Sun 12-2 D served all week 6.30-9.30 (Sun 12-2.30) **Brewery/Company:** Free House 🍺: Mr Chubbs, Good Old Boy, Guinness, Boddingtons, guest ale ♀: 8 **Children's Facilities:** Play area (Wendy house) Menu/Portions Games Highchair Food warming **Nearby:** Legoland, Beale Park, Bath **Notes:** Dogs allowed in bar Garden: Fenced garden with play area **Parking:** 30

HUNGERFORD

The Swan Inn ★★★★ INN

Craven Road Lower Green Inkpen RG17 9DX

☎ 01488 668326 📠 01488 668306

Email: enquiries@theswaninn-organics.co.uk

Web: www.theswaninn-organics.co.uk

Dir: *S down Hungerford High St (A338), under rail bridge, turn left to Hungerford Common. Turn right signed Inkpen 3m.* The Swan lies just below Combe Gibbet and Walbury Hill, the highest points in this part of southern England. Local organic beef farmers Bernard and Mary Harris own the Swan, and almost everything on the menus makes use of fresh organic, GMO-free produce.

Open: 12-2.30 7-11 (Open all day wknds summer) Closed: 25-26 Dec **Bar Meals:** L served all week 12-2 D served all week 7-9.30 (Sat 12-2.30, Sun 12-3) Av main course £10 **Restaurant Meals:** L served Wed-Sun 12-2.30 D served Wed-Sat 7-9.30 (Sunday-lunch only, 12-3) Av 3 course alc £25 **Children's Facilities:** Play area (Swing) Menu/Portions Highchair Food warming Baby changing **Notes:** Garden: terraces with seating and tables **Parking:** 50

HURST

The Green Man ♀

Hinton Road RG10 OBP

☎ 0118 934 2599 📠 0118 934 2939

Email: info@thegreenman.uk.com

Web: www.thegreenman.uk.com

Dir: *off the A321 next to Hurst Cricket Club* Once part of Windsor Great Park, this building dates from 1646. Low ceilings and log fires make for a cosy interior, where good beers and some value-for-money wines can be enjoyed. Food choices are varied and include light bites, salads and more elaborate specials.

Open: 11-3 5.30-11 (Sun 12-3, 6-10.30) **Bar Meals:** L served all week 12-2.30 D served all week 6.30-9.30 (Sun 12-3 & 6.30-9 Win, 6.30-9.30 Sum) **Restaurant Meals:** L served all week 12-2.30 D served all week 6.30-9.30 **Brewery/Company:** Brakspear 🍺: Brakspear Bitter, Special & Seasonal Ales ♀: 7 **Children's Facilities:** Licence Play area (in garden) Menu/Portions Cutlery Food warming **Nearby:** Legoland, Dinton Pastures Park, Bracknell Adventure Swimming Pool **Notes:** Garden: Large, with umbrellas on heated patio **Parking:** 40

BERKSHIRE

KNOWL HILL
Bird In Hand Country Inn 🍷
Bath Road Twyford RG10 9UP
☎ 01628 826622 & 822781 📄 01628 826748
Email: sthebirdinhand@aol.com
Web: www.birdinhand.co.uk
Dir: *On A4, 5m W of Maidenhead, 7m E of Reading*
Legend has it that in the late 1700s, George III sought the hospitality of this inn when his horse threw a shoe whilst hunting. Such was his gratitude that he granted a royal charter to the landlord. Bar snacks are available, whilst the restaurant menu offers an appealing mix of modern and classic dishes.
Open: 11-3 6-11 (Sun 12-10:30) **Bar Meals:** L served all week 12-2.30 D served all week 6.30-10 (Sun 12-9.30) Av main course £9.95 **Restaurant Meals:** L served all week 12-2.30 D served all week 7-10 (Sun 7-9.15) Av 3 course alc £27.50 **Brewery/Company:** Free House 🍺: Brakspear Bitter, Hogsback TEA 🍷: 12 **Children's Facilities:** Menu/Portions Highchair Food warming Baby changing **Nearby:** Legoland, Coral Reef, Odds Park Farm **Notes:** Dogs allowed in bar, in garden Garden: patio with fountain **Parking:** 86

MARSH BENHAM
The Red House ⊚ 🍷
Newbury RG20 8LY
☎ 01635 582017 📄 01635 581621
Email: cyrilgrell@btconnect.com
Web: www.theredhousepub.com
Dir: *5m from Hungerford, 3m from Newbury & 400yds off the A4*
Known at one time as the Water Rat, this striking brick-and-thatch pub lies close to the banks of the River Kennet, one of Britain's prettiest chalk streams. There's an ever-popular set-price bistro menu, and the suntrap patio is just the place in which to relax in summer.
Open: 11.30-3 6-11 (Sun 11.30-3.30) **Bar Meals:** L served Mon-Sat 11.30-2.30 D served Mon-Sat 7-9.30 (Sun 11.30-2.45) Av main course £9.95 **Restaurant Meals:** L served Mon-Sat 12-2.30 D served Mon-Sat 7-9.30 (Sun 11.30-2.45) Av 3 course alc £31.50 **Brewery/Company:** Free House 🍺: Bombardier, Stella, Amstel & Murphy's 🍷: 15 **Children's Facilities:** Menu/Portions Highchair Food warming **Nearby:** Highclere Castle, Newbury Racecourse & Rainforest **Notes:** Garden: Terrace, Lawn **Parking:** 40

READING
The Flowing Spring 🍷
Henley Road Playhatch RG4 9RB
☎ 0118 969 3207
Email: flowingspring@aol.com
Dir: *3m N of Reading*
A lovely country pub overlooking the Thames flood plain at the point where the Chiltern Hills strike out north east towards Bedfordshire. The proprietor likes his establishment to be known as "a pub that serves good food, rather than a restaurant that serves lousy beer". Representative dishes on the combined bar/restaurant menu include home-made curries, shoulder of lamb, and rib-eye steaks. It's a Fullers pub, so Chiswick, London Pride and ESB are all well kept on tap.
Open: 12-11 **Bar Meals:** L served Mon-Sun 12-2.30 D served Wed-Sat 6.30-9.30 Av main course £6.50 🍺: London Pride, ESB, Chiswick 🍷: 7 **Children's Facilities:** Play area Menu/Portions Cutlery Highchair Food warming **Notes:** Dogs allowed in bar Garden: Large garden bounded by streams **Parking:** 40

STANFORD DINGLEY
The Bull Country Inn 🍷
Nr Reading RG7 6LS
☎ 0118 974 4409 🖷 0118 974 5249
Email: admin@thebullatstanforddingley.co.uk
Web: www.thebullatstanforddingley.co.uk
Dir: *A4/A340 to Pangbourne. 1st left to Bradfield. Through Bradfield, 0.3m left into Back Lane. At end left, pub 0.25m on left*
A family-owned, 15th-century traditional village inn. Serves varied main courses and snack menus.
Open: 12-3 6-11 (Sun 7-10.30) **Bar Meals:** L served all week 12-2.30 D served all week 6.30-9.30 (Sun 7-9.30) Av main course £9.50 **Restaurant Meals:** L served all week 12.30-2.30 D served all week 6.30-9.30 (Sun 7-9.30) Av 3 course alc £21.50 **Brewery/Company:** Free House 🍺: West Berkshire Brewery Ales, Brakspear Bitter, Bass 🍷: 7 **Children's Facilities:** Fam room Menu/Portions Highchair Food warming **Nearby:** Bucklebury Farm Park, Beale Park, Wellington Country Park **Notes:** Dogs allowed in bar, in garden, Water Garden: Large secure area, plenty of tables **Parking:** 50

STANFORD DINGLEY
The Old Boot Inn 🍷
RG7 6LT
☎ 0118 974 4292 🖷 0118 974 4292
Web: www.theoldbootinn.co.uk
Dir: *M4 junct 12, A4/A340 to Pangbourne. 1st left to Bradfield. Through Bradfield, follow Stanford Dingley signs*
Set in the glorious Pang Valley, in a village of Outstanding Natural Beauty, the original 18th-century Old Boot has been extended to include a popular, non-smoking conservatory. Fresh seafood choices are announced daily, and include the likes of seabass, cod, scallops, haddock and swordfish.
Open: 11-3 6-11 (Sun 12-3, 7-10.30) **Bar Meals:** L served all week 12-2.15 D served all week 7-9.30 (Sun 12-2.30 7-9.30) **Restaurant Meals:** L served all week 12-2.15 D served all week 7-9.30 **Brewery/Company:** Free House 🍺: Brakspear Bitter, Interbrew Bass, West Berkshire Dr Hexters, Archers Best, Thomas Hardy Royal Oak 🍷: 8 **Children's Facilities:** Play area (Climbing frame) Menu/Portions Highchair Food warming **Nearby:** Buckleberry Farm Park, River Pang **Notes:** Dogs allowed in bar, in garden Garden: 0.5 acre over-looking farmland **Parking:** 40

THEALE
Thatchers Arms 🍷
North Street RG7 5EX
☎ 0118 930 2070 🖷 0118 930 2070
Web: www.thatchersarms.com
Dir: *Telephone for directions*
A warm, friendly country pub in a rural area, The Thatchers Arms is surrounded by many footpaths and lanes for walkers. Although in a small hamlet, the pub is only a five minute drive from the M4. There are good garden facilities and a separate patio area. The menu features a range of steaks, and a variety of fish and seafood dishes. Many family facilities are available, and senior citizen's day is on Wednesday.
Open: 12-2.30 5.30-11 (Sat 12-3, 6-11, Sun 12-3, 7-10.30) **Bar Meals:** L served all week 12-2 D served all week 7-9.30 Av main course £10 **Restaurant Meals:** L served all week 12-2 D served all week 7-9.30 Av 3 course alc £17 **Brewery/Company:** Avebury Taverns Limited 🍺: Fuller's London Pride, Shepherd Neame Spitfire, John Smiths Smooth 🍷: 8 **Children's Facilities:** Menu/Portions Games Highchair Food warming **Nearby:** Beale Park , Didicot Steam Railway **Notes:** Dogs allowed in bar, in garden, Water **Parking:** 15

BERKSHIRE / BUCKINGHAMSHIRE

WINKFIELD
Rose & Crown 🍷
Woodside Windsor Forest SL4 2DP
☎ 01344 882051 📠 01344 885346
Email: info@roseandcrownascot.com
Web: www.roseandcrownascot.com
Dir: *M3 junct 3 from Ascot racecourse on A332 take 2nd exit from Heatherwood Hosp rdbt, then 2nd left*
A 200-year-old traditional pub complete with old beams and low ceilings. Hidden down a country lane, it has a peaceful garden overlooking open fields where you can see horses and llamas at pasture.
Open: 11-12 (9am Royal Ascot week) **Bar Meals:** L served all week 12-2.30 D served Tue-Sat 7-9.30 (Sun 12-2.30) Av main course £8 **Restaurant Meals:** L served all week 12-2.30 D served Tue-Sat 7-9.30 (Sun 12-2.30) Av 3 course alc £16 **Brewery/Company:** Greene King 🍺: Morland Original, Greene King IPA, Morland Original & Guest Ale 🍷: 9 **Children's Facilities:** Play area (Swings) Menu/Portions Games Highchair Food warming Baby changing **Nearby:** Legoland, Windsor Castle & Ascot Racecourse **Notes:** Garden: Set in rural area next to large field **Parking:** 24

AMERSHAM
Hit or Miss Inn 🍷
Penn Street Village HP7 0PX
☎ 01494 713109 📠 01494 718010
Email: hit@ourpubs.co.uk
Web: www.ourpubs.co.uk
Dir: *Off Amersham - High Wycombe Rd (A404)*
You'll find The Hit or Miss in lovely countryside between Amersham and Beaconsfield, overlooking the cricket pitch where the pub's namesake team plays. It is a cottage-style establishment, in business since 1798, with a country garden complete with lawn, patio and picnic tables. A good choice of dishes, freshly prepared and cooked on the premises, might include leek and feta parcel with tzatziki, and house smoked salmon with garlic mushrooms and potato gratin.
Open: 11-11 (Sun 12-10.30) **Bar Meals:** L served all week 12-2.30 D served all week 6.45-9.30 (Sun 12-8) Av main course £11 **Restaurant Meals:** L served all week 12-2.30 D served all week 6.45-9.30 (Sun 12-8) Av 3 course alc £19 **Brewery/Company:** Hall & Woodhouse 🍺: Badger Best, Tanglefoot, Sussex, Hofbrau & Stella 🍷: 12 **Children's Facilities:** Menu/Portions Games Highchair Food warming Baby changing **Nearby:** Bekonscot Model Village, Zoom Indoor Play Centre, Odds Farm Rare Breeds **Notes:** Dogs allowed in bar, in garden, Water bowls Garden: Lawn and patio area with picnic tables **Parking:** 40

BEACONSFIELD
The Royal Standard of England 🍷
Brindle Lane Forty Green HP9 1XT
☎ 01494 673382
Email: theoldestpub@btinternet.com
Web: www.rsoe.co.uk
Dir: *A40 to Beaconsfield, right at church rdbt onto B474 towards Penn, left onto Forty Green Road 1m.*
Striking stained glass windows, beams, flagstone floors, and a large inglenook fireplace set the scene in this welcoming country inn that dates from the 12th century, reputed to be the oldest in England. Situated in a part of the world renowned for Civil War battles and skirmishes, the inn became a Royalist headquarters, which accounts for its splendid name. The place is so haunted it even has its own ghost book in which you can log your experiences! It is also a perfect base for walking or recuperating after a long hike, cooling your blisters and refuelling with the hearty food. Steak and kidney pudding; cod and chips; and Welsh mountain lamb with roast potatoes and vegetables are likely choices. For lighter appetites there are nibbles such as hummus with pitta bread; garlic prawns; and Welsh rarebit.
Open: 11-12 (Sun 12-11) **Bar Meals:** L served all week 12-10 D served all week 12-10 Av main course £10 **Brewery/Company:** Free House 🍺: Marston's Pedigree, Brakspear Bitter, Rebellion IPA & Guest Beers 🍷: 12 **Children's Facilities:** Licence Fam room Menu/Portions Food warming **Nearby:** Bekonscot Model Village, Open Air Museum & Rare Breeds Centre **Notes:** Dogs allowed in bar, in garden, Water & dog treats Garden: Paved area, grass lawn & floral borders **Parking:** 125

BOLTER END
The Peacock ♟
Lane End High Wycombe HP14 3LU

☎ 01494 881417

Email: andy.callen@the peacockbolterend.co.uk

Web: www.thepeacockbolterend.co.uk

Dir: *Located on B482 Manlow to Stokenchurch road. 2m from junct 5 of M40.*

The oldest part of this pub dates from 1620, featuring original beams and a fireplace dating from the early 1800s. It is situated on top of the Chiltern Hills overlooking the common. Children are particularly welcome as there are two specially designated areas just for them.

Open: 12-3 5.30-11 (Sat 11.30-11, Sun 12-10.30 Winter closed Sun eve and Mon) **Bar Meals:** L served all week 12-2.30 D served Mon-Sat 6.30-9.30 (Sun 12-3) Av main course £11 **Restaurant Meals:** L served Mon-Sun 12-2.30 D served Mon-Sat 6.30-9.30 (Sun 12-3) Av 3 course alc £18.50 🍴: Brakspear, Shepherd Neame Spitfire ♟: 8 **Children's Facilities:** Licence Fam room Menu/Portions Cutlery Games Food warming **Notes:** Dogs allowed in bar **Garden:** Food served **Parking:** 30

BUCKINGHAM
The Old Thatched Inn ♟
Adstock MK18 2JN

☎ 01296 712584 📠 01296 715375

Email: manager@theoldthatched.co.uk

Web: www.theoldthatchedinn.co.uk

Listed in 1645, this lovely old thatched and beamed inn has come through a refurbishment with its traditional beams and inglenook fireplace intact. The spacious interior consists of a formal conservatory and a bar with comfy furniture and a welcoming atmosphere. Fresh fish is a speciality with fillet of sea bass, white cabbage, bacon and capers a typical example. Meat options might include roast duck breast with celeriac purée, braised chicory and griottes cherry sauce.

Open: 12-3 6-11 (open all day bank holidays & week-ends) **Bar Meals:** L served all week 12-2.305 D served all week 6-9.30 (Sat 12-9.30, Sun 12-9) Av main course £12 **Restaurant Meals:** L served all week 12-2.30 D served all week 6-9.30 Av 3 course alc £22.50 🍴: Hook Norton Best, Sharps Doom Bar, Tom Wood, Deuchars ♟: 8 **Children's Facilities:** Play area (Highchairs) Menu/Portions Games Highchair Food warming **Nearby:** Stowe Gardens, Claydon House & Milton Keynes **Notes:** Dogs allowed in bar, in garden, Water provided **Garden:** Floral terrace with tables, lawned area **Parking:** 20

BUCKINGHAM
The Wheatsheaf ♟
Main Street Maids Moreton MK18 1QR

☎ 01280 815433 📠 01280 814631

Web: www.thewheatsheaf.uk.com

Dir: *From M1 junct 13 take A421 to Buckingham, then take A413.*

Three hundred year old village pub serving real ales, quality bar snacks, and an à la carte menu in the spacious conservatory overlooking the secluded beer garden. Options include chicken breast in a cream and stilton sauce, duck breast with Madeira sauce, or stilton and broccoli pasta. Fish specialities include breaded Whitby fish and chips, king prawn crevettes, and salmon steak in a lemon and lime sauce. Children will enjoy the outdoor play equipment.

Open: 12-3 6-11 (Sun 6-10.30) **Bar Meals:** L served Mon-Sat 12-2.15 D served Mon-Sat 7-9.30 (Sun 12.2) Av main course £10.95 **Restaurant Meals:** L served Mon-Sat 12-2.15 D served Mon-Sat 7-9.30 (Sun 12-2) Av 3 course alc £25 **Brewery/Company:** Free House 🍴: Hook Norton, Black Sheep, John Smiths, Side Pocket For A Toad & Reverend James ♟: 10 **Children's Facilities:** Fam room Play area (Wooden outdoor play equipment) Menu/Portions Games Highchair Food warming Baby changing **Nearby:** Stowe Landscape Gardens, Gullivers Land, Silverstone Race Track & Xscape **Notes:** Dogs allowed in bar, in garden, Water **Garden:** Large secluded garden, chairs on lawn/patio **Parking:** 15

CHALFONT ST GILES

The Ivy House ★★★★ INN 🍷

London Road HP8 4RS

☎ 01494 872184 📠 01494 872870

Email: enquiries@theivyhouse-bucks.co.uk

Web: www.theivyhouse-bucks.co.uk

Dir: *On A413 2m S of Amersham & 1.5m N of Chalfont St Giles*

A much loved 17th-century pub is set in the heart of the Chilterns. It is as popular with cask ale fans and wine drinkers as it is with diners. Serves award-winning food.

Open: 12-3 6-11 (Sat 12-11, Sun 12-10.30) **Bar Meals:** L served all week 12-2.30 D served all week 6.30-9.30 (Sat 12-10, Sun 12-9) Av main course £12.95 **Restaurant Meals:** L served all week 12-2.30 D served all week 6.30-9.30 (Sat 12-10, Sun 12-9) Av 3 course alc £25 **Children's Facilities:** Play area (Colouring sheets & pens, Wendy house) Menu/Portions Cutlery Games Highchair Food warming Baby changing **Nearby:** Odds Farm Rare Breeds Animal Park, Chiltern Open Air Museum, Milton's Cottage **Notes:** Dogs allowed in bar, in garden, Not in restaurant Garden: Patio, court-yard & garden, outstanding views **Parking:** 45

CHALFONT ST PETER

The Greyhound Inn 🍷

SL9 9RA

☎ 01753 883404 📠 01753 891627

Email: reception@thegreyhoundinn.net

Web: www.thegreyhoundinn.net

Dir: *M40 junct 1/M25 junct 16, follow signs for Gerrards Cross, then Chalfont St Peter*

The 14th-century Greyhound has a macabre place in English history. Not only are its grounds believed to be where the last man hanged for stealing sheep was executed, but a former patron was Sir George Jeffreys, known as the Hanging Judge for his harsh sentencing policy during the Monmouth Rebellion. While still a local magistrate he held court in a room above the restaurant. The cooking style is essentially classic British with a modern twist, producing starters such as moules marinière, shallots, parsley, white wine and cream; chargrilled chicken Caesar salad; and avocado, orange and prawn salad with Marie Rose sauce. From a well balanced list of main courses choose from deep-fried haddock in beer batter; whole baked sea bass; pan-fried calf's liver; home-made shepherd's pie; or leg of duck confit, among many others.

Open: 11-11 Closed: 1 Jan **Bar Meals:** L served all week 12-3 D served all week 6-9 Av main course £10 **Restaurant Meals:** L served all week 12-3 D served all week 6-9 Av 3 course alc £22.50 **Brewery/Company:** Enterprise Inns 🍺: London Pride 🍷: 12 **Children's Facilities:** Licence Games Highchair Food warming Baby changing **Notes:** Dogs allowed in bar Garden: Outside terrace: tables, chairs & umbrellas **Parking:** 25

CHOLESBURY

The Full Moon 🍷

Hawridge Common Nr Chesham HP5 2UH

☎ 01494 758959 📠 01494 758797

Email: annie@alberto1142.freeserve.co.uk

Dir: *At Tring on A41 turn for Wiggington & Cholesbury. Equal distance between Chesham, Tring, Berkhampstead and Wendover. On Common in front of windmill*

High in the Chilterns this 16th-century former coaching inn has beams, flagstones, and a windmill-backed setting. One menu serves the two bars and the restaurant.

Open: 12-3 5.30-11 (Sat open all day, Sun 12-10.30) Closed: 25 Dec **Bar Meals:** L served all week 12-2 D served all week 6.30-9 (Sun 6-8) Av main course £11 **Restaurant Meals:** L served all week 12-2 D served all week 6.30-9 (Sun 6-8) Av 3 course alc £22.50 **Brewery/Company:** Enterprise Inns 🍺: Interbrew Bass & Adnams, Fuller's London Pride, Brakspear Special, and Guest Ales 🍷: 7 **Children's Facilities:** Menu/Portions Highchair Food warming Baby changing **Notes:** Dogs allowed in bar, in garden, Water Garden: canopy, heat lamps **Parking:** 28

CUDDINGTON
The Crown ♀

Spurt Street HP18 0BB

☎ 01844 292222

Email: david@anniebaileys.com

Web: www.thecrowncuddington.co.uk

Dir: *Off A418 between Aylesbury and Thame*

This characterful Grade II listed pub functions equally well as a popular local and a serious dining pub. There's a locals' bar and several low-beamed dining areas. There is also a small patio area providing outside seating and an opportunity for alfresco dining in the summer. Food-wise, the eclectic menus should please all comers. The good value set menu offers a choice of two or three courses or there's a hearty selection of pubby main courses.
Open: 12-3 6-11 (All day Sun) **Bar Meals:** L served all week 12-2.30 D served all week 6.30-10 (Sun 12-8) Av main course £11 **Restaurant Meals:** L served all week 12-2.30 D served all week 6.30-10 (Sun 12-8) Av 3 course alc £22 **Brewery/Company:** Fullers ◼: Fullers London Pride, Adnams, Guinness ♀: 9 **Children's Facilities:** Menu/Portions Games Food warming Baby changing **Notes:** Garden: Small patio **Parking:** 12

GREAT HAMPDEN
The Hampden Arms ♀

Nr Great Missenden HP16 9RQ

☎ 01494 488255 📄 01494 488094

Email: louise@thehamptonarms.fsnet.co.uk

Dir: *From M40 take A4010, right before Princes Risborough. Great Hampden signed*

Whether you're celebrating a special occasion or just want a quiet pint of real ale, you'll find a warm and friendly welcome at this mock Tudor pub restaurant in the heart of the beautifully wooded Hampden Estate. The menu features such dishes as game pie set on a rich port sauce; baked halibut steak with a watercress, mussel and cream sauce; and roasted vegetables set on a rocket and Parmesan salad. Lighter snacks are available, and there is a good choice of hot puddings.
Open: 12-3 6-11 (Sun 7-10.30) **Bar Meals:** L served all week 12-2 D served all week 6.30-9 (Fri & Sat 6.30-9.30, Sun 12-3, 7-9) Av main course £10.95 **Restaurant Meals:** L served all week 12-2 D served all week 6.30-9 (Sun 12-3, 7-9) Av 3 course alc £20 **Brewery/Company:** Free House ◼: Adnams Bitter, Hook Norton, Tetley ♀: 7 **Children's Facilities:** Fam room Menu/Portions Highchair Food warming **Nearby:** Hampden Common, Laceygreen Windmill, Speen Rest Home for Horses **Notes:** Dogs allowed in bar, in garden Garden: Grass & outside eating **Parking:** 30

GREAT MISSENDEN
The Polecat Inn ♀

170 Wycombe Road Prestwood HP16 0HJ

☎ 01494 862253 📄 01494 868393

Email: polecatinn@btinternet.com

Dir: *On the A4128 between Great Missenden and High Wycombe*

The colourful three-acre garden with its interesting herbaceous borders is a huge attraction at this charming 17th-century free house, set amidst rolling Chilterns countryside. Owner John Gamble, who bought the closed and dilapidated Polecat sixteen years ago, renovated and extended the building to create an attractive inn that still retains many of its original features. Now, the small low-beamed rooms that radiate from the central bar are the setting for a wide-ranging menu and daily blackboard specials, freshly prepared using local ingredients and herbs from the garden. Lunchtime brings sausages in French bread; filled jacket potatoes; and hot roast beef in stotty bread. Larger appetites might choose beef Wellington; salmon fish cakes with tomato and basil; parsnip and stilton croquettes; or shepherd's pie with cheddar mash.
Open: 11.30-2.30 6-11 (Sun 12-3) Closed: Dec 25-26, Jan 1 **Bar Meals:** L served all week 12-2 D served Mon-Sat 6.30-9 **Brewery/Company:** Free House ◼: Marston's Pedigree, Morland Old Speckled Hen, Interbrew Flowers IPA & Brakspears Bitter ♀: 16 **Children's Facilities:** Fam room Play area (2 swings & climbing frame) Menu/Portions Food warming **Notes:** Dogs allowed in bar, in garden Garden: Extensive with herbaceous borders & plants **Parking:** 40

GREAT MISSENDEN
The Rising Sun ♟

Little Hampden HP16 9PS

☎ 01494 488393 & 488360 📠 01494 488788

Email: sunrising@rising-sun.demon.co.uk

Web: www.rising-sun.demon.co.uk

Dir: *From A413, N of Gt Missenden, take Rignall Rd on left signed for Princes Risborough 2.5m. Turn right signed Little Hampden only.*

Reached down a single track this 250-year-old inn is tucked away in the Chiltern Hills. An interesting menu offers starters which can double as snacks, and an extensive à la carte selection for lunch and dinner. **Open:** 11.30-3 6.30-10 (Sun 12-3 only, Open BH lunchtime) **Bar Meals:** L served Tue-Sun 12-2 D served Tue-Sat 7-9 (Sun lunch 12-2) Av main course £9.95 **Restaurant Meals:** L served Tue-Sun 12-2 D served Tue-Sat 7-9 (Sun lunch 12-2) Av 3 course alc £23 🍺: Adnams, Brakspear Bitter, Spitfire, Youngs Special, Marstons Pedigree ♟: 10 **Children's Facilities:** Menu/Portions Highchair Food warming **Nearby:** Bekonscott Model Village, Shire Horse Centre, Roald Dahl Museum **Notes:** Garden: With seating area **Parking:** 20

KINGSWOOD
Crooked Billet ♟

Ham Green Aylesbury HP18 0QJ

☎ 01296 770239 📠 01296 770094

Email: info@crookedbillet.com

Web: www.crookedbillet.com

Dir: *On A41 between Aylesbury & Bicester*

Located in peaceful Buckinghamshire countryside, this 200-year-old pub offers an extensive and tempting choice of food. Starters may include port and stilton rarebit with date and walnut bread, and tomato Cumberland sauce, or salad of queenie scallops with smoked salmon. Among the main courses can be found pasta alla Fiorentina smothered in cream cheeses and spinach; roasted sea bass fillet with shrimp velouté and parsley mash; or gratin of fine herb gnocchi with chard, turnips and carrots. **Open:** 11-11 **Bar Meals:** L served Mon-Sat 12-2.30 D served Mon-Sat 6-9.30 (Sun 12-3.30) **Restaurant Meals:** L served Mon-Sat 12-2.30 D served Mon-Sat 6-9.30 (Sun 12-3.30) **Brewery/Company:** Free House 🍺: Hook Norton, Guinness, Tetley's, Carlsberg & Carlsberg Export ♟: 15 **Children's Facilities:** Play area Menu/Portions Cutlery Highchair Food warming **Notes:** Garden: Large seated area surrounded by woodland **Parking:** 50

LITTLE CHALFONT
The Sugar Loaf Inn ♟

Station Road HP7 9NP

☎ 01494 765579 📠 01494 766908

Email: info@thesugarloafinn.com

Web: www.thesugarloafinn.com

There's a contemporary gastro feel to this classic 1930s pub, which has recently enjoyed a major refit at the hands of its new owners. Inside there is a bar and two dining rooms. Outside, the large rear garden is just the place for alfresco summer dining. Service is informal, and the menu features a variety of traditional European dishes with a modern twist. **Open:** 12-11 Closed: 25-26 Dec & 1 Jan **Bar Meals:** L served all week 12-3 D served Av main course £7 **Restaurant Meals:** L served all week 12-3 D served all week 6-10.30 (Sun/Sat 12-4) Av 3 course alc £22.25 **Brewery/Company:** Punch Taverns 🍺: Adnams, Guinness, London Pride, Hoegaarden & Staropramen ♟: 10 **Children's Facilities:** Licence Menu/Portions Games Highchair Food warming Baby changing **Nearby:** Odds Farm, Model Village & Chess Valley Walk **Notes:** Dogs allowed Garden: to the rear **Parking:** 20

MARLOW
The Kings Head ♀
Church Road Little Marlow SL7 3RZ
☎ 01628 484407 📄 01628 484407
Dir: *M40 junct 4 take A4040 S, then A4155*
This flower-adorned pub, only ten minutes from the
Thames Footpath, dates back to 1647. It has a cosy,
open-plan interior with original beams and open fires.
From sandwiches and jacket potatoes, the menu extends
to the likes of sea bass with ginger, sherry and spring
onions; lamb shank with rich minty gravy, mash and fresh
vegetables; pheasant casserole; tuna and mozzarella fish-
cakes; and stir-fry duck with plum sauce.
Open: 11-11 **Bar Meals:** L served all week 12-2.15 D
served all week 6.30-9.30 (Sun 12-8) Av main course
£8.95 **Restaurant Meals:** L served all week 12-2.15 D
served all week 6.30-9.30 (Sun 12-8)
Brewery/Company: Enterprise Inns 🍺: Fuller's London
Pride, Timothy Taylor Landlord, Adnam Broadside &
Deuchars IPA ♀: 9 **Children's Facilities:** Menu/Portions
Highchair Food warming Baby changing **Nearby:** Odds
Farm & River Thames Marlow **Notes:** Garden: behind
pub, lots of tables & chairs **Parking:** 50

OVING
The Black Boy ♀
Church Lane Aylesbury HP22 4HN
☎ 01296 641258 📄 01296 641271
Email: theblackboyoving@aol.com
Web: www.theblackboyoving.co.uk
Dir: *4.6m N of Aylesbury*
Oliver Cromwell and his soldiers camped in the Black
Boy's huge garden after sacking nearby Bolebec Castle
during the Civil War. Today, the 16th-century pub is a
rural oasis, with spectacular views over the Vale of
Aylesbury to Stowe School and beyond. Choices in the
dining room include Scottish salmon with new potatoes
and seasonal greens; local lamb shank with minted gravy
and root vegetables; and a vegetarian cheese and onion
filo parcel.
Open: 12-3 6-11 **Bar Meals:** L served Tues-Sun 12-2
D served Tues-Sat 6.30-9 (Sun 12-3.30) Av main course
£11.50 **Restaurant Meals:** L served Tues-Sun 12-2 D
served Tues-Sat 6.30-9 (Sun 12-3.30) Av 3 course alc
£20 🍺: Spitfire, Youngs Bitter, Batemans Bitter,
Deuchars & Gales ♀: 10 **Children's Facilities:**
Menu/Portions Cutlery Games Food warming **Nearby:**
Waddesdon Manor, Quainton Railway, Gullivers World
Notes: Dogs allowed in bar, Water Garden: Large with
views of Aylesbury Vale **Parking:** 20

SKIRMETT
The Frog ♀
Henley on Thames RG9 6TG
☎ 01491 638996 📄 01491 638045
Email: jim.crowe@btinternet.com
Web: www.thefrog.co.uk
Dir: *Turn off A4155 at Mill End, pub 3m on*
This privately owned pub and restaurant is tucked away
in the beautiful Hambleden valley. The simple set menu
offers great value for money with options like salad of
Gravadlax, followed by roast loin of pork, and sticky toffee
pudding to finish. The carte offers a range of starters like
soup, garlic bread or bruschetta; followed by mains like
pan-seared salmon with curried lentils.
Open: 11.30-3 6.30-11 **Bar Meals:** L served all week
12-2.30 D served all week 6.30-9.30 Av main course
£10.50 **Restaurant Meals:** L served all week 12-2.30
D served all week 6.30-9.30 Av 3 course alc £25
Brewery/Company: Free House 🍺: Adnams Best, Hook
Norton, Rebellion, Fullers London Pride **Children's
Facilities:** Fam room Menu/Portions Games Highchair
Food warming **Notes:** Dogs allowed in bar Garden: Beer
garden, patio, outdoor eating **Parking:** 15

TURVILLE
The Bull & Butcher 🍷

Henley on Thames RG9 6QU

☎ 01491 638283 📄 01491 638836

Email: info@thebullandbutcher.com

Web: www.thebullandbutcher.com

Dir: *M40 junct 5 follow Ibstone signs. Right at T-junct. Pub 0.25m on left*

Even if you've never been to Turville or this delightful black-and-white-timbered 16th-century pub, you may well recognise them immediately you arrive here. The village has earned itself celebrity status over the years as a popular location for numerous film and television productions, most notably *Midsomer Murders* and *The Vicar of Dibley*. Movies shot in the area include *Chitty Chitty Bang Bang*. An appetising menu ranges from smoked fish platter and venison and vegetable casserole, to oven-roasted rump of lamb, and chicken, mushroom and tarragon pie.

Open: 12-11 (Sun and BH 12-10.30) **Bar Meals:** L served all week 12-2.30 D served all week 6.30-9.30 (Sun 12-9) Av main course £11.95 **Restaurant Meals:** L served all week 12-2.30 D served all week 7-9.45 (Sun 12-9) Av 3 course alc £24 **Brewery/Company:** Brakspear 🍺: Brakspear Bitter, Brakspear Special, Hooky Dark and Brewers selections 🍷: 36 **Children's Facilities:** Play area (Childrens seats at end of garden under tree) Menu/Portions Cutlery Food warming **Nearby:** Chitty Chitty Bang Bang Windmill, Classical Riding Centre, **Notes:** Dogs allowed in bar, Water on request **Garden:** Large outdoor patio with seating **Parking:** 30

WEST WYCOMBE
The George and Dragon Hotel 🍷

High Street HP14 3AB

☎ 01494 464414 📄 01494 462432

Email: sue.raines@btconnect.com

Web: www.george-and-dragon.co.uk

Dir: *On A40, close to M40*

Built on the site of a 14th-century hostelry, this 18th-century former coaching inn in a National Trust village has welcomed generations of visitors. The range of real ales is excellent, and the eclectic menu draws influences from all over the globe.

Open: 11-2.30 5.30-11 (Sat 11-3, 5.30-11, Sun 12-3, 6-9.30) **Bar Meals:** L served all week 12-2 D served all week 6-9.30 Av main course £12.50 **Brewery/Company:** Enterprise Inns 🍺: Courage Best, Wells Bombardier Premium, Greene King Abbot Ale, Adnams Broadside, Marston's Pedigree 🍷: 8 **Children's Facilities:** Fam room Play area (Climbing frame, swings) Menu/Portions Cutlery Highchair Food warming **Nearby:** West Wycombe Caves, Bekonskot Model Village **Notes:** Dogs allowed in bar, in garden, in bedrooms, Water **Garden:** Large garden adjacent to car park **Parking:** 35

BABRAHAM
The George Inn at Babraham 🍷

High Street Cambridge CB2 4AG

☎ 01223 833800

Email: george@inter-mead.com

Web: www.georgeinnbabraham.co.uk

Dir: *Babraham High St, just off A11/A505 & A1307*

Following a devastating fire in 2004, the 18th-century George was completely rebuilt. New kitchens and three restaurant areas were incorporated into this beautifully furnished and decorated village dining pub. The food is a pairing of traditional English with more worldwide influences.

Open: 11.30-3 5.30-11 (Open all day summer w/ends) **Bar Meals:** L served all week 12-2.15 D served all week 6.30-9 **Restaurant Meals:** L served all week 12-2.15 D served all week 6.30-9 **Brewery/Company:** Free House 🍺: Old Speckled Hen, Guinness, Greene King Abbot Ale 🍷: 8 **Children's Facilities:** Menu/Portions Cutlery Games Highchair Food warming Baby changing **Nearby:** Audley End, Newmarket Races & Duxford Air Museum **Notes:** **Garden:** Covered terrace, large lawn and tables **Parking:** 41

BARRINGTON
The Royal Oak ♀
West Green nr Cambridge CB2 5RZ
☎ 01223 870791 📠 01223 870791
Dir: *From Barton off M11 S of Cambridge*
One of the oldest thatched pubs in England is this
rambling, timbered 13th-century building overlooking
what is (coincidentally) the largest village green in
England. Yet it is only six miles from Cambridge, three
miles from the M11 and a mile from Shepreth Station. A
wide range of fish dishes includes scallops, trout, scampi,
tuna, swordfish, tiger prawns, squid and other seasonal
offerings. There is also a carvery on Sunday.
Open: 11.30-2.30 6-11 (Sun 12-10.30 high season
only) **Bar Meals:** L served Mon-Sat 12-2.30 D served
Mon-Thu 6.30-9 (Sun 12-2.30, Fri-Sat 6.30-9.30) Av

main course £7.50 **Restaurant Meals:** L served Sun
D served 6.30-9 Av 3 course alc £25
Brewery/Company: Old English Inns & Hotels 🍺: IPA
Potton Brewery, Adnams, Elgoods, Nethergates, guest
♀: 6 **Children's Facilities:** Play area (The largest village
green in England) Menu/Portions Cutlery Games
Highchair Food warming **Nearby:** Willers Mill Wildlife
Park, Duxford Airfield, Wimpole Hall **Notes:** Garden:
village green **Parking:** 50

CAMBRIDGE
Cambridge Blue
85 Gwydir Street CB1 2LG
☎ 01223 361382 📠 01223 505110
Email: c.lloyd13@ntlworld.com
Dir: *Town centre*
A convivial, community-spirited pub, with an unexpectedly
huge rear garden, in a long terraced street. Noisy
machines, including mobile phones, have no place within.
Rowing memorabilia and pictures cover the walls, and
daily papers and local publications are provided. Hearty
regulars include steak and stout with mash, Suffolk
seafood pie, and a choice of sausages with mash and
gravy. Lighter bites include toasted ciabattas and jacket
potatoes.
Open: 12-2.30 5.30-11 (Sat & Sun 12-3, Sun 6-10.30)

Bar Meals: L served all week 12-2.30 D served all
week 6-9.30 (No food 25-Dec) Av main course £6.50
Brewery/Company: Free House 🍺: Woodforde's Wherry,
Hobson's Choice, Adnams, Elgoods Black Dog Mild,
Guest Ales **Children's Facilities:** Fam room Play area
(Toys) Menu/Portions Games Food warming **Notes:** Dogs
allowed in bar, in garden, Water (dogs on leads) **Garden:**
Grass, wooden picnic tables on paving slabs

ELSWORTH
The George & Dragon ♀
41 Boxworth Road Cambridge CB3 8JQ
☎ 01954 267236 📠 01954 267080
Dir: *SE of A14 between Cambridge & Huntingdon*
Set in a pretty village just outside Cambridge, this pub
offers a wide range of satisfying food to locals and
visitors alike. Expect Mediterranean king prawns; prime
Scottish steaks; and fresh cod, haddock or plaice from
Lowestoft. For a lighter meal, ploughman's lunches and
sandwiches are available: try rump steak in a focaccia
sandwich roll. Monday night special menus - pheasant
suppers, roast duck feasts and more - offer good value
set price meals.
Open: 11-3 6-11 (Sun 12-3, 6.30-10.30) **Bar Meals:** L
served all week 12-2 D served Mon-Sat 6.30-9.30 (Sun

12-3, 6-9) Av main course £10 **Restaurant Meals:** L
served all week 12-2 D served Mon-Sun 6.30-9.30
(Sun 12-2.30, 6-9) **Brewery/Company:** Free House
🍺: Greene King IPA, Ruddles County, Morland Old
Speckled Hen ♀: 8 **Children's Facilities:** Menu/Portions
Highchair Food warming **Notes:** Garden: Patio area and
garden with fountain **Parking:** 50

CAMBRIDGESHIRE

CAMBRIDGESHIRE

ELTISLEY
The Leeds Arms
The Green St Neots Huntingdon PE19 6TG
☎ 01480 880283 📠 01480 880379
Web: www.theleedsarms.co.uk
Dir: *On A428 between Cambridge & St Neots*
Built towards the end of the 18th century and named after a local landowner, the Leeds Arms has recently been taken over by a new team, and is now a Charles Wells pub. A sample menu includes lamb shank with a mint jus, medallions of pork with Calvados sauce, chicken breast wrapped in bacon on mashed potatoes, and wild mushroom and avocado hotpot. Meat is sourced from an organic farm.
Open: 11.30-2.30 6.30-11 **Bar Meals:** L served all week 12-2 D served all week 6.30-9.45 Av main course £7.95 **Restaurant Meals:** L served all week 12-2 D served all week 6.30-9.45 (Sun 12-2, 7-9) Av 3 course alc £15 **Brewery/Company:** Charles Wells ⌕: Charles Wells Smooth, 3 Guest Ales **Children's Facilities:** Play area Menu/Portions Games Highchair Food warming **Nearby:** Croyton Organic Farm & Wimpole Hall **Notes:** Dogs allowed in bar Garden: Patio, tables, grass area **Parking:** 30

ELTON
The Black Horse 🍷
14 Overend nr Peterborough PE8 6RU
☎ 01832 280240 & 280875
Dir: *Off A605 (Peterborough to Northampton rd)*
Antique furnishings and open log fires crank up the old world charm in this 17th-century inn, while the delightful one-acre rear garden overlooks Elton's church and rolling open countryside. The pub was once the village jail, and the building later became a morgue. Today's clientele are very much alive, and its current landlord has had to extend the car park to meet demand. Superb selection of food ranges from bar snacks to a full à la carte.
Open: 12-11.30 **Bar Meals:** L served all week 12-2 D served Mon-Sat 6-9 (Sun 12-3) Av main course £13.50 **Restaurant Meals:** L served all week 12-2 D served Mon-Sat 6-9 Av 3 course alc £25 **Brewery/Company:** Free House ⌕: Bass, Everards Tiger, Nethergate, Barnwell Bitter 🍷: 14 **Children's Facilities:** Fam room Play area Menu/Portions Cutlery Highchair Food warming Baby changing **Notes:** Dogs allowed in bar, in garden, Water provided **Garden:** patio with various sport facilities **Parking:** 30

ELY
The Anchor Inn 🍷
Sutton Gault CB6 2BD
☎ 01353 778537 📠 01353 776180
Email: anchorinn@popmail.bta.com
Web: www.anchorsuttongault.co.uk
Dir: *From A14, B1050 to Earith, take B1381 to Sutton. Sutton Gault on left*
Built in 1650, the Anchor Inn has evolved to combine modern comforts with timeless charm and character. The pub has won wide recognition for its modern British cuisine. There's an emphasis on seasonal and traditional ingredients and, in summer, meals can be enjoyed on the terrace overlooking the New Bedford River.
Open: 12-3 7-11 Closed: Dec 26 **Bar Meals:** L served all week 12-2 D served all week 7-9 (Sat 6.30-9.30) Av main course £10 **Restaurant Meals:** L served all week 12-2 D served all week 7-9 (Sat 6.30-9.30) Av 3 course alc £27 ⌕: City of Cambridge Hobson's Choice, Boathouse Bitter 🍷: 8 **Children's Facilities:** Menu/Portions Games Highchair Food warming **Nearby:** Mepal Outdoor Centre, Oliver Cromwell's House (Ely) **Notes:** Garden: Terrace overlooking river **Parking:** 16

FENSTANTON
King William IV ♥

High Street nr Huntingdon PE28 9JF

☎ 01480 462467 🖹 01480 468526

Email: kingwilliam@thefen.fsnet.co.uk

Web: www.kingwilliamiv.co.uk

Dir: *Off A14 between Cambridge & Huntingdon*

Originally three 17th-century cottages, this rambling old inn stands next door to the clock tower in the heart of the village. Inside are low beams, a lively bar and the appropriately named Garden Room. Fresh food is cooked daily, with pork and leek sausages and King Bill vegetarian burger among the lunchtime options, while the à la carte menu offers the likes of lemon sole fillet, mignons of chicken fillet, and risotto of butternut squash.

Open: 11-11 (Sun 12-10.30)   **Bar Meals:** L served all week 12-2.15   D served Mon-Sat 6.30-9.45 (Sun 12-3.30) **Restaurant Meals:** L served all week 12-2   D served Mon-Sat 7-9.45 (Sun 12-3.30) **Brewery/Company:** Greene King 🍺: Greene King Abbot Ale & IPA, Guest Ales ♥: 9 **Children's Facilities:** Games Highchair Food warming **Notes:** Dogs allowed in bar, Water   Garden: Patio area **Parking:** 14

FORDHAM
White Pheasant ♥

Nr Newmarket CB7 5LQ

☎ 01638 720414

Email: whitepheasant@whitepheasant.com

Web: whitepheasant.com

Dir: *From Newmarket A142 to Ely, approx 5 miles to Fordham. Pub on left*

Standing in a fenland village between Ely and Newmarket, this white-painted free house dates from the 1600s. In many ways little has changed down the years, yet today's wooden floors, pine furniture and pastel shades bring the interior harmoniously and stylishly up to date. The emphasis is on 'traditional British food with a fusion', with restaurant mains including home-made chicken Kiev, thyme-roasted sea bass, and wild mushroom Stroganoff. Bar snacks include salads and filled breads.

Open: 12-3 6-11 (Sun 7-10.30) Closed: 26-29 Dec & 1 Jan **Bar Meals:** L served all week 12-2.30 D served all week **Restaurant Meals:** L served all week 12-2.30 D served all week 6-9.30 (Sun 12-2.30 & 7-9) Av 3 course alc £25 **Brewery/Company:** Free House 🍺: Woodforde's Nelson's Revenge, Norfolk Nog, Admirals Reserve, Wherry, Youngs ♥: 14 **Children's Facilities:** Menu/Portions Cutlery Games Highchair Food warming **Nearby:** Anglesey Abbey, City of Ely, Wicken Fen, Newmarket & Planet Zoom **Notes:** Garden: Pleasant area, child friendly **Parking:** 30

GOREFIELD
Woodmans Cottage

90 High Road Wisbech PE13 4NB

☎ 01945 870669 🖹 01945 870631

Email: magtuck@aol.com

Dir: *3m NW of Wisbech*

Friendly, newly refurbished, family-run traditional village pub in Cambridgeshire's Fenland, only a mere 2mtrs above the level of the sea nearly 10 miles away. It offers a good range of pub food including steaks, mixed grill, lamb shank, home-made steak and kidney pie, lasagne, battered cod, plaice and haddock, and lobster tails. Jumbo sausages and ploughman's feature among the snacks, while vegetarian options include vegetable curry.

Open: 11-2.30 7-11 Closed: 25 Dec **Bar Meals:** L served all week 12-2 D served all week 7-10 Av main course £8 **Restaurant Meals:** L served all week 12-2 D served all week 7-10 **Brewery/Company:** Free House 🍺: Greene King IPA & Abbot Ale, Interbrew Worthington Bitter, Cours Lager & Stella **Children's Facilities:** Menu/Portions Games Highchair Food warming **Nearby:** Play Today and Bowling Alley Park **Notes:** Garden: Walled patio area **Parking:** 40

CAMBRIDGESHIRE

CAMBRIDGESHIRE

HOLYWELL

The Old Ferryboat Inn ★★ HL ♟

Back Lane St Ives PE27 4TG

☎ 01480 463227 🖺 01480 463245

Dir: *A14 then right onto A1096 then A1123 right to Holywell*

Renowned as England's oldest inn, built some time in the 11th century, but with a hostelry history that goes back to the 6th, the Old Ferryboat has immaculately maintained thatch, white stone walls, and cosy interior. A pleasant atmosphere - despite the resident ghost of a lovelorn teenager - in which to enjoy hot chicken curry, roast rack of lamb, steak and ale pie, fish and chips, and Greene King ales.

Open: 11.30-11 **Bar Meals:** L served all week 12-2.30 D served all week 6-9.30 (Sun 12-2.30, 6-9) Av main course £8.95 **Brewery/Company:** Old English Inns & Hotels 🍺: Greene King Abbot Ale/IPA, Old Speckled Hen, guest ales ♟: 6 **Children's Facilities:** Menu/Portions Games Highchair Food warming **Notes:** Garden: Food served outside, river views **Parking:** 100

HUNTINGDON

The Old Bridge Hotel ★★★ HL ◉◉ ♟

1 High Street PE29 3TQ

☎ 01480 424300 🖺 01480 411017

Email: oldbridge@huntsbridge.co.uk

Web: www.huntsbridge.com

Dir: *Signed from A1 & A14*

Ivy covers every inch of the handsome 18th-century façade of this thriving town house hotel. Formerly a private bank, the building stands right on the edge of the town centre overlooking the River Ouse. From the panelled dining room and main lounge with their fine fabrics, quality prints and comfortable chairs, to the 24 individually styled bedrooms, the opulent décor reflects the building's original character. Walls in the more informal Terrace dining area are all hand-painted, one particular work having taken over 4 months to complete. The food reflects the individuality of chef Chris Tabbitt, whose aim is simply to make the best ingredients taste as good as possible. Scotch broth or hot chorizo sausage with olives might introduce the bargain lunch menu, followed by wild mushroom lasagne; sea bass fillet with caviar butter; or roast venison with braised sweetheart cabbage. Naturally, everything is home made.

Open: 11-11 (Sun 12-10.30) **Bar Meals:** L served all week 12-2.30 D served all week 6.30-10.30 **Restaurant Meals:** L served all week 12-2.30 D served all week 6.30-10.30 **Brewery/Company:** Huntsbridge 🍺: Adnams Best, Hobsons Choice, Bateman XXXB ♟: 15 **Children's Facilities:** Menu/Portions Cutlery Games Highchair Food warming **Nearby:** Wimpole Hall Home Farm, Grafham Water, Cambridge **Parking:** 60

HUNTINGDON

The Three Horseshoes ★★★ INN ♟

Moat Lane Abbots Ripton PE28 2PA

☎ 01487 773440 🖺 01487 773440

Email: abbotsripton@aol.com

Web: www.thethreehorseshoes.com

Dating back to 1654 and retaining many original features, the picturesque Three Horseshoes once had the lowest ceiling of any pub in the county. Stepping inside today, customers are greeted by three bar areas, a restaurant and a range of hand pumped Adnams real ales. Typical food includes Sunday roasts like rib of beef with Yorkshire pudding, roast loin of pork with crackling and apple sauce; and grilled tuna steak.

Open: 11.30-3 6-11 **Bar Meals:** L served Tue-Sun 12-2 D served Tue-Sat 6.30-9.30 (Sun 12-2.30) Av main course £8 **Restaurant Meals:** L served Tue-Sat 12-2 D served Tue-Sat 6.30-9.30 🍺: Adnams Bitter, Adnams Broadside, Oakhams & JHB ♟: 12 **Children's Facilities:** Fam room Menu/Portions Highchair Food warming Baby changing **Nearby:** Hamerton Wildlife Centre, Huntingdon Marina **Notes:** Garden: Large garden at rear, pond and seats at front **Parking:** 100

KEYSTON
The Pheasant Inn ☺ ♥
Village Loop Road Huntingdon PE28 0RE
☎ 01832 710241 🖷 01832 710340
Email: thepheasant@cyberwave.co.uk
Web: www.huntsbridge.com
Dir: *Signed from A14, W of Huntingdon*
The Pheasant is a charming 15th-century, thatched free house in a sleepy farming village. It is part of a privately-owned small group of chef-managed dining pubs in the Huntingdon/Peterborough area, sister establishments being The Falcon at Fotheringay, The Three Horseshoes at Madingley and The Old Bridge at Huntingdon. At the Pheasant you will find a large traditional bar, and three distinct dining areas offering a choice of comfortable and relaxed places to eat and drink. The latest addition is a garden at the rear of the pub, and there are also table outside at the front. The food is an eclectic mix, with favourite influences coming from the south of France. Dishes tend to be simple rather than fussy, making good use of seasonal ingredients in both traditional and modern ways.
Open: 12-3 6-11 **Bar Meals:** L served all week 12-2 D served all week 6.30-9.30 Av main course £10.95
Restaurant Meals: L served all week 12-2 D served all week 6.30-9.30 Av 3 course alc £23
Brewery/Company: Huntsbridge Ltd 🍺: Adnams, Village Bike Potton Brewery, Augustinian Nethergate Brewery
♥: 16 **Children's Facilities:** Menu/Portions Games Highchair Food warming Baby changing **Nearby:** Grafton Water, Wicksteed Park **Notes:** Garden: at rear, tables at front **Parking:** 40

NEWTON
The Queen's Head ♥
Cambridge CB2 5PG
☎ 01223 870436
Dir: *6m S of Cambridge on B1368, 1.5m off A10 at Harston, 4m from A505*
A quintessential English, 17th-century pub with the same family (here since 1962) still running it, steadfastly banning fruit machines and piped music from the two small bars. Lunches are limited to home-made soup, Aga-baked potatoes, toast with beef dripping, and sandwiches. In the evening it's just soup and cold platters. There's no specials board since, as the landlord says, "We have no specialist!"
Open: 11.30-2.30 6-11 (Sun 12-2.30, 7-10.30) Closed: 25-26 Dec **Bar Meals:** L served all week 11.30-2.15 D served all week 7-9.30 (Sun 7-9.30) Av main course £4
Brewery/Company: Free House 🍺: Adnams Southwold, Broadside, Fisherman, Bitter & Regatta ♥: 8 **Children's Facilities:** Fam room (Games room, well behaved children only) Menu/Portions Food warming **Nearby:** Duxford Air Museum, Cambridge Colleges, Wimpole Hall & House Farm **Notes:** Dogs allowed in bar, Water Garden: Food/drink served on village green/seating **Parking:** 15

STRETHAM
The Lazy Otter ♥
Cambridge Road nr Ely CB6 3LU
☎ 01353 649780 🖷 01353 649314
Email: swilkilazyotter@aol.com
Dir: *Telephone for directions*
With a large beer garden and riverside restaurant overlooking the marina, the Lazy Otter lies just off the A10 between Ely and Cambridge. The pub's location beside the Great Ouse river makes it very popular in summer. Typical dishes include jumbo cod, lemon sole topped with crab meat, and fisherman's medley, as well as a selection of steaks and grills. The marina holds 30 permanent boats, as well as up to 10 day boats.
Open: 11-11 **Bar Meals:** L served all week 12-2.30 D served all week 6-9.30 (Sun 12-4) **Restaurant Meals:** L served all week 12-2.30 D served all week 6-9.30 (Sun 12-4) 🍺: Marston's Pedigree, Scottish Courage John Smith's & Courage Best ♥: 8 **Children's Facilities:** Play area Menu/Portions Highchair Food warming **Notes:** Garden: Large beer garden along river front **Parking:** 50

ESSEX

CASTLE HEDINGHAM
The Bell Inn ♀
St James Street Halstead CO9 3EJ
☎ 01787 460350
Email: bell-inn@ic24.net
Web: www.bell-castle.co.uk
Dir: *On A1124 N of Halstead, right to Castle Hedingham*
Only gravity-fed beer is served at this former coaching inn. Other traditional features include beams, wooden floors and open fires inside and a large walled orchard garden outside. Quality ingredients are carefully sourced, locally where possible, for the simple pub food.
Open: 11.45-3 6-11 (Fri 11.45am-12am, Sat 12-11.30 & Sun 12-11) Closed: 25 Dec (eve) **Bar Meals:** L served all week 12-2 D served all week 7-9.30 (Sat/Sun 12-2.30, Sun 7-9) Av main course £8.50

Brewery/Company: Grays ◀: Mild, Mighty Oak, Greene King IPA , Adnams Bitter ♀: 8 **Children's Facilities:** Fam room Play area (swings,high chairs,nappy changing facilities) Games Highchair Food warming Baby changing **Nearby:** Steam Trains & Castle **Notes:** Dogs allowed in bar by arrangement only Garden: Large walled orchard garden **Parking:** 15

CLAVERING
The Cricketers ♀
Saffron Walden CB11 4QT
☎ 01799 550442 📄 01799 550882
Email: cricketers@lineone.net
Web: www.thecricketers.co.uk
Dir: *From M11 junct 10, A505 E. Then A1301, B1383. At Newport take B1038*
Celebrity chef Jamie Oliver first learnt to cook in this 16th-century country pub, which is still run by his parents, Trevor and Sally. Seasonally changing menus are offered, fixed-price in the restaurant, and carte in the bar. The cooking shows a strong Italian influence.
Open: 10.30-11 Closed: 25-26 Dec **Bar Meals:** L served all week 12-2 D served all week 7-10
Restaurant Meals: L served all week 12-2 D served all

week 7-10 Av 3 course alc £26 ◀: Adnams Bitter, Carlsberg-Tetley Tetley Bitter, Greene King IPA & Adnams Broadside ♀: 10 **Children's Facilities:** Fam room Play area (Fenced patio) Menu/Portions Highchair Food warming **Nearby:** Audley End Model Railway, Stansted Castle & Toy Museum **Notes:** Garden: One patio and one courtyard **Parking:** 100

COLCHESTER
The Rose & Crown Hotel ★★★ HL ◉◉
East Street CO1 2TZ
☎ 01206 866677 📄 01206 866616
Email: info@rose-and-crown.com
Web: www.rose-and-crown.com
Dir: *From M25 junct 28 take A12 N. Follow Colchester signs*
In 1400, Colchester had 13 inns, and this was one. Today, it's the oldest hotel in England's oldest town, with a bar made of cell doors from the jail that once stood on the site. Eating in the oak-beamed brasserie means traditional food - fish and chips, or gammon steak, for example - while in the candlelit Oak Room the style is Indian/French fusion - green chicken tikka salad; spicy sea bass; and wild mushroom risotto, for example.

Open: 11-2.30 6-11 (Sat-Sun all day) **Bar Meals:** L served all week 12-2 D served all week 6-10 (Sun 12-3) **Restaurant Meals:** L served all week 12-2 D served Mon-Sat 7-9.45 **Brewery/Company:** Free House ◀: Carlsberg-Tetley Tetley's Bitter, Rose & Crown Bitter, Adnams Broadside **Children's Facilities:** Fam room Menu/Portions Cutlery Highchair Food warming Baby changing **Nearby:** Colcester Zoo, Rollerworld, Gobananas **Parking:** 50

DEDHAM

The Sun Inn ★★★★ INN 🍷

High Street CO7 6DF

☎ 01206 323351

Email: info@thesuninndedham.com

Web: www.thesuninndedham.com

Dir: *From A12 follow signs to Dedham for 1.5m, pub on village high street.*

A quiet pint goes hand in hand with robust food and wine at this independent free house. Owner Piers Baker has restored original features such as oak floorboards and the elm bar top, and brought all four open fires back into use. A decent selection of real ales is backed by a respectable wine list. Here you can read the newspapers or play board games in comfort, whilst the large walled garden and sun-trap terrace come into their own for alfresco summer wining and dining. Locally sourced seasonal ingredients govern the menu of modern British dishes.

Open: Closed: 25-27 Dec **Bar Meals:** L served all week 12-2.30 D served all week 6.30-9.30 (Wknds 12-3, Fri/Sat 6.30-10) Av main course £10 **Restaurant Meals:** L served all week 12-2.30 D served all week 6.30-9.30 (Wknds 12-3, Fri/Sat 6.30-10) Av 3 course alc £20 **Brewery/Company:** Free House : Brewer's Gold Crouch Vale, Adnam's Broadside, Canary from Lowestoft, Titanic & Kaltenberg 🍷: 16 **Children's Facilities:** Licence Fam room (Swing, slide in garden and pub games) Menu/Portions Games Highchair Food warming Baby changing **Nearby:** Colchester Zoo, Beth Chatto Gardens & Waterworld Colchester **Notes:** Dogs allowed in bar, Water Garden: Walled, trees, terrace & lawn **Parking:** 15

FELSTED

The Swan at Felsted 🍷

Station Road Dunmow CM6 3DG

☎ 01371 820245 📠 01371 821393

Email: info@theswanatfelsted.co.uk

Web: www.theswanatfelsted.co.uk

Dir: *Exit M11 junct 8, onto A120 signed Felsted. The Swan is in centre of Felsted*

The Swan, which was rebuilt after a fire in the early 20th century, is ideally situated for exploring the pretty Essex countryside. Food includes everything from light dishes at lunchtime to more serious fare in the evening.

Open: 11-11 (Sun 12-4) **Bar Meals:** L served all week 12-3 D served Mon-Sat 6-10 (Sun 12-4) Av main course £10 **Restaurant Meals:** L served all week 12-3 D served Mon-Sat 6-10 (Sun 12-4) Av 3 course alc £22.50 **Brewery/Company:** Greene King : IPA, Fosters, Stella, Prospect, Scrumpy Jack, Guinness & Guest Beer 🍷: 9 **Children's Facilities:** Licence Menu/Portions Cutlery Games Highchair Food warming Baby changing **Notes:** Dogs allowed in bar Garden: Enclosed courtyard, patio heaters, parasols **Parking:** 4

ESSEX

GOSFIELD

The Green Man 🍷

The Street Halstead CO9 1TP

☎ 01787 472746

Email: www.deb@thegreenmangosfield.co.uk

Web: www.thegreenmangosfield.co.uk

Dir: *Take A131 N from Braintree then A1017 to village*

Traditional yet smart village dining pub. The menu and daily specials owe much to good fresh produce, whether traditional cod in beer batter, steak and kidney pudding, or more adventurous possibilities such as roast salmon fillet with a lime butter sauce, steak and kidney pudding, grilled or battered skate wings, or pork and apple casserole with herb dumplings. From March to November there's an impressive buffet-style cold table.

Open: 11-3 6.15-11 (Sun 12-4) **Bar Meals:** L served all week 12-2 D served Mon-Sat 6.45-9 (Sun 12-2.30) Av main course £9 **Restaurant Meals:** L served all week 12-2 D served Mon-Sat 6.45-9 (Sun 12-2.30) **Brewery/Company:** Greene King : Greene King IPA, Old Speckled Hen & Abbot Ale 🍷: 9 **Children's Facilities:** Licence Menu/Portions Cutlery Games Highchair Food warming **Nearby:** Gosfield Lake, The Pits Country Park **Notes:** Dogs allowed in bar, Water Garden: 10 Tables, paved patio area **Parking:** 25

LITTLE CANFIELD
The Lion & Lamb ♟
Dunmow CM6 1SR
☎ 01279 870257 🗎 01279 870423
Email: info@lionandlamb.co.uk
Web: www.lionandlamb.co.uk
Dir: *M11 junct 8, B1256 towards Takeley*
There's a friendly welcome at this traditional country pub restaurant, with its soft red bricks, oak beams and winter log fires.There is a wide-ranging choice from the bar menu, restaurant and fresh fish board.
Open: 11-11 (Sun 12-11) **Bar Meals:** L served all week 11-10 D served all week 11-10 (Sun 12-10) Av main course £8.50 **Restaurant Meals:** L served all week 11-10 D served all week 11-10 (Sun 12-10) Av 3 course alc £28 **Brewery/Company:** Greene King ◀: Ridleys

IPA, Old Bob, Prospect & Seasonal Beers, Old Speckled Hen, Greene King IPA, Ridleys Rumpus & Old Bob Fireside ♟: 10 **Children's Facilities:** Play area (Garden, Wendy house, baby changing facility) Menu/Portions Cutlery Games Highchair Food warming Baby changing **Nearby:** Hatfield Forest **Notes:** Garden: Large enclosed garden overlooking farmland **Parking:** 50

MANNINGTREE
The Mistley Thorn ◉ ♟
High Street Mistley CO11 1HE
☎ 01206 392821 🗎 01206 390122
Email: info@mistleythorn.com
Web: www.mistleythorn.com
Dir: *Exit A12 at Hadleigh and follow signs to E Berholt & Maningtree/Mistrey.*
Nowadays a casual but upscale bistro-style restaurant, this historic free house was built in 1723. It stands in the centre of Mistley, on the estuary of the River Stour near Colchester. Owner Sherri Singleton, who is also the proprietor of the Mistley Kitchen cookery school, serves up an accomplished menu with a strong emphasis on locally sourced and seasonal produce, organic where possible.
Open: 12-11 **Bar Meals:** L served all week 12-2.30 D

served all week 7-10 (All day Sat-Sun) Av main course £8.50 **Restaurant Meals:** L served all week 12-2.30 D served all week 7-9.30 (Sat-Sun all Day) Av 3 course alc £21 ◀: Greene King IPA, Adnams, St. Peters ♟: 8 **Children's Facilities:** Menu/Portions Cutlery Games Highchair Food warming Baby changing **Notes:** Dogs allowed in bar Garden: Patio seats 14 **Parking:** 6

NORTH FAMBRIDGE
The Ferry Boat Inn
Ferry Lane Chelmsford CM3 6LR
☎ 01621 740208
Email: sylviaferryboat@aol.com
Web: ferryboatinn.net
Dir: *From Chelmsford take A130 S then A132 to South Woodham Ferrers, then B1012. right to village*
A 500-year-old traditional weatherboard inn with beams, log fires and a resident ghost. It is tucked away at the end of a lovely village on the River Crouch, next to the marina, and was once a centre for smugglers. Offers an extensive menu.
Open: 11.30-3-11 (Sun 12-4) **Bar Meals:** L served all week 12-2 D served all week 7-9.30 (Sun 12-2.45, 7-9) Av main course £6 **Restaurant Meals:** L served all

week 12-1.30 D served all week 7-9
Brewery/Company: Free House ◀: Greene King IPA, Abbot Ale, Ruddles County **Children's Facilities:** Fam room (Garden) Menu/Portions Highchair Food warming **Nearby:** Marsh Farm Country Park, Butterfly Farm, Museum of Power **Notes:** Dogs allowed in bar Garden: 1 acre, grassed, benches **Parking:** 50

RADWINTER
The Plough Inn ♟

Saffron Walden CB10 2TL

☎ 01799 599222

Dir: *4m E of Saffron Walden, at junct of B2153 & B2154*
An Essex woodboard exterior, old beams and a thatched roof characterise this listed inn, once frequented by farm workers. A recent refurbishment program has added a 50-seat restaurant, and turned the Plough from a purely local village pub into a destination gastro-pub, without losing too much of the village pub feel. A typical menu includes the likes of smoked haddock parcels, lamb noisettes, partridge, duck breast, and a variety of home-made pies.

Open: 12-3 6-11 (Sun 12-10.30) **Bar Meals:** L served all week 12-2 D served Mon-Sat 6.30-9 (Sun 12-3) Av main course £7.95 **Restaurant Meals:** L served all week 12-2 D served Mon-Sat 6.30-9 (Sun 12-3) Av 3 course alc £20 **Brewery/Company:** Free House ▥: Adnams Best, IPA, Woodfordes Wherry, Archers, guest ♟: 15 **Children's Facilities:** Menu/Portions Highchair Food warming **Nearby:** Mole Hall Wildlife Park, Linton Zoo, Norman Village, Toy Museum **Notes:** Dogs allowed in bar, Water **Garden:** Patio under pergola, large lawn **Parking:** 28

SAFFRON WALDEN
The Cricketers' Arms ★★★★ INN ◉ ♟

Rickling Green CB11 3YG

☎ 01799 543210 ▤ 01799 543512

Email: reservations@cricketers.demon.co.uk

Web: www.thecricketersarms.com

Dir: *Exit B1383 at Quendon. Pub 300yds on left opp cricket ground.*
This historic inn was built as a terrace of timber-framed cottages, and overlooks the cricket green. The cricketing connection began in the 1880s when Rickling Green became the venue for London society cricket matches, and associations with the England team and the county game continue today. The pub has been beautifully refurbished in a stripped-back, modern style, retaining traditional features, but bringing in contemporary comforts such as big leather sofas and, outside, a pretty Japanese terrace garden. One modern, all-pleasing menu serves all three dining areas. Typical dishes include risotto of crayfish, caramelized onion, fresh herbs and parmesan; and monkfish wrapped in bacon with chilli, coriander and yellow pea purée.

Open: 12-11 **Bar Meals:** L served all week 12-2.30 D served all week 7-9.30 (Sun 7-9) Av main course £12 **Restaurant Meals:** L served all week 12-2.30 D served all week 7-9.30 (Sun 12-2.30, 7-9) Av 3 course alc £25 **Brewery/Company:** Free House ▥: Greene King IPA, Jennings Cumberland & Ruddles County ♟: 8 **Children's Facilities:** Fam room Menu/Portions Games Highchair Food warming **Nearby:** Wildlfie Park, Toy Museum & Minature Railway **Notes:** Garden: Front terrace, Japanese garden **Parking:** 40

WICKHAM BISHOPS
The Mitre

2 The Street CM8 3NN

☎ 01621 891378 ▤ 01621 894932

Dir: *Off B1018 between Witham and Maldon*
Originally the Carpenter's Arms, this friendly pub changed its name in the mid-1890s, presumably to reflect the one-time possession of the village by the Bishops of London. The pub's regular range of meat choices includes mixed grills, pies and curries, steaks, and dishes featuring duck, pork, lamb and chicken. Fish is strongly represented by dishes based on salmon, haddock, cod, snapper, trout, sea bass, mahi mahi, plaice, Dover sole, red mullet and sea bream.

Open: 11.30-11 **Bar Meals:** L served all week 12-2.30 D served all week 7-9.30 (All day Sat-Sun) Av main course £7 **Restaurant Meals:** L served all week 12-2.30 D served all week 7-9.30 (All Day Sat-Sun) Av 3 course alc £18 **Brewery/Company:** Ridley & Sons Ltd ▥: Greene King IPA, Greene King Abbott **Children's Facilities:** Play area (enlcosed beer garden) Menu/Portions Highchair Food warming **Notes:** Dogs allowed in bar, dog bowl **Garden:** Enclosed with patio and BBQ **Parking:** 20

ESSEX

CASTEL
Hotel Hougue du Pommier ★★★ HL ⊛ ♉

Hougue du Pommier Road Guernsey GY5 7FQ
☎ 01481 256531 🖹 01481 256260
Email: hotel@houguedupommier.guernsey.net
Web: www.hotelhouguedupommier.com
Old Guernsey farmhouse with the only feu du bois
(literally 'cooking on the fire') in the Channel Islands. Fish,
steaks, chicken and vegetarian dishes are offered along
with a selection of bar meals. Play 'get the hook on the
nose of the large black bull', again, the only one left in
Guernsey. The 10-acre garden has a swimming pool,
barbecue and medieval area, where banquets are held
the first Saturday of the month.
Open: 10.30-11.45 **Bar Meals:** L served all week 12-
2.15 D served all week 6.30-9 **Restaurant Meals:** L
served Sun 12-2.30 D served all week 6.30-9
Av 3 course alc £25 🍺: John Smith's, Extra Smooth,
Guernsey Best Bitter ♉: 8 **Children's Facilities:** Licence
Menu/Portions Games Highchair Food warming Baby
changing **Nearby:** Sausmarez Park, Oatlands Activity
Centre **Notes:** Dogs allowed in garden, in bedrooms
Garden: Ten acre, BBQ & swimming pool **Parking:** 60

ALRESFORD
The Globe on the Lake

The Soke Broad Street SO24 9DB
☎ 01962 732294 🖹 01962 732221
Email: duveen-conway@supanet.com
Web: theglobeonthelake.co.uk
Dir: *Telephone for directions*
In an outstanding setting on the banks of a reed-fringed
lake and wildfowl sanctuary, The Globe is a convivial
hostelry facing a prime Hampshire waterscape. Waterfowl
sunbathe in the garden.
Open: 11-3 6-11 (Summer Sat-Sun all day) Closed: 25-
26 Dec **Bar Meals:** L served all week 12-2 D served all
week 6.30-9 (Wknds 12-2.30) Av main course £9.50
Restaurant Meals: L served all week 12-2 D served all
week 6.30-9 (Wknds 12-2.30) Av 3 course alc £20
Brewery/Company: Unique Pub Co Ltd 🍺: Wadworth
6X, Ringwood, Henley Brakspear Bitter, Fuller's London
Pride, Itchen Valley Godfathers ♉: 6 **Children's
Facilities:** Fam room Play area (over 14 in bar, play
house) Menu/Portions Cutlery Highchair Baby changing
Nearby: Watercress Line Steam Railway **Notes:** Garden:
Large lakeside garden with benches

AXFORD
The Crown at Axford ♉

Basingstoke RG25 2DZ
☎ 01256 389492 🖹 01256 389149
Email: thecrowninn.axford@virgin.net
Web: www.crownataxford.com
The Crown is a small country inn set at the northern
edge of the pretty Candover Valley. Here you can enjoy
your choice from a selection of real ales and wines, with
some bread and olives to keep you going, and order
dishes like pork, beer and watercress sausages. The food
is all home cooked from local produce wherever possible,
including fish, game, and veggie dishes from the board.
Organic specials are now included.
Open: 12-3 6-11 (Sat 12-11 Sun 12-10.30) **Bar
Meals:** L served all week 12-2.30 D served all week
6.30-9.30 Av main course £9.50 **Restaurant Meals:** L
served all week 12-2.30 D served all week 6.30-9 (Fri
Sat 9.30, Sun 8.30) Av 3 course alc £16.50
Brewery/Company: Free House 🍺: London Pride,
Youngs Bitter, Triple FFF, Fosters, Stella Artois & Guest
Ale ♉: 7 **Children's Facilities:** Licence Menu/Portions
Games Highchair Food warming **Notes:** Dogs allowed in
bar, in garden, Water Garden: Large Patio **Parking:** 30

BASINGSTOKE
Hoddington Arms 🍷
Upton Grey RG25 2RL
☎ 01256 862371 📄 01256 862371
Email: monca777@aol.com
Web: www.hoddingtonarms.com
Dir: *Telephone for directions*
Log fires, 18th-century beams - this relaxing pub has no shortage of traditional charm. It's located near the duck pond at Upton Grey, Hampshire's best kept village for several years. In addition to a choice of bar snacks and a set price menu of the day, blackboard specials include dishes such as honey glazed breast of duck with dauphinoise potatoes; minted lamb casserole; and home-cooked Hoddington pies. There's also a peaceful rear terrace and garden.

Open: 12-3 6-11 (Sun 7-10.30) **Bar Meals:** L served all week 12-2 D served Mon-Sat 6-9 Av main course £9.50 **Restaurant Meals:** L served all week 12-2 D served Mon-Sat 6-9 Av 3 course alc £20 **Brewery/Company:** Greene King 🍺: Greene King IPA, Old Speckled Hen, Ruddles Best 🍷: 7 **Children's Facilities:** Fam room Play area (Outside) Menu/Portions Games Highchair Food warming **Notes:** Dogs allowed in bar, in garden, Water **Garden:** Large patio **Parking:** 30

BEAUWORTH
The Milburys 🍷
Alresford SO24 0PB
☎ 01962 771248 📄 01962 7771910
Email: info@themilburys.co.uk
Web: www.themilburys.co.uk
Dir: *A272 towards Petersfield, after 6m turn right for Beauworth*
A rustic hill-top pub dating from the 17th century and named after the Bronze Age barrow nearby. It is noted for its massive, 250-year-old treadmill that used to draw water from the 300ft well in the bar, and for the far-reaching views across Hampshire that can be savoured from the lofty garden. The African Oasis restaurant has a distinctly South African flavour.
Open: 11-3 6-11 (Sun 6-10.30) **Bar Meals:** L served all week 12-2 D served all week 6.30-9.30 Av main course £9 **Restaurant Meals:** L served all week 12-2 D served all week 6.30-9.30 Av 3 course alc £10 **Brewery/Company:** Free House 🍺: Theakstons Old Peculier, Triple FFF Altons Pride, Deuchars, guest ale 🍷: 8 **Children's Facilities:** Menu/Portions Highchair Food warming **Notes:** Dogs allowed in bar, in garden, Water provided **Garden:** Beautiful view of valley **Parking:** 60

BENTLEY
The Bull Inn
Nr Farnham GU10 5JH
☎ 01420 22156 📄 01420 520772
Dir: *2m from Farnham on A31 towards Winchester*
15th-century beamed coaching inn in a Hampshire village made famous by reality radio and television series over the years. Inside are open log fires, two separate bars and a restaurant. Extensive selection of pub food complemented by braised shank of lamb with sweet potato mash and rosemary sauce; pan-fried fillet of salmon with a lemon and chive butter; and roasted hook of ham with swede and potato purée.
Open: 11-11 **Bar Meals:** L served all week 12-2.30 D served all week 6.30-9.30 (Sun 12-3, 6-8.45) Av main course £12.95 **Restaurant Meals:** L served all week 12-2.30 D served all week 6.30-9.30 **Brewery/Company:** Free House 🍺: Scottish Courage Courage Best, Hogs Back TEA, Young's Bitter, Fullers London Pride **Children's Facilities:** Play area Menu/Portions Cutlery Highchair Food warming **Nearby:** Birdworld, Alresford Steam Railway **Notes:** Dogs allowed in bar, Water **Garden:** Patio at front of pub **Parking:** 40

HAMPSHIRE

BENTWORTH
The Sun Inn ♟
Sun Hill Alton GU34 5JT
☎ 01420 562338
This flower-decked pub is either the first building you pass as you enter Bentworth from the Basingstoke-Alton road, or the last one out, depending on which way you are travelling, and it always seems to come as a surprise. Originally two cottages, it now has three interconnecting rooms, each with its own log fire and brick and wood floors. Food is hearty and traditional. There is much to see and do in the area: Gilbert White's House and the Oates Museum in Selborne are not far away, and neither are Jane Austen's House at Chawton, nor the Watercress Line at Alresford. Also within easy reach is Basing House in Old Basing, on the outskirts of Basingstoke.

Open: 12-3 6-11 (Sun 12-10.30) **Bar Meals:** L served all week 12-2 D served all week 7-9.30
Brewery/Company: Free House 🍺: Cheriton Pots Ale, Ringwood Best & Old Thumper, Brakspear Bitter, Fuller's London Pride **Children's Facilities:** Fam room Cutlery Highchair Food warming **Notes:** Dogs allowed in bar, in garden, Water

BROOK
The Bell Inn ★★★ HL ☺
nr Lyndhurst SO43 7HE
☎ 023 80812214 📄 023 80813958
Email: bell@bramshaw.co.uk
Web: www.bramshaw.co.uk
Dir: *From M27 junct 1 (Cadnam) take B3078 signed Brook, 0.5m on right*
Since it was established in 1782 The Bell has been owned continuously by the same family. Features of the handsome building include white-painted window shutters, an inglenook fireplace and beamed bedrooms. Bar food ranges from hot and cold snacks to daily specials featuring fresh fish and local game in season.
Open: 11-11 (Sun 12-10.30) **Bar Meals:** L served all week 12-2.30 D served all week 6.30-9.30 **Restaurant**

Meals: D served all week 6.30-9.30
Brewery/Company: Free House 🍺: Ringwood Best, Winter Brew, Fosters, Kronenbourg & Guinness
Children's Facilities: Fam room Play area (Play area in garden) Menu/Portions Cutlery Games Highchair Food warming Baby changing **Nearby:** Beaulieu & Paultons Park **Parking:** 60

BUCKLERS HARD
The Master Builders House Hotel
★★★ HL ☺☺ ♟
Beaulieu SO42 7XB
☎ 01590 616253 📄 01590 616297
Email: res@themasterbuilders.co.uk
Web: www.themasterbuilders.co.uk
The former house of the master shipbuilder Henry Adams is a fine 18th-century building in the historic ship-building village of Bucklers Hard, with a grassy area In front running down to the Beaulieu River. It has been carefully refurbished to create a smart hotel and the beamed Yachtsman's Bar. The bar offers ploughman's, jackets, sandwiches, children's choices and a short lunch and evening menu with the likes of pheasant terrine, pie of the day, and chilli con carne.

Open: 11-11 (Nov-Mar 11-6 Sun-Thu) **Bar Meals:** L served all week 12-2.30 D served all week 7-9 Av main course £9.95 **Restaurant Meals:** L served all week 12-3 D served all week 7-10 Av 3 course alc £20
Brewery/Company: Free House 🍺: Greene King IPA, Youngs, Tetleys, Broadside ♟: 6 **Children's Facilities:** Menu/Portions Games Highchair Food warming **Nearby:** Maritime Museum, Motor Museum & Paultons Park **Notes:** Dogs allowed in bar, Water **Parking:** 60

CHALTON
The Red Lion 🍷
Waterlooville PO8 0BG
☎ 023 9259 2246 📠 023 9259 6915
Email: redlionchalton@aol.com
Dir: *Just off A3 between Horndean & Petersfield. Take exit near Queen Elizabeth Country Park*
Believed to be Hampshire's oldest pub, the Red Lion began life in 1147 as a workshop and residence for the craftsmen who built the Norman church across the road. Today, there are spectacular views of the South Downs from the large garden and modern dining room. There is a snack menu, as well as light meals and children's dishes. The main specials board changes daily.
Open: 11-3 6-11 **Bar Meals:** L served all week 12-2 D served Mon-Sat 6.30-9.30 (Sun 12-2.30) **Restaurant**

Meals: L served all week 12-2 D served Mon-Sat 6.30-9.30 **Brewery/Company:** George Gale & Co 🍺: Gales Butser, Winter Brew, GB & HSB 🍷: 20 **Children's Facilities:** Fam room Menu/Portions Cutlery Games Highchair Food warming **Nearby:** Roman Villa, Buster Ancient Farm, Country Park **Notes:** Dogs allowed in bar, in garden **Garden:** Spectacular views **Parking:** 80

CHAWTON
The Greyfriar
Winchester Road GU34 1SB
☎ 01420 83841
Email: info@thegreyfriar.co.uk
Web: www.thegreyfriar.co.uk
Dir: *just off A31 near Alton. Access to Chawton via the A31/A32 junct. Signed Jane Austen's House.*
A terrace of cottages in the 16th century, a 'beer shop' by 1847, and from 1871 a proper pub, known as the Chawton Arms. The simple lunch menu offers baguettes, ploughman's, quiches, burgers and breaded scampi tails. The evening menu, which changes most days, might well come up with milk-fed lamb with leeks; fillet of gurnard with tomatoes and olive sauce; and gammon steak with bubble and squeak. Jane Austen's house is opposite.

Open: 12-11 (Mon-Fri 12-11, Sun 12-10.30) **Bar Meals:** L served all week 12-2 D served all week 7-9.30 (Sun 12-3, 6-8.30) Av main course £10.95 **Restaurant Meals:** L served all week 12-2 D served all week 7-9.30 (Sun 12-3, 6-8.30) 🍺: Fuller's London Pride, Chiswick & ESB, Discovery & Seasonal Ales 🍷: 6 **Children's Facilities:** Play area Menu/Portions Games Food warming **Nearby:** Gilbert White's House, Jane Austen's House & Watercress Line **Notes:** Dogs allowed in bar, in garden, Water **Garden:** Paved area, sun trap, picnic tables **Parking:** 16

CRAWLEY
The Fox and Hounds 🍷
nr Winchester SO21 2PR
☎ 01962 776006 📠 01962 776006
Email: liamlewisairey@aol.com
Web: www.foxandhoundscrawley.co.uk
Dir: *A34 onto A272 then 1st right into Crawley*
Just north west of Winchester, at the heart of a peaceful Hampshire village, this mock Tudor inn enjoys a burgeoning reputation for simple well-cooked food. Recently restored to former glories, it features beamed rooms warmed by log fires that create a welcoming, lived-in atmosphere. Typical menu choices include Old English sausages on bubble and squeak, steak and ale pie, salmon fillet with Hollandaise sauce, dressed crab salad, or pork fillet with black pudding.

Open: 12-3 6-11 (Sun 12-4) **Bar Meals:** L served all week 12-2 D served all week 6-9 Av main course £6.95 **Restaurant Meals:** L served all week 12-2 D served all week 7-9 Av 3 course alc £15
Brewery/Company: Free House 🍺: Wadworth 6X, Ringwood Best, Gales HSB, Fullers London Pride 🍷: 15 **Children's Facilities:** Licence Play area **Notes:** Garden: Small terraced area, family garden to rear **Parking:** 17

HAMPSHIRE

HAMPSHIRE

DAMERHAM
The Compasses Inn ★★★★ INN ☉
Nr Fordingbridge SP6 3HQ
☎ 01725 518231 📄 01725 518880
Email: info@compassesinn.net
Web: www.compassesinn.net
Dir: *From Fordingbridge (A338) follow signs for Sandleheath/Damerham. Or signs from B3078*
The 425-year-old Compasses is a perfect example of a traditional country free house. The freshly prepared meals may be eaten in the bar, dining room or lovely garden.
Open: 11-3 6-11 (all day Sat, Sun 12-4, 7-10.30) **Bar Meals:** L served all week 12-2.30 D served all week 7-9.30 (Sun 7-9) Av main course £8 **Restaurant Meals:** L served all week 12-2.30 D served all week 7-9.30 (Sun 7-9) Av 3 course alc £17 **Brewery/Company:**

Free House 🍺: Ringwood Best, Hop Back Summer Lightning, Courage Best, Gales Best plus guest ☉: 8 **Children's Facilities:** Licence Menu/Portions Cutlery Highchair Food warming Baby changing **Nearby:** Paultons Park, Moors Valley Country Park, New Forest **Notes:** Dogs allowed by arrangement in bar **Garden:** Large garden by village green **Parking:** 30

EAST MEON
Ye Olde George Inn ☉
Church Street Nr Petersfield GU32 1NH
☎ 01730 823481 📄 01730 823759
Email: yeoldgeorge@aol.com
Dir: *S of A272 (Winchester/Petersfield). 1.5m from Petersfield turn left opposite church*
This 15th-century inn is located in a lovely old village on the River Meon, close to a magnificent Norman church. Its open fires, heavy beams and rustic artefacts create an ideal setting for a good choice of real ales and freshly prepared food in the bar or restaurant. Fish dishes features strongly.
Open: 12-3 6-11 (Sat 11-3) **Bar Meals:** L served all week 12-2 D served all week 7-9 Av main course £9.50 **Restaurant Meals:** L served all week 12-2 D served all week 7-9 Av 3 course alc £16.95 **Brewery/Company:** Hall & Woodhouse 🍺: Badger Best, Tanglefoot & King & Barnes Sussex ☉: 8 **Children's Facilities:** Menu/Portions Games Highchair Food warming **Nearby:** Butser Hill, Quen Elizabeth Country Park, Southsea **Notes:** Dogs allowed in bar **Garden:** Heated patio **Parking:** 30

EVERSLEY
The Golden Pot ☉
Reading Road RG27 0NB
☎ 0118 9732104
Web: www.golden-pot.co.uk
Dir: *Between Reading and Camberley on the B3272 about 0.25m from the Eversley cricket ground*
Dating back to the 1700s, this welcoming pub became the first smoke free pub in North Hampshire early in 2005. A warming fire connects the bar and restaurant, and both offer wide-ranging menus, with baguettes at lunchtime, and a variety of hot bar and restaurant dishes.
Open: 11.30-3 5.30-11 Closed: Dec 25-26, Jan 1 **Bar Meals:** L served all week 12-2.15 D served Mon-Sat 6-9.15 (Sun lunch 12-2) Av main course £9 **Restaurant Meals:** L served Sun-Fri 12-2 D served Mon-Sat 7-9 (Sun Lunch 12-2) Av 3 course alc £24 **Brewery/Company:** Greene King 🍺: Greene King Ruddles Best, Abbot Ale, Greene King IPA ☉: 8 **Children's Facilities:** Menu/Portions Games Highchair Food warming **Nearby:** Wellington Country Park **Notes:** Dogs allowed in bar, in garden **Garden:** Pergola, picnic tables **Parking:** 30

FORDINGBRIDGE
The Augustus John ♟
116 Station Road SP6 1DG
☎ 01425 652098
Email: enquiries@augustusjohn.com
Web: www.augustusjohn.com
The renowned British portrait painter lived in the village and drank here, long before it became known as a smart dining pub. Lunches range from sandwiches and baguettes to salads, by way of jackets and light meals. The carte offers Aberdeen Angus steaks, broccoli and cauliflower bake, rack of Welsh lamb, and fillet of pork tenderloin, with fresh fish and daily specials on the blackboard. There is also a tempting Thai menu.
Open: 11.30-3.30 6-12 **Bar Meals:** L served all week 11.30-2 D served all week 6.30-9 (Sun 7-9)

Restaurant Meals: L served all week 11.30-2 D served all week 6.30-9 **Brewery/Company:** Eldridge Pope
🍺: Flowers IPA, Ringwood Best, John Smiths & Courage Directrors ♟: 8 **Children's Facilities:** Menu/Portions Cutlery Highchair Food warming **Nearby:** New Forest
Notes: Dogs allowed in bar **Parking:** 40

HOOK
Crooked Billet ♟
London Road RG27 9EH
☎ 01256 762118 🖷 01256 761011
Email: richardbarwise@aol.com
Web: www.thecrookedbillethook.co.uk
Dir: *From M3 take Hook Ring Road. At third rdbt turn right on A30 towards London, pub on left 0.5m by river.*
The present pub dates back to 1934, though there has been a hostelry on this site since the 1600s. Food to suit all appetites includes half shoulder of lamb in mint gravy; home-made steak and kidney pie; and a range of ploughman's with hot French bread.
Open: 11.30-3 6-11 **Bar Meals:** L served all week 12-2.30 D served all week 7-9.30 (Sun 12-3, 7-9.30. Fri & Sat 7-10) **Brewery/Company:** Free House 🍺: Scottish

Courage Courage Best & Directors & John Smith's, Hogs Back TEA, Timothy Taylors Landord ♟: 8 **Children's Facilities:** Play area (climbing frame, swings, slide) Menu/Portions Cutlery Games Highchair Food warming **Nearby:** Wellington Country Park, Legoland, Birdworld
Notes: Dogs allowed in bar, in garden, Water **Garden:** Large garden next to Whitewater River **Parking:** 60

HORSEBRIDGE
John O'Gaunt Inn ♟
SO20 6PU
☎ 01794 388394 🖷 01794 388394
Dir: *A3057 Stockbridge to Romsey. Horsebridge is 4m from Stockbridge, turn right at brown info board.*
Walkers from the nearby Test Way, fishermen from the River Test and the winter shooting fraternity all frequent this small country inn, five miles north of Romsey. It provides a great atmosphere for well-kept ales and generously priced food. The specials board showcases fresh local produce, notably pheasant, duck, rabbit and pigeon, while seafood like tuna, salmon, trout, sea bass and scampi are always available.
Open: 11-3 6-11 (Sat-Sun 11-11) Closed: 4-5 Jan **Bar Meals:** L served Tue-Sun 12-2.45 D served Tue-Sat 6-

9.30 Av main course £7.95 **Restaurant Meals:** L served Tue-Sun 12-2.45 D served Tue-Sat 6-9.45 Av 3 course alc £20 **Brewery/Company:** Free House
🍺: Ringwood Best Bitter, Ringwood Fortyniner, Palmers IPA, Carlsberg & Thatchers ♟: 8 **Children's Facilities:** Licence Menu/Portions Games Highchair Food warming **Nearby:** Test Way Walk, Motisfont Gardens, Horsebridge Springs Fly Fishing **Notes:** Dogs allowed in bar Garden: Small area with tables, chairs and umbrellas **Parking:** 12

HAMPSHIRE

ITCHEN ABBAS
The Trout 🍷
Main Road SO21 1BQ
☎ 01962 779537 📠 01962 791046
Email: thetroutinn@aol.com
Web: www.thetrout-inn-itchenabbas.co.uk
Dir: *Exit M3 junct 9, follow A34, bear to right on A33, follow signs to Itchen Abbas, pub is 2m on the left.*
A 19th-century coaching inn in the Itchen Valley close to the river. It is said to have been the location that inspired Charles Kingsley to write The Water Babies. Serves freshly cooked, local produce in the bar and restaurant.
Open: 12-3 6-11 (All day Sat-Sun Mar-Oct) Closed: 26 Dec & 1 Jan **Bar Meals:** L served all week 12-2.15 D served all week 6.30-9 (Sun 12-5) Av main course £11
Restaurant Meals: L served all week 12-2.15 D served Mon-Sat 6.30-9 Av 3 course alc £21 🍺: Greene King IPA, Morland Speckled Hen 🍷: 9 **Children's Facilities:** Licence Play area (Swings & playhouse) Menu/Portions Games Highchair Food warming **Nearby:** Marwell Zoo, South Down Walks, Watercress line **Notes:** Dogs allowed in bar **Garden:** Large garden with lots of seating
Parking: 30

LYMINGTON
Mayflower Inn 🍷
Kings Saltern Road SO41 3QD
☎ 01590 672160 📠 01590 679180
Email: info@themayflower.uk.com
Web: www.themayflower.uk.com
Dir: *A337 towards New Milton, left at rdbt by White Hart, left to Rookes Ln, right at mini-rdbt, pub 0.75m*
A favourite with yachtsmen and dog walkers, this solidly built mock-Tudor inn overlooks the Lymington River, with glorious views to the Isle of Wight. There's a magnificent garden with a purpose-built play area for children and an on-going summer barbecue in fine weather. Light bites and big bowl salads are backed up with heartier choices like vegetable stir-fry; steak and mushroom pudding; and baked salmon with prawns, cheese and leeks.
Open: 11-12 (Sun 12-10.30) **Bar Meals:** L served all week 12-9.30 D served all week 6.30-9.30 Av main course £8.50 **Restaurant Meals:** L served all week 12-9.30 D served all week 6.30-9.30 **Brewery/Company:** Enterprise Inns 🍺: Ringwood Best, Fuller's London Pride, 6X, Goddards Fuggle Dee Dum 🍷: 8 **Children's Facilities:** Play area (garden) Menu/Portions Highchair Food warming Baby changing **Nearby:** New Forest **Notes:** Dogs allowed in bar Water **Garden:** Large lawns, decking area, awnings, heaters **Parking:** 30

LYNDHURST
New Forest Inn 🍷
Emery Down SO43 7DY
☎ 023 8028 2329 📠 8028 3216
Delightfully situated in the scenic New Forest, this rambling inn lies on land claimed from the crown by use of squatters' rights in the early 18th-century. Ale was once sold from a caravan which now forms the front lounge porchway. Lovely summer garden and welcoming bars with open fires and an extensive menu listing local game in season and plenty of fresh fish - whole Dover sole, fresh tuna, monkfish thermidor - alongside traditional pub meals.
Open: 11-11 **Bar Meals:** L served all week 12-3 D served all week 6-9.30 Av main course £9.50
Restaurant Meals: L served all week 11-10 D served all week 6-10 **Brewery/Company:** Enterprise Inns 🍺: Ringwood Best, Fullers London Pride, Abbot Ale, Old Hooky, Ringwood 49, Speckled Hen **Children's Facilities:** Licence Play area Menu/Portions Highchair Food warming **Nearby:** Paultons Park, Beaulieu **Notes:** Dogs allowed in bar, in garden Water **Garden:** Food served outside **Parking:** 20

LYNDHURST
The Trusty Servant

Minstead SO43 7FY

☎ 023 8081 2137

Email: enquiries@trustyservant.co.uk

Web: www.trustyservant.co.uk

Popular New Forest pub overlooking the village green and retaining many Victorian features. The famous sign is taken from a 16th-century Winchester scholar's painting portraying the qualities of an ideal college servant. The menu prides itself on its real food, good value and generous portions. You might sample snacks, Tony's home-made pies, steaks from the grill, venison or tenderloin of pork. There's also a good choice of vegetarian dishes, such as sizzling Thai vegetable stir-fry. **Open:** 11-11 (Sun 12-10.30) **Bar Meals:** L served all week 12-9 D served all week 7-10 **Restaurant Meals:** L served all week 12-2.30 D served all week 7-10 **Brewery/Company:** Enterprise Inns ◼: Ringwood Best, Fuller's London Pride, Wadworth 6X, Timothy Taylor Landlord **Children's Facilities:** Fam room Menu/Portions Highchair Food warming **Nearby:** Paultons Park, Longdown Dairy Farm, Owl & Otter Centre **Notes:** Dogs allowed in bar, in garden, Water **Garden:** Heated barn area seats 30, picnic benches **Parking:** 16

MAPLEDURWELL
The Gamekeepers ♟

Tunworth Road RG25 2LU

☎ 01256 322038 📄 01256 322038

Email: costellophil@hotmail.com

Web: www.thegamekeepers.co.uk

Dir: *Exit M3 junct 6, turn right at The Hatch pub on A30 towards Hook. Gamekeepers is signposted.*

A very rural location for this 19th-century pub, which has a large secluded garden and, unusually, a well inside. All the food on the extensive menu is made on the premises. **Open:** 12-3 5-1 **Bar Meals:** L served all week 12-2.30 D served all week 6.30-9.30 (Sun 12-4) Av main course £8 **Restaurant Meals:** L served all week 12-2.30 D served all week 5.30-9.30 (Sun 12-4) Av 3 course alc £25 **Brewery/Company:** Free House ◼: Badgers First Gold, London Pride, Ringwood Best, Moondance, Alton's Pride, Liberation Ale ♟: 12 **Children's Facilities:** Licence Menu/Portions Cutlery Highchair Food warming **Nearby:** Old Basing House, King Johns Castle & Basingstoke Canal **Notes:** Dogs allowed in bar, in garden, Water **Garden:** Large, secluded garden area **Parking:** 50

MONXTON
The Black Swan ♟

High Street SP11 8AW

☎ 01264 710260 📄 01264 710961

Dir: *Exit A303, at rdbt follow signs for Monxton, pub on main road.*

The Black Swan stands on the Portway, the Roman road that used to link Old Sarum, just north of Salisbury, and Winchester. It dates from 1662, possibly earlier. It offers a menu combining French, English and New World ideas, as well as regular pub grub. Children are welcome in the courtyard and restaurant for lunch and early suppers. **Open:** 12-11 Closed: 25 Dec, 1 Jan **Bar Meals:** L served all week 12-2 D served all week 6-9.30 (Fri-Sat 12-2.30, 6-10 Sun 7-9.30) Av main course £13 **Restaurant Meals:** L served all week 12-2 D served all week 6-9.30 (Fri-Sun 12-2.30, 6-10) **Brewery/Company:** Enterprise Inns ◼: Timothy Taylor Landlords, Ringwood Best Bitter, Summer Lightning, London Pride ♟: 9 **Children's Facilities:** Licence Menu/Portions Highchair Food warming **Nearby:** The Hawk Conservatory **Notes:** Dogs allowed in garden **Parking:** 40

HAMPSHIRE

NORTH WALTHAM
The Fox 🍷
Basingstoke RG25 2BE

☎ 01256 397288 🖹 01256 398564

Email: info@thefox.org

Web: www.thefox.org

Dir: *From M3 junct 7 take A30 towards Winchester. Village signed on R. Take 2nd signed road*

A peaceful village pub situated down a quiet country lane enjoying splendid views across fields and farmland. Built as three farm cottages in 1624, The Fox can offer families three large level gardens, one of which is a children's play area. The menu offers traditional dishes using seasonal produce as it becomes available.

Open: 10-12 **Bar Meals:** L served all week 12-2.30 D served all week 6.30-10 **Restaurant Meals:** L served all week 12.30-2.30 D served all week 6.30-10 **Brewery/Company:** Punch Taverns 🍺: Gales HSB, Spitfire, Brakspear & Ringwood Best Bitter 🍷: 11 **Children's Facilities:** Licence Play area Menu/Portions Games Highchair Food warming **Notes:** Dogs in bar, Water Garden: Large grass areas, countryside views **Parking:** 40

OWSLEBURY
The Ship Inn 🍷
Whites Hill nr Winchester SO21 1LT

☎ 01962 777358 🖹 01962 777458

Email: theshipinn@freeuk.com

Dir: *M3 junct 11 take B3335. Follow Owslebury signs*

Situated on a windswept chalk ridge on the edge of a pretty village, the Ship dates back more than 300 years. A quaint old bar with low beams and ship's timbers add to the appeal. From the pub there are striking views towards the Solent and the South Downs. Daily menus and a good choice of lunchtime meals and snacks.

Open: 11-3 6-11 (Jul-Aug 11-11 all week) **Bar Meals:** L served all week 12-2 D served all week 6.30-9.30 (Sun 12-3) **Restaurant Meals:** L served all week 12-2 D served all week 6.30-9.30 (Sun 12-3, 6.30-9) 🍺: Greene King IPA, Morland Original, Pots & Abbots 🍷: 12 **Children's Facilities:** Play area (Sand pit, swings, play area) Menu/Portions Games Highchair Food warming Baby changing **Nearby:** Marwell Zoo, Intech Science Park, Winchester Cathedral **Notes:** Dogs allowed in bar, in garden, Water Garden: BBQ, pond, horse park **Parking:** 50

PILLEY
The Fleur de Lys 🍷
Pilley Street Lymington SO41 5QG

☎ 01590 672158

Probably the oldest pub in the New Forest, with a list of landlords from 1498, the Fleur de Lys is known to date back to 1096. The traditional thatched inn has been sympathetically refurbished under new ownership, with an open fire and two wood burning stoves. Outside is a large landscaped garden with wooden tables and chairs. Dishes include award-winning local sausages, mille-feuille of roasted peppers, and fillet of salmon wrapped in Parma ham.

Open: 11.30-3 6-11 (Sun 12-3, 7-10.30) **Bar Meals:** L served all week 12-2.15 D served all week 6.30-9.30 (Sun 7-9) Av main course £12 **Restaurant Meals:** L served all week 12-2.15 D served all week 6.30-9.30 (Sun 7-9) Av 3 course alc £24 **Brewery/Company:** Enterprise Inns 🍺: Ringwood Best, plus guest ales 🍷: 6 **Children's Facilities:** Play area (Swings) Menu/Portions Cutlery Highchair Food warming **Nearby:** Beaulieu Motor Museum, Longdown Dairy Farm & Paultons Park **Notes:** Dogs allowed in bar, Water Garden: Lawned area with chairs/tables/parasols **Parking:** 18

ROCKBOURNE
The Rose & Thistle ♟
Fordingbridge SP6 3NL
☎ 01725 518236
Email: enquiries@roseandthistle.co.uk
Web: www.roseandthistle.co.uk
Dir: *Follow Rockbourne signs from B3078 & A354*
This is a picture postcard pub if ever there was one, with
a stunning rose arch, flowers around the door and a
delightful village setting. The 16th-century free house is
well placed for visiting the New Forest, Breamore House,
and Rockbourne's very own Roman villa. Landlord Tim
Norfolk maintains a tradition of serving fine fresh food.
Open: 11-3 6-11 (Oct-Apr Sun close at 8) **Bar Meals:** L
served all week 12-2.30 D served all week 6.30-9.30
(Sun seasonal variation) Av main course £10 **Restaurant**

Meals: L served all week 12-2.30 D served all week
6.30-9.30 Av 3 course alc £18 🍺: Fuller's London
Pride, Adnams Broadside, Hop Back Summer Lightning,
Strongs Best Bitter, Palmers Copper Ale ♟: 18 **Children's**
Facilities: Licence Menu/Portions Cutlery Highchair Food
warming **Nearby:** Monkey World **Notes:** Garden: An
English country garden **Parking:** 28

ROCKFORD
The Alice Lisle ♟
Rockford Green Ringwood BH24 3NA
☎ 01425 474700 📠 01425 483332
Well-known New Forest pub with landscaped gardens
overlooking a lake, popular with walkers and visitors to
the region. It was named after the widow of one of
Cromwell's supporters who gave shelter to two fugitives
from the Battle of Sedgemoor. Choose from a varied
menu which might include salmon and crab cakes,
honey minted lamb shoulder, liver and bacon, and
Mexican enchilada. There's a good range of starters
and children's dishes.
Open: 11-3 5.30-11 (Sun all day) **Bar Meals:** L served
all week 12-2 D served all week 6-9 (Sun 12-8) Av main
course £7.95 **Restaurant Meals:** L served all week 12-

2 D served all week 6-9 (Sun 12-8)
Brewery/Company: George Gale & Co 🍺: HSB,
Ringwood, Winter Brew, 49er ♟: 7 **Children's**
Facilities: Licence Fam room Play area (Climbing
fortress, slides) Menu/Portions Cutlery Games Highchair
Food warming Baby changing **Nearby:** Moors Valley
Country Park, Alice in Wonderland, Paultons Park **Notes:**
Dogs allowed in bar Garden: Large garden with lots of
seating, aviary **Parking:** 150

ROWLAND'S CASTLE
The Fountain Inn ◆◆◆◆
34 The Green PO9 6AB
☎ 023 9241 2291 📠 023 9241 2291
Email: fountaininn@amserve.com
Situated on the village green in pretty Rowlands Castle,
The Fountain is a lovingly refurbished Georgian inn
complete with resident ghost. Food is served in the Italian
restaurant, bistro and wine bar, where dishes include
hand rolled, stone baked pizzas; warm salads;
Mediterranean tapas; and specials such as beef
Wellington.
Open: 5-11 (Fri-Sun 12pm-11pm) **Restaurant Meals:** L
served Fri-Sun 12 D served Mon-Sat 6.30-10
Brewery/Company: Free House 🍺: Ruddles IPA, Abbot,
Ruddles Cask **Children's Facilities:** Play area (Slides

swings & climbing frame) Menu/Portions Highchair Food
warming **Nearby:** Staunton Park, Hayling Island,
Stansted House **Notes:** Dogs allowed in bar, in garden,
in bedrooms Garden: Enclosed back garden, eight tables
Parking: 20

HAMPSHIRE

HAMPSHIRE

SELBORNE
The Selborne Arms ♔
High Street GU34 3JR

☎ 01420 511247 🖹 01420 511754

Web: www.selbornearms.co.uk

Dir: *From A3 follow B3006, pub is on the left in centre of village of Selborne*

A traditional village pub, 17th-century in origin, known for its friendly atmosphere and good food; the latter sourced extensively from Hampshire growers and suppliers, and all GM-free. There are plenty of light lunch and dinner choices with blackboards listing specials and desserts.
Open: 11-3 6-11 (Sun all day, Fri 5.30-11) **Bar Meals:** L served all week 12-2 D served all week 7-9
Restaurant Meals: L served Wed-Sun 12-2 D served Wed-Sat 7-9 Av 3 course alc £18 🍺: Courage Best,
Ringwood 49er, Cheriton Pots, local guest ales ♔: 10
Children's Facilities: Play area (Climbing equipment/playhouse, swing & slide) Menu/Portions Games Food warming **Nearby:** Birdworld, Watercress Line Steam Railway & Lavender & Sunflower Farm
Notes: Dogs allowed in garden, Water bowls Garden: Lawn, patio, wishing well, BBQ **Parking:** 7

SPARSHOLT
The Plough Inn ♔
Main Road Nr Winchester SO21 2NW

☎ 01962 776353 🖹 01962 776400

Dir: *From Winchester take B3049 (A272) W, left to Sparsholt, Inn 1m.*

The Plough, in the same village as the well-known agricultural college, is close enough to Winchester to draw many of its well-heeled citizens out for a meal or just a drink. From the outside, you can see that it has been much extended but, once inside, the main bar and dining areas blend together very harmoniously. Booking is definitely advised for any meal.
Open: 11-3 6-11 (Sun 12-3, 6-10.30) Closed: 25 Dec
Bar Meals: L served all week 12-2 D served all week 6-9 Av main course £12 **Restaurant Meals:** L served all week 12-2 D served all week 6-9 **Brewery/Company:** Wadworth 🍺: Wadworth Henry's IPA, 6X, Old Timer & JCB ♔: 14 **Children's Facilities:** Fam room Play area (Play fort, donkey paddock) Highchair Food warming
Nearby: Marwell Zoo & Romsey Rapids **Notes:** Dogs allowed in bar, Dogs on leads Garden: Patio, lawn, and play area **Parking:** 90

ST MARY BOURNE
The Bourne Valley Inn ♔
nr Andover SP11 6BT

☎ 01264 738361 🖹 01264 738126

Email: bournevalleyinn@btinternet.com

Located in the charming Bourne Valley, this popular traditional inn is the ideal setting for conferences, exhibitions, weddings and other notable occasions. The riverside garden abounds with wildlife, and children can happily let off steam in the special play area. Typical menu includes deep fried Brie or a cocktail of prawns, followed by rack of lamb with a redcurrant and port sauce, salmon and prawn tagliatelle, steak and mushroom pie, crispy haddock and chips and warm duck salad.
Open: 11-11 (Sun 12-10.30) **Bar Meals:** L served all week 12-2 D served all week 7-9 **Restaurant Meals:** L served all week 12-2 D served all week 7-9
Brewery/Company: Free House 🍺: Guest ales ♔: 8
Children's Facilities: Licence Play area (Outdoor play, climbing area) Menu/Portions Cutlery Highchair Food warming **Notes:** Dogs allowed in bar, Water & biscuits provided Garden: Riverside, secluded **Parking:** 50

STRATFIELD TURGIS
The Wellington Arms ★★★ HL ♟

Hook RG27 0AS

☎ 01256 882214 🖹 01256 882934

Email: wellington.arms@virgin.net

Web: www.innforanight.co.uk

Dir: *On A33 between Basingstoke & Reading*

Looking at this Grade II listed hotel today, it is hard to believe it was originally a farmhouse. The Wellington Arms is an ideal base for visiting the nearby Stratfield Saye estate, formerly the home of the Duke of Wellington. Well-kept real ales complement a good selection of eating options, including liver and bacon served with bubble and squeak; steak and kidney pudding; fanned avocado, cherry, tomato and bacon salad; and smoked salmon and prawn platter.

Open: 11-11 (Sun 12-10.30) **Bar Meals:** L served all week 12-10 D served all week 12-10 (Sun 9.30) **Restaurant Meals:** L served Sun-Fri 12-2 D served Mon-Sat 6.30-9.30 Av 3 course alc £24 **Brewery/Company:** Hall And Woodhouse Retail ⌑: Badger Best Bitter & Tanglefoot ♟: 12 **Children's Facilities:** Menu/Portions Games Highchair Food warming Baby changing **Nearby:** Wellington Country Park, Legoland, Aldershot Military Museum **Notes:** Dogs allowed in garden, in bedrooms **Garden:** Patio area with grass area to side and rear **Parking:** 60

UPPER FROYLE
The Hen & Chicken Inn ♟

Nr Alton GU34 4JH

☎ 01420 22115 🖹 01420 23021

Email: bookings@henandchicken.co.uk

Web: www.henandchicken.co.uk

Dir: *2m from Alton, on A31 next to petrol station*

A 16th-century inn, once the haunt of highwaymen and retaining a traditional atmosphere enhanced by large open fires, panelling and beams. Close by is the delightful old Georgian town of Farnham, famous for its castle, Maltings arts complex and various listed buildings. The tempting menu has everything from fillet of halibut, char-grilled rib eye steak, and rich venison casserole, to Cumberland sausages, and penne pasta. Specials might include risotto of Cornish crab and grilled marlin loin.

Open: 11-3 5.30-11 (Sun 12-10.30, Fri-Sat 11-11) **Bar Meals:** L served all week 12-2.30 D served all week 6-9 (Sun 12-9) Av main course £7.50 **Restaurant Meals:** L served all week 12-2.30 D served all week 6-9 (Sun 12-9) Av 3 course alc £22 **Brewery/Company:** Hall & Woodhouse ⌑: Badger Best, Tanglefoot, King & Barnes Sussex Ale ♟: 8 **Children's Facilities:** Play area (assault course) Menu/Portions Cutlery Highchair Food warming **Nearby:** Watercress Line, Birdworld, Marwell **Notes:** Dogs allowed in bar **Garden:** large, food served outside **Parking:** 36

WARSASH
The Jolly Farmer Country Inn ♟

29 Fleet End Road Southampton SO31 9JH

☎ 01489 572500 🖹 01489 885847

Email: mail@thejollyfarmeruk.com

Dir: *Exit M27 junct 9, towards A27 Fareham, right onto Warsash Rd. Follow for 2m then left onto Fleet End Rd*

Multi-coloured classic cars are lined up outside this friendly pub close to the Hamble river, and it boasts its own golf society and cricket team. The bars are furnished in a rustic style with farming equipment on the walls and ceilings. There's also a patio and a purpose-built children's play area. Grills, including 8oz gammon steaks, and house specialities such as shank of lamb, chicken Stroganoff, and fresh fillet of plaice characterise the wide-ranging menu.

Open: 11-11 **Bar Meals:** L served all week 12-2.30 D served all week 6-10 **Restaurant Meals:** L served all week 12-2.30 D served all week 6-10 **Brewery/Company:** Whitbread ⌑: Gale's HSB, Fuller's London Pride, Interbrew Flowers IPA **Children's Facilities:** Fam room Play area (Swings, See-saw, Wendy house, castle) Menu/Portions Cutlery Games Highchair Food warming **Notes:** Dogs allowed in bar, Water **Garden:** Large play area **Parking:** 50

HAMPSHIRE

HAMPSHIRE / HERTFORDSHIRE

WHITCHURCH
Watership Down Inn ♟
Freefolk Priors RG28 7NJ
☎ 01256 892254
Email: mark@watershipdowninn.co.uk
Web: www.watershipdowninn.co.uk
Dir: *On B3400 between Basingstoke & Andover*
Enjoy an exhilarating walk on Watership Down before relaxing with a pint of well-kept local ale at this homely 19th-century inn named after Richard Adams' classic tale of rabbit life. The menu choices range from sandwiches, jacket potatoes, salads and ploughman's through to liver and bacon casserole, sausage and mash, mushroom Stroganoff, Somerset chicken, and braised lamb shank in a red wine gravy. Just don't expect any rabbit dishes!
Open: 11.30-3.30 6-11 **Bar Meals:** L served all week

12-2.30 D served all week 6-9.30 (Sun 12-2.30 & 7-8.30) **Brewery/Company:** Free House 🍺: Oakleaf Bitter, Butts Barbus Barbus, Triple FFF Pressed Rat & Warthog, Hogs Back TEA, Stonehenge Danish Dynamite ♟: 8 **Children's Facilities:** Play area (Fully enclosed) Menu/Portions Highchair Food warming **Notes:** Garden: Beer garden, patio, heaters **Parking:** 18

WHITSBURY
The Cartwheel Inn ♟
Whitsbury Road Nr Fordingbridge SP6 3PZ
☎ 01725 518362
Dir: *From Ringwood follow A338 to Salisbury. After 8m turn off at Fordingbridge North and Whitsbury. Turn into 4th road on right (Alexandria Road), continue to end and turn right, Inn is 3m*
Handy for exploring the New Forest, visiting Breamore House and discovering the remote Mizmaze on the nearby downs, this extended, turn-of-the-century one-time wheelwright's and shop has been a pub since the 1920s. Venue for a beer festival held annually in August, with spit-roast pigs, barbecues, Morris dancing and a range of 30 real ales. Popular choice of well kept beers in the bar too. Home-made food on daily specials boards - steak

and kidney pudding, fisherman's pie and chicken curry. Like their postcard says: "Off the beaten track, but never in a rut!"
Open: 11.30-3 6-11 (All day Sat, Sun 12-10.30) **Bar Meals:** L served all week 12-2 D served all week 6-9 (Sun 12-2.30) Av main course £6 **Brewery/Company:** Ringwood 🍺: Ringwood 49er, Old Thumper, Ringwood Best, Ringwood Seasonal, guest ales ♟: 20 **Children's Facilities:** Play area (Large garden with play equipment) Menu/Portions Games Baby changing **Nearby:** New Forest, Bremore House, Rockbourne Roman Villa **Notes:** Dogs allowed in bar, Water, Biscuits **Garden:** Lawn, rockery borders **Parking:** 25

ALDBURY
The Greyhound Inn ♟
19 Stocks Road nr Tring HP23 5RT
☎ 01442 851228 📠 01442 851495
Email: tim@valianttrooper203.freeserve.co.uk
Web: www.greyhoundaldbury.co.uk
Nestling beneath the Chiltern Hills and close to the National Trust's renowned Ashridge Estate, the Greyhound is understandably a favourite with walkers. Log fires warm the bar in winter, whilst summer brings the option of an alfresco lunch overlooking the village pond. Bar snacks like rustic ploughman's with Cropwell Bishop stilton are a local legend, and hot menu choices include butternut squash, red onion and sage risotto; and rump of lamb with bacon and garlic potatoes.
Open: 11-11 Closed: 25 Dec **Bar Meals:** L served all

week 12-2.30 D served Mon-Sat 6.30-9.30 **Restaurant Meals:** L served all week 12-2.30 D served Mon-Sat 7-10 **Brewery/Company:** Hall & Woodhouse 🍺: Badger Best, Tanglefoot, King & Barnes & Sussex ♟: 10 **Children's Facilities:** Fam room Menu/Portions Highchair Food warming **Nearby:** Tring Museum, Grand Union Canal, Ashridge Forest & Whipsnade Zoo **Notes:** Dogs allowed in bar, Water **Garden:** Courtyard, Food served outside **Parking:** 9

ALDBURY
The Valiant Trooper ♀
Trooper Road nr Tring HP23 5RW
☎ 01442 851203 📠 01442 851071
Dir: *A41 at Tring junct, follow railway station signs, 0.5m and at village green turn right then 200yds on left*
Family-run free house in a pretty village whose ancient stocks and duckpond often feature in films. The deeds date back to 1752, when it was The Royal Oak; it became The Trooper Alehouse in 1803, allegedly because the Duke of Wellington once discussed tactics here with his troops. In the 1880s a landlord would remove his wooden leg and bang it on the counter - maybe his way of calling 'Time!' The old stable block, which has also served as scout hut and local bikers' club, is now a comfortable 40-seater restaurant offering daily black-board specials. Hikers and cyclists descend from the surrounding Chiltern Hills for a pint of Tring Brewery's Jack O' Legs, or regularly changing guest beers. Dogs are welcome too.
Open: 11.30-11 (Sun 12-10.30) **Bar Meals:** L served all week 12-2 D served Tue-Sat 6.30-9.15 (Sun 12-2.30) **Restaurant Meals:** L served all week 12-2 D served Tue-Sun 6.30-9.15 (Sun 12-2.30)
Brewery/Company: Free House 🍺: Fuller's London Pride, Oakham J.H.B, Tring Jack O'Legs & 2 Guest Beers ♀: 8 **Children's Facilities:** Fam room Play area (Wendy house) Menu/Portions Cutlery Highchair Food warming
Nearby: Ashridge Monument, Woodland & Recreation Ground **Notes:** Dogs allowed in bar, Water bowls Garden: Large grassed area with picnic tables & patio **Parking:** 36

ARDELEY
The Jolly Waggoner
nr Stevenage SG2 7AH
☎ 01438 861350
Cream-washed 500-year-old pub with exposed beams, roaring fires, antique furniture and a popular cottage garden. The inn also benefits from a lovely village setting and a variety of local walks. All the food is homemade from fresh ingredients, ranging from appetising sandwiches to à la carte dining. Fish is something of a speciality, like dressed crab salad, swordfish or sea bass. Alternatively, try loin of lamb, calves' liver or steak and kidney pie.
Open: 12-3 6-11 **Bar Meals:** L served all week 12-2 D served all week 6.30-9. (Sun 12-3) Av main course £12
Restaurant Meals: L served all week 12.30-2 D served all week 6.30-9 **Brewery/Company:** Greene King 🍺: Greene King IPA & Abbot Ale **Children's Facilities:** Menu/Portions Games Highchair Food warming **Notes:** Garden: Pretty cottage garden, wooden fruniture **Parking:** 15

ASHWELL
The Three Tuns ♀
High Street SG7 5NL
☎ 01462 742107 📠 01462 743662
Email: claire@tuns.co.uk
Web: www.tuns.co.uk
Many original features survive at this 19th-century inn, helping to create an old-world atmosphere in the heart of Ashwell village. The freshly prepared menu changes daily, and includes best end of roast rack of lamb; fillet of pork Normandy with a creamy Calvados and apple sauce; Provençal pinto bean stew; and seafood kebabs with a spicy chilli dip and savoury rice. To follow, try home-made profiteroles with butterscotch sauce, or frangipane tart with redcurrant glaze.
Open: 11-11.30 (Fri-Sat 11-midnight, Sun 12-10.30)
Bar Meals: L served all week 12-2.30 D served all week 6.30-9.30 **Restaurant Meals:** L served all week 12-2.30 D served all week 6.30-9.30
Brewery/Company: Greene King 🍺: Greene King IPA, Ruddles, Abbot ♀: 7 **Children's Facilities:** Fam room Play area Menu/Portions Games Highchair Food warming
Notes: Dogs allowed in bar, in garden Garden: Large, terrace at top, seats around 100 **Parking:** 20

HERTFORDSHIRE

HERTFORDSHIRE

BARLEY
The Fox & Hounds
High Street SG8 8HU
☎ 01763 848459 📠 01763 849274
Email: jamesburn1972@aol.com
Dir: *A505 onto B1368 at Flint Cross, pub 4m*
Set in a pretty village, this former 17th-century hunting lodge is notable for its pub sign which extends across the lane. It has real fires, a warm welcome and an attractive garden. The new owners have already made their mark with their home-cooked food, offering a menu with a good range of dependable choices, including sirloin steak with chips and onion rings; barbecued ribs; chilli and lasagne.
Open: 12-11 (Sun 12-10.30, Winter Mon-Fri 12-3, all day Sat & Sun) **Bar Meals:** L served all week 12-10 D served all week 12-10 (Sun 12-9) Av main course £8 **Restaurant Meals:** L served 12-10 D served 12-10 Av 3 course alc £13.95 **Brewery/Company:** Punch Taverns 🍺: IPA, 6X, Adnams Best, Old Speckled Hen & Guest Beers **Children's Facilities:** Play area Menu/Portions Games Food warming **Notes:** Dogs allowed in bar Garden: L-shaped garden with tables and chairs **Parking:** 35

BUNTINGFORD
The Sword Inn Hand ★★★★ INN ♇
Westmill SG9 9LQ
☎ 01763 271356
Email: theswordinnhand@btconnect.com
Web: www.theswordinnhand.co.uk
Dir: *Off A10 1.5m S of Buntingford*
This delightful 14th-century free house is set in a peaceful village amid rolling Hertfordshire countryside. A wealth of oak beams, flagstone floors and an open fire-place welcomes visitors to the bar, with its excellent local ales and guest beers. The menu includes sandwiches, baguettes and omelettes, as well as hot dishes like lamb's liver with bubble and squeak; spinach and red pepper lasagne; and breaded scampi with chips and mixed salad.
Open: 12-3 5-11 (All day Fri-Sun) **Bar Meals:** L served Mon-Sun 12-2.30 D served Mon-Sun 6.30-9.30 (Sun winter 12-5 summer 12-7) Av main course £8 **Restaurant Meals:** L served Mon-Sun 12-2.30 D served Mon-Sun 6.30-9.30 (Sun 12-5) Av 3 course alc £22 **Brewery/Company:** Free House 🍺: Greene King IPA, Young's Bitter, Shephard Neame Spitfire & Guest Ales **Children's Facilities:** Play area (Football Goal & Trampoline) Menu/Portions Highchair Food warming **Nearby:** Broxbourne Wildlife Park, Willers Mill Farm **Notes:** Dogs allowed in bar, in garden Garden: Large, beautiful view, patio area, pergola **Parking:** 25

HEXTON
The Raven ♇
Hitchin SG5 3JB
☎ 01582 881209 📠 01582 881610
Email: jack@ravenathexton.f9.co.uk
Web: www.theraven.co.uk
Dir: *5m W of Hitchin. 5m N of Luton, just outside Barton le Clay.*
Named after Ravensburgh Castle in the neighbouring hills, this 1920s pub has comfortable bars and a large garden. Snacks include ploughman's and salad platters; tortilla wraps, filled baguettes and jacket potatoes. The varied main menu includes lots of steak options.
Open: 11-3 6-11 (Sun 12-10.30, Sat 11-11) **Bar Meals:** L served all week 12-2 D served all week 6-10 (Sat-Sun 12-9) **Restaurant Meals:** L served all week 12-2 D served all week 6-10 Av 3 course alc £15 **Brewery/Company:** Enterprise Inns 🍺: Greene King Old Speckled Hen, Fullers London Pride, Greene King IPA ♇: 24 **Children's Facilities:** Play area (Swings) Cutlery Games Highchair Food warming Baby changing **Nearby:** Woburn, Whipsnade **Notes:** Garden: Benches & tables, seats 50 **Parking:** 40

HUNSDON
The Fox and Hounds ♈
2 High Street SG12 8NH

☎ 01279 843999 📄 01279 841092

Email: info@foxandhounds-hunsdon.co.uk

Web: www.foxandhounds-hunsdon.co.uk

Dir: *From A414 between Ware & Harlow take B180 in Stanstead Abbotts N to Hundson.*

Tucked away in sleepy Hunsdon in the heart of the Hertfordshire countryside, this pub has a friendly, informal atmosphere. Meals are served in the bar, the lounge and the large, homely dining room. Expect serious, inspired cooking that combines classics with modern touches.

Open: 12-4 6-11 Closed: 2 weeks in Jan/Feb **Bar Meals:** L served Tue-Sat 12-3 D served Tue-Sat 6-10.30 (Sun 12-4) Av main course £12 **Restaurant Meals:** L served Sun 12-3 D served Thu-Sat 7-10 Av 3 course alc £30 🍺: Adnams Bitter, Adnams Broadside, Budvar, Guinness, De-Koninck ♈: 7 **Children's Facilities:** Licence Play area (Swings & rocking horse) Menu/Portions Games Highchair Food warming Baby changing **Notes:** Dogs allowed in bar **Garden:** Large, attractive quiet garden and patio area **Parking:** 40

OLD KNEBWORTH
The Lytton Arms ♈
Park Lane SG3 6QB

☎ 01438 812312 📄 01438 817298

Email: thelyttonarms@btinternet.com

Web: www.the-lytton-arms.co.uk

Dir: *From A1(M) take A602. At Knebworth turn right at rail station. Follow Codicote signs. Pub 1.5m on right*

The pub was designed around 1877 by Lord Lytton's brother-in-law, the architect Sir Edwin Lutyens. The pub offers a simple, wide-ranging menu.

Open: 11-11 (Sun 12-10.30) **Bar Meals:** L served Mon-Sun 12-2.30 D served Mon-Sat 6.30-9.30 (Sun 12-5) Av main course £8 **Restaurant Meals:** L served Mon-Sun 12-2.30 D served Mon-Sat 6.30-9.30 (Sun 12-5) Av 3 course alc £17.50 **Brewery/Company:** Free House 🍺: Fuller's London Pride, Adnams Best Bitter, Broadside, Wherry, Deuchars IPA ♈: 30 **Children's Facilities:** Licence Menu/Portions Highchair Food warming Baby changing **Nearby:** Knebworth Park, Hatfield House, Stevenage Leisure Centre **Notes:** Dogs allowed, Water **Garden:** Large umbrella protected decking and heating **Parking:** 40

ROYSTON
The Cabinet Free House and Restaurant ◉♈
High Street Reed SG8 8AH

☎ 01763 848366 📄 01763 849407

Email: thecabinet@btopenworld.com

Web: www.thecabinetinn.co.uk

Dir: *2m N of Royston just off the A10*

The Cabinet, meaning small room or meeting place, is a 16th-century country inn and restaurant located in the little village of Reed just off the A10 London to Cambridge road. Food is prepared from the best local produce but draws inspiration from around the world to offer an interesting variety of dishes including traditional favourites. There is a good menu choice.

Open: 12-3 6-11 (Open all day Sat-Sun (summer)) Closed: 25-26 Dec **Bar Meals:** L served Tue-Sun 12-2.30 D served Tue-Sat 6-10 (Sun 12-3.30) **Restaurant Meals:** L served Tue-Sun 12-2.30 D served Tue-Sat 6-10 Av 3 course alc £28 🍺: London Pride, Greene King IPA ♈: 50 **Children's Facilities:** Fam room Menu/Portions Cutlery Highchair Food warming **Notes:** Dogs allowed in bar, in garden **Garden:** 1 acre **Parking:** 40

HERTFORDSHIRE

WALKERN

The White Lion ♈

31 The High Street nr Stevenage SG2 7PA

☎ 01438 861251

Email: tydies@aol.com

Web: www.whitelionwalkern.com

Dir: B1037 from Stevenage

In rolling chalk downland, Walkern manages to keep a respectable distance from nearby Stevenage, Britain's first 'new town'. The bar in this 16th-century pub has oak beams, an inglenook, leather sofas, newspapers and a PC for those who still need to surf the net over a pint of Greene King or cup of hot chocolate. The informal restaurant offers a traditional pub menu, with ham, egg and chips, fillet of beef Stroganoff, and succulent steaks.

Open: 12-2.30 4.30-11.30 (Fri 12-2, 4.30-12, Sat 12-12, Sun 12-10.30) **Bar Meals:** L served all week 12-2.30 D served Tue-Sat 6-9.30 (Sun 12-5) Av main course £4.95 **Restaurant Meals:** L served all week 12-2.30 D served Tue-Sat 6-9.30 (Sun 12-5) Av 3 course alc £17 **Brewery/Company:** Greene King 🍺: Greene King IPA & Abbot Ale, Guinness, Stella Artois & Fosters ♈: 8 **Children's Facilities:** Play area (Climbing frame, slide) Menu/Portions Games Highchair Food warming Baby changing **Nearby:** Paradise Park, Knebworth House & Benington Lordship **Notes:** Dogs allowed in bar **Garden:** Large mature garden and patio **Parking:** 30

GOREY

Castle Green Gastropub ♈

La Route de la Cote St Martin JE3 6DR

☎ 01534 853103 📠 01534 853103

Email: castlegreenpub@hotmail.com

A superbly located pub overlooking Gorey harbour and, in turn, overlooked by dramatic Mont Orgueil Castle. The views from the wooden sun terrace are breathtaking. An imaginative menu offers pan-Pacific-style dishes like Moroccan spiced lamb shoulder; Thai chicken burger; sushi and sashimi plate with pickled ginger and wasabi; along with fresh fillets of the day's catch, and summer seafood platter.

Open: 11-11 (Open 7 days Jun-Sep) Closed: 2 weeks early Jan **Bar Meals:** L served all week 12-2.30 D served all week 6-9 (Winter no lunch Mon, no dinner Sun-Mon) Av main course £7.95 **Restaurant Meals:** L served all week 12-2.30 D served all week 6-9 Av 3 course alc £16 🍺: Stella, Directors, Fosters, John Smith Extra Smooth, Theakstons ♈: 8 **Children's Facilities:** Menu/Portions Games Highchair Food warming **Nearby:** Mont Orange Castle, Jersey Pottery, **Notes:** Garden: Wooden terrace **Parking:** 10

ST BRELADE

La Pulente Hotel ♈

La Route de la Pulente JE3 8HG

☎ 01534 744487 📠 01534 498846

Dir: West side of the Island, 5m from St Helier

Amazing sea views, open fires on cold winter days and an inviting atmosphere are promised at this welcoming pub. The artistic bar and the rustic restaurant are complemented in summer by a balcony and terrace, where freshly-caught fish can be enjoyed along with choices from the specials menu. Thai vegetable curry, pan-fried chicken supreme, home-made steak and ale pie, lobster and prawn salad, and braised lamb shank are typical.

Open: 11-11 **Bar Meals:** L served all week 12-2.15 D served Mon-Sat 6-9 (Sun 12-2.45) Av main course £7.50 **Restaurant Meals:** L served all week 12-2.15 D served Mon-Sat 6-9 (Sun 12-2.45) Av 3 course alc £15 **Brewery/Company:** Randalls Brewery 🍺: Bass Bitter, Theakstons Best, Breda ♈: 11 **Children's Facilities:** Menu/Portions Highchair Food warming **Nearby:** Beach, Bowling, Mini-golf **Parking:** 30

ST MARTIN
Royal Hotel ♟
La Grande Route de Faldouet JE3 6UG
☎ 01534 856289 📠 01534 857298
Email: johnbarker@jerseymail.co.uk
Dir: *2m from Five Oaks rdbt, towards St Martin. Pub on right next to St Martin's Church*

A friendly atmosphere, value for money, and great food and drink are the hallmarks of this friendly local in the heart of St Martin. Roaring log fires welcome winter visitors, and there's a sunny beer garden to relax in during the summer months. Among the traditional home-made favourites are steak and ale pie, fresh grilled trout, monkfish and prawn Thai curry, and vegetarian lasagne. Ploughman's lunches, filled jacket potatoes, grills and children's choices are also on offer.

Open: 9.30-11.30 (Sun 11-11.30) **Bar Meals:** L served all week 12-2.15 D served Mon-Sat 6-8.30 (Sun 12-2.30 Winter, 6-8.30 Summer) Av main course £7 **Restaurant Meals:** L served all week 12-2.15 D served Mon-Sat 6-8.30 🍺: Fosters, John Smiths Smooth, Theakstons cool, Guinness, Ringwood Real Ale ♟: 9 **Children's Facilities:** Play area (Swings, slide) Menu/Portions Games Highchair Food warming Baby changing **Nearby:** Jersey Zoo & Beach **Notes:** Garden: Beer garden, large patio **Parking:** 80

BRABOURNE
The Five Bells ♟
The Street Ashford TN25 5LP
☎ 01303 813334 📠 01303 814667
Email: fivebells@aol.com
Web: www.thefivebellspub.co.uk
Dir: *5m E of Ashford*

A 16th-century free house pub surrounded by rolling hills and orchards and the perfect pit stop for walkers and cyclists. Originally a poor house, the old stocks are located across the road. There is an extensive menu and a range of popular daily specials.

Open: 11.30-3 6.30-11 **Bar Meals:** L served all week 12-2 D served all week 6.30-9.30 Av main course £8 **Restaurant Meals:** L served all week 12-2 D served all week 6.30-9.30 (Sun 12-2.30, 6.30-9.30)

Brewery/Company: Free House 🍺: Shepherd Neame Master Brew, London Pride, Greene King IPA, Adnams ♟: 12 **Children's Facilities:** Play area (Slide, see-saw, swing,) Menu/Portions Cutlery Games Highchair Food warming Baby changing **Notes:** Dogs allowed in bar, in garden, Water Garden: Lawn, seating for 80 persons **Parking:** 65

BROOKLAND
Woolpack Inn
Romney Marsh TN29 9TJ
☎ 01797 344321

A remote 15th-century inn noted for its strong links with smuggling and surrounded by dykes and reed beds. The place oozes charm and character with open beams and an inglenook fireplace adding to the atmosphere. An old spinning wheel, used to divide up the smuggling contraband, can still be seen mounted from the ceiling. Wholesome home-made pub food includes mixed grill; battered cod with chips and peas; vegetable curry; and chicken Kiev.

Open: 11-3 6-11 (Sat 11-11, Sun 12-10.30) **Bar Meals:** L served all week 12-2 D served all week 6-9 (Sat-Sun 12-9) Av main course £7

Brewery/Company: Shepherd Neame 🍺: Shepherd Neame Spitfire Premium Ale, Master Brew Bitter **Children's Facilities:** Fam room Play area (Play area, animals) Menu/Portions Highchair Food warming Baby changing **Nearby:** Camber Sands, Lydd Raceway, Wind Surfing, fishing **Notes:** Dogs allowed in bar, Water Garden: Large secluded beer garden with 18 tables **Parking:** 80

JERSEY / KENT

KENT

CANTERBURY
The Chapter Arms ♥
New Town Street Chartham Hatch CT4 7LT
☎ 01227 738340 🖹 01227 732536
Web: chapterarms.com
Dir: *3m from Canterbury. Off A28 in Chartham Hatch*
A flower-bedecked free house on the Pilgrims' Way with a garden featuring fish ponds and fruit trees. The property was once three cottages owned by Canterbury Cathedral's Dean and Chapter - hence the name. Daily menus rely on plenty of excellent fresh fish. Other choices might be slow roast shoulder of local pork with apple sauce, pan fried beef fillet strips on rosti with rose peppercorn sauce, or roast pepper, aubergine and cherry tomato tart, topped with goats' cheese. Lighter snacks, such as filled baps, are also available.

Open: 11-3 6.30-11 (Sun 12-10.30) Closed: 25 Dec (eve) **Bar Meals:** L served all week 12-2 D served all week 6.30-8.30 (Sun 12-2.30, 6.30-8.30) Av main course £8 **Restaurant Meals:** L served all week 12-2 D served all week 7-9 (Sun 6.30-8.30) Av 3 course alc £22.50 **Brewery/Company:** Free House 🍺: Shepherd Neame Master Brew, guest ales ♥: 8 **Children's Facilities:** Play area Menu/Portions Highchair Food warming **Notes:** Dogs allowed in bar, in garden, Water Garden: 1 acre of lawn, fish ponds & flower beds **Parking:** 40

CANTERBURY
The Old Coach House ♥
A2 Barnham Downs CT4 6SA
☎ 01227 831218 🖹 01227 831932
Web: www.oldcoachhousecanterbury.com
Dir: *7m S of Canterbury on A2. Turn at Jet petrol station.*
A former stop on the original London to Dover coaching route, and listed in the 1740 timetable, this inn stands some 300 metres from the Roman Way. Noteworthy gardens with home-grown herbs and vegetables, week-end spit-roasts, and unabashed continental cuisine mark it as an auberge in the finest Gallic tradition. Food options include seafood, venison and other game in season, plus perhaps rib of beef with rosemary, pot au feux, and grilled lobster with brandy sauce.
Open: 4-11 **Bar Meals:** D served all week 6.30-9

Restaurant Meals: D served all week 6.30-9
Brewery/Company: Free House 🍺: Interbrew Whitbread Best Bitter **Children's Facilities:** Menu/Portions Cutlery Highchair Food warming Baby changing **Parking:** 60

CANTERBURY
The White Horse Inn ⊚♥
53 High Street Bridge CT4 5LA
☎ 01227 832814 🖹 01227 832814
Web: www.whitehorsebridge.co.uk
Dir: *3m S of Canterbury, just off A2. 15m N of Dover*
This medieval and Tudor building was originally a staging post close to a ford on the main Dover to Canterbury road, and still provides a stirling service to modern travellers. An enormous log fire burning in the beamed bar during the winter months provides a guaranteed warm welcome, whilst the extensive garden is popular for al fresco dining on warmer days. Fullers and Shepherd Neame are amongst the real ales served in the bar, with up to ten wines available by the glass. You'll find a strong emphasis on food, with seasonal dishes created from the best local ingredients. Choose between the relaxed blackboard bar menu, and more formal dining in the restaurant.
Open: 11-3 6-11 (Sun 12-5) Closed: 25 Dec, 1 Jan **Bar Meals:** L served all week 12-2 D served all week 6.30-9 **Restaurant Meals:** L served Tue-Sun 12-2 D served Tue-Sat 7-9 🍺: Shepherd Neame Masterbrew, Greene King Abbot Ale, Fullers London Pride, Greene King IPA, Gadds No. 5 ♥: 10 **Children's Facilities:** Menu/Portions Games Highchair Food warming Baby changing **Notes:** Garden: Large grass area, mature trees, benches **Parking:** 20

CHIDDINGSTONE
Castle Inn ♟

TN8 7AH

☎ 01892 870247 📠 01892 871420
Email: info@castleinn.co.uk
Web: www.castleinn.co.uk
Dir: *1.5m S of B2027 between Tonbridge & Edenbridge.*
Movie location finders know the Castle well. Films it has
featured in include *Elizabeth R*, *Room with a View*, *The
Life of Hogarth* and *The Wicked Lady*. In the saloon bar
the menu meets informal dining needs, or there is the
more extensive restaurant menu. Behind the inn is a
vine-hung courtyard garden with its own bar.
Open: 11-11 **Bar Meals:** L/D served all week 11-9.30
(Sun 12-6) **Restaurant Meals:** L served Wed-Mon 12-2
D served Wed-Mon 7.30-9.30 **Brewery/Company:** Free

House 🍺: Larkins Traditional, Harveys Sussex, Young's
Ordinary, Larkins Porter 🍷: 10 **Children's Facilities:**
Licence Menu/Portions Cutlery Games Highchair Food
warming Baby changing **Nearby:** Hever Castle,
Penshurst Place, Knole Park **Notes:** Dogs allowed in
bar, in garden, Water and chews **Garden:** Patio, lawn,
sheltered, bar

CHISLET
The Gate Inn ♟

North Stream Canterbury CT3 4EB

☎ 01227 860498
Dir: *From Canterbury on A28 turn left at Upstreet*
This rural retreat is surrounded by marshland and
pasture, with a beautiful garden overlooking a stream
populated by ducks and geese. It might be a challenge
to decide on what to eat in the family-friendly
interconnecting bars, since the huge menu offers a wide
range of snacks and sustaining meals. There are 17
sandwich fillings; 9 different 'ploughpersons'; jacket
potatoes with 16 different fillings; and 'Gateburgers'
filled with various delights.
Open: 11-2.30 6-11 (Sun 12-4, 7-10.30) **Bar Meals:** L
served all week 12-2 D served all week 6-9

Brewery/Company: Shepherd Neame 🍺: Shepherd
Neame Master Brew, Spitfire, Seasonal Beers 🍷: 11
Children's Facilities: Fam room (Family room)
Menu/Portions Cutlery Games Highchair Food warming
Baby changing **Notes:** Dogs allowed in bar, in garden,
Water & dog biscuits **Garden:** Beside a stream
Parking: 14

DOVER
The Clyffe Hotel ♟

High Street St Margaret's at Cliffe CT15 6AT

☎ 01304 852400 📠 01304 851880
Email: stay@theclyffehotel.com
Web: www.theclyffehotel.com
Dir: *3m NE of Dover*
Quaint Kentish clapperboard building dating back to the
late 16th-century. In its time it has been a shoemaker's
and an academy for young gentlemen. Just a stone's
throw from the Saxon Shore Way and the renowned
White Cliffs of Dover. The main bar and neatly furnished
lounge lead out into the delightful walled rose garden.
Seared fillet of tuna and lightly steamed halibut are
among the seafood specialities; other options include
pan-fried chicken breast and penne pasta.

Open: 11-12 (Wknds 11am-1am) **Bar Meals:** L served
all week 12-2.30 D served Mon-Sat 6-9.30 Av main
course £9 **Restaurant Meals:** L served all week 12-
2.30 D served Mon-Sat 6-9.30 Av 3 course alc £22
Brewery/Company: Free House 🍺: Interbrew Bass,
Boddingtons, Fullers London Pride 🍷: 30 **Children's
Facilities:** Licence Play area (Large garden, playhouse,
toys) Menu/Portions Games Highchair Food warming
Nearby: Wingham Wild Life Park, Howletts Zoo, Kids
Safari **Notes:** Dogs allowed in bar, Water bowls **Garden:**
Traditional English walled garden **Parking:** 20

KENT

KENT

FAVERSHAM
Shipwrights Arms ♀
Hollowshore ME13 7TU
☎ 01795 590088
Dir: *A2 through Osprince then right at rdbt. Turn right at T-junct then left opp Davington School & follow signs*
A classic pub on the Kent marshes, first licensed in 1738, and once a haunt of pirates and smugglers. There are numerous nooks and crannies, and Kent-brewed real ales are served traditionally by gravity straight from the cask. The self-sufficient landlord generates his own electricity and draws water from a well. Home-cooked food might include mushroom Stroganoff, and sausage and mash, with an emphasis on English pies and puddings during the winter.
Open: 12-3 6-11 (Sun 12-3, 6-10.30)   **Bar Meals:** L served Tue-Sun 12-2.30   D served Tue-Sat 7-9   Av main course £6.95 **Brewery/Company:** Free House ▣: Local Beers **Children's Facilities:** Fam room (open space) Menu/Portions Highchair Food warming **Notes:** Dogs allowed in bar   Garden: Large open area adjacent to Faversham Creek **Parking:** 30

FAVERSHAM
The Albion Tavern ♀
Front Brents Faversham Creek ME13 7DH
☎ 01795 591411   🖺 01795 591587
Email: albiontavern@tiscali.co.uk
Web: www.albiontavern.co.uk
Dir: *From Faversham take A2 W. In Ospringe turn R just before Ship Inn, at Shepherd Neame Brewery 1m turn L over creek bridge*
A quaint, white-weatherboarded gem built in 1748 overlooking historic Faversham Creek. The small bar, which has a distinct nautical atmosphere, serves an attractive, contemporary menu.
Open: 11-3 6-11 (Sun 12-10.30)   **Bar Meals:** L served all week 12-2.30   D served Mon-Sat 6.30-9.30 Av main course £7 **Restaurant Meals:** L served all week 12-2.30   D served Mon-Sat 6.30-10 (Sun 11-9.30)   Av 3 course alc £16 **Brewery/Company:** Shepherd Neame ▣: Spitfire, Master Brew, Shepherd Neame, Seasonal Ales ♀: 10 **Children's Facilities:** Play area (Changing facilities) Menu/Portions Games Highchair Food warming Baby changing **Nearby:** Walks, swimming pool, playgrounds **Notes:** Dogs allowed in bar **Parking:** 20

FOLKESTONE
The Lighthouse ★★★ INN ♀
Old Dover Road Capel le Ferne CT18 7HT
☎ 01303 223300   🖺 01303 842270
Web: www.thelighthouseinn.co.uk
Perched on the edge of Dover's famous White Cliffs, with sweeping Channel views, the Lighthouse began as an ale house in 1840, later becoming, successively, a billiard hall, convalescent home, psychiatric hospital and country club, while more recently still Channel Tunnel builders headquartered here. Most food is home made, from traditional bar meals like chilli con carne, to items on the carte and specials board, both of which offer a good choice of fish dishes.
Open: 11-11 **Bar Meals:** L served all week 12-2.30   D served all week 6-9 (Sun 12-8.30) **Restaurant Meals:** L served all week 12-2.30   D served all week 6-9 (Sun 12-8.30) ▣: Abbot Ale & Guest Ales ♀: 8 **Children's Facilities:** Licence Fam room Play area (garden area/equipment) Menu/Portions Cutlery Games Highchair Food warming Baby changing **Notes:** Garden: lawn, large patio **Parking:** 80

LAMBERHURST

The Swan at the Vineyard 🍷

The Down TN3 8EU

☎ 01892 890170 📠 01892 890401

Web: www.theswan.org

With a large village green at the front and acres of Kentish vineyard to the rear, the Swan declares that it is 'not a traditional pub grub place', so don't expect jacket potatoes or chips. Instead choose from a comprehensive menu featuring Mediterranean vegetables with blue Stilton creamed fondue; grilled sea-bass fillet with Cajun coriander prawns; and veal escalope poached in milk, garlic and nutmeg with dauphinoise potato.

Open: 12-3 6-11 (Sun 12-5) **Bar Meals:** L served all week 12-2.15 D served all week 6-9.30 Av main course £7.50 **Restaurant Meals:** L served all week 12-2.15 D served all week 6-9.30 Av 3 course alc £20 🍺: Harveys Best, Adnams Broadside, Bombardier, Adnams Regatta, guest beers 🍷: 7 **Children's Facilities:** Play area (Large, enclosed garden fort) Menu/Portions Games Highchair Food warming **Nearby:** Pets Corner, Bewl Water, Vineyard Tourist Centre **Notes:** Dogs allowed in bar Garden: Grass and patio area, seating **Parking:** 30

LINTON

The Bull Inn 🍷

Linton Hill Maidstone ME17 4AW

☎ 01622 743612

Email: thebullinlinton@yahoo.co.uk

Web: www.lintonhillbull.co.uk

Dir: *S of Maidstone on A229 Hastings road*

A traditional 17th-century coaching inn in the heart of the Weald with stunning views from the glorious garden, and a large inglenook fireplace and wealth of beams inside. A tasty bar menu includes lasagna, spinach and ricotta tortellini, cod and chips, and bubble and squeak, as well as sandwiches, baguettes, and ploughman's. From the restaurant menu comes pan-fried venison steak wrapped in pancetta, served on sautéed oyster mushrooms.

Open: 11-3 5-11 (Sun 12-10.30, Sat 11-11) **Bar Meals:** L served all week 12-2.30 D served Mon-Sat 7-9.30 (Sun 12-3.30) Av main course £8.95 **Restaurant Meals:** L served all week 12-2.30 D served all week 7-9.30 (Sun 12-3.30) Av 3 course alc £25 **Brewery/Company:** Shepherd Neame 🍺: Shepherd Neame Master Brew & Spitfire, Seasonal Ale 🍷: 7 **Children's Facilities:** Menu/Portions Cutlery Highchair Food warming **Nearby:** The Hop Farm **Notes:** Dogs allowed in bar, in garden Garden: Large garden, ample seating, stunning views **Parking:** 30

LITTLEBOURNE

King William IV

4 High Street Canterbury CT3 1UN

☎ 01227 721244 📠 01227 721244

Email: sam@bowwindow.co.uk

Web: www.thebowwindow.co.uk

Dir: *From A2 follow signs to Howletts Zoo. After zoo & at end of road, pub is straight ahead*

Located just outside the city of Canterbury, the King William IV overlooks the village green and is well placed for Sandwich and Herne Bay. With open log fires and exposed oak beams, this friendly inn is a good place for visitors and locals.

Open: 11-11 (Sun 12-10.30) **Bar Meals:** L served all week 12-2.30 D served Tue-Sat 6-9 Av main course £10 **Restaurant Meals:** L served all week 12-2.30 D served Tue-Sat 6-9 **Brewery/Company:** Free House 🍺: Scottish Courage John Smith's, Sussex Harveys **Children's Facilities:** Menu/Portions Games Highchair Food warming Baby changing **Nearby:** Howletts Zoo, Wingham Bird Park, Canterbury Tales **Parking:** 15

KENT

MARKBEECH
The Kentish Horse
Cow Lane Edenbridge TN8 5NT
☎ 01342 850493
Surrounded by Kent countryside, this pub is popular
with ramblers, cyclists and families. The inn dates from
1340 and is said to have a smuggling history; it also
boasts a curious street-bridging Kentish sign. The wide-
ranging menu offers fresh starters such as Greek feta
salad, or pint of shell-on prawns, followed by spinach
and ricotta cannelloni; sausage and mash with onion
gravy; and steak and Guinness pie. Regular folk festivals
and other events.
Open: 12-11 (Sun 12-10.30) **Bar Meals:** L served all
week 12-2.30 D served Tue-Sat 7-9.30 (Sun 12-3.30)
Av main course £8.95 **Restaurant Meals:** L served all
week 12-2.30 D served all week 7-9.30 (Sun 12-3.30)
Av 3 course alc £15.50 ◖: Harvey's Larkins, plus guest
ales **Children's Facilities:** Play area (Swings, slide,
climbing fort) Highchair Food warming **Nearby:** Hever
Castle, Chiddingstone Village, Penshurst Place **Notes:**
Dogs allowed, Water, biscuits **Garden:** Big garden with
spectacular views **Parking:** 40

PENSHURST
The Bottle House Inn ♀
Coldharbour Road Tonbridge TN11 8ET
☎ 01892 870306 📄 01892 871094
Email: info@thebottlehouseinnpenshurst.co.uk
Web: www.thebottlehouseinnpenshurst.co.uk
Dir: *From Tunbridge Wells take A264 W then B2188 N*
Built as a farmhouse in 1492, the building was later
divided into two properties and one became the pub.
Today the daily-changing menu offers extensive choice
and, as far as possible, everything is made from locally
supplied fresh produce.
Open: 11-11 (Sun 11-10.30) Closed: Dec 25 **Bar
Meals:** L served all week 12-10 D served all week
12-10 (Sun 11.30-9) Av main course £10.95
Restaurant Meals: L served all week 12-10 D served
all week 12-10 (Sun 11.30-9) Av 3 course alc £21
Brewery/Company: Free House ◖: Larkins Ale, Harveys
Sussex Best Bitter ♀: 8 **Children's Facilities:** Licence
Menu/Portions Games Highchair Food warming **Nearby:**
Hever Castle, Penhurst Place, Groombridge Place **Notes:**
Dogs allowed in bar, in garden, Water **Garden:** Front
raised terrace garden and side patio **Parking:** 36

PLUCKLEY
The Mundy Bois ♀
Mundy Bois Ashford TN27 0ST
☎ 01233 840048 📄 01233 840193
Email: helen@mundybois.com
Web: www.mundybois.com
An ale house since 1780 and formerly named the Rose
and Crown, this creeper-clad pub is on the outskirts of
Pluckley, considered to be the most haunted place in
England. The bar menu offers home-made meals and
snacks like Aberdeen Angus burgers or pork and cider
gourmet sausage and mash. A new patio dining area
allows alfresco eating, and the garden has an
adventure playground.
Open: 11.30-3 6-11 (Fri-Sun 11.30-11, May-Sep open
10am Sat-Sun) **Bar Meals:** L served all week 12-2.30
D served all week 7-9.30 (May-Sep open 10am Sat-Sun
for brunch) **Restaurant Meals:** L served all week 12-
2.30 D served all week 7-9.30 **Brewery/Company:**
Free House ◖: Master Brew, Wadworth 6X ♀: 10
Children's Facilities: Adventure play area Menu/Portions
Cutlery Games Highchair Food warming **Nearby:** Rare
breeds centre, Leeds Castle, Steam Railway Line **Notes:**
Dogs allowed in bar, garden only , Water provided
Garden: Alfresco dining **Parking:** 30

ROYAL TUNBRIDGE WELLS
The Beacon ★★★★ INN ♟
Tea Garden Lane Rusthall TN3 9JH
☎ 01892 524252 📠 01892 534288
Email: beaconhotel@btopenworld.com
Web: www.the-beacon.co.uk
Dir: *From Tunbridge Wells take A264 towards East Grinstead. Pub 1m on L*
The Beacon stands high on a sandstone outcrop overlooking one of the best views in south-east England. The menus fuse contemporary with classical, and are updated quarterly to take full seasonal advantage of county-grown produce. Children may explore the 17 acres of grounds, with lakes, woodland walks and the Chalybeate Spring.
Open: 11-11 (Sun 12-10.30) **Bar Meals:** L served all week 12-2.30 D served all week 6.30-9.30 **Restaurant**

Meals: L served all week 12-2.30 D served all week 6-9.30 (Fri/Sat 12-2.30, 6.30-10, Sun 12-5, 6.30-9.30) Av 3 course alc £26.30 **Brewery/Company:** Free House 🍺: Harveys Best, Timothy Taylor Landlord, Larkins Traditional ♟: 12 **Children's Facilities:** Licence Play area (17 acres) Menu/Portions Highchair **Notes:** Garden: Decking area **Parking:** 40

ROYAL TUNBRIDGE WELLS
The Crown Inn ♟
The Green Groombridge TN3 9QH
☎ 01892 864742
Email: crowngroombridge@aol.com
Web: www.crowngroombridge.co.uk
Dir: *Take A264 W of Tunbridge Wells, then B2110 S*
Dating back to 1585, this charming free house was a favourite haunt for Keira Knightley and the cast of *Pride and Prejudice* during filming at Groombridge Place in 2005. Low beams and an inglenook fireplace are the setting for the lunchtime bar menu, which features toasted ciabattas, jackets and hot pub favourites. Evening diners might choose grilled cod with prawn and parsley butter; chicken and home-made ratatouille; or sun-blushed tomato pasta with peppers and roquette.

Open: 11-3 6-11 (Summer Fri-Sun open all day) **Bar Meals:** L served all week 12-3 D served Mon-Sat 7-9 (Sun 12-4) **Restaurant Meals:** L served all week 12-3 D served Mon-Sat 7-9 (Sun 12-4) **Brewery/Company:** Free House 🍺: Harveys IPA, Greene King IPA & Abbot Ale, Larkins ♟: 8 **Children's Facilities:** Play area (Large garden away from road) Games Highchair Food warming **Nearby:** Groombridge Place Gardens, Spa Valley Railway, Forest Way **Notes:** Dogs allowed in bar, in garden, Water bowls Garden: Benches, overlooks village green **Parking:** 35

KENT

SEVENOAKS
The White Hart Inn ♟
Tonbridge Road TN13 1SG
☎ 01732 452022
Email: sportingheros@btclick.com
A 16th-century inn close to Knole House, one of Kent's most famous and historic homes, noted for its glorious deer park. The pub's attractive garden, spacious terrace and traditional period interior draw customers from all corners of the county. The menu offers everything from shank of lamb with garlic mash, and breast of chicken in artichoke sauce, to steak and kidney pudding, and beer-battered cod, as well as good snacks.
Open: 11-3.30 6-12 **Bar Meals:** L served all week 12-2.30 D served Mon-Sat 6-9.30 (Sun 12-4.30) Av main course £8.50 **Restaurant Meals:** L served all week 12-

2.30 D served Mon-Sat 6-9 (Sun 12-4.30) Av 3 course alc £21 🍺: Harveys Sussex, Shepherd Neame Spitfire, Adnams Best, guest beers ♟: 8 **Children's Facilities:** Licence Fam room Play area (Canadian adventure route and climbing) Menu/Portions Cutlery Games Highchair Food warming Baby changing **Notes:** Garden: Garden terrace and beer garden to seat 130 **Parking:** 50

SMARDEN
The Chequers Inn ★★★★ INN ♟

The Street TN27 8QA

☎ 01233 770217 📄 01233 770623

Email: reception@thechequerssmarden.com

Web: www.thechequerssmarden.com

Dir: *Through Leeds village, left to Sutton Valence/Headcorn then left for Smarden. Pub in village centre*

A ghost is said to haunt the bedrooms of the Chequers - an atmospheric 14th-century inn with a clapboard façade in the centre of one of Kent's prettiest villages. The inn has its own beautiful landscaped garden with large duck pond and attractive south-facing courtyard. Here the food ranges from club sandwiches and jacket potatoes to smoked ham, eggs and chips, and lambs' liver with bacon. For an à la carte meal two separate restaurants offer a choice of ambience: the Red Restaurant has an opulent and romantic setting, while the Gold Restaurant is less formal in style and suitable for the whole family; both serve the same menus.

Open: 11-11 (Sun 12-10.30) **Bar Meals:** L served all week 12-2.30 D served all week 6-9.30 (Sun 12-3, 6-8.30) Av main course £9.95 **Restaurant Meals:** L served all week 12-2.30 D served all week 6.30-9.30 (Sun 12-3, 6-8.30) Av 3 course alc £22.50 **Brewery/Company:** Free House 🍺: Harveys, IPA, Abbot, Speckled Hen ♟: 9 **Children's Facilities:** Menu/Portions Games Highchair Food warming **Nearby:** Leeds Castle **Notes:** Dogs allowed in bar Garden: Landscaped with natural pond **Parking:** 15

STALISFIELD GREEN
The Plough Inn ♟

Faversham nr Charing ME13 0HY

☎ 01795 890256 📄 01795 890940

Dir: *A20 to Charing, on dual carriageway turn left for Stalisfield*

Originally a farmhouse, this 15th-century free house inn has been unspoilt by time, and boasts a lady ghost among its original beams and log fires. Set in a pretty village on top of the North Downs, the interesting menus are supplemented by specials which may include gravadlax, baked cod fillet with pancetta and mozzarella, chicken supreme in a white wine cream sauce, or smoked haddock with leek mash. The Plough featured in an episode of the TV series, *The Darling Buds of May*.

Open: 12-3 7-1 **Bar Meals:** L served Tue-Sat 12-3 D served Tue-Sat 7-9.30 (Sun 12-3, 7-9.30) **Restaurant Meals:** L served Tue-Sun 12-3 D served Tue-Sun 7-9.30 Av 3 course alc £14.45 **Brewery/Company:** Free House 🍺: Adnams Bitter, Wadworth 6X, Spitfire, monthly changing guest beer ♟: 8 **Children's Facilities:** Fam room Menu/Portions Highchair Food warming Baby changing **Notes:** Dogs allowed in bar, in garden Garden: Large beer garden, excellent view, heaters **Parking:** 100

TENTERDEN
White Lion Inn ★★★ INN ♟

57 High Street TN30 6BD

☎ 01580 765077 📄 01580 764157

Email: whitelion@celticinnspubs.co.uk

Web: www.celticinns.co.uk

Dir: *on the A28 Ashford/Hastings road*

A 16th-century coaching inn on a tree-lined street of this old Cinque Port, with many original features retained. The area is known for its cricket connections, and the first recorded county match between Kent and London was played here in 1719. The menu offers plenty of choice, from calves' liver and bacon, shoulder of lamb, and Cumberland cottage pie to tuna pasta bake and various ploughman's.

Open: 7-11 **Bar Meals:** L served all week 12-2.30 D served all week 6-9.30 (Sun 6-8.30) Av main course £7.95 **Restaurant Meals:** L served all week 12-2.30 D served all week 6-9.30 (Sun 6-8.30) Av 3 course alc £20 **Brewery/Company:** Lionheart Inns 🍺: Greene King IPA, Adnams Broadside ♟: 10 **Children's Facilities:** Menu/Portions Highchair Food warming **Nearby:** Kent & East Suusex Steam Railway, Bodiam Castle, Rare Breeds Farm **Notes:** Dogs allowed in bar, Accommodation available Garden: Large patio area with tables and chairs **Parking:** 30

WROTHAM
The Green Man
Hodsoll Street Ash-cum-Ridley Sevenoaks TN15 7LE
☎ 01732 823575
Email: the.greenman@btopenworld.com
Web: www.greenmanpub.com
Dir: *Between Brands Hatch & Gravesend*
A family-run 300-year-old pub located in the picturesque village of Hodsoll Street on the North Downs. An extensive menu is prepared to order using fresh local produce, and includes a wide variety of fish (especially on Wednesday, which is fish night) including mixed fish grill; haddock on Bombay potatoes, lamb shank, roast duck, and chicken stuffed with king prawns. Those who enjoy a good pint will be pleased with the well-kept cellar.
Open: 11-2.30 6-11 (Fri & Sat 11-11, Sun 12-10.30)

Bar Meals: L served all week 12-2 D served all week 6.30-9.30 (Sun 6.30-9) Av main course £12 **Restaurant Meals:** L served all week 12-2 D served all week 6.30-9.30 (Sun 6.30-9) **Brewery/Company:** Enterprise Inns ▮: Youngs Bitter, Fuller's London Pride, Harveys, Flowers Original **Children's Facilities:** Licence Play area (Climbing frame) Food warming **Nearby:** Howletts Zoo & Digger Land **Notes:** Dogs allowed in bar, in garden, Water **Garden:** Large grassed area with many picnic benches **Parking:** 42

LONDON E14
The Gun ☺ ♟
27 Coldharbour Docklands
☎ 020 7515 5222 ▤ 020 7515 4407
Email: info@thegundocklands.com
Web: www.thegundocklands.com
Dir: *From South Quay DLR go E along Marsh Wall to mini rdbt. Turn left, over bridge and 1st right.*
This grade II listed 18th-century pub stands on the banks of the Thames directly across the water from the Millennium Dome and a stone's throw from Canary Wharf. The surrounding area was once home to the dockside iron foundries which produced guns for the Royal Navy fleets. The pub was almost destroyed by fire five years ago, but re-opened its doors after painstaking restoration works carried out in close consultation with

English Heritage. The food served here is one of its strengths: chef Scott Wade, who has worked for Marco Pierre White at Mirabelle, prides himself on preparing high quality British food with a few foreign excursions.
Open: 11-12 (Sat 10.30-12, Sun 10.30-10.30) **Bar Meals:** L served all week 12-3 D served all week 6-10.30 (Sat 10.30-4.30, 6-10.30 Sun 10.30-4.30, 6-9.30) Av main course £10 **Restaurant Meals:** L served all 12-3 D served all week 6-10.30 (Sat 10.30-4.30, 6-10.30 Sun 10.30-4.30, 6-9.30) Av 3 course alc £25 ▮: Lowenbrau, Guinness, San Miguel, Hoegaarden, Carlsberg♟: 22 **Children's Facilities:** Licence Menu/Portions Food warming **Notes:** Garden: Beer garden, BBQ, good views over Thames

LONDON EC1
The Well ♟
180 Saint John St Clerkenwell EC1V 4JY
☎ 020 7251 9363 ▤ 020 7404 2250
Email: drink@downthewell.co.uk
Web: www.downthewell.com
Dir: *Telephone for directions*
A gastro-pub where the emphasis is on modern European and Mediterranean-style food served on two floors. The lower ground features the leather-panelled aquarium bar with exotic tropical fish occupying huge tanks set into the walls. Try the crispy pork belly with roasted leeks, Jerusalem artichokes and pied bleu mushrooms with a mustard and brandy cream sauce; or slow-roasted rib eye steak with dauphinoise potatoes, roasted garlic and crispy bacon. Large choice of wines

by the glass, and European bottled beers.
Open: 11-12 (Sun 11-11) **Bar Meals:** L served Mon-Sun 12-3 D served Mon-Sun 6-10.30 (Food served all day Sat-Sun) Av main course £12.50 **Restaurant Meals:** L served Mon-Sun 12-3 D served Mon-Sun 6-10.30 Av 3 course alc £20 ▮: San Miguel, Paulaner, Red Stripe, Weissbier ♟: 15 **Children's Facilities:** Licence (High Chair) Menu/Portions Highchair Food warming

LONDON N1
The Barnsbury 🍷
209-211 Liverpool Road Islington N1 1LX
☎ 020 7607 5519 📠 020 7607 3256
Email: info@thebarnsbury.co.uk
Web: www.thebarnsbury.co.uk
The Barnsbury, in the heart of Islington, is a welcome addition to the London scene as a gastropub that gets both the prices and food right. The recent addition of a walled garden has added a secluded and sought-after summer oasis for alfresco dining. The food is cooked from daily supplies of fresh produce which have been bought direct from the market, resulting in interesting menus with a slight nod to international cuisine.
Open: 12-11 Closed: 24-26 Dec, 1 Jan **Bar Meals:** L served all week 12-3 D served all week 6.30-10 (Sun 6.30-9.30) Av main course £12 **Restaurant Meals:** L served all week 12-3 D served all week 6.30-10 (Sun 6.30-9.30) Av 3 course alc £22 **Brewery/Company:** Free House 🍺: Timothy Taylor Landlord, Fullers London Pride, guest ale 🍷: 12 **Children's Facilities:** Menu/Portions Games Highchair Food warming Baby changing **Notes:** Garden: Walled garden with seating

LONDON N1
The Duke of Cambridge 🍷
30 St Peter's Street N1 8JT
☎ 020 7359 3066 📠 020 7359 1877
Email: duke@dukeorganic.co.uk
Web: www.dukeorganic.co.uk
The first organic pub in the UK, the Duke of Cambridge opened in December 1998 and was the first UK pub to receive Soil Association certification. Founder and MD Geetie Singh combines her skills and passion for food and ethical business to create a value-driven company with minimal environmental impact. There is no music, TV or electronic machinery. The company recycles and re-uses wherever possible and operates a fish purchasing policy approved by the Marine Conservation Society. Even the electricity is wind and solar sourced, and with 100% organic wines and twice-daily changing blackboard menu you can really feel virtuous while tucking into a few courses and a glass or two of your favourite tipple. Try a starter like wild duck, apple and celeriac salad; followed perhaps by baked organic trout wrapped in Parma ham.
Open: 12-11 (Sun 12-10.30) Closed: Dec 25-26 **Bar Meals:** L served all week 12.30-3 D served all week 6.30-10.30 (Sat 12.30-3.30, Sun 12.30-3.30, 7-10) Av main course £12 **Restaurant Meals:** L served all week 12.30-3 D served all week 6.30-10.30 (Sat 12.30-3.30, Sun 12.30-3.30, 7-10) **Brewery/Company:** Free House 🍺: Eco Warrior, St Peter's Best Bitter, East Kent Golding 🍷: 12 **Children's Facilities:** Licence Menu/Portions Cutlery Games Highchair Food warming Baby changing **Notes:** Dogs allowed in bar Garden: paved area, seats 20

LONDON NW1
The Engineer 🍷
65 Gloucester Avenue Primrose Hill NW1 8JH
☎ 020 7722 0950 📠 020 7483 0592
Email: info@the-engineer.com
Web: www.the-engineer.com
Situated in a very residential part of Primrose Hill close to Camden Market, this corner street pub is worth seeking out. Built by Isambard Kingdom Brunel in 1841, it attracts a discerning dining crowd for imaginative, well-prepared food and a friendly, laid-back atmosphere. Inside it is fashionably rustic, with a spacious bar area, sturdy wooden tables with candles, simple decor and changing art exhibitions in the restaurant area. A walled, paved and heated garden to the rear is extremely popular in fine weather. The fortnightly-changing menu features an eclectic mix of inspired home-made dishes and uses organic or free-range meats. Typical examples could be miso-marinated cod with wasabi mash and soy sherry sauce; or chicken breast stuffed with pumpkin, ricotta and sage with warm pasta and asparagus. Side dishes include Baker fries or rocket and parmesan salad.
Open: 9-11 **Bar Meals:** L served all week 12-3 D served all week 7-11 (Sun 12.30-4) Av main course £13.50 **Restaurant Meals:** L served all week 12-3 D served all week 7-11 (Sun 12.30-4) Av 3 course alc £26 **Brewery/Company:** Six Continents Retail 🍺: Erdinger, Leffe, Bombardier, Hook Norton 🍷: 10 **Children's Facilities:** Licence Fam room Games Highchair Food warming Baby changing **Nearby:** Regents Park & Zoo, Camden Canal Cruises **Notes:** Dogs allowed in bar, Water bowls Garden: Tables, seating approx 100

LONDON NW10

The Greyhound 🍷

64-66 Chamberlayne Road NW10 3JJ

☎ 020 8969 8080 📠 020 8969 8081

Email: greyhoundnw10@aol.com

Web: www.thegreyhound@needtoeat.co.uk

This pub was recently created from a derelict building, much to the delight of the locals, who have been flocking in ever since. Customers range from a smattering of supermodels to young families and older couples, all clearly enjoying the friendly atmosphere. There's an eclectic wine list, and a menu each for the bar and dining room. Since it opened a few years ago there has been a change of ownership.

Open: 11-11 (Fri-Sat 11-12, Sun 11-10.30) Closed: 25-26 Dec, 1 Jan **Bar Meals:** L served Tue-Sun 12.30-3 D served all week 6.30-10 (Sun 12.30-7) Av main course £9 **Restaurant Meals:** L served Tue-Sun 12.30-3 D served all week 6.30-10.30 (Sun 12.30-7) Av 3 course alc £19 **Brewery/Company:** Free House: Guinness, Kronenbourg, Bitburger & Guest ales 🍷: 14 **Children's Facilities:** Menu/Portions Games Highchair Food warming **Notes:** Dogs allowed in bar, Water Garden: Tranquil urban space, plants, heaters, BBQ

LONDON SE1

The Fire Station 🍷

150 Waterloo Road SE1 8SB

☎ 020 7620 2226 📠 020 7633 9161

Email: firestation.waterloo@pathfinderpubs.co.uk

Dir: *Turn right at exit 2 of Waterloo Station*

Close to Waterloo Station, and handy for the Old Vic Theatre and the Imperial War Museum, this remarkable conversion of a genuine early-Edwardian fire station has kept many of its former trappings intact. The rear dining room faces the open kitchen. An interesting menu includes dishes such as Fire Station avocado Caesar salad, baked cod with cheese polenta and pimento and pesto dressing, roast spiced pork belly with sticky rice and pak choi. Alternatively try Tandoori seared yellowfin tuna loin, calves' liver with bacon or mustard mash or lemon sole with Jerusalem artichokes. There are also imaginative midweek and Sunday set-price lunches.

Open: 11-11 (Mon-Tue 11-12, Wed-Thu 11-1) Closed: 25-26 Dec, 1 Jan **Bar Meals:** L served all week 12-5.30 D served all week 5.30-10.30 Av main course £6.95 **Restaurant Meals:** L served all week 12-2.45 D served all week 5-11 (Sat 12-11, Sun 12-9.30) Av 3 course alc £14.50 **Brewery/Company:** Pathfinder Pubs: Adnams Best Bitter, Fuller's London Pride, Young's Bitters, Shepherd Neame Spitfire,Marstons Pedigree 🍷: 8 **Children's Facilities:** Play area (highchairs, baby changing facilities) Menu/Portions Highchair Food warming **Nearby:** Aquarium, London Eye **Notes:** Garden: Tables outside on pavement

---

LONDON SE10

North Pole Bar & Restaurant 🍷

131 Greenwich High Road Greenwich SE10 8JA

☎ 020 8853 3020 📠 020 8853 3501

Email: north-pole@btconnect.com

Web: www.northpolegreenwich.com

The North Pole manages to be three venues in one: the stylish Piano Restaurant with resident ivory-tinkler from Thursday to Sunday evenings; the funky cocktail bar, and finally there is the basement night club. A few years ago the whole building was refurbished to a high standard, and now also includes a VIP bar for private parties. An extensive bar menu is available all day everyday from 12 until 10.30pm. The restaurant takes pride in offering modern European cooking with a French twist.

Open: 12-12 **Bar Meals:** L/D served all week 12-10.30 Av main course £6 **Restaurant Meals:** L served Sun 12-4 D served all week 6-11 Av 3 course alc £25 **Brewery/Company:** Free House: Stella Artois, Staropramen, Leffe, Carling, Guinness 🍷: 20 **Children's Facilities:** Menu/Portions Games Highchair Food warming Baby changing **Nearby:** Maritime Museum, Royal Observatory, Greenwich Park

LONDON

LONDON SE21
The Crown & Greyhound ♇
73 Dulwich Village SE21 7BJ
☎ 020 8299 4976 📄 020 8693 8959
With a tradition of service and hospitality reaching back
to the 18th century, the Crown and Greyhound counts
Charles Dickens and John Ruskin amongst its celebrated
patrons. Modern day customers will find three bars and a
restaurant in the heart of peaceful Dulwich Village. The
weekly-changing menu might feature bean cassoulet with
couscous; or an 8oz Angus burger with Cheddar cheese
and potato wedges. There are daily salads, pasta and fish
dishes, too.
Open: 11-11 (Sun 12-10.30) **Bar Meals:** L/D served all
week 12-10 (Sun 12-9) Av main course £7 **Restaurant
Meals:** L served all week 12-10 D served all week (Sun

12-9) 🍺: Fuller's London Pride & guest ales ♇: 15
Children's Facilities: Fam room Menu/Portions Highchair
Food warming Baby changing **Notes:** Dogs allowed
Garden: 2 levels, paved with trees and BBQ area

LONDON SE22
Franklins ◉ ♇
157 Lordship Lane Dulwich SE22 8HX
☎ 020 8299 9598
Email: info@franklinsrestaurant.com
Web: www.franklinsrestaurant.com
Franklins is a little more bar/restaurant than pub, but
nonetheless there are real ales and lagers on tap here,
including Young's, Kronenbourg and Guinness. The
interior is stripped-back, modern and stylish with bare
floors, exposed brick walls and smartly clothed tables.
The upwardly mobile and appreciative clientele enjoy the
no-frills short menu, which opens with the likes of Irish
rock oysters; curried parsnip soup; and kipper pâté. Main
courses continue in the same unfussy vein, with choices
such as Oxford Down lamb with aubergine and anchovy;

saddle of venison with potatoes dauphinoise; and calves'
liver with onion and bacon. Traditional and comforting
desserts include Bakewell tart; spotted dick; and rhubarb
crumble. From Monday to Friday the excellent value set
lunch menus allow the option of two or three courses,
with three courses being only £3 the dearer.
Open: 12-12 Closed: 25-26, 31 Dec, 1 Jan **Bar Meals:**
L served all week 12-6 D served all week 6-10.30 (Sun
1-10.30) Av main course £14 **Restaurant Meals:** L
served all week 12-6 D served all week 6-10.30 (Sun
1-10.30) Av 3 course alc £22 **Brewery/Company:**
Free House 🍺: Youngs, Estrella, Guinness, Becks,
Kronenbourg ♇: 11 **Children's Facilities:**
Menu/Portions Games Highchair Food warming Baby
changing **Nearby:** Horniman Museum, Dulwich Picture
Gallery & Park **Notes:** Dogs allowed in bar

LONDON SE5
The Sun and Doves ♇
61-63 Coldharbour Lane Camberwell SE5 9NS
☎ 020 7924 9950 📄 020 7924 9330
Email: mail@sunanddoves.co.uk
Web: www.sunanddoves.co.uk
This attractive Camberwell venue was originally just The
Sun until a Mr Dove bought it in the mid-19th century. It
survived bomb damage during the last war, and today
it's recognized for good food, drink and art - the pub
showcases local artists, many of whom are well known.
For a London pub it has a decent sized garden, planted
in Mediterranean style, and a paved patio offers fixed
seating for the summer months. The menu is stylishly
simple, with snacks like the pub's club sandwich; Welsh
rarebit; or merguez with rocket. The honestly priced lunch

and dinner menu has starters ranging from quiche of the
day to a plate of Serrano ham and salami. Mains include
cottage pie; hand-made sausages; eggs Benedict; and
char-grilled rib-eye steak. The sought-after puddings
include death by chocolate, and crumble with custard.
Open: 11-12 Closed: 25-26 Dec **Bar Meals:** L served
all week 12-10.30 D served all week 12-10.30 (Sun
12-9) Av main course £10 **Restaurant Meals:** L served
all week 11-11 D served all week 10.30 Av 3 course
alc £18 🍺: Old Speckled Hen, San Miguel & Ruddles ♇:
8 **Children's Facilities:** Play area (Garden/Patio paved
with fixed seating) Menu/Portions Cutlery Games
Highchair Food warming Baby changing **Nearby:**
Brockwell Park, Ruskin Park & Myatt's Fields Park
Notes: Dogs allowed in bar, in garden, Water bowl
Garden: Secluded, warm, spacious & south facing

LONDON SW18
The Old Sergeant ♟
104 Garrett Lane Wandsworth SW18 4DJ
☎ 020 8874 4099 📄 020 8874 4099
Traditional, friendly and oozing with character, The Old Sergeant enjoys a good reputation for its beers, but also offers some good malt whiskies. It's a good place to enjoy home-cooked food too: the menu could include salmon fish cakes with a sweet chili sauce, duck and orange sausages with coriander mash and gravy, or Thai fishcakes. One of the first pubs bought by Young's in the 1830s.
Open: 12-11 (Sun 12-10.30) **Bar Meals:** L served all week 12-2.30 D served all week 6-9.30 (Sun 12-9) Av main course £7.50 **Restaurant Meals:** L served Mon-Fri D served Mon-Fri (Thu-Sat 7-9.30 only) Av 3 course

alc £20 **Brewery/Company:** Youngs 🍺: Youngs Ordinary, Youngs Special ♟: 12 **Children's Facilities:** Play area (Changing Room) Menu/Portions Food warming Baby changing **Nearby:** Youngs Brewery Tour, Wandle Park **Notes:** Dogs allowed in bar, dog bowl **Garden:** Seats 50

LONDON SW3
The Phene Arms ♟
Phene Street Chelsea SW3 5NY
☎ 020 7352 3294 📄 020 7352 7026
Email: info@thephenearms.com
Web: www.thephenearms.com
Dir: *200yds from Kings Road.*
Built in 1851 and named after a doctor who introduced tree planting to London's streets, the pub was once George Best's local. It has a bar, a restaurant area, and a roof terrace, great for basking in the summer. New co-owner Christian Sandefeldt (with wife Kerstin) offers a northern French/Scandinavian menu, thus Swedish meatballs with lingonberries appear alongside roasted halibut with white haricot beans. Fondue and raclette are served on Sundays and Mondays.

Open: 11-midnight (Sun 12-10.30) **Bar Meals:** L served all week 12-4 D served all week 4-10 (Sun 4-9 Av main course £8 **Restaurant Meals:** L served only Avail. for large pre-booked groups 12-7 D served all week 7-10 (Sun 7-9) Av 3 course alc £23 **Brewery/Company:** Free House 🍺: Adnams Bitter Broadside, Fullers London Pride ♟: 12 **Children's Facilities:** Menu/Portions Games Highchair Food warming **Nearby:** Natural History Museum, Chelsea Sports Centre **Notes:** Dogs allowed in bar **Garden:** Quiet fenced garden and terrace

LONDON SW4
The Royal Oak ♟
8-10 Clapham High Street SW4 7UT
☎ 020 7720 5678
Email: savagecorp@mac.com
Home to pubs, bars and restaurants galore, these days Clapham High Street has a real neighbourhood feel about it. Maybe this traditional London boozer doesn't look much from outside, but its funky gastropub interior admirably compensates. A typical menu offers rib of beef with horseradish; mushroom and tarragon sausage toad-in-the-hole; and fresh fish, including oysters, and potted salmon. Seaside-brewed Adnams real ales are very much at ease in this urban environment.
Open: 12-11 (Sun 12-10.30) **Bar Meals:** L served all week 12-6 D served all week 6-10.30 Av main course

£8.50 **Brewery/Company:** Enterprise Inns 🍺: Adnams Broadside, Adnams Bitter, Hoegarden, Kronenburg & Guinness ♟: 8 **Children's Facilities:** Licence Fam room Menu/Portions Food warming **Notes:** Dogs allowed in bar

LONDON

LONDON / NORFOLK

LONDON SW4
The Windmill on the Common ♟
Clapham Common South Side SW4 9DE
☎ 020 8673 4578 📠 020 8675 1486
Email: windmillhotel@youngs.co.uk
Web: www.youngs.co.uk
Dir: *5m from London - Northern Line for tube and just off South Circular 205 where the 205 meets the A24 at Clapham*

The original part of this unusually-named pub was known as Holly Lodge and at one time was the property of the founder of Youngs Brewery. The varied menu offers such dishes as steak and ale pie, salmon fillet, traditional lamb moussaka, chicken stir-fry with vegetables, bangers and mash, Thai fishcakes, and Windmill burger with bacon, cheese and onions.

Open: 11-11 (Sun 12-10.30) **Bar Meals:** L served all week 12-3 D served all week 6-10.30 (Sat 12-10, Sun 12-9) Av main course £7 **Brewery/Company:** Young & Co Brewery Plc 🍺: Youngs Bitter, Guinness ♟: 17 **Children's Facilities:** Licence Fam room Highchair Food warming **Nearby:** Clapham Common **Notes:** Dogs allowed in bar, in garden **Garden:** Benches in outside area, not grassed **Parking:** 20

LONDON W4
The Devonshire House ♟
126 Devonshire Road Chiswick W4 2JJ
☎ 020 8987 2626 📠 020 8995 0152
Email: info@thedevonshire.co.uk
Web: www.thedevonshirehouse.co.uk
Dir: *150yds off Chiswick High Rd. 100yds from Hogarth rdbt & A4*

Laid back and unpretentious perfectly describes this 'unique' London gastropub, located in the quiet leafy district of Chiswick. Previously the Manor Tavern, the Devonshire House was extensively refurbished and transformed a few years ago into an attractive, light and airy bar and restaurant. The menu is an interesting mix of modern British and Mediterranean dishes, and changes daily depending upon what fresh produce is available.

You can whet your appetite with some olives, nuts or farmhouse bread before trying a starter like warm salad of beignets of sweetbreads with red onion marmalade. Main courses might feature a simple pizza Margarita, or perhaps chicken Maryland with confit tomato, sweetcorn fritters and caramelised bananas. Children are made to feel welcome with a secure garden to play in plus books, crayons and games to keep them entertained.

Open: 12-11 Closed: 25-26 Dec **Bar Meals:** L served Tue-Sun 12-3 D served Tue-Sun 7-11 Av main course £12 **Restaurant Meals:** L served Tue-Sun 12-3 D served Tue-Sun 7-11 **Brewery/Company:** Unique 🍺: Stella, Kronenbourg 1664, London Pride, Guinness ♟: 15 **Children's Facilities:** Play area (Books, crayons, games) Menu/Portions Games Highchair Food warming **Notes:** Dogs allowed in bar

BLAKENEY
The Kings Arms ♟
Westgate Street Holt NR25 7NQ
☎ 01263 740341 📠 01263 740391
Email: info@blakeneykingsarms.co.uk
Web: www.blakeneykingsarms.co.uk

This Grade II listed free house is located on the beautiful North Norfolk coast, close to the famous salt marshes, and is run by Marjorie and Howard Davies, who settled here after long and successful showbiz careers. The Kings Arms is an ideal centre for walking, or perhaps a ferry trip to the nearby seal colony and world-famous bird sanctuaries. Locally-caught fish and seasonal seafood feature on the menu, together with local game, home-made pies and pastas.

Open: 11-11 **Bar Meals:** L served all week 12-9.30 D served all week 12-9.30 (Sun 12-9) **Brewery/Company:** Free House 🍺: Greene King Old Speckled Hen, Woodfordes Wherry Best Bitter, Marston's Pedigree, Adnams Best Bitter ♟: 12 **Children's Facilities:** Fam room Play area (swings) Menu/Portions Games Highchair Food warming Baby changing **Nearby:** Dinosaur Park, Beaches & Seal trips **Notes:** Dogs allowed in bar, in garden, in bedrooms, Water **Garden:** Very safe large patio and grass area **Parking:** 10

BLAKENEY
White Horse Hotel ♀
4 High Street NR25 7AL
☎ 01263 740574 📠 01263 741303
Email: enquiries@blakeneywhitehorse.co.uk
Web: www.blakeneywhitehorse.co.uk
Dir: *From A148 (Cromer to King's Lynn rd) turn onto A149 signed to Blakeney.*
A short, steep stroll from Blakeney quayside stands the 17th-century White Horse, formerly a coaching inn. A twice-yearly changing menu is based loosely around the shellfish seasons. All the shellfish and much of the fish comes from along this very stretch of coast.
Open: 11-3 6-11 **Bar Meals:** L served all week 12-2.15 D served all week 6-9 Av main course £10 **Restaurant Meals:** D served all week 7-9 Av 3 course alc £25

Brewery/Company: Free House 🍺: Adnams Bitter, Woodfordes Wherry, Greene King IPA & Abbott ♀: 12 **Children's Facilities:** Fam room Menu/Portions Cutlery Highchair Food warming Baby changing **Nearby:** Crabbing on Blakeney Quay, Seal Trips **Notes:** Garden: Courtyard, picnic tables and umbrellas **Parking:** 14

BRANCASTER STAITHE
The White Horse ★★ HL ⊛ ♀
Main Road King's Lynn PE31 8BY
☎ 01485 210262 📠 01485 210930
Email: reception@whitehorsebrancaster.co.uk
Web: www.whitehorsebrancaster.co.uk
Dir: *A149 coast road, midway between Hunstanton & Wells-next-the-Sea.*
Stunning views of North Norfolk's heritage coast are the perfect companion to well kept ales and local seafood at this gloriously situated dining pub. It has an enviable reputation for imaginative food, which can be enjoyed in the conservatory restaurant, or sun deck in summer.
Open: 11-11 (Sun 12-10.30) **Bar Meals:** L served all week 12-2 D served all week **Restaurant Meals:** L served all week 12-2 D served all week 6.45-9 Av 3

course alc £24 🍺: Adnams Best Bitter, Fullers London Pride, Woodfordes Wherry & Guest ♀: 12 **Children's Facilities:** Games Highchair Food warming Baby changing **Nearby:** Sea Life Centre, Hunstanton Fun Fair, Sandy Brancaster Beach & Seal Trips **Notes:** Dogs allowed in bar, in garden **Garden:** Sun deck terrace overlooking tidal marshes **Parking:** 85

BURNHAM THORPE
The Lord Nelson ♀
Walsingham Road King's Lynn PE31 8HL
☎ 01328 738241 📠 01328 738241
Email: david@nelsonslocal.co.uk
Web: www.nelsonslocal.co.uk
Dir: *B1355 Burnham Market to Fakenham Rd, pub 9m from Fakenham & 1.75m from Burnham Market. Located near church opposite the playing fields.*
The pub was renamed after Horatio Nelson, who was born in Burnham Thorpe. Families are welcome, and children will enjoy the huge garden.
Open: 11-3 6-11 (Sun 6.30-10.30) **Bar Meals:** L served all week 12-2 D served Mon-Sat 7-9 (Sat/Sun 12-2.30, Fri/Sat 7-9.30) **Restaurant Meals:** L served all week 12-2 D served Mon-Sat 7-9 (Sat/Sun 12-2.30,

Fri/Sat 7-9.30) Av 3 course alc £26 **Children's Facilities:** Play area (Large wooded play area with equipment & toys) Menu/Portions Games Highchair Food warming Baby changing **Nearby:** Pensthorpe Wildlife Reserve, Holkham Hall & Hunstanton Seaworld **Notes:** Dogs allowed in bar, in garden, Water **Garden:** Seating, children's play area, BBQ **Parking:** 30

NORFOLK

CLEY NEXT THE SEA
The George Hotel ☉

High Street Holt NR25 7RN

☎ 01263 740652 🖹 01263 741275

Email: thegeorge@cleynextthesea.com

Web: www.thegeorgehotelcley.com

Dir: *On A149 through Cley next the Sea, approx 4m from Holt.*

A rambling country property full of character with a modern twist, set within the beautiful and historic village of Cley next the Sea. A classic Edwardian Norfolk inn, The George has an excellent reputation for freshly prepared food made from local ingredients.

Open: 11-11 (Sun & BHs 11-10.30) **Bar Meals:** L served all week 12-2 D served all week 6.30-9 (Sun 12-2.30) Av main course £10.95 **Restaurant Meals:** L served all week 12-2 D served all week 6.30-9 (Sun 12-2.30) Av 3 course alc £20 **Brewery/Company:** Free House 🍺: Greene King IPA, Abbot Ale, Yetmans Beers & Leffe ☉: 8 **Children's Facilities:** Fam room Menu /Portions Cutlery Highchair Food warming Baby changing **Nearby:** Seal Trips, Beaches **Notes:** Dogs allowed in bar, in garden, Water Bowls **Parking:** 15

COLTISHALL
Kings Head ☉

26 Wroxham Road Norwich NR12 7EA

☎ 01603 737426 🖹 01603 736542

Dir: *A47 Norwich ring road onto B1150 to North Walsham at Coltishall. Right at petrol station, follow rd to right past church, on right next to car park*

This 17th-century free house stands on the banks of the River Bure, right in the heart of the Norfolk Broads. Hire cruisers are available at nearby Wroxham, and fishing boats can be hired at the pub. If you prefer to stay on dry land you'll find a warm welcome at the bar, with a range of real ales that includes Adnams Bitter, Directors and Marston's Pedigree. There's an inviting menu, too, served in both the bar and the non-smoking restaurant.

Open: 11-3 6-11 (Sun all day) Closed: 26 Dec **Bar Meals:** L served all week 12-2 D served all week 7-9 Av main course £12.50 **Restaurant Meals:** L served all week 12-2 D served all week 7-9 Av 3 course alc £25 **Brewery/Company:** Free House 🍺: Adnams Bitter, Directors, Marston's Pedigree ☉: 10 **Children's Facilities:** Menu/Portions Highchair Food warming **Nearby:** Luroxham Barns **Notes:** Garden: Terraced area at front of pub **Parking:** 20

FAKENHAM
The Wensum Lodge Hotel

Bridge Street NR21 9AY

☎ 01328 862100 🖹 01328 863365

Email: enquiries@wensumlodge.fsnet.co.uk

Web: www.wensumlodge.co.uk

Dir: *20m from Norwich, 20m from King's Lynn*

Wensum Lodge is a converted mill dating from around 1700, idyllically located by the River Wensum, for which the hotel has fishing rights. Home-cooked food is prepared from locally supplied ingredients, with baguettes, jacket potatoes and an all-day breakfast on the light bite menu. The carte might have baby peeled prawns on dressed leaves with chilli dip; and Wensum burger topped with bacon, cheese, salad and relish in a toasted bun served with fries.

Open: 11-11 **Bar Meals:** L served all week 11.30-3 D served all week 6.30-9.30 (Sun 12-3, 6.30-9) Av main course £7.50 **Restaurant Meals:** L served all week 11.30-3 D served all week 6.30-9.30 (Sun 12-3, 6.30-9) Av 3 course alc £18 **Brewery/Company:** Free House 🍺: Greene King Abbot Ale & IPA, Old Mill Bitter, Carling **Children's Facilities:** Menu/Portions Games Highchair Food warming Baby changing **Nearby:** Wildlife Park, Dinosaur Adventure Park, Penshorpe Waterfowl Park **Notes:** Garden: Small with stream **Parking:** 20

FAKENHAM
The White Horse Inn ★★★★ INN
Fakenham Road East Barsham NR21 0LH
☎ 01328 820645 📠 01328 820645
Email: subalpine19@whsmith.net.co.uk
Web: norfolkinns.co.uk
Dir: *1.5m N of Fakenham on the minor road to Little Walsingham.*
Ideally located for birdwatching, walking, cycling, fishing, golf and sandy beaches, this refurbished 17th-century inn offers en suite rooms and a characterful bar with a log-burning inglenook. Good range of beers and malt whiskies. Fresh ingredients are assured in daily specials, with fish especially well represented. There is also a grill menu. Birdwatching tours can be arranged.
Open: 11.30-3 6.30-11 **Bar Meals:** L served all week 12-2 D served all week 7-9.30 Av main course £9.95 **Restaurant Meals:** L served all week 12-2 D served all week 7-9.30 🍺: Adnams Best, Adnams Broadside, Tetley, Wells Eagle IPA **Children's Facilities:** Menu/Portions Games Highchair Food warming **Nearby:** Sandringham, Dinosaur Park, Thursford **Notes:** Garden: Patio area & enclosed courtyard **Parking:** 50

GREAT RYBURGH
The Boar Inn
Fakenham NR21 0DX
☎ 01328 829212 📠 01328 829421
Dir: *Off A1067 4m S of Fakenham*
The village, deep in rural Norfolk, has one of the county's unusual round-towered Saxon churches. Opposite is the 300-year-old Boar, dispensing a good variety of food, including beef Madras with rice, sweet and sour chicken with noodles, plaice fillet with prawns in Mornay sauce, scallops, lemon sole, and prime Norfolk steaks. Specials include skate wing with garlic and herb butter, and wild boar steak with cranberry and red wine jus. Bar/alfresco snacks and children's meals.
Open: 12-2.30 5.30-12 (All day 1 May-30 Sep) **Bar Meals:** L served all week 12-2 D served all week 7-9 **Restaurant Meals:** L served all week 12-2 D served all week 7-9 Av 3 course alc £15 **Brewery/Company:** Free House 🍺: Courage Best & guest ale **Children's Facilities:** Fam room (Pool & games room) Menu/Portions Games Highchair Food warming **Notes:** Garden: Food served outside **Parking:** 30

HAPPISBURGH
The Hill House 🍷
NR12 0PW
☎ 01692 650004 📠 01692 650004
Dir: *5m from Stalham, 8m from North Walsham*
16th-century coaching inn with original timbers situated in an attractive North Norfolk coastal village. Sir Arthur Conan Doyle stayed here and was inspired to write a Sherlock Holmes story called *The Adventure of The Dancing Men*. Changing guest ales; good value bar food; large summer garden. Look out for the likes of steaks, chicken breast with leek and Stilton, or seafood platter, plus various Greek, Italian and French dishes. Beer festival each June, on the Summer Solstice.
Open: 12-3 7-11 (Thu-Sun all day, Summer all day) **Bar Meals:** L served all week 12-2.30 D served all week 7-9.30 Av main course £6 **Restaurant Meals:** D served all week 7-9.30 Av 3 course alc £25
Brewery/Company: Free House 🍺: Shepherd Neame Spitfire, Buffy's, Woodforde's Wherry , Adnams Bitter, House Bitter 🍷: 9 **Children's Facilities:** Fam room Menu/Portions Cutlery Games Highchair Food warming **Notes:** Dogs allowed in bar, Water Garden: Large, by the sea **Parking:** 20

HEVINGHAM
Marsham Arms Freehouse ☻
Holt Road Norwich NR10 5NP
☎ 01603 754268
Email: nigelbradley@marshamarms.co.uk
Web: www.marshamarms.co.uk
Dir: *On B1149 N of Norwich airport, 2m through Horsford towards Holt*
Victorian philanthropist and landowner Robert Marsham built what is now the Marsham Arms as a hostel for poor farm labourers. A good range of traditional pub fare is offered, featuring lots of fresh fish.
Open: 11-11 **Bar Meals:** L served all week 11.30-2.30 D served all week 6-9.30 (Sun 12-2.30, 6.30-9) Av main course £9.50 **Restaurant Meals:** L served all week 12-2.30 D served all week 6-9.30 (Sun 6.30-9)

Av 3 course alc £19.50 ☎: Adnams Best, Woodforde's Wherry Best Bitter, Mauldens, Worthington, Broadside
☻: 8 **Children's Facilities:** Fam room Play area Menu/Portions Cutlery Highchair Food warming Baby changing **Nearby:** Dinosaur Park, Splash Pools, Wildlife Park **Notes:** Garden: Large lawn with patio & marquee seats 20 **Parking:** 100

HOLKHAM
Victoria at Holkham ★★ SHL ◉◉ ☻
Park Road NR23 1RG
☎ 01328 711008 📠 01328 711009
Email: victoria@holkham.co.uk
Web: www.victoriaatholkham.co.uk
Dir: *On A149, 3m W of Wells-next-the-sea*
How could Thomas William Coke have considered calling his new hotel anything else? He opened it in 1838, the year after the young Queen Victoria had elevated him to the peerage. The interior of the colonial-style Victoria is opulent and colourful. The food is modern yet traditional, fresh, seasonal and local: crabs from Cromer, oysters from Thornham, and mussels from Brancaster.
Open: 12-12 **Bar Meals:** L served out of season only D served all week Av main course £10 **Restaurant**

Meals: L served all week 12-2.30 D served all week 7-9 Av 3 course alc £30 ☎: Adnams Best, Woodfordes Wherry, guest ale ☻: 12 **Children's Facilities:** Licence Play area (swings, cimbing frames, slides) Menu/Portions Cutlery Games Highchair Food warming Baby changing **Nearby:** Holkham Estate, Holkham beach **Notes:** Dogs allowed in bar Garden: seasonal BBQ **Parking:** 50

HORSTEAD
Recruiting Sergeant ☻
Norwich Road Norwich NR12 7EE
☎ 01603 737077 📠 01603 738827
Dir: *on the B1150 between Norwich & North Walsham*
The name of this inviting country pub comes from the tradition of recruiting servicemen by giving them the King or Queen's shilling in a pint of beer. It offers good food, ales and wines in homely surroundings with a patio and lawned garden for alfresco dining. The menu is ever changing, with inventive dishes such as fresh oysters with a tabasco, lime and red onion dressing, duck breast on an apple and potato rosti and chicken breast stuffed with mozzarella and chorizo. There is also a vast daily specials menu, including fish and vegetarian dishes.
Open: 11-11 **Bar Meals:** L served all week 12-2 D

served all week 6.30-9 (Fri-Sat 6.30-9.30) Av main course £15 **Restaurant Meals:** L served all week 12-2 D served all week 6.30-9.30 Av 3 course alc £20
Brewery/Company: Free House ☎: Adnams, Woodefordes, Greene King Abbot Ale, Scottish Courage
☻: 13 **Children's Facilities:** Play area (high chairs) Menu/Portions Highchair Food warming Baby changing **Nearby:** Wroxham Barns, Yale Valley Railway **Notes:** Dogs allowed in bar, in garden, Water Garden: Large patio, seats approx 40, enclosed lawn **Parking:** 50

ITTERINGHAM
Walpole Arms ♥
Aylsham NR11 7AR
☎ 01263 587258 📠 01263 587074
Email: goodfood@thewalpolearms.co.uk
Web: www.thewalpolearms.co.uk
Dir: *Leave Aylsham in Blickling direction. After Blickling Hall take 1st right to Itteringham*
Andy Parle, a veteran of Michelin-starred restaurants, and his team of chefs create meals that are more than the sum of their parts, using fresh local, seasonal produce.
Open: 12-3 6-11 (Sun 7-10.30) Closed: 25 Dec **Bar Meals:** L served all week 12-2 D served Mon-Sat 7-9.30 (Sun 12.30-2.30) Av main course £11.50
Restaurant Meals: L served Sat-Sun 12-2 D served Mon-Sat 7-9.30 (Sun 12.30-2.30) Av 3 course alc

£22.50 🍺: Adnams Broadside, Woodfordes Wherry Best Bitter & Walpole ♥: 12 **Children's Facilities:** Play area (Large fully fenced garden) Menu/Portions Cutlery Highchair Food warming Baby changing **Nearby:** Norfolk Wildlife Park, Dinosaur Adventure Park, Blickling Hall **Notes:** Dogs allowed in bar & garden, Water **Garden:** 2 grassed areas & vine covered patio **Parking:** 100

LARLING
Angel Inn ♥
Norwich NR16 2QU
☎ 01953 717963 📠 01953 718561
Dir: *5m from Attleborough, 8m from Thetford and 1m from station.*
A 17th-century former coaching inn on the Norwich to Thetford road. In the comfortable lounge bar, wheel-back chairs, an oak-panelled settle, a wood-burning stove and a huge collection of water jugs help create its homely atmosphere. Main dishes include steaks and grills, salmon and asparagus crêpe, seafood platter, lamb balti, and burgers. Try one of the specials - spicy pork stir-fry, Adnams-battered fillet of fresh cod, or maybe vegetable korma.
Open: 10-11 **Bar Meals:** L served Sun-Sat 12-2 D

served Sun-Sat 6.30-9.30 (Fri & Sat 12-10, Sun 12-9.30) Av main course £7.95 **Restaurant Meals:** L served all week 12-2 D served all week 6.30-9.30 (Fri & Sat 12-10, Sun 12-9.30) **Brewery/Company:** Free House 🍺: Adnams Bitter, Wolf Bitter, Caledonian Deuchars IPA, Timothy Taylor Landlord & Mauldons ♥: 7 **Children's Facilities:** Play area (swings) Menu/Portions Highchair Food warming **Nearby:** Banham Zoo, The Brecks, Snetterton Race Curcuit **Notes:** Garden: Large, garden tables **Parking:** 100

LITTLE FRANSHAM
The Canary and Linnet
Main Road NR19 2JW
☎ 01362 687027 📠 01362 687021
Email: ben@canaryandlinnet.co.uk
Web: www.canaryandlinnet.co.uk
Dir: *Situated on A47 between Dereham and Swaffham*
A pretty, former blacksmith's cottage fulfilling the key requirements of a traditional English country pub - low ceilings, exposed beams and an inglenook fireplace. Its sign once showed footballers in Norwich City (Canaries) and Kings Lynn (Linnets) strips, but now features two birds in a cage. Food offered throughout the bar, conservatory restaurant and garden includes steak and ale pie, medallions of pork in stilton sauce, and tempura battered red mullet fillets with sweet chilli sauce.

Open: 12-3 6-11 (Sun 12-3 7-10) **Bar Meals:** L served Mon-Sun 12-2 D served all week 6-9.30 **Restaurant Meals:** L served all week 12-2 D served Mon-Sun 6-9.30 **Brewery/Company:** Free House 🍺: Greene King IPA, Tindall's Best, Adnams Bitter, Wolf, Blue Moon **Children's Facilities:** Menu/Portions Highchair Food warming **Notes:** Dogs allowed in bar **Parking:** 70

NORFOLK

LITTLE WALSINGHAM
The Black Lion Hotel ♙
Friday Market Place NR22 6DB
☎ 01328 820235 🖹 01328 821407
Email: lionwalsingham@btinternet.com
Web: www.blacklionwalsingham.com
Dir: *From King's Lynn take A148 and B1105 or from Norwich take A1067 and B1105.*
A former coaching inn, dating in part from 1310, with the northern end built to accommodate Edward III and Queen Philippa of Hainault when they visited the shrine at Walsingham (the hotel takes its name from her coat of arms). The friendly bar has a welcoming fire in winter, and in the restaurant the seasonal menu might offer scrumpy pork hock; rainbow trout Cleopatra; and spinach, cherry tomato and mozzarella herb pudding.
Open: 11-3 6-1am (Sat & Sun 11am-1am) **Bar Meals:** L served all week 12-2.30 D served all week 7-9 (Sun Lunch 12-3) Av main course £7.95 **Restaurant Meals:** L served all week 12-2.30 D served all week 7-9 (Sun Lunch 12-3) Av 3 course alc £16
Brewery/Company: Enterprise Inns 🍺: Woodforde's Wherry, Blacksheep Special, John Smiths Smooth, Fosters & Woodforde's Nelson's Revenge ♙: 7
Children's Facilities: Menu/Portions Cutlery Games Highchair Food warming **Nearby:** Pensthorpe Wildfowl Centre, Wells-Walsingham Light Railway & Thursford Collection **Notes:** Dogs allowed in bar, in garden, Water, food on request **Garden:** Courtyard, picnic tables, well

MARSHAM
The Plough Inn
Norwich Road Norwich NR10 5PS
☎ 01263 735000 🖹 01263 735407
Email: enquiries@ploughinnmarsham.co.uk
Web: www.ploughinnmarsham.co.uk
Dir: *9m from Norwich, 1m from Aylsham on A140.*
An attractive, traditional 18th-century country pub and restaurant, extended and modernised over the years. The menus are carefully annotated and chosen to provide foods for people with special dietary requirements.
Open: 12-3 5-11 (Sun 5-10.30, Sun Etr-Sep 30 all day)
Closed: Dec 25 **Bar Meals:** L served all week 12-2.30
D served all week 6.30-9 (All day Sun Etr-Sep 30) Av main course £10 **Restaurant Meals:** L served all week 12-2.30 D served all week 6.30-9 (Sun Etr-Sep 30 12-9) Av 3 course alc £20 🍺: IPA Greene King, Fosters, Stella, Kronenburg, John Smiths Smooth **Children's Facilities:** Licence Menu/Portions Games Highchair Food warming Baby changing **Nearby:** Bure Valley Railway, Norfolk Broads, Cromer & Sheringham Coats **Notes:** **Garden:** Large lawn, seating, flowers, trees **Parking:** 60

MUNDFORD
Crown Hotel
Crown Road Thetford IP26 5HQ
☎ 01842 878233 🖹 01842 878982
Dir: *Take A11 to Barton Mills junct, then A1065 to Brandon & on to Mundford*
Built in 1652, the Crown has been many things - a famous hunting lodge; the local magistrates' court; and even a doctors' waiting room. Its most unusual feature, in these pancake-flat parts, is that it is set into a hill! Traditional food is served in the bar, and a more elaborate menu is available in the restaurant; perhaps tian of Brixham crab followed by lamb rump with flageolet purée, fondant potato, garlic confit and mint jus.
Open: 11-2 **Bar Meals:** L served all week 12-3
D served all week 7-10 **Restaurant Meals:** L served all week 12-3 D served all week 7-10
Brewery/Company: Free House 🍺: Courage Directors, Marston Pedigree, Archers, Greene King IPA & Guest ales
Children's Facilities: Menu/Portions Highchair Food warming **Nearby:** Thetford Forest Centre, Banham Zoo, High Lodge **Notes:** Dogs allowed in bar **Garden:** beer garden patio, food served outside **Parking:** 30

REEPHAM
The Old Brewery House Hotel
Market Place NR10 4JJ
☎ 01603 870881 📄 01603 870969
Dir: *Off the A1067 Norwich to Fakenham road, B1145 signed Aylsham*
A grand staircase, highly polished floors and wooden panelling characterise this hotel, originally built as a private residence in 1729. It became a hotel in the 1970s, retaining many of its Georgian features. Alongside the real ales and fine wines, there's a bar menu of freshly produced dishes.
Open: 11-11 (Sun 12-10.30) **Bar Meals:** L served all week 12-2 D served all week 6.30-9.15 (Sun 12-2.15, 7-9) Av main course £7 **Restaurant Meals:** L served all week 12-2 D served all week 6.30-9.30 Av 3 course alc £20 **Brewery/Company:** Free House 🍺: IPA, Greene King Abbot Ale & Old Speckled Hen **Children's Facilities:** Play area (indoor heated pool) Menu/Portions Highchair Food warming Baby changing **Nearby:** Dinosaur Park, Aqua Park, Seaside **Notes:** Dogs allowed in bar, in garden **Garden:** Garden with pond & benches **Parking:** 80

SALTHOUSE
The Dun Cow
Coast Road NR25 7XG
☎ 01263 740467
Dir: *On A149 coast road, 3m E of Blakeney, 6m W of Sheringham*
Overlooking some of the country's finest freshwater marshes, the front garden of this attractive pub is inevitably popular with birdwatchers and walkers. The bar area was formerly a blacksmith's forge, and many original 17th-century beams have been retained. Children are welcome, but there's also a walled rear garden reserved for adults. The menu includes snacks, pub staples like burgers and jacket potatoes, and main courses like gammon steak, pasta and meatballs, plaice and chips, and lasagne.
Open: 11-11 (Sun 12-10.30) **Bar Meals:** L served all week 12-8.45 D served all week 12-8.45 Av main course £7 **Brewery/Company:** Pubmaster 🍺: Greene King IPA & Abbot Ale, Adnams Broadside 🍷: 6 **Children's Facilities:** Fam room Games Highchair Food warming Baby changing **Notes:** Dogs allowed in bar **Garden:** Garden & courtyard overlooking marshes **Parking:** 8

SNETTISHAM
The Rose & Crown ★★ HL 🏆 🍷
Old Church Road King's Lynn PE31 7LX
☎ 01485 541382 📄 01485 543172
Email: info@roseandcrownsnettisham.co.uk
Web: www.roseandcrownsnettisham.co.uk
Dir: *N from King's Lynn on A149 signed Hunstanton. Inn in village centre between market square & church*
A perfect example of a traditional country pub that has taken on a new lease of life, the Rose & Crown dates back to the 14th century, and promises great food and appealing surroundings. The three bar areas all have timbered ceilings, open fires and marvellous worn pamment-tiled floors. Twisting passages and cosy nooks and crannies radiate from the pub's ancient core. A regularly changing menu presents dishes such as baked fillet of halibut with herb mash potatoes and caviar fish cream. There's also a good choice of sandwiches and Rose & Crown 'Classics'.
Open: 11-11 (Sun 12-10.30) **Bar Meals:** L served all week 12-2 D served all week 6.30-9 (Sat-Sun 2.30, Fri & Sat 9.30) Av main course £10 **Restaurant Meals:** L served all week 12-2 D served all week 6.30-9 Av 3 course alc £20 **Brewery/Company:** Free House 🍺: Adnams Bitter & Broadside, Interbrew Bass, Fuller's London Pride, Greene King IPA 🍷: 20 **Children's Facilities:** Fam room Play area (Large play fort, crayons etc) Menu/Portions Cutlery Games Highchair Food warming Baby changing **Nearby:** Park Farm, Sandringham & Beaches **Notes:** Dogs allowed in bar, in garden, in bedrooms, Water **Garden:** Large walled garden, seating & shade **Parking:** 70

STOKE HOLY CROSS
The Wildebeest Arms ⊚⊚ ♀
82-86 Norwich Road Norwich NR14 8QJ
☎ 01508 492497 🖹 01508 494353
Email: wildebeest@animalinns.co.uk
Web: www.animalinns.co.uk
This pub changed its name from the Red Lion in honour, if that's the right word, of a former landlord known to his regulars as 'the wild man' and 'beasty'. A sophisticated calm now imbues the large open-plan, oak-beamed bar and dining area, furnished with bare wooden tables - it's actually all quite rustic. What inevitably strikes the first-time visitor is the collection of African tribal art - masks, primitive instruments, large carved hippos and a giraffe. The food is modern European.
Open: 12-3 6-11 (Sun 12-3 7-10.30) Closed: Dec 25-26

Bar Meals: L served all week D served all week Av main course £13.95 **Restaurant Meals:** L served all week 12-2 D served all week 7-10 Av 3 course alc £25 **Brewery/Company:** Free House ◧: Adnams ♀: 12 **Children's Facilities:** Menu/Portions Games Highchair Food warming **Notes:** Garden: Beer garden, beautifully landscaped **Parking:** 40

SWANTON MORLEY
Darbys Freehouse
1&2 Elsing Road Dereham NR20 4NY
☎ 01362 637647 🖹 01362 637928
Email: louisedarby@hotmail.co.uk
Dir: *From A47 (Norwich to King's Lynn) take B1147 to Dereham*
Built in the 1700s as a large country house, then divided into cottages in the late 19th century. In 1987, after the village's last traditional pub closed, it was converted into the pub you see today, while retaining its old beams and inglenooks. Traditional pub food includes steak and mushroom pudding, braised lamb shank, chargrilled pork loin, scampi, beer-battered haddock, steaks, curries and a vegetarian selection. Children have their own menu and a play area.

Open: 11.30-3 6-11 (Sat 11.30-11, Sun 12-10.30)
Bar Meals: L served all week 12-2.15 D served all week 6.30-9.45 (Sat 12-9.45, Sun 12-8.45)
Restaurant Meals: L served all week 12-2.15 D served all week 6.30-9.45 **Brewery/Company:** Free House ◧: Woodforde's Wherry, Badger Tanglefoot, Adnams Broadside, Adnams Best, Theakstons Mild & 3 Guests **Children's Facilities:** Fam room Play area (Play area, toy box) Cutlery Games Highchair Food warming **Notes:** Dogs allowed in bar Garden: Beer garden & outdoor eating **Parking:** 75

THOMPSON
Chequers Inn ♀
Griston Road Thetford IP24 1PX
☎ 01953 483360 🖹 01953 488092
Email: richard@chequers_inn.wanadoo.co.uk
Web: www.thompsonchequers.co.uk
Dir: *Between Watton and Thetford off A1075*
The 16th-century Chequers, with its unusual low-slung thatched roof, is hidden among the trees on the edge of Thompson village. Food may be chosen from the bar menu, carte or daily specials board.
Open: 11.30-2.30 6.30-11 (Sun 12-3, 6.30-10.30) **Bar Meals:** L served all week 12-2 D served all week 6.30-9.30 Av main course £8.50 **Restaurant Meals:** L served all week 12-2 D served all week 6.30-9.30 Av 3 course alc £18 **Brewery/Company:** Free House

◧: Fuller's London Pride, Adnams Best, Wolf Best, Greene King IPA, Woodforde's Wherry Best Bitter ♀: 7 **Children's Facilities:** Play area (Swings & climbing frame) Menu/Portions Highchair Food warming Baby changing **Nearby:** Melsop Farm Park, Thetford Forest & Banham Zoo **Notes:** Dogs allowed in bar, in garden Garden: Lawned area, views **Parking:** 35

THORNHAM

Lifeboat Inn ★★ HL 🍴🍷

Ship Lane PE36 6LT

☎ 01485 512236 📄 01485 512323

Email: reception@lifeboatinn.co.uk

Web: www.lifeboatinn.co.uk

Dir: *A149 to Hunstanton, follow coast road to Thornham, pub 1st left*

The 16th-century inn overlooking the salt marshes and Thornham Harbour has a welcoming atmosphere. The conservatory is renowned for its ancient vine. The best available fish and game feature on the menus in the form of traditional country fare. Bowls of steaming mussels are legendary, harvested daily by local fishermen.

Open: 11-11 **Bar Meals:** L served all week 12-2.30 D served all week 6.30-9.30 Av main course £9

Restaurant Meals: D served all week 7-9.30 **Brewery/Company:** Free House 🍺: Woodforde's Wherry, Adnams, Greene King Abbot Ale & IPA 🍷: 10 **Children's Facilities:** Fam room Play area (Wooden play fort) Menu/Portions Highchair Food warming **Nearby:** Sealife Centre, beach **Notes:** Dogs allowed in bar, in garden Garden: Enclosed wall patio **Parking:** 100

THORPE MARKET

Green Farm Restaurant & Hotel ★★ HL

North Walsham Road Norwich NR11 8TH

☎ 01263 833602 📄 01263 833163

Email: enquiries@greenfarmhotel.co.uk

Web: www.greenfarmhotel.co.uk

Dir: *Situated on A149*

This 16th-century flint-faced former farmhouse overlooks the village green and features a pubby bar as well as a restaurant with an interesting menu. Typical dishes may include grilled marinated breast of duck served on a herbal ratatouille with a sage and balsamic jus, or seabass on roasted fennel and lemon cream sauce.

Open: 10-11 **Bar Meals:** L served all week 12-2 D served all week 6.30-8.30 (Fri-Sat 6.30-9) Av main course £9.50 **Restaurant Meals:** L served all week

12-2 D served all week 6.30-8.30 (Fri-Sat 6.30-9) Av 3 course alc £30 **Brewery/Company:** Free House 🍺: Greene King IPA, Wolf Best Bitter **Children's Facilities:** Menu/Portions Cutlery Games Highchair Food warming Baby changing **Nearby:** Shire Horse Centre, Elephant Play Barn **Notes:** Dogs allowed in bar Garden: Facing village green & enclosed side garden **Parking:** 60

TITCHWELL

Titchwell Manor Hotel ★★ HL 🍴🍴

Brancaster Kings Lynn PE31 8BB

☎ 01485 210221 📄 01485 210104

Email: margaret@titchwellmanor.com

Web: www.titchwellmanor.com

Dir: *A149 between Brancaster & Thornham*

This century old manor house has been updated. Smart public rooms include a lounge, informal bar, and a conservatory restaurant. The sea is a major influence on the menus. Families are particularly welcome and there is a colourful children's menu for under 12s.

Open: 11-11 **Bar Meals:** L served all week 12-2 D served all week 6.30-9.30 Av main course £10

Restaurant Meals: L served all week 12-2 D served all week 6.30-9.30 Av 3 course alc £20

Brewery/Company: Free House 🍺: Greene King IPA **Children's Facilities:** Play area (Books, games & garden) Menu/Portions Cutlery Games Highchair Food warming Baby changing **Nearby:** Hunstanton Sealife Centre, Bircham Windmill & Brancaster Beach **Notes:** Dogs allowed in bar, in garden water, kennel Garden: Large walled garden, views, summerhouse **Parking:** 50

NORFOLK

WELLS-NEXT-THE-SEA
The Crown Hotel ◉ ♟

The Buttlands NR23 1EX

☎ 01328 710209 📄 01328 711432

Email: reception@thecrownhotelwells.co.uk

Web: www.thecrownhotelwells.co.uk

Dir: *10m from Fakenham on B1105*

A former coaching inn, The Crown overlooks the tree-lined green known as The Buttlands. Food is served in the bar with its old beams and open fire, the sunny restaurant or vibrant conservatory. In fine weather you can sit outside on the sun deck. Diners can be sure of freshly prepared food from the best ingredients and flavours from around the world.

Open: 11-11 **Bar Meals:** L served all week 12-2.30 D served all week 6.30-9.30 Av main course £9

Restaurant Meals: D served all week 7-9 ◖: Adnams Bitter, Woodefordes Wherry, Adnams Guest Ale, Bitburger ♟: 12 **Children's Facilities:** Licence Menu/Portions Cutlery Games Highchair Food warming Baby changing **Nearby:** Wells-Walsingham Light Railway, Children's sack House, Seal trips **Notes:** Dogs on leads allowed in bar, in garden, Water bowls **Garden:** Decking area

WEST BECKHAM
The Wheatsheaf ♟

Manor Farm Church Road Holt NR25 6NX

☎ 01263 822110

Web: www.wheatsheaf.org.uk

Dir: *2m inland from Sheringham on A148*

Former manor house converted to a pub in 1984 and retaining many original features. Sample one of the real ales from Woodfordes Brewery and relax in the large garden. The specials board may feature saddle of lamb stuffed with spinach and stilton with a brandy gravy, pork and oregano meatballs in a tomato sauce on tagliatelle with garlic bread, or chick pea, pepper and pineapple curry served with rice and home-made chapattis.

Open: 11.30-3 6.30-11 (Winter 12-3, 6.30-11, Sun 12-3, 7-10) **Bar Meals:** L served all week 12-2 D served Mon-Sat 6.30-9 Av main course £7.50 **Restaurant Meals:** L served Tue-Sun 12-2 D served Tue-Sat 7-9 **Brewery/Company:** Free House ◖: Woodforde's Wherry Best Bitter, Nelson's Revenge, Norfolk Nog, Greene King IPA & Guest Ales ♟: 7 **Children's Facilities:** Fam room Play area (games room, tractor, rabbit run, swings) Menu/Portions Highchair Food warming **Nearby:** Sheringham Country Park, beach, Steam Railway **Notes:** Dogs allowed in bar, in garden, Water **Garden:** Large garden with gazebo and covered patio **Parking:** 50

WINTERTON-ON-SEA
Fishermans Return ♟

The Lane Great Yarmouth NR29 4BN

☎ 01493 393305 📄 01493 393951

Email: fishermans_return@btopenworld.com

Web: www.fishermans-return.co.uk

Dir: *8m N of Great Yarmouth on B1159*

This 300-year-old brick and flint pub is within walking distance of long beaches and National Trust land, where you can enjoy bird or seal watching. Under the same ownership for over 30 years, the pub has a popular menu with dishes such as Whitby scampi, burgers, and seafood omelette, plus daily specials.

Open: 11-2.30 6-11 (Sat 11-11, Sun 12-10.30) **Bar Meals:** L served all week 12-2 D served all week 6.30-9 Av main course £9.25 **Brewery/Company:** Free House ◖: Woodforde's Wherry & Norfolk Nog, Adnams Best Bitter & Broadside and Greene King IPA & Guest Ales ♟: 10 **Children's Facilities:** Fam room Play area (Slide, climbing frame & swing) Menu/Portions Cutlery Highchair Food warming **Nearby:** Sandy Beach, Broadland Boats **Notes:** Dogs allowed in bar, in garden **Garden:** enclosed, with tables **Parking:** 50

WOODBASTWICK
The Fur & Feather Inn ♟
Slad Lane Norwich NR13 6HQ
☎ 01603 720003 🖹 01603 722266
Web: www.thefurandfeatherinn.co.uk
Dir: *Leave Norwich on Salhouse/Wroxham road, follow brown signs for Woodfordes Brewery.*
This idyllic country pub is ideal for real ale lovers: Woodforde's Brewery is next door, and all eight ales are offered here, straight from the cask. The pub was originally two farm cottages, and now boasts three cosy bar areas and a smart restaurant where you can enjoy meals made using Woodforde's ales - chicken, leek and Great Eastern Ale pie, for example, alongside other interesting choices such as pot roasted venison or stuffed plaice fillets.

Open: 11.30-3 6-11 (Summer Mon-Sat 11.30-11, Sun 12-10.30) **Bar Meals:** L served all week 12-2 D served all week 6-9 (Sun 12-2.30) Av main course £8 **Restaurant Meals:** L served all week 12-2 D served all week 6-9 (Sun 12-2.30) **Brewery/Company:** Woodforde'S 🍺: Woodforde's Wherry, Great Eastern, Norfolk Nog, Nelsons Revenge, Fur and Feather Bitter ♟: 8 **Children's Facilities:** Highchair Food warming Baby changing **Nearby:** Salhouse Broad **Notes:** Garden: Large garden with fenced pond **Parking:** 100

ABINGDON
The Merry Miller ♟
Cothill OX13 6JW
☎ 01865 390390 🖹 01865 390040
Email: rob@merrymiller.co.uk
Web: www.merrymiller.co.uk
Dir: *1m from the Marcham interchange on the A34*
Any inventory of the Merry Miller must include its wealth of risqué prints. Despite the beams, flagstones and stripped pine tables, the interior of this 17th-century former granary is more redolent of Tuscany - which at least ensures that the pasta dishes feel at home! But lunch could just as easily be a club sandwich or seafood salad bowl, whilst evening diners might choose roasted Gressingham duck; or tomato, goats' cheese and Puy lentil tartlettes.

Open: 12-2.45 (Fri/Sat 12-11, Sun 12-10.30) **Bar Meals:** L served all week 12-2.45 D served all week 6.30-9.45 (Sun all day) **Restaurant Meals:** L served all week 12-2.45 D served all week 6.30-9.45 Av 3 course alc £20 **Brewery/Company:** Greene King 🍺: Greene King IPA & Old Speckled Hen ♟: 15 **Children's Facilities:** Menu/Portions Cutlery Games Highchair Food warming Baby changing **Notes:** Dogs allowed in bar Garden: small patio, 20 parasol-covered seats **Parking:** 60

ARDINGTON
The Boars Head ★★★★ INN 🏵🏵 ♟
Church Street Wantage OX12 8QA
☎ 01235 833254 🖹 01235 833254
Email: info@boarsheadardington.co.uk
Web: www.boarsheadardington.co.uk
Dir: *Off A417 E of Wantage*
The pretty, 400-year-old Boars Head is tucked away beside the church within the beautifully maintained Lockinge Estate. Ardington is an ideal base for walking or cycling, and has paths winding down to nearby villages or running up to the ancient Ridgeway. For food, look to the full menu or the reasonably-priced 'menu rapide'.
Open: 12-3 6.30-11 **Bar Meals:** L served all week 12-2.30 D served all week 7-10 **Restaurant Meals:** L served all week 12-2.30 D served all week 7-10 Av 3 course alc £33 🍺: Hook Norton Old Hooky, West Berkshire Brewery Dr. Hexter's, Warsteiner, Butts Brewery, Barbus Barbus, Coteswold Lager ♟: 8 **Children's Facilities:** Menu/Portions Games Highchair Food warming Baby changing **Nearby:** White Horse at Uffington, Didcot Steam Railway Centre **Notes:** Garden: Patio area, three tables **Parking:** 20

BAMPTON
The Romany
Bridge Street nr Witney OX18 2HA
☎ 01993 850237 📄 01993 852133
Email: romany@barbox.net
A shop until 20 years ago, The Romany is housed in an 18th-century building of Cotswold stone with a beamed bar, log fires and intimate dining room. The choice of food ranges from bar snacks and bar meals to a full à la carte restaurant menu, with home-made specials like hotpot, Somerset pork, or steak and ale pie. There is a good range of vegetarian choices. Regional singers provide live entertainment a couple of times a month.
Open: 11-11 **Bar Meals:** L served all week 12-2 D served all week 6.30-9 Av main course £6 **Restaurant Meals:** L served all week 12-2 D served all week 6.30-9 **Brewery/Company:** Free House 🍺: Archers Village, plus guests **Children's Facilities:** Play area Menu/Portions Games Highchair Food warming **Notes:** Dogs allowed, Water Garden: Food served outside **Parking:** 8

BANBURY
The Wykham Arms 🍷
Temple Mill Rd Sibford Gower OX15 5RX
☎ 01295 788808 📄 01295 788806
Email: info@wykhamarms.co.uk
Web: www.wykhamarms.co.uk
Dir: *Between Banbury and Shipston on Stour off B4035. 20m S of Stratford-Upon-Avon*
An early 17th-century thatched inn built of mellow Hornton stone and originally part of William of Wykham's estate. The bar menu is typified by dishes like Hooky braised beef pie with crisp pastry croute. Restaurant mains include dishes such as baked Cornish plaice with ratatouille and dill crushed potato
Open: 11-3 6-11.30 **Bar Meals:** L served Tue-Sun 12-2.30 D served Tue-Sat 6-9.45 (Sun 12-3.30) Av main course £13 **Restaurant Meals:** L served Tue-Sun 12-2.30 D served Tue-Sat 7-9.45 (Sun 12-3) Av 3 course alc £27.50 **Brewery/Company:** Free House 🍺: Hook Norton Best, Guinness 🍷: 12 **Children's Facilities:** Licence Menu/Portions Highchair Food warming **Notes:** Garden: Views of village Oxfordshire countryside **Parking:** 30

BANBURY
Ye Olde Reindeer Inn
47 Parsons Street OX16 5NA
☎ 01295 264031 📄 01295 264018
Email: tonypuddifoot@aol.com
Dir: *1m from M40 junct 11, in town centre just off market square*
Oliver Cromwell stayed in the Reindeer during the Battle of Edge Hill in 1642, and royalty, as well as the merely plain rich, used the magnificent Globe Room on their way to and from the capital. The original panelling was removed from here before the First World War and stored in London, finally being returned in 1964. The menu comprises hot or toasted sandwiches, ploughman's, omelettes, salads and other snacks, with daily specials.
Open: 11-11 (Sun 12-3.30) **Bar Meals:** L served Mon-Sat 11-2.30 D served Mon -Sat11-2.30 (Sun 12-3) Av main course £4.95 **Restaurant Meals:** L served all week 12-2 D served all week 12-2 (Sun 12-3) **Brewery/Company:** Hook Norton Brewery 🍺: Hook Norton, Best , Hook Norton Haymaker, Hook Norton Old, Hook Norton 12 days, Hook Norton Dark **Children's Facilities:** Fam room Menu/Portions Cutlery Games Highchair Food warming **Notes:** Garden: Courtyard, tables and chairs **Parking:** 14

BARNARD GATE
The Boot Inn ♟
Eynsham OX29 6XE
☎ 01865 881231
Email: info@theboot-inn.com
Web: www.theboot-inn.com
Dir: *Off the A40 between Witney & Eynsham*
Not surprisingly, this popular pub is renowned for its collection of boots and other footwear given to the pub by a host of celebrities, including The Bee Gees, George Best and Jeremy Irons. Run by Australian-born chef Craig Foster, the Boot offers a welcoming bar and secluded dining areas. A typical lunch menu might include Cumberland sausage ring; traditional gammon, egg and chips; and home-made burger with brie and bacon. Good choice of salads and snacks and extensive wine list.

Open: 11-3 6-11 (All day in summer) **Bar Meals:** L served all week 12-2.30 D served all week 7-10 **Restaurant Meals:** D served 7-9.30 Av 3 course alc £20 **Brewery/Company:** Free House ▩: Hook Norton Best, Adnams Best, Fullers London Pride, Youngs Best ♟: 7 **Children's Facilities:** Menu/Portions Highchair Food warming **Parking:** 20

BLACK BOURTON
The Vines ♟
Burford Road Bampton Black Bourton OX18 2PF
☎ 01993 843559 ▤ 01993 840080
Email: vinesrestaurant@aol.co.uk
Web: www.vinesblackbourton.co.uk
Dir: *From A40 Witney, take A4095 to Faringdon, then 1st right after Bampton to Black Bourton*
Tucked away in the beautiful village of Black Bourton, this picturesque Cotswold stone hotel offers excellent food and wine. John Clegg of the BBC's Real Rooms Team has recently renovated the stylish restaurant, where the appetising menus feature modern British dishes with an international twist.
Open: 12-3 6-11 (Mon 6-11) **Bar Meals:** L served Tue-Sun 12-2 D served Mon-Sun 6.30-9.30 Av main course

£6.50 **Restaurant Meals:** L served Tue-Sun 12-2 D served Tue-Sun 6.30-9.30 (Closed Mon lunch) Av 3 course alc £22 ▩: Old Hookey, Tetley Smooth, Carlsberg-Tetley ♟: 7 **Children's Facilities:** Licence Menu/Portions Highchair Food warming **Nearby:** Cotswold Wildlife Park, Blenheim Palace **Notes:** Garden: Lawn area, seating & 'Aunt Sally' facility **Parking:** 70

BLOXHAM
The Elephant & Castle
Nr Banbury OX15 4LZ
☎ 01295 720383
Email: elephant.bloxham@btinternet.com
Web: www.elephantandcastle.tablesir.com
Dir: *Just off A361*
The arch of this 15th-century Cotswold-stone coaching inn still straddles the former Banbury to Chipping Norton turnpike. Locals play darts or shove-ha'penny in the big wood-floored bar, whilst the two-roomed lounge boasts a bar-billiards table and a large inglenook fireplace. The reasonably priced menu offers a range of sandwiches and crusty filled baguettes, plus pub favourites like roast chicken breast with stuffing, crispy battered cod, and seafood platter.

Open: 10-3 5-11 (Sat, Sun-open all day) **Bar Meals:** L served Mon-Sat 12-2 Av main course £5.50 **Restaurant Meals:** L served Mon-Sat 12-2 **Brewery/Company:** Hook Norton Brewery ▩: Hook Norton Best Bitter, Hook Norton Seasonal Ales, Guest Ales **Children's Facilities:** Fam room Play area (Enclosed lawn) Menu/Portions Food warming Baby changing **Nearby:** Wild Fowl Centre, Hook Norton Brewery Visitor Centre, Broughton Castle **Notes:** Garden: Raised lawn in flower filled garden, patio **Parking:** 20

BURFORD
Golden Pheasant ♥
91 High Street OX18 4QA
☎ 01993 823223 🖺 01993 822621
Email: robrichardson@goldenpheasant-burford.co.uk
Web: www.goldenpheasant-burford.co.uk
Dir: *M40 junct 8 and follow signs A40 Cheltenham into Burford*
Built of mellow Cotswold limestone, this 18th-century private hotel has a cheery stone-flagged, stone-walled bar, with adjacent lounge and brasserie. Seek out the gravadlax with lemon mayonnaise, antipasti, or deep-fried camembert with warm cranberry sauce starters, then consider smoked haddock with spring onion mash and Welsh rarebit sauce; beef stroganoff with mushrooms and rice; or stir-fried vegetable curry.

Open: 9-11 **Bar Meals:** L served all week 12-2.30 D served all week 6.30-9.30 Av main course £11.45 **Restaurant Meals:** L served all week 12-2.30 D served all week 6.30-9 🍺: Abbot, IPA ♥: 7 **Children's Facilities:** Menu/Portions Highchair Baby changing **Nearby:** Cotswold Wildlife Park, Burford Animal Centre **Notes:** Dogs allowed in bar Garden: Patio **Parking:** 12

BURFORD
The Inn for All Seasons ★★ HL ♥
The Barringtons OX18 4TN
☎ 01451 844324 🖺 01451 844375
Email: sharp@innforallseasons.com
Web: www.innforallseasons.com
Dir: *3m W of Burford on A40*
This Grade II-listed Cotswolds coaching inn has served travellers on the London to Wales road since the 16th century. Within its solid walls is a treasure-trove of ancient oak beams, inglenooks and contemporary furniture. There are several guest ales, among them always a Wychwood from nearby Witney, and a large selection of wines by the glass. The Sharp family has owned the Inn since 1986; Matthew Sharp, the chef, has worked with the Roux Brothers and Anton Mosimann. Connections with the right people in Brixham guarantee a wonderful supply of fish for dishes such as poached wing of skate with a caper and shallot butter, or grilled Dover sole.

Open: 11-2.30 6-11 (Sun 12-3, 7-10.30) **Bar Meals:** L served all week 11.30-2.30 D served all week 6.30-9.30 (Sun 12-2.30, 7-9) Av main course £9.95 **Restaurant Meals:** L served all week 11.30-2.30 D served all week 6.30-9.30 (Sun 12-2.30, 7-9) **Brewery/Company:** Free House 🍺: Wadworth 6X, Interbrew Bass, Wychwood, Badger, Sharps & Doom Bar ♥: 15 **Children's Facilities:** Play area (Garden) Menu/Portions Cutlery Games Highchair Food warming Baby changing **Nearby:** Cotswold Wildlife Park, Birdland & Model Village Bourton on Water **Notes:** Dogs allowed in bar, in garden, in bedrooms, Water Garden: Small grass area, tables, good views **Parking:** 80

CHALGROVE
The Red Lion Inn ♥
The High Street OX44 7SS
☎ 01865 890625
Email: annie@redlionchalgrove.co.uk
Dir: *B480 from Oxford Ring road, through Stadhampton, left then right at mini-rdbt, at Chalgrove Airfield right fork into village*
Parts of this lovely cream-painted and beamed pub date back to the 11th century. Later in its life, in 1637, it became the property of the church and provided free dining and carousing for the church wardens. The emphasis today is on a warm welcome, a good pint of real ale, and both traditional and imaginative eating.
Open: 12-3 6-11.30 (Winter 12-2.30, Sun 7-11) Closed: 1 Jan **Bar Meals:** L served all week 12-2 D served Mon-Sat 6.30-9 Av main course £9.50 **Restaurant Meals:** L served all week 12-2 D served Mon-Sat 6.30-9 Av 3 course alc £19 **Brewery/Company:** Free House 🍺: Fuller's London Pride, Adnams Best, Timothy Taylors Landlord ♥: 8 **Children's Facilities:** Play area Menu/Portions Cutlery Food warming **Notes:** Dogs allowed in bar, in garden Garden: Large, with seating

CHINNOR

Sir Charles Napier ☺☺ ♀

Spriggs Alley OX39 4BX

☎ 01494 483011 📠 01494 485311

Web: www.sircharlesnapier.co.uk

Dir: *M40 junct 6 to Chinnor. Turn right at rdbt, up hill to Spriggs Alley*

High in the beechwood-covered Chilterns is this welcoming pub with huge log fires, comfortable sofas and a jumble of old chairs and tables. In the summer, lunch is served on the vine- and wisteria-shaded terrace overlooking the extensive lawns and herb gardens. Come winter and locals bring in edible fungi and berries, as well as pigeons and pheasants for the pot. Inside and out are works by local sculptor Michael Cooper.

Open: 12-3.30 6.30-12 Closed: 25-26 Dec **Bar Meals:**

L served Tue-Fri 12-2.30 D served Tue-Thu 7-9.30 Av main course £11.50 **Restaurant Meals:** L served Tue-Sun 12-2.30 D served Tue-Sat 7-10 (Sun 12-3.30) **Brewery/Company:** Free House ◀: Wadworth 6X, Wadwoth IPA ♀: 15 **Children's Facilities:** Menu/Portions Highchair Food warming **Notes:** Garden: Large garden and terrace **Parking:** 50

CUDDESDON

Bat & Ball Inn ♀

28 High Street Wheatley OX44 9HJ

☎ 01865 874379 📠 01865 873363

Email: bb@traditionalvillageinns.co.uk

Web: www.traditionalvillageinns.co.uk

Dir: *Through Wheatley towards Garsington, take left turn, signed Cuddesdon*

Do not be surprised to discover that the bar of this former coaching inn is packed to the gunnels with cricketing memorabilia. The owners claim that their collection puts to shame even that of Lords cricket ground! The comprehensive menu, supplemented by daily specials, is likely to feature steaks, fresh-baked pie of the day, herb-battered fresh cod, and maybe chargrilled Toulouse sausages. Lighter meals include homemade lasagne,

lamb Peshwari, and warm spinach and pancetta salad.
Open: 11-11 **Bar Meals:** L served all week 12-2.45 D served all week 6.30-9.45 (Sun 12-9.30) Av main course £11 **Restaurant Meals:** L served all week 12-2.30 D served all week 6.30-9.30 (Sun 12-9.30) Av 3 course alc £22 **Brewery/Company:** Free House ◀: Marston's Pedigree, House LBW Bitter, Guinness, Stella & Carlsberg ♀: 10 **Children's Facilities:** Menu/Portions Cutlery Games Highchair Food warming **Nearby:** Millets Farm, Shotover Country Park **Notes:** Dogs allowed in bar, Water Bowls Garden: Small patio overlooking Oxfordshire Downs **Parking:** 20

CUMNOR

Bear & Ragged Staff ♀

28 Appleton Road nr Oxford OX2 9QH

☎ 01865 862329 📠 01865 865947

Dir: *A420 from Oxford, right to Cumnor on B4017.*

A 700-year-old pub allegedly haunted by the mistress of the Earl of Warwick. With a tad more certainty it is believed that Oliver Cromwell frequented the pub, which may explain the removal of the royal crest above one of the two massive, original fireplaces, which with the wooden beams and floors, help to create a powerfully historic atmosphere. The pub caters for a wide cross-section of locals, as well as being popular with visitors from further afield, many drawn by the extensive menu that includes home-made steak and kidney pudding and the locally renowned Cape bobotie.

Open: 12-11 (Sun 12-10.30) **Bar Meals:** L served all week 12-2.30 D served all week 6-9.30 **Restaurant Meals:** L served all week 12-3 D served all week 6-9 **Brewery/Company:** Morrells Of Oxford ◀: IPA, Old Speckled Hen, Abbot Ale, Old Hooky, plus guest ales **Children's Facilities:** Play area Highchair **Notes:** Garden: Food served outdoors, patio, BBQ **Parking:** 60

CUMNOR
The Vine Inn ♀

11 Abingdon Road OX2 9QN

☎ 01865 862567 📄 01865 862567

Dir: *A420 from Oxford, right onto B4017*

An old village pub whose name, when you see the frontage, needs no explanation. In 1560, the suspicious death of an Earl's wife in Cumnor Place first had people asking "Did she fall, or was she pushed?". A typical menu here could include lamb shank with a red wine and mint sauce, pan-fried fillet steak with brandy and mushroom sauce, and the day's fresh fish. There's also a good range of snacks. Children love the huge garden.
Open: 11-3 6-11 (Sun 12-10.30) **Bar Meals:** L served all week 12-2.15 D served all week 6-9.15 (Sat 12-3, Sun 12-6) **Restaurant Meals:** L served all week 12-2.15 D served all week 6.30-9.15 (Sat 12-3 Sun 12-6) **Brewery/Company:** Punch Taverns 🍺: Adnams Bitter, Carlsberg-Tetely Tetely Bitter, Hook Norton, guest beers ♀: 7 **Children's Facilities:** Licence Play area (Climbing frame, swings & slide) Menu/Portions Cutlery Games Highchair Food warming Baby changing **Notes:** Dogs allowed in bar, in garden, in bedrooms, Water **Garden:** Fenced with tables and chairs & lawn area **Parking:** 45

CUXHAM
The Half Moon

nr Watlington OX49 5NF

☎ 01491 614151 📄 01491 614606

Email: reservations@halfmooncuxham.com

Web: www.halfmooncuxham.com

Alain Madoui presides over this 16th-century thatched pub, tucked away beside a stream in a quiet village 4 miles from the M40 (J6). Completely refitted after a fire a few years ago, the Half Moon offers a cosy, homely welcome along with plenty of characterful nooks and crannies, and quaint little fireplaces. Ingredients for their menus are sourced locally or from France, and are combined into delicious dishes such as veal kidneys served with a mustard sauce; red mullet with capers and orange sauce; or palm heart, Roquefort cheese, grape and pine nut salad.
Open: 12-2.30 5.30-11 (Sun 12-10.30) **Bar Meals:** L served all week 12-2 D served all week 7-9 Av main course £11 **Restaurant Meals:** L served all week 12-2 D served all week 7-9.30 Av 3 course alc £60 🍺: Brakspear Ordinary , 4 Seasons **Children's Facilities:** Fam room Play area (Play area) **Notes:** Garden: food served outside **Parking:** 20

DORCHESTER
The White Hart ★★★ HL ◉◉ ♀

High Street OX10 7HN

☎ 01865 340074 📄 01865 341082

Email: whitehart@oxfordshire-hotels.co.uk

Web: www.oxfordshire-hotels.co.uk

Dir: *A4074 Oxford to Reading, 5m junct 7 M40 A329 to Wallingford*

The White Hart is located eight miles south of Oxford right at the centre of the High Street in the historic village of Dorchester-on-Thames. The inn has been providing hospitality to travellers for around 400 years, and the bars attract locals, residents and diners alike. Innovative dishes are prepared from fresh ingredients. A good-value fixed-price lunch is available Monday to Saturday, and the carte menu doubles your choice.
Open: 11-11 **Bar Meals:** L served all week 12-2.30 D served all week 6.30-9.30 **Restaurant Meals:** L served all week 12-2.30 D served all week 6.30-9.30 Av 3 course alc £28 🍺: Greene King, Marstons Pedigree, St Austell Tribute, Deucars Caledeonian IPA ♀: 12 **Children's Facilities:** Menu/Portions Highchair Food warming **Nearby:** LegoLand **Parking:** 28

FARINGDON
The Lamb at Buckland 🌐🍷
Lamb Lane Buckland SN7 8QN
☎ 01367 870484 📠 01367 870675
Email: enquiries@thelambatbuckland.co.uk
Web: www.thelambatbuckland.co.uk
Dir: *Just off A420 3m E of Faringdon*

In a Cotswold-fringe village in the Vale of the White Horse, the 18th-century Lamb displays a fair few appropriately ovine artefacts. Its reliable menu, supplemented by daily specials, offers roast rack of English lamb with mint and sorrel sauce; beefsteak and kidney wholemeal pastry pie; roast breast of Gressingham duck with apple and Calvados sauce; and whole sea bass stuffed with roasted fennel and fresh herbs, accompanied by a light Pernod sauce.

Open: 10.30-3 5.30-11 Closed: 24 Dec-7 Jan **Bar Meals:** L served Tue-Sun 12-2 D served Tue-Sat 6.30-9.30 Av main course £10 **Restaurant Meals:** L served Tue-Sun 12-2 D served Tue-Sat 6.30-9.30 Av 3 course alc £22.50 **Brewery/Company:** Free House 🛢: Hook Norton, Adnams Broadside, Arkells 3Bs 🍷: 12 **Children's Facilities:** Menu/Portions Games Highchair Food warming **Nearby:** Cotswold Wildlife Park, White Horse Hill & Oxford Story **Notes:** Garden: Food served outside **Parking:** 50

FARINGDON
The Trout at Tadpole Bridge 🍷
Buckland Marsh SN7 8RF
☎ 01367 870382
Email: info@trout-inn.co.uk
Web: www.trout-inn.co.uk
Dir: *Halfway between Oxford & Swindon on the A420, take road signed Bampton, pub is approx 2m.*

This 17th-century pub lies deep in the countryside on the south bank of the River Thames. First a coal storage house, then cottages, it became an inn towards the end of the 19th century. In 1996 it was bought by Chef/patron Chris Green who has transformed it into a light and airy hostelry, with polished wooden tables, oak beams, flagstone floors, a roaring log fire in winter, and a very pretty riverside garden. Isolated it may be, but its popularity is in no small measure due to the well-above average food, stylishly cooked using fresh local produce. A meal could begin with pressed terrine of ham hock, foie grass and ox tongue with piccalilli and follow with the likes of roast loin of venison with mustard galette.
Open: 11.30-3 6-11 (Closed Sun eve) Closed: 25,31 Dec, 1 Jan & 1st wk in Feb **Bar Meals:** L served all week 12-2 D served Mon-Sat 7-9 Av main course £12.95 **Restaurant Meals:** L served all week 12-2 D served Mon-Sat 7-9 **Brewery/Company:** Free House 🛢: Ramsbury Bitter, Youngs PA Bitter, Butts Barbus, West Berkshire Brewery Mr Chubbs Lunchtime Bitter, Full Circle 🍷: 10 **Children's Facilities:** Cutlery Highchair Food warming **Nearby:** Cotswold Wildlife Park, Blenheim Palace & River Thames **Notes:** Dogs allowed in bar Garden: next to the River Thames **Parking:** 70

FIFIELD
Merrymouth Inn 🍷
Stow Road OX7 6HR
☎ 01993 831652 📠 01993 830840
Email: tim@merrymouthinn.fsnet.co.uk
Web: www.hotelinthecotswolds.co.uk
Dir: *On A424 between Burford (3m) & Stow-on-the-Wold (4m)*

A beautifully restored Cotswold inn dating back to the 13th century. A blackboard of fresh fish, vegetarian and other daily specials supplements standard menu main dishes such as roast sirloin of beef.
Open: 12-2.30 6-10.30 (Closed Sun eve in winter) **Bar Meals:** L served all week 12-2 D served all week 6.30-9 (Sun 7-8.30) Av main course £10 **Restaurant Meals:** L served all week 12-2 D served all week 6.30-9 (Sun 7-9) Av 3 course alc £19 **Brewery/Company:** Free House 🛢: Hook Norton Best Bitter, Adnams Broadside 🍷: 7 **Children's Facilities:** Menu/Portions Games Highchair Food warming **Nearby:** Cotswold Wildlife Park, Birdland, Cotswold Farm Park **Notes:** Dogs allowed in bar, in garden Garden: Small patio & enclosed garden at pubs front **Parking:** 70

FILKINS
The Five Alls ♦♦♦ ⚲

GL7 3JQ

☎ 01367 860306

Email: info@thefivealls.co.uk

Web: www.thefivealls.co.uk

Dir: *A40 exit Burford, Filkins 4m, A361 to Lechlade*

An 18th-century inn in a peaceful village on the edge of the Cotswolds. Home-made fare ranges from steak and chips to lobster with spaghetti in tomato and cream sauce. Sandwiches and omelettes are available at lunch. The garden has an over-sized chess set and quoits. **Open:** 11-3 5.30-11 (Sat/Sun all day) **Bar Meals:** L served all week 12-2.30 D served all week 6.30-9 (Sun 12-7) Av main course £10 **Restaurant Meals:** L served all week 12-2.30 D served all week 6.30-9 (Sun 12-7)

Av 3 course alc £20 🍺: Brakspear Bitter, Brakspear Special & Brakspear/Wychwood Seasonal Ales ⚲: 8 **Children's Facilities:** Play area (Garden) Menu/Portions Cutlery Highchair Food warming **Nearby:** Burford Wildlife Park, Cotswold Water Park, Blenheim Palace **Notes:** Dogs allowed in bar, in garden **Garden:** Large lawned garden with patio **Parking:** 40

GORING
Miller of Mansfield ⚲

High Street nr Reading RG8 9AW

☎ 01491 872829 📠 01491 873100

Email: reservations@millerofmansfield.com

Web: www.millerofmansfield.co.uk

Dir: *From Pangbourne A329 to Streatley, then R on B4009, 0.5m to Goring*

This beautiful old building has recently been renovated. There is a bar menu and a restaurant open for breakfast, lunch and dinner 365 days a year. Modern European menus might offer roast loin of venison or grilled fillet of sea bass in the restaurant, and fish and chips in the bar. **Open:** 8-11 **Bar Meals:** L served all week 11-10 D served all week 11-10 (Sun 12-4, 6.30-9.30) Av main course £11.95 **Restaurant Meals:** L served all week

12-3 D served all week 6-10 Av 3 course alc £22 **Brewery/Company:** Free House 🍺: Good Old Boy, Rebellion IPA, Organic Jester, San Miguel & Kronenberg ⚲: 15 **Children's Facilities:** Menu/Portions Games Highchair Food warming Baby changing **Notes:** Dogs allowed in bar, Water **Garden:** Seating, plants, statues, canopy & heaters **Parking:** 3

HAILEY
Bird in Hand ⚲

Whiteoak Green Nr Witney OX29 9XP

☎ 01993 868321 📠 01993 868702

Email: welcome@birdinhandinn.co.uk

Web: www.birdinhandinn.co.uk

Dir: *From Witney travel N onto B4022 through Hailey to Whiteoak Green for 5m. At Charlbury continue S onto B4022 for 5m.*

Classic Cotswold stone inn, a Grade II listed building dating from the 16th century, set in the Oxfordshire countryside just outside Hailey. The restaurant offers imaginative cooking using local produce. **Open:** 11-11 **Bar Meals:** L served all week 12-3 D served all week 6-9 (Fri-Sat dinner 6-10, Sun 12-6) Av main course £12 **Restaurant Meals:** L served all week

12-3 D served all week 6-9 (Fri-Sat 10, Sun 12-6) Av 3 course alc £25 **Brewery/Company:** Heavitree 🍺: Old Speckled Hen, Brakspear, Hobgoblin & Old Hooky ⚲: 8 **Children's Facilities:** Menu/Portions Highchair Food warming Baby changing **Nearby:** Cogges Museum, Deer Park, Blenheim Palace & Bourton on the water **Notes:** **Garden:** Food served, patio & lawn areas **Parking:** 100

HENLEY-ON-THAMES
The Cherry Tree Inn ★★★★ RR ◉ ♟
Stoke Row RG9 5QA

☎ 01491 680430 📄 01491 682168

Email: info@thecherrytreeinn.com
Web: www.thecherrytreeinn.com

There's a confident blend of ancient and modern inside this 400-year-old listed building. Originally three flint cottages, the Cherry Tree has been re-fitted by its new owners, who have complemented the original features with contemporary decor, strong colours and modern furnishings. Service is informal, with a variety of classic European dishes prepared from fresh local ingredients.
Open: 12-11 (Sun 12-10.30) Closed: 25-26 Dec & 1 Jan
Bar Meals: L served all week12-3 D served all week Av main course £7.50 **Restaurant Meals:** L served all week 12-3 D served all week 7-10.30 (Sun 12-4, 7-10) Av 3 course alc £21 **Brewery/Company:** Brakspear
🍺: Brakspear Bitter, Brakspear Special, Stella, Guinness & Hoegaarden ♟: 10 **Children's Facilities:** Licence Menu/Portions Games Highchair Food warming Baby changing **Notes:** Dogs allowed in bar Garden: Large, south facing with lots of seats **Parking:** 25

HENLEY-ON-THAMES
The Five Horseshoes ♟
Maidensgrove RG9 6EX

☎ 01491 641282 📄 01491 641086

Email: admin@thefivehorseshoes.co.uk
Web: www.thefivehorseshoes.co.uk
Dir: *From Henley-on-Thames take A4130, after 1m take B480 to the right, signed Stonor. At Stonor, turn left and follow through woods and over common, pub on left.*
The Five Horseshoes is located in an area of outstanding natural beauty with two gardens offering stunning views over the Chiltern Hills. One garden has a barbecue, and hog roasts are held in summer. Inside are two snug bar areas and a large restaurant.
Open: 12-3.30 6-11 (Sat 12-11, Sun 12-6) **Bar Meals:** L served all week 12-2.30 D served all week 6.30-10 (Sat 12-3, Sun 12-4) Av main course £9.50 **Restaurant Meals:** L served all week 12-2.30 D served all week 6.30-10 (Sat 12-3, Sun 12-4) **Brewery/Company:** Brakspear 🍺: Brakspear Ordinary, Special & Seasonal ♟: 9 **Children's Facilities:** Menu/Portions Games Highchair Food warming **Notes:** Dogs allowed in bar, in garden Garden: 2 gardens, 1 with a BBQ **Parking:** 85

HENLEY-ON-THAMES
The Golden Ball ♟
Lower Assendon RG9 6AH

☎ 01491 574157 📄 01491 574157

Email: thegoldenball@tiscali.co.uk
Dir: *A4130, right onto B480, pub 300yds on left*
Traditional country pub in the Stonor Valley a mile from Henley-on-Thames. It is a listed brick and flint building, originally two 17th-century cottages. Dick Turpin frequented the place and hid from capture in a recess by the chimney upstairs. There's a south facing beer garden for fine weather, while log fires keep things cosy in winter. Food includes sandwiches, pies, butcher's sausage of the day and beer-battered haddock.
Open: 11-3 6-11 **Bar Meals:** L served all week 12-2.30 D served all week 7-9 Av main course £9.60 🍺: Brakspear Ordinary, Brakspear Seasonal, Brakspear Special, Fosters & Kronenbourg ♟: 11 **Children's Facilities:** Licence Play area (Swings, slide & tower) Menu/Portions Cutlery Games Highchair Food warming **Nearby:** Nature Reserve **Notes:** Dogs allowed in bar, must be on lead, Water provided Garden: Large south facing with seating **Parking:** 30

OXFORDSHIRE

OXFORDSHIRE

HENLEY-ON-THAMES
The White Hart Nettlebed ★★★ HL ⬢⬢ ♀
High Street Nettlebed RG9 5DD
☎ 01491 641245 📄 01491 649018
Email: Info@whitehartnettlebed.com
Web: www.whitehartnettlebed.com
Dir: *On the A4130 between Henley-on-Thames and Wallingfrod*
Once used as a billeting house for Cavalier troops during the English Civil War, this beautifully restored building dates from the 17th century. With its chic bar, restaurant and bistro it attracts those who seek stylish surroundings and a welcoming atmosphere. Dining styles vary from bar sandwiches, to an à la carte restaurant menu.
Open: 7-11 **Bar Meals:** L served all week 12-2.30 D served all week 6-10 (Sun 12-4) **Restaurant Meals:** L served all week 12-2.30 D served all week 6-10 (Sun 12-4) Av 3 course alc £20 🍺: Brakspear, Guinness, Fosters, Stella & Strongbow ♀: 12 **Children's Facilities:** Licence Fam room Play area Menu/Portions Cutlery Games Highchair Food warming Baby changing **Nearby:** Riverides, Rowing Museum and Parks, Legoland & Coral Reef **Notes:** Garden: Large lawned area with seating

HOOK NORTON
The Gate Hangs High ★★★★ INN
Whichford Road Nr Banbury OX15 5DF
☎ 01608 737387 📄 01608 737870
Email: gatehangshigh@aol
Web: www.gatehangshigh.com
Dir: *Off A361 SW of Banbury*
A charming country pub in beautiful countryside near the mystical Rollright Stones, and Hook Norton, from whose renowned brewery come its cask-conditioned, dry-hopped ales. The pub is on the old drovers' road from Wales to Banbury; a tollgate that once stood outside was said to hang high enough for small creatures to pass under, but owners of larger creatures had to pay. The Gate is well known for dishes featuring black pudding; its rösti version, topped with bacon and poached egg, is one. Also typical are salmon and prawn pie; roasted half-duck with leeks and marmalade; and fillet steak with stilton and bacon. The blackboard offers daily fish and other specials. Children have their own play area outside.
Open: 12-3 6-11 (All day at wknds, Sun 12-4, 7-10.30) Closed: 25 Dev Eve **Bar Meals:** L served all week 12-2.30 D served all week 6-10 Av main course £8.95 **Restaurant Meals:** L served all week 12-2.30 D served all week 6-10 (Sat 12-11, Sun 12-10.30) Av 3 course alc £8.95 **Brewery/Company:** Hook Norton Brewery 🍺: Hook Norton - Best, Old Hooky, Haymaker & Generation **Children's Facilities:** Menu/Portions Highchair Food warming **Nearby:** Water Fowl Park Wigginton, Wildlife Park Burford **Notes:** Dogs allowed in bar, in garden, Water Garden: Wonderful views overlooking fields, courtyard **Parking:** 30

KELMSCOT
The Plough Inn
nr Lechlade GL7 3HG
☎ 01367 253543 📄 01367 252514
Email: plough@kelmscottgl7.fsnet.co.uk
Web: www.theploughatkelmscott.co.uk
Dir: *From M4 onto A419 then A361 to Lechlade & A416 to Faringdon, pick up signs to Kelmscot*
A restored 17th-century inn in an attractive village close to Kelmscott Manor and the Thames. It is popular with the walking and boating fraternity, and has a lawn and patio area for outdoor eating. Dishes range from steak and kidney pudding to mustard-roasted ham hock with bubble and squeak, or grilled mullet and Thai noodles.
Open: 11-3 7-11 **Bar Meals:** L served all week 12-2.30 D served all week 7-9 **Restaurant Meals:** L served all week 12-2.30 D served all week 7-9 Av 3 course alc £21.50 **Brewery/Company:** Free House 🍺: Hook Norton, Timothy Taylor, Wychwood & Archers **Children's Facilities:** Menu/Portions Games Highchair Food warming **Nearby:** Cotswold Wildlife Park **Notes:** Dogs allowed in bar, in garden, Water provided Garden: Grassed area with patio **Parking:** 4

LEWKNOR

The Leathern Bottel ♛

1 High Street OX49 5TW

☎ 01844 351482

Run by the same family for more than 25 years, this 16th-century coaching inn is set in the foothills of the Chilterns. Walkers with dogs, families with children, parties for meals or punters for a quick pint are all made equally welcome. In winter there's a wood-burning stove, a good drop of Brakspears ale, nourishing specials and a quiz on Sunday. Summer is the time for outdoor eating, the children's play area, Pimm's and Morris dancers. **Open:** 11-3 6-11 Closed: 25-26 Dec **Bar Meals:** L served all week 12-2 D served all week 7-9.30 Av main course £7.95 **Brewery/Company:** Brakspear ▥: Brakspear Ordinary, Special ♛: 12 **Children's**

Facilities: Fam room Play area (adventure play area) Menu/Portions Food warming **Notes:** Dogs allowed in bar, Water Garden: Large garden enclosed with hedge **Parking:** 35

LOWER SHIPLAKE

The Baskerville Arms ◆◆◆◆ ♛

Station Road Henley-on-Thames RG9 3NY

☎ 0118 940 3332 ▤ 0118 940 7235

Email: enquiries@thebaskerville.com

Web: www.thebaskerville.com

Dir: *Just off the A4155, 1.5m from Henley.*

This welcoming pub stands on the popular Thames Path just a few minutes from historic Henley-on-Thames. It is brick-built on the outside, modern-rustic inside. Light meals are served in the bar, while the restaurant offers the likes of seared sea bass with shellfish bisque and saffron risotto. **Open:** 11.30-2.30 6-11 (Sun 11.30-2.30, 5.30-11) **Bar Meals:** L served all week 12-2 D served Mon-Sat 7-9.30 Av main course £10.25 **Restaurant Meals:** L served Mon-Sun 12-2 D served Mon-Sat 7-9.30 ▥: London Pride, Brakspear, Stella Artois, Castlemaine & Hoppit, Bass ♛: 8 **Children's Facilities:** Play area (Purpose-built) Menu/Portions Highchair Food warming **Nearby:** Rowing Museum, Boat trips on River Thames **Notes:** Dogs on leads allowed in bar Garden: Spacious with play area & BBQ **Parking:** 12

MARSTON

Victoria Arms ♛

Mill Lane OX3 0PZ

☎ 01865 241382

Email: kyffinda@yahoo.co.uk

Dir: *From A40 follow signs to Old Marston, sharp right into Mill Lane, pub in lane 500yrds on left.*

Friendly country pub situated on the banks of the River Cherwell, occupying the site of the old Marston Ferry that connected the north and south of the city. The old ferryman's bell is still behind the bar. Popular destinations for punters, and fans of TV sleuth Inspector Morse, as the last episode used this as a location. Typical menu includes lamb cobbler, steak and Guinness pie, spicy pasta bake, battered haddock, and ham off the bone. **Open:** 11.30-11 (Oct-Apr closed afternoons) **Bar Meals:** L served all week 12-2.30 D served all week 6-9 (Sun 12-6) Av main course £5.95 **Brewery/Company:** Wadworth ▥: Henrys IPA, Wadworth 6X, JCB, guest beers ♛: 15 **Children's Facilities:** Fam room Menu/Portions Games Highchair Food warming Baby changing **Notes:** Dogs allowed Garden: Food served outside Patio & lawn area **Parking:** 70

MURCOTT

The Nut Tree Inn 🍷

Main Street Nr Kidlington OX5 2RE

☎ 01865 331253 📠 01865 331977

Web: www.nuttreeinn.co.uk

Dir: *Off B4027 NE of Oxford via Islip & Charlton-on-Moor*

This 15th-century thatched inn is full of rustic charm, set in extensive fenced and hedged gardens with trees and lawns. Inside too, there are exposed beams, wood-burning stoves in inglenook fireplaces, real ales and home-cooked meals. Two menus are offered, the regular carte and the traditional menu of butties and light bites (pasta bake, pizza and deep-fried cod). Dishes from the carte include plaice paupiette, fillet Diane, and chicken provençale.

Open: 12-3 6-11 (Sun 12-5) **Bar Meals:** L served Tue-Sat 12-2.30 D served Tue-Sat 6-9 (Sun 12-3) Av main course £9.95 **Restaurant Meals:** L served Tue-Sun 12-2.30 D served Tue-Sat 6-9 (Sun 12-3) Av 3 course alc £22.50 **Brewery/Company:** Free House 🍺: Hook Norton, Adnams 🍷: 6 **Children's Facilities:** Fam room Play area Menu/Portions Highchair Food warming **Notes:** Dogs allowed in garden, Kennel Garden: Fenced and hedged with trees and lawns **Parking:** 40

ROKE

Home Sweet Home 🍷

Wallingford OX10 6JD

☎ 01491 838249 📠 01491 835760

Dir: *Just off the B4009 from Benson to Watlington, signed on B4009*

Long ago converted from adjoining cottages by a local brewer, this pretty 15th-century inn stands in a tiny hamlet surrounded by lovely countryside. Oak beams and the large inglenook fireplace dominate a friendly bar with an old-fashioned feel. Starters might include spicy nachos topped with cheese for two to share; while main courses run to Cornish crab fishcakes with home-made tartare sauce; or calves' liver and bacon with an onion gravy. Extensive Sunday menu.

Open: 11-2.30 6-11 (Sun 12-3, closed Sun eve) Closed: Dec 25-26 **Bar Meals:** L served all week 12-2 D served Mon-Sat 6-9 **Restaurant Meals:** L served Mon-Sun 12-2 D served Mon-Sat 7-9 **Brewery/Company:** Free House 🍺: Black Sheep, Loddon Brewery Beers-Hoppit & Branoc 🍷: 10 **Children's Facilities:** Play area (Children's license) Menu/Portions Highchair Food warming **Notes:** Dogs allowed, Water **Parking:** 60

SHENINGTON

The Bell 🍷

Banbury OX15 6NQ

☎ 01295 670274

Email: the_bellshenington@hotmail.com

Web: www.banburytown.co.uk/thebell/

Dir: *M40 junct 11 take A422 towards Stratford. Continue through Wroxton and Shenington is signed on the left.*

Overlooking a picturesque village green surrounded by mellow stone houses, this attractive and comfortable 300-year-old pub is conveniently located for exploring much of the nearby Oxfordshire countryside as well as the Cotswolds. The pub offers home-cooked food prepared in-house, and the blackboard menu changes frequently.

Open: 12-2.30 7-11 **Bar Meals:** L served Tue-Sun 12-2 D served all week 7-11 Av main course £8.95 **Restaurant Meals:** L served Tues-Sun12-2 D served all week 7-10 **Brewery/Company:** Free House 🍺: Hook Norton, Flowers 🍷: 8 **Children's Facilities:** Menu/Portions Highchair Food warming **Notes:** Dogs allowed in bar, Water Garden: Beer garden, outdoor eating

SHIPTON-UNDER-WYCHWOOD
The Shaven Crown Hotel ♟

High Street OX7 6BA

☎ 01993 830330 📄 01993 832136

Email: relax@theshavencrown.co.uk

Web: www.theshavencrown.co.uk

Dir: *On A361, halfway between Burford and Chipping Norton opposite village green and church*

Believed to be one of the ten oldest inns in England, The Shaven Crown is steeped in history, having been built as a hospice to the neighbouring Bruern Monastery. Offers varied bar and restaurant food.

Open: 12-2.30 5-11 (All day Sat-Sun) **Bar Meals:** L served all week 12-2 D served all week 6-9.30 (All day Sat-Sun) Av main course £10.95 **Restaurant Meals:** L served Sun 12-2 D served all week 7-9 Av 3 course alc £20 **Brewery/Company:** Free House 🍺: Hook Norton Best, Old Hooky & Archers Wychwood 🍷: 10 **Children's Facilities:** Play area (high chairs, cots) Menu/Portions Games Highchair Food warming **Nearby:** Cotswold Wildlife Park, Birdland, The Model Village **Notes:** Dogs allowed in bar, in garden, in bedrooms, Water **Garden:** Enclosed courtyard, lawned area with trees **Parking:** 15

SOUTH MORETON
The Crown Inn ♟

High Street Didcot OX11 9AG

☎ 01235 812262

Email: sallyandjohn@tesco.net

Dir: *From Didcot take A4130 towards Wallingford. Village on right*

Friendly village pub located midway between Wallingford and Didcot. It prides itself on its home-prepared food, and has real ale on tap. Families are welcome and customers come from far and wide. During the summer the garden is very popular. Dishes include steaks, shoulder of lamb, fresh battered haddock, and salmon fillet hollandaise. Recent change of ownership.

Open: 11-3 5.30-11 (Sun 12-3, 7-10.30) Closed: Dec 25-26 **Bar Meals:** L served all week 12-2 D served all week 7-9.30 Av main course £9.50 **Restaurant Meals:** L served all week 12-2 D served all week 7-9.30 **Brewery/Company:** Wadworth 🍺: Wadworth 6X & Henrys IPA, guest beers 🍷: 8 **Children's Facilities:** Menu/Portions Cutlery Highchair Food warming **Notes:** Dogs allowed in bar, in garden, Water **Garden:** 2 areas with bench style seating **Parking:** 30

SOUTH STOKE
The Perch and Pike ♟

RG8 0JS

☎ 01491 872415 📄 01491 875852

Email: eating@perchandpike.com

Web: www.perchandpike.com

Dir: *(On The Ridgeway between Reading and Oxford)*

The Perch and Pike, just two minutes' walk from the River Thames, was the village's foremost beer house back in the 17th century. There is plenty of atmosphere in the original pub and in the adjoining barn conversion, which houses the 42-seater restaurant. Food ranges from a selection of sandwiches to the likes of smoked haddock and salmon fish cakes, and venison with celeriac mash and Madeira jus.

Open: 12-3 6-11 (Sun 12-5) **Bar Meals:** L served all week 12-3 D served all week 6.30-10 Av main course £9.50 **Restaurant Meals:** L served all week 12-3 D served Mon-Sat 6.30-10 Av 3 course alc £18 **Brewery/Company:** Brakspear 🍺: Brakspear beers 🍷: 12 **Children's Facilities:** Licence Play area Menu/Portions Games Highchair Food warming Baby changing **Nearby:** Ridgeway Walk, Zoo **Notes:** Dogs allowed in bar, Water bowls **Garden:** Tiered, grassed area with benches **Parking:** 40

STANTON ST JOHN
Star Inn ♀
Middle Road OX33 1EX
☎ 01865 351277 📄 01865 351006
Email: murwin@aol.com
Web: www.welcometothestar.co.uk
Dir: *B4027 take Stanton exit, then 3rd left into Middle Rd, pub is 200yds on left.*
Although the Star is only a short drive from the centre of Oxford, this popular pub still retains a definite 'village' feel. The oldest part dates from the early 17th century, and in the past, the building has been used as a butcher's shop and an abattoir. The garden is peaceful and secluded. There's a varied menu.
Open: 11-2.30 6.30-11 **Bar Meals:** L served all week 12-2 D served Mon-Sat 6.30-9.30 Av main course £8.95 **Brewery/Company:** Wadworth 🍺: Wadworth 6X, Henrys IPA & JCB ♀: 7 **Children's Facilities:** Fam room Play area Menu/Portions Cutlery Games Highchair Food warming **Nearby:** Cotswold Wildlife Park, The Oxford Experience & Waterperry Gardens **Notes:** Dogs allowed in bar, in garden, Water bowls **Garden:** Large secure garden **Parking:** 50

STANTON ST JOHN
The Talkhouse ♀
Wheatley Road Nr Oxford OX33 1EX
☎ 01865 351648 📄 01865 351085
Email: manager@thetalkhouse.co.uk
Web: www.thetalkhouse.co.uk
Dir: *Stanton St John signed from the Oxford ring road*
First recorded as a pub in 1783, the Talkhouse comprises three bar and dining areas, all with a Gothic look and a welcoming atmosphere. An interesting modern menu reflects a range of classic British ingredients often treated with French influences: Welsh rarebit on toast, or terrine of game à la Richelieu to start, and saddle of venison Wellington with sauce Périgueux; or grilled rib-eye steak with béarnaise noisette to follow perhaps.
Open: 12-3 6-11 (Fri & Sat 12-11, Sun 12-9, Open all day Summer) **Bar Meals:** L served all week 12-2 D served all week 6-9 (Sun 12-6) Av main course £16 **Restaurant Meals:** L served all week 12-2 D served all week 7-10 (Sun 12-9) Av 3 course alc £30 **Brewery/Company:** Gastronomic Pub Company 🍺: Hook Norton, Adnams, Landlord, Carlsberg, Tetley Smooth & Guinness ♀: 10 **Children's Facilities:** Menu/Portions Games Highchair Baby changing **Notes:** Garden: Courtyard garden **Parking:** 60

SWALCLIFFE
Stag's Head ♀
Banbury OX15 5EJ
☎ 01295 780232 📄 01295 788977
Dir: *6M W of Banbury on the B4035*
This friendly, 600 year-old thatched village inn enjoys picture postcard looks and a pretty village setting. Blending a traditional pub feel with a family-friendly environment, the Stag also offers a beautiful terraced garden and play area. Freshly prepared dishes include goat's cheese tart with chips or salad; and moules marinière with chorizo and crusty bread. Look out for the landlord's own paintings of local scenes.
Open: 12-2.30 6-11 (Closed Sun eve) **Bar Meals:** L served Tue-Sun 12-2 D served Tue-Sat 6.30-9.30 (Sun 12-3) Av main course £7.95 **Restaurant Meals:** L served Tue-Sun 12-2 D served Tue-Sat 6.30-9.30 (Sun 12-3) **Brewery/Company:** Free House 🍺: Hook Norton Hooky, Adnams Bitter, Deuchars IPA, Moorhouse Pride of Pendle & Black Sheep ♀: 8 **Children's Facilities:** Play area (Play area in garden) Menu/Portions Cutlery Games Highchair Food warming Baby changing **Notes:** Dogs allowed in bar, in garden Garden

SWERFORD
The Mason's Arms ⊚

Banbury Road Chipping Norton OX7 4AP

☎ 01608 683212 ▤ 01608 683105

Email: themasonschef@hotmail.com

Web: www.masonarms.co.uk

Dir: *Between Banbury and Chipping Norton A361*

A short hop from the 'Glorious Cotswolds', and built from the region's ubiquitous honey-coloured stone, this 300-year-old pub was once rundown and empty, until proprietor Bill Leadbeater and his wife, Charmaine, arrived. Over the years they have won a heap of awards. **Open:** 10-3 6-11 Closed: 25-26 Dec **Bar Meals:** L served Mon-Sun 12-2.15 D served Mon-Sun 7-9.15 (Sun lunch 12-3) Av main course £7 **Restaurant Meals:** L served all week 12-2.15 D served all week 7-9.15

Av 3 course alc £25 **Brewery/Company:** Free House ◖: Hook Norton Best & Brakspear Special ♟: 6 **Children's Facilities:** Licence Menu/Portions Highchair Food warming Baby changing **Nearby:** Burford wildlife Park, Hook Norton Brewery & Pottery, Wiggington Water Fowl Sanctuary **Notes:** Garden: Large grassed area, with seating, views **Parking:** 50

WITNEY
The Bell Inn

Standlake Road Ducklington OX29 7UP

☎ 01993 702514 ▤ 01993 706822

Dir: *One mile south of Witney in Ducklington village off A415 Abingdon road.*

Nearly 700 years have passed since the men building the adjacent church also erected their own living accommodation. Their hostel eventually became the Bell, and much extended over the years, it even embraces William Shepheard's former brewery, which closed in 1886. Today it is a popular, traditional village local, with many original features - and a collection of some 500 bells. Home-made pies, stews and burgers are a speciality, and there's a pig roast on Boxing Day. **Open:** 12-3 5-11 (Fri-Sun 12-11) Closed: Dec 25 **Bar**

Meals: L served all week 12-2 D served Mon-Sat 6-9 Av main course £9 **Restaurant Meals:** L served all week 12-2 D served Mon-Sat 6-9 Av 3 course alc £16 ◖: Greene King, IPA & Old Speckled Hen, Morland Original,Guinness **Children's Facilities:** Play area (Climbing frame, swings) Menu/Portions Cutlery Games Highchair Food warming **Nearby:** Burford Wildlife Park, Cogges Farm Museum, Lower Windrush Valley walk **Notes:** Garden: Terrace at front and rear of pub seating 50 **Parking:** 12

WYTHAM
White Hart ♟

OX2 8QA

☎ 01865 244372

Email: whitehartwytham@aol.com

Dir: *Just off A34 NW of Oxford*

Tucked away in the quiet village of Wytham is this smart gastropub, concealed within a traditional Cotswold stone inn. If it looks familiar, it may be because it has featured in some of the Inspector Morse television programmes. It serves real ale, but is predominantly a place to eat. The proprietor sources eggs, chicken, pork and bacon from a local farm less than a mile away, and all the meat is either free range or organic. The well presented menu is supplemented by the specials boards with fresh fish and game dishes always featured in season.

Open: 12-12 **Bar Meals:** L served all week 12-3 D served Mon-Sun 6.30-10 Av main course £13.50 **Restaurant Meals:** L served all week 12-3 D served Mon-Sun 6.30-10 ◖: Hook Norton, Leffe & Landlord ♟: 60 **Children's Facilities:** Menu/Portions Highchair Food warming **Notes:** Garden: Mediterranean Terrace **Parking:** 80

BURY ST EDMUNDS
The Linden Tree
7 Out Northgate IP33 1JQ
☎ 01284 754600
Dir: *Opposite railway station*
Built to serve the railway station, this is a big, friendly Victorian pub, with stripped pine bar, dining area, non-smoking conservatory and charming garden. The family-orientated menu ranges from beef curry, home-made pies, and liver and bacon, to crab Thermidor, fresh sea bass, and mushroom and lentil moussaka. Youngsters will go for the burgers, scampi, Quorn or pork chipolatas. Freshly filled ciabattas at lunchtime.
Open: 11-3 5-11 **Bar Meals:** L served all week 12-2 D served all week 6-9.30 (Sun and BH 12-3 5.30-9) Av main course £6 **Restaurant Meals:** L served all week 12-2 D served all week 6-9.30 (Sun 12-3 & 5.30-9) Av 3 course alc £16 **Brewery/Company:** Greene King ■: Greene King, IPA & Old Speckled Hen & Guest **Children's Facilities:** Play area (Swing, See-saw) Menu/Portions Games Highchair Food warming Baby changing **Nearby:** Play World, Abbey Gardens **Notes:** Dogs allowed Dog bowl Garden: Large, picnic tables, play area, seats 20

BURY ST EDMUNDS
The Three Kings ★★★★ INN ♀
Hengrave Road Fornham All Saints IP28 6LA
☎ 01284 766979
Email: thethreekings@keme.co.uk
Plenty of exposed wood and interesting artifacts create a traditional atmosphere at this pretty pub. Bedroom accommodation is also provided in converted Grade II listed outbuildings. Food is served in the bar, conservatory, restaurant and courtyard, with at least four fresh grilled fish dishes every day, a choice of steaks, and old favourites like steak and ale pie or liver and bacon. Recent change of hands.
Open: 12-11 **Bar Meals:** L served all week 12-2 D served all week 5.30-9 (Sun 12-2.30, 6-8) Av main course £8 **Restaurant Meals:** L served Sun 12-2 D served Sat 7-9 (Sun 12-2.30) Av 3 course alc £15 **Brewery/Company:** Greene King ■: Greene King IPA, Abbot & Ridleys Rumps ♀: 14 **Children's Facilities:** Licence Menu/Portions Cutlery Highchair Food warming **Nearby:** West Stow Country Park, Abbey Gardens, Ickworth Park **Notes:** Garden: Patio area, benches **Parking:** 28

CAVENDISH
Bull Inn
High Street CO10 8AX
☎ 01787 280245
Dir: *A134 Bury St Edmunds to Long Melford, then R at green, pub 3m on R*
A Victorian pub set in one of Suffolk's most beautiful villages, with an unassuming façade hiding a splendid 15th-century beamed interior. Expect a good atmosphere and decent food, with the daily-changing blackboard menu listing perhaps curries, shank of lamb, fresh fish and shellfish, and a roast on Sundays. Outside there's a pleasant terraced garden.
Open: 11-3 6-11 (Sun 12-4) **Bar Meals:** L served Mon-Sun 12-2 D served Tue-Sat 6.30-9 (Sun 12-2.30) Av main course £9 **Restaurant Meals:** L served Sun-Sat 12-2 D served Mon-Sat 6.30-9 (Sun 12-2.30) Av 3 course alc £16 **Brewery/Company:** Adnams ■: Adnams Bitter & Broadside, Nethergate Suffolk County ♀: 6 **Children's Facilities:** Menu/Portions Highchair Food warming **Notes:** Dogs allowed Garden: Patio **Parking:** 30

COCKFIELD
Three Horseshoes 🍷

Stow's Hill Bury St Edmunds IP30 0JB

☎ 01284 828177 📄 01284 828177

Email: john@threehorseshoespub.co.uk

Web: www.threehorseshoespub.co.uk

Dir: *A134 towards Sudbury, then left onto A1141 towards Lavenham*

Originally a thatched long hall, The Three Horseshoes was built around 1350. Eat amid the old world charm of the restaurant and bar, or in the conservatory with country-side views. There are over 100 dishes to choose from. **Open:** 10-3 6-11 (Sun 10.30) **Bar Meals:** L served Wed-Mon 12-2 D served Wed-Mon 6-9.30 (Sun 12-3, 6-9) Av main course £7.50 **Restaurant Meals:** L served Wed-Mon 12-2.30 D served Wed-Mon 7-9.30

(Sun 12-2.30, 6-9) Av 3 course alc £16 🍺: Horseshoes Bitter, Adnams, Directors, Theakstons XB & Websters Yorkshire 🍷: 13 **Children's Facilities:** Play area (Indoor puzzles, outdoor activities) Cutlery Games Highchair Food warming **Nearby:** Colchester Zoo, Kentwell Hall, Thetford Forest **Notes:** Dogs allowed in bar, Water **Garden:** Enclosed with gazebo and water feature **Parking:** 90

COTTON
The Trowel & Hammer Inn

Mill Road Stowmarket IP14 4QL

☎ 01449 781234 📄 01449 781765

Web: www.trowelandhammer.co.uk

Dir: *From A14 follow signs to Haughley,then Bacton,then turn left for Cotton.*

At first sight, this thatched, wisteria-covered pub hardly looks 550 years old, but the interior conveys a much better idea of its age. Merchants and cotton traders heading inland from the coast used to stop here, and the poet Milton drank here when he lived locally. **Open:** 12-11 (Fri/Sat 12pm-1am) **Bar Meals:** L served all week 12-2 D served all week 6-9 (All day Sun) Av main course £7.50 **Restaurant Meals:** L served all week 12-2 D served Mon-Sat 6-9 Av 3 course alc £20

Brewery/Company: Free House 🍺: Adnams Bitter, Greene King IPA & Abbot Ale, Nethergates, Mauldons **Children's Facilities:** Play area (Swimming pool, table tennis & games) Menu/Portions Cutlery Games Highchair Food warming **Nearby:** Cotton Music Museum, Snetterton Market, Thornham Walks **Notes:** Garden: Large garden with swimming pool **Parking:** 50

DENNINGTON
The Queens Head

The Square Woodbridge IP13 8AB

☎ 01728 638241 📄 01728 638037

Email: denningtonqueen1@btinternet.com

Dir: *From Ipswich take A14 to turn off for Lowestoft (A12). Turn off to Framlingham on the B1116, from Framlingham follow signs to Dennington.*

This 16th-century inn with earlier origins is reputedly haunted. Features include a large garden with seating and an attractive Koi pond at the rear. Locally brewed cider is available alongside the real ales. Extensive menus range from lunchtime sandwiches, ploughman's and baked potatoes through to a vegetarian menu, griddle selection, children's menu and even a gluten free menu. Sample dishes are Thai fishcakes and sweet chilli

dip to start, and home-made meat pie of the day. **Open:** 9-3 6.30-11 (Close at 10 Winter w/days and Sundays, Summer 6-11) Closed: 25-26 Dec **Bar Meals:** L served all week 12-2 D served all week 6.30-9 Av main course £8 **Restaurant Meals:** L served all week 12-2 D served all week 6.30-9 Av 3 course alc £16 **Brewery/Company:** Free House 🍺: Adnams, St Peters, Woodfordes & Mauldons **Children's Facilities:** Fam room Play area Menu/Portions Cutlery Games Food warming **Nearby:** Stoneham Barns Owl Sanctuary & Framlingham Castle **Notes:** Garden: Large pond, seating and fountain **Parking:** 30

SUFFOLK

DUNWICH

The Ship Inn

St James Street nr Saxmundham IP17 3DT

☎ 01728 648219 📠 01728 648675

Email: shipinn@tiscali.co.uk

Dir: *N on A12 from Ipswich through Yoxford, right signed Dunwich*

This old smugglers' haunt exudes great warmth and character, and is noted for traditional food and local ales. As one would expect, fresh local fish features prominently on the menu, including cod, mackerel, prawns, scampi, and fishcakes. The specials board may supplement these with sole, haddock, sardines and crab according to availability, and in fine weather the Dunwich fish can be eaten in the garden.

Open: 11-11 (Sun 12-10.30) **Bar Meals:** L served all week 12-3 D served all week 6-9 **Restaurant Meals:** L served all week 12-3 D served all week 6-9 (Sat-Sun 12-6 6-9) **Brewery/Company:** Free House 🍺: Adnams, Mauldons **Children's Facilities:** Play area (high chairs) Menu/Portions Highchair Food warming **Notes:** Dogs allowed in bar, in garden, in bedrooms **Garden:** Large terraced area **Parking:** 10

ERWARTON

The Queens Head

The Street Ipswich IP9 1LN

☎ 01473 787550

Dir: *From Ipswich take B1456 to Shotley*

This handsome 16th-century Suffolk free house provides an atmospheric stop for a pint of locally-brewed Adnams or Greene King ales. There's a relaxed atmosphere in the bar with its bowed black oak beams, low ceilings and cosy coal fires, and magnificent views over the fields to the Stour estuary. The wide-ranging menu offers traditional hot dishes and snacks, while daily specials include pheasant casserole, spinach and red lentil curry, and home-made fishcakes.

Open: 11-3 6.30-11 (Sun 12-3, 7-10.30) Closed: 25 Dec **Bar Meals:** L served all week 12-1.45 D served all week 7-9 Av main course £8 **Restaurant Meals:** L served all week 12-2.45 D served all week 7-9.30 **Brewery/Company:** Free House 🍺: Adnams Bitter & Broadside, Greene King IPA, Aspall Cider, Guinness & Strongbow **Children's Facilities:** Play area (children welcome in restaurant only) Menu/Portions Highchair Food warming **Parking:** 30

EYE

The White Horse Inn ★★★★ INN

Stoke Ash IP23 7ET

☎ 01379 678222 📠 01379 678800

Email: mail@whitehorse-suffolk.co.uk

Web: www.whitehorse-suffolk.co.uk

Dir: *On the main A140 between Ipswich & Norwich*

A 17th-century coaching inn set amid lovely Suffolk countryside. The heavily-timbered interior accommodates an inglenook fireplace, two bars and a restaurant. There are seven spacious motel bedrooms in the grounds, as well as a patio and secluded grassy area. An extensive menu is supplemented by lunchtime snacks, grills and daily specials from the blackboard. Grilled butterflied breast of chicken, Lincolnshire sausages and mash, lasagne, and salmon and haddock tagliatelle are typical.

Open: 10-11 (Sun 11-10.30) **Bar Meals:** L served all week 11-9.30 D served all week 11-9.30 **Restaurant Meals:** L served all week 11-9.30 D served all week 11-9.30 **Brewery/Company:** Free House 🍺: Adnams, Greene King Abbot, IPA Smooth **Children's Facilities:** Licence Menu/Portions Cutlery Games Highchair Food warming **Nearby:** Bressingham Steam Museum, Barnham Zoo, Thornham Walks **Notes:** Garden: Patio & grass area **Parking:** 60

GREAT GLEMHAM
The Crown Inn ♟
Saxmundham IP17 2DA

☎ 01728 663693

Dir: *A12 Ipswich to Lowestoft, in Stratford-St-Andrew L at Shell garage. Crown 1.5m*

Cosy 17th-century village pub overlooking the Great Glemham Estate and within easy reach of the Suffolk Heritage Coast. You can eat in the extensively renovated bars and large flower-filled garden, where moussaka, carbonnade of beef, Somerset lamb casserole, roasted vegetables with pasta, and spinach and feta cheese tart from the specials menu might be followed by fresh fruit Pavlova or traditional sherry trifle.

Open: 11.30-2.30 6.30-11 (Closed Mon) **Bar Meals:** L served Tue-Sun 11.30-2.30 D served Tue-Sun 6.30-10

Brewery/Company: Free House 🍺: Adnams Bitter & Broadside ♟: 7 **Children's Facilities:** Play area Menu/Portions Games Highchair Food warming Baby changing **Nearby:** Easton Farm Park & Framlingham Castle **Notes:** Dogs allowed in bar Garden: Large lawn, flower border, picnic table **Parking:** 20

HALESWORTH
The Queen's Head ♟
The Street Bramfield IP19 9HT

☎ 01986 784214 🖨 01986 784797

Email: qhbfield@aol.com

Web: www.queensheadbramfield.co.uk

Dir: *2m from A12 on the A144 towards Halesworth*

The owners of the Queen's Head are supporters of the 'local and organic' movement - reflected by the pub's daily changing menu which proudly names the farms and suppliers from which the carefully chosen ingredients are sourced. The pub is a lovely old building in the centre of Bramfield on the edge of the Suffolk Heritage Coast.

Open: 11.45-2.30 6.30-11 (Sun 12-3, 7-10.30) Closed: 26 Dec **Bar Meals:** L served all week 12-2 D served all week 6.30-10 (Sun 7-9) Av main course £9.95

Brewery/Company: Adnams 🍺: Adnams Bitter & Broadside ♟: 7 **Children's Facilities:** Fam room (Books, toys) Menu/Portions Games Highchair Food warming Baby changing **Nearby:** Kessingland Wildlife park, Beaches of Southwold & Southwold Pier **Notes:** Dogs allowed in bar, in garden Water Garden: Enclosed garden with seating, willow dome **Parking:** 15

HOLBROOK
The Compasses
Ipswich Road nr Ipswich IP9 2QR

☎ 01473 328332 🖨 01473 327403

Email: rickandjayne@tiscali.co.uk

Dir: *From A137 S of Ipswich, take B1456/B1080*

Holbrook is bordered by the rivers Orwell and Stour, and this traditional country pub, which dates back to the 17th century, is on the Shotley peninsula. The menu is varied and appetizing, and always features a good seafood selection on the specials board, including seafood lasagna, fish pie, and grilled salmon with bonne femme sauce.

Open: 12-2.30 6-11 (Sun 12-3, 6-10.30) Closed: 25-26 Dec, 1 Jan **Bar Meals:** L served all week 12-2.15 D served all week 6-9.15 (Sun 12-2.15, 6-9.15) Av main course £8.95 **Restaurant Meals:** L served all week 12-2.15 D served all week 6-9.15 (Sun 12-2.15, 6-9.15) Av 3 course alc £17.50 **Brewery/Company:** Punch Taverns 🍺: Carlsberg, Greene King IPA, Adnams Bitter, Kronenbourg & Guest Ales **Children's Facilities:** Play area (Slide, swings, wendy house) Menu/Portions Highchair **Nearby:** Bourne Hill Ski Slope, Alton Water (water sports) **Notes:** Garden: Six picnic benches, childrens play area **Parking:** 30

SUFFOLK

HONEY TYE
The Lion

Leavenheath nr Colchester CO6 4NX

☎ 01206 263434 🖶 01206 263434

Web: www.thelionleavenheath.co.uk

Dir: *On A134 between Colchester & Sudbury*

Traditional country dining pub on the Essex/Suffolk border, with low-beamed ceilings and an open log fire inside and a patio with tables and umbrellas for outside eating and drinking. The menu offers a good choice of daily fresh fish (oven baked red snapper supreme with tomato and prawn confit), pub favourites (home-made steak and ale pie), and main dishes such as braised lamb shank with rosemary, garlic and red wine jus. **Open:** 11-3 5-11 (Sun 12-10.30) **Bar Meals:** L served all week 12-2 D served all week 6-9.30 (Sun 12-9.30)

Restaurant Meals: L served all week 12-2 D served all week 6-9.30 (Sun 12-9.30) **Brewery/Company:** Free House 🍺: Greene King IPA, Adnams Bitter, Guest ale, Stella Artois, Carling **Children's Facilities:** Menu/Portions Highchair Food warming **Notes:** Dogs allowed in garden Garden: Patio with tables and umbrellas **Parking:** 40

KETTLEBURGH
The Chequers Inn

Woodbridge IP13 7JT

☎ 01728 723760 & 724369 🖶 01728 723760

Email: info@thechequers.net

Web: www.thechequers.net

Dir: *From Ipswich A12 onto B1116, left onto B1078 then right through Easton*

The Chequers is set in beautiful countryside on the banks of the River Deben. The landlord serves a wide range of cask ales, including two guests. In addition to snack and restaurant meals, the menu in the bar includes local sausages and ham with home-produced free-range eggs. The riverside garden covers two acres and can seat up to a hundred people. **Open:** 12-2.30 6-11 **Bar Meals:** L served all week 12-

2 D served all week 7-9.30 (Sun 12-2 7-9) Av main course £5 **Restaurant Meals:** L served all week 12-2 D served all week 7-9.30 (Sun 12-2, 7-9) Av 3 course alc £16 **Brewery/Company:** Free House 🍺: Greene King IPA, Black Dog Mild & 3 Guest Ales **Children's Facilities:** Play area (play/tree house) Highchair Food warming **Nearby:** Easton Park Farm, Framlington Castle, Stonham Barns **Notes:** Dogs allowed in bar, Water Garden: Two acre riverside garden, large terrace **Parking:** 40

LAVENHAM
Angel Hotel ★★ HL 🏵 🍷

Market Place CO10 9QZ

☎ 01787 247388 🖶 01787 248344

Email: angellav@aol.com

Web: www.theangelhotel.com

Dir: *7m from Sudbury on A1141 between Sudbury & Bury St Edmunds*

First licensed in 1420, this attractive, bustling inn does its best to source all its produce from local suppliers and everything on its award-winning restaurant and bar menu is prepared on the premises. **Open:** 11-11 (Sun 12-10.30) Closed: 25-26 Dec **Bar Meals:** L served all week 12-2.15 D served all week 6.45-9.15 Av main course £10 **Restaurant Meals:** L served all week 12-2.15 D served all week 6.45-9.15

Av 3 course alc £20 🍺: Adnams Bitter, Nethergate, Greene King IPA, Broadside & Old Growler 🍷: 9 **Children's Facilities:** Licence (Highchairs, toys, cots, baby listening) Menu/Portions Cutlery Games Highchair Food warming Baby changing **Nearby:** Hollowtrees Farm, Colchester Zoo & Kingfisher Leisure Centre **Notes:** Garden: Lawn and patio with tables **Parking:** 105

LIDGATE
The Star Inn
The Street Newmarket CB8 9PP
☎ 01638 500275 📄 01638 500275
Email: tereaxon@aol.com
Dir: *From Newmarket, clocktower in High st, follow signs toward Clare on B1063. Lidgate 7m from Newmarket*
It may look like a traditional English pub, but The Star also houses a much-loved Spanish restaurant serving appealingly hearty food, which is particularly popular with trainers on Newmarket race days, and with dealers and agents from all over the world during bloodstock sales. The star of the Star is the owner, a Catalan landlady who has made her mark with Spanish dishes plus some imaginative international and British choices.
Open: 11-3 5-11 Closed: 25-26 Dec, 1 Jan **Bar Meals:**

L served all week 12-2 D served Mon-Sat 7-10 (Sun 12-2.30, 7-11) Av main course £13.50 **Restaurant Meals:** L served all week 12-2 D served Mon-Sat 7-10 (Sun 12-2.30) **Brewery/Company:** Greene King
🍺: Greene King IPA, Old Speckled Hen & Abbot Ale
Children's Facilities: Menu/Portions Highchair Food warming **Parking:** 12

MELTON
Wilford Bridge
Wilford Bridge Road Woodbridge IP12 2PA
☎ 01394 386141 📄 01394 386141
Email: wilfordbridge@yahoo.com
Dir: *Head to the coast from the A12, follow signs to Bawdsey & Orford, cross railway lines, next pub on left.*
Run by Mike and Anne Lomas for the past 16 years, this free house is just down the road from the famous Saxon burial ship at Sutton Hoo (NT). Mike is a former West End chef and concentrates on traditional fare, especially fish dishes, using best quality produce.
Open: 11-3 6.30-11 (Open all day summer wknds) Closed: 25-26 Dec **Bar Meals:** L served all week 11.30-2 D served all week 6.30-9.30 (Food served all day wknds) Av main course £10 **Restaurant Meals:** L

served all week 11.30-2 D served all week 6.30-9.30 (Food served all Day wknds) Av 3 course alc £18 🍺: Adnams Best, Broadside, Scottish Courage John Smith's & guest Ales 🍷: 7 **Children's Facilities:** Menu/Portions Highchair Food warming **Nearby:** Melton Duck Pond, National Trust Site, Sutton Hoo & Woodbridge Tide Mill **Notes:** Garden: Patio, seats 30 people **Parking:** 40

NAYLAND
Anchor Inn
26 Court Street Colchester CO6 4JL
☎ 01206 262313 📄 01206 264166
Email: enquiries@anchornayland.co.uk
Web: www.anchornayland.co.uk
Dir: *From Colchester follow signs to N railway station, continue under railway bridge, take A134 towards Sudbury, turn right towards Nayland signed Horkesley Rd. Pass bridge, pub on right.*
The Anchor Inn, with the River Stour right on its doorstep, is the only pub in this picturesque Suffolk village. Dating back to the 15th century, it is reported to be the last remaining place from which press gangs recruited their 'volunteers'. Today there is a superb bar with a lively warm atmosphere, fine ales and good food. The inn has

its own smokery, and produce from the smokehouse is often featured on the menu, including fish and cheeses. The 'light bites and nibbles' menu offers filled huffers (triangular bread rolls). From the main menu come starters like shellfish risotto with shaved parmesan, followed by kid curry with pilaf rice and onion bhaji.
Open: 11-3 5-11 (Sat 11-11, Sun 11-10.30) **Bar Meals:** L served all week 12-2.30 D served all week 6.30-9 (Fri-Sat 6.30-9.30 Sun 10-3, 4.30-8.30) Av main course £9 **Restaurant Meals:** L served all week 12-2.30 D served all week 6.30-9 (Fri-Sat 6.30-9.30 Sun 10-3, 4.30-8.30) Av 3 course alc £18.50
Brewery/Company: Free House 🍺: Adnams, IPA, Mild
🍷: 6 **Children's Facilities:** Menu/Portions Highchair Food warming Baby changing **Notes:** Garden: Riverside terrace, views of valley **Parking:** 10

POLSTEAD
The Cock Inn
The Green CO6 5AL

☎ 01206 263150   📠 01206 263150

Email: mail@cockinn.info

Web: www.geocities.com/cockatpolstead

Dir: *Colchester/A134 towards Sudbury then right, follow signs to Polstead*

The 17th-century farmhouse overlooks the green in a lovely village in the heart of Constable country. The menu changes frequently and there's always a great choice.
Open: 11-3 6-11 (Sat-Sun (Apr-Sep) 11-11) **Bar Meals:** L served Tues-Sun11.30-2.30 D served Tues-Sun 6.30-9.30 (Sun 12-2.30, 6.30-9) Av main course £8
Restaurant Meals: L served Tue-Sun 11.30-2.30 D served Tue-Sun 6.30-9.30 (Sun 12-2.30, 6.30-9)

Av 3 course alc £17 🍺: Greene King IPA, Adnams, Ansels Mild, Carlsberg & Guinness **Children's Facilities:** Play area (Swings, slide, seesaw, climbing frame) Menu/Portions Cutlery Games Highchair Food warming **Nearby:** Colchester Go Bananas **Notes:** Dogs allowed in bar, in garden, Water and treats **Garden:** Picnic tables, pretty garden, water feature **Parking:** 20

SNAPE
Plough & Sail 🍷
Snape Maltings IP17 1SR

☎ 01728 688413   📠 01728 688930

Email: enquiries@snapemaltings.co.uk

Web: www.snapemaltings.co.uk

An enjoyable and popular part of any visit to Snape Maltings, the Plough and Sail rubs shoulders with the famous Concert Hall, art gallery and shops. The rambling interior includes a restaurant, and the large terrace provides summer seating. Sweet potato moussaka or wild boar sausages with green pea mash are typical light lunches, whilst evening diners might expect a slow braised lamb shank, or baked cod with Welsh rarebit and creamed leeks.
Open: 11-3 5.30-11 **Bar Meals:** L served all week 12-2.30 D served all week Av main course £11.95
Restaurant Meals: L served all week 12-2.30 D served all week 7-9 (Sat-Sun 7-9.30) Av 3 course alc £17
Brewery/Company: Free House 🍺: Adnams Broadside, Adnams Bitter, Explorer, Fishermans, Old Ale 🍷: 10
Children's Facilities: Menu/Portions Cutlery Games Highchair Food warming Baby changing **Nearby:** Easton Farm Park, Kessingland Zoo & Thorpeness Mere **Notes:** Dogs allowed in bar, in garden, Water bowls **Garden:** Enclosed courtyard, paved garden area **Parking:** 100

SOUTHWOLD
The Randolph ◎ 🍷
41 Wangford Road Reydon IP18 6PZ

☎ 01502 723603   📠 01502 722194

Email: reception@therandolph.co.uk

Web: www.therandolph.co.uk

Dir: *A1095 from A12 at Blythburgh, 4m, Southwold 1m from Darsham Train Station.*

This grand late-Victorian pile in large gardens was built by Adnams, the ubiquitous local brewers, who named it after Lord Randolph Churchill, Sir Winston's father. Standing just out of town, it successfully combines its functions as pub, restaurant and hotel; more accurately perhaps, this happy state of affairs is all down to owners David and Donna Smith. The menus are full of interesting twists - the 'Randolph breakfast' starter, for example, consists of chorizo, black pudding, pancetta, haricot beans, fried bread and quail's egg. Similarly, main courses, such as confit of pork belly with egg noodles and stir-fry; grilled plaice fillets with cucumber and caper butter; and roasted vegetable koulibiac with red pepper coulis and aubergine crisps. Finish with rich chocolate tart, caramelised orange and crème Chantilly.
Open: 11-12 **Bar Meals:** L served all week 12-2 D served all week 6.30-9 Av main course £8.95
Restaurant Meals: L served all week 12-2 D served all week 6.30-9 Av 3 course alc £19.95 🍺: Adnams Bitter, Adnams Broadside, guest ale 🍷: 6 **Children's Facilities:** Menu/Portions Cutlery Games Highchair Food warming **Nearby:** Pirate Petes, Animal Adventure Park & Kessingland **Notes:** Garden: Large fenced area with garden tables **Parking:** 60

STOWMARKET

The Buxhall Crown ♟

Mill Road Buxhall IP14 3DW

☎ 01449 736521 ▤ 01449 736528

Email: trevor@buxhallcrown.fsnet.co.uk

Web: www.thebuxhallcrown.co.uk

When Trevor Golton and Cathy Clarke bought the Buxhall Crown in 1999, their aim was to create their own 'dream pub', serving good food in a relaxed, sociable environment. Together, they've transformed the 17th-century building from just another rundown village local into one of East Anglia's most welcoming and applauded gastro-pubs. Hand-pumped real ales and an extensive wine list complement an interesting and varied menu that changes every few weeks. Fire up your palate with shredded duck and hoi sin sauce pancake rolls; or a simple, warm smoked chicken Caesar salad. Main courses range from the ever-popular haddock in beer batter with home-cut chips to more adventurous fare: try chestnut potato cakes with rarebit topping and port sauce; roasted lambs' hearts with apricot stuffing, mashed potato and red wine gravy; or suet crust game pie with juniper gravy and seasonal vegetables. **Open:** 12-3 6.30-11 Closed: 25-26 Dec **Bar Meals:** L served Tue-Sun 12-2 D served Tue-Sat 6.30-9.30 Av main course £25 **Restaurant Meals:** L served Tue-Sun 12-2 D served Tue-Sat 6.30-9.30 **Brewery/Company:** Greene King ◖: Greene King IPA, Woodforde's Wherry, Tindals Best Bitter, Cox & Holbrook ♟: 30 **Children's Facilities:** Menu/Portions Cutlery Highchair Food warming **Notes:** Dogs allowed in bar, Water **Garden:** Patio with wooden furniture, heaters **Parking:** 25

THORPENESS

The Dolphin Inn ♟

Peace Place Aldeburgh IP16 4NA

☎ 01728 454994

Email: info@thorpenessdolphin.com

Web: www.thorpenessdolphin.com

Dir: *(Signed Thorpeness)*

In the heart of Thorpeness, this traditional village inn offers good food, and alfresco dining in the summer. Pan-fried pigeon breasts are served as a starter with red pepper dressing; lamb kleftiko is marinated in red wine and served the Cypriot way with onions, herbs, rice and Greek salad; and there's a fish selection too. **Open:** 11-3 6-11 (Restricted hours in winter) **Bar Meals:** L served all week 12-2 D served all week 6.30-9 Av main course £9 **Restaurant Meals:** L served all week 12-2 D served all week 6.30-9 Av 3 course alc £18 ◖: Adnams Best, Adnams Broadside ♟: 8 **Children's Facilities:** Menu/Portions Cutlery Highchair Food warming Baby changing **Nearby:** Beach **Notes:** Dogs allowed in bar **Garden:** Large garden with awning, BBQ **Parking:** 14

WALBERSWICK

Bell Inn ♟

Ferry Road Southwold IP18 6TN

☎ 01502 723109 ▤ 01502 722728

Email: bellinn@btinternet.com

Web: www.blythweb.co.uk/bellinn

Dir: *From A12 take B1387, follow along untill after village green and bear right down track.*

The inn dates back 600 years and is located at the heart of the lovely coastal village of Walberswick, near the green, beach and the ancient fishing harbour on the River Blyth. Food is home cooked with local produce featuring strongly, particularly fresh fish. A further treat is afternoon tea in the bar, with a choice of teas, coffees and pastries. **Open:** 11-3 6-11 (Sun 12-10.30, Fri/Sat 6-12) **Bar Meals:** L served all week 12-2 D served all week 6-9 (Sun 12-2.30) Av main course £8.50 **Restaurant Meals:** D served Fri-Sat 7-9 Av 3 course alc £20 ◖: Adnams Best, Broadside, Regatta, Old Ale, Oyster Stout, Explorer ♟: 15 **Children's Facilities:** Fam room Cutlery Games Highchair Food warming Baby changing **Nearby:** Seaside **Notes:** Dogs allowed on leads in bar **Garden:** Large with beach and sea views **Parking:** 10

WESTLETON

The Westleton Crown ★★★ HL ⍟⍟
The Street Nr Saxmundham IP17 3AD
☎ 01728 648777 📠 01728 648239
Email: reception@westletoncrown.co.uk
Web: www.westletoncrown.co.uk
Dir: *Turn off the A12 just past Yoxford N bound, follow signs for Westleton for 2m*
The original buildings belonged to nearby Sibton Abbey. Nestled in a quiet village close to the coast and RSPB bird reserves, it offers genuine hospitality and food made from fresh, locally-sourced ingredients - perhaps steak and kidney suet pudding or grilled fillet of sea bass.
Open: 11-11 (Sun 12-10.30) **Bar Meals:** L served all week 12-2.15 D served all week 7-9.30 Av main course £13 **Restaurant Meals:** L served all week 12-2.15 D served all week 7-9.30 Av 3 course alc £30 **Brewery/Company:** Free House 🍺: Adnams, Greene King IPA, Aspalls Cider, Guest Ales **Children's Facilities:** Fam room Menu/Portions Games Highchair Food warming Baby changing **Nearby:** Beach, RSPB Minsmere & Pleasurewood Hills **Notes:** Dogs allowed in bar **Garden:** Award winning tiered sections **Parking:** 30

BETCHWORTH

The Red Lion 🍷
Old Reigate Road RH3 7DS
☎ 01737 843336 📠 01737 845242
Email: info@redlion-betchworth.com
Web: www.redlion-betchworth.com
Set in 18 acres with a cricket ground and rolling countryside views, this award-winning, 200-year-old pub offers an extensive menu. Beyond baguettes and ploughman's lunches the choice includes sole and smoked salmon, Barbary duck breast, aubergine and broccoli fritters, deep-fried plaice and chips, Toulouse sausage and mash, and steak and ale pie. The area is ideal for walkers.
Open: 12-11.30 (Sun 12-11) **Bar Meals:** L served all week 12-3 D served all week 6-10 (Sun 12-8.30) **Restaurant Meals:** L served all week 12-3 D served all week 6-10 (Sun 12-8.30) Av 3 course alc £18 **Brewery/Company:** Punch Taverns 🍺: Fullers London Pride, Greene King, IPA, Adnams Broadside 🍷: 6 **Children's Facilities:** Games Highchair Food warming **Notes:** **Garden:** Large beer garden, seats 50 **Parking:** 50

CHURT

The Pride of the Valley ★★★★ BB 🍷
Tilford Road Farnham GU10 2LH
☎ 01428 605799 📠 01428 605875
Email: reservations@prideofthevalleyhotel.com
Web: www.prideofthevalleyhotel.com
Dir: *4m from Farnham on outskirts of Churt Valley*
Charming and traditional, the Pride of the Valley is in the heart of the beautiful Surrey countryside and sits within its own idyllic country garden. The menu is extensive and international in its flavours. Catering for all tastes, ages and appetites in both the restaurant and the bistro, the well-prepared food is available everyday for lunch and dinner.
Open: 10.30-11 **Bar Meals:** L served all week 12-2.30 D served all week 6.30-9.30 **Restaurant Meals:** L served all week 12-2.30 D served all week 6.30-9.30 **Brewery/Company:** Free House 🍺: Dooms Bar, Hogs Back brewery beers 🍷: 8 **Children's Facilities:** Menu/Portions Cutlery Games Highchair Food warming **Nearby:** Frensham Pond, Sculpture Park **Notes:** Dogs allowed In reception/garden **Garden:** Idyllic country garden **Parking:** 60

COBHAM

The Cricketers 🍷

Downside KT11 3NX

☎ 01932 862105 📄 01932 868186

Email: info@thecricketersdownside.co.uk

Web: www.thecricketersdownside.co.uk

Dir: *From M25 exit junct 10 & join A3 towards London. Take 1st exit signed to Cobham. Leave A3 turn right to Cobham. Strait over 1st rdbt & right at 2nd. After 1m turn right opposite Waitrose into Downside Bridge Rd.*

Traditional, family-run pub, parts of which date back to 1540, with beamed ceilings and log fires. The inn's charming rural setting makes it popular with walkers, and the pretty River Mole is close by. There is a salad and light meals menu, with dishes like fishcakes and Barnsley chops. The main menu offers pan-fried cod fillet with saffron mash, steamed mussels and creamy sorrel sauce, or lamb shank cooked in aromatics and red wine sauce. **Open:** 11-11 **Bar Meals:** L served all week 12-3 D served Mon-Sat 6.30-10 (Sun 12-8) Av main course £10 **Restaurant Meals:** D served Tue-Sat 10 (Sun 12-4) Av 3 course alc £27.50 **Brewery/Company:** Enterprise Inns 🍺: Speckled Hen, London Pride, Gales, 1664 & Foster 🍷: 9 **Children's Facilities:** Licence Play area Menu/Portions Food warming **Notes:** Dogs allowed in bar, in garden Garden: Field at front seats 110, BBQ & sports **Parking:** 75

DUNSFOLD

The Sun Inn 🍷

The Common GU8 4LE

☎ 01483 200242 📄 01483 201141

Email: suninn@dunsfold.net

Dir: *A281 thru Shalford & Bramley, take B2130 to Godalming. Dunsfold on left after 2m*

This 500-year-old family-run inn overlooks the village cricket green and offers a warm welcome, blazing fires and a broad selection of food. Typical starters include deep fried brie with cranberry sauce, prawn and avacado salad, and Sun Inn special nachos. Follow with a choice of popular favourites such as steak and kidney pudding, italian meatballs, creamy fish pie, trio of speciality sausages and mash, or salmon fishcakes with lime and mango salsa.

Open: 11-3 5-11 (Sun 12-10.30) **Bar Meals:** L served all week 12-2.30 D served all week 7-9.30 (Sun 12-2.30, 7-8.30) Av main course £7.95 **Restaurant Meals:** L served all week 12-2.30 D served all week 7-9.30 (Sun 7-8.30) **Brewery/Company:** Punch Taverns 🍺: Harveys Sussex, Adnams, guest ales 🍷: 9 **Children's Facilities:** Fam room (Enclosed garden with guinea pigs) Menu/Portions Cutlery Games Food warming Baby changing **Nearby:** Winkworth Arboretum, Sydney Woods, Butterfly Conservation Woods **Notes:** Dogs allowed in bar, in garden, Water & Biscuits Garden: Large patio garden to side **Parking:** 40

ELSTEAD

The Woolpack 🍷

The Green nr Godalming GU8 6HD

☎ 01252 703106 📄 01252 705914

Dir: *A3 S, take Milford exit and follw signs for Elstead on the B3001*

Built as a store for woollen bales, this quaint old pub has also served as a butcher's shop, bicycle repair works and the local Co-op. Remnants of the wool industry, including weaving shuttles and cones of wool, form appealing features in the bar. There are good cask-conditioned ales and large blackboard menus that are frequently changed. The pub has a reputation for its generously-proportioned old English and colonial' food.

Open: 11-3 5.30-11 (Sat 11-11, Sun 12-10.30) **Bar Meals:** L served all week 12-2 D served all week 7-9.30 (Sun 12-2, 7-9) **Restaurant Meals:** L served all week 12-2 D served all week 7-9.30 (Sun 12-2, 7-9) **Brewery/Company:** Punch Taverns 🍺: Greene King Abbot Ale, Brakspears, Spitfire 🍷: 11 **Children's Facilities:** Fam room Play area Menu/Portions **Notes:** Dogs allowed in bar, in garden, Water Garden: Walled garden at rear **Parking:** 15

FARNHAM
The Bat & Ball Freehouse ♟

15 Bat & Ball Lane Boundstone GU10 4SA

☎ 01252 792108 🖷 01252 794564

Email: info@thebatandball.co.uk

Web: www.thebatandball.co.uk

Dir: *From A31 follow signs to Bird World. Turn left before The Bengal Lounge PH onto School Ln. Cross over x-rds into Sandrock Hill. After 0.25m take left onto Upper Bourne Ln, follow signs.*

With a name like this it should be no surprise to find cricketing memorabilia in this 150-year-old inn. The menu features traditional British and European dishes, some with a bit of spice, and a good vegetarian selection. **Open:** 11-11 (Sun 12-10.30) **Bar Meals:** L served all week 12-2.15 D served all week 7-9.30 (Sun 12-3, 6-8.30) **Restaurant Meals:** L served all week 12-2.15 D served all week 7-9.30 (Sun 12-3, 6-8.30) **Children's Facilities:** Fam room Play area (Off-ground playhouse and walkway) Menu/Portions Food warming Baby changing **Nearby:** Birdworld, Alice Holt Forest, Frensham Ponds **Notes:** Dogs allowed in bar, in garden **Garden:** Patio area with planted vines, seating, BBQ **Parking:** 40

HINDHEAD
Devil's Punchbowl Inn ♟

London Road GU26 6AG

☎ 01428 606565 🖷 01428 605713

Email: devilspunchbowl@ep-ltd.com

Web: www.roomattheinn.info

Dir: *from M25 take A3 to Guildford, then A3 & follow Portsmouth signs*

The inn, which dates from the early 1800s, stands 900ft above sea level with wonderful views as far as London on a clear day. The 'punchbowl' is a large natural bowl in the ground across the road. The menu has something for everybody with deep fried camembert with cranberry sauce, whitebait, and smoked haddock fishcakes as starters; mains include steaks, grilled sea bass and Cumberland sausages. There is a separate snack menu. **Open:** 11-11 **Bar Meals:** L served all week 12-6 D served all week 6-10 (Sun 12-9) Av main course £7.95 **Restaurant Meals:** L served all week 12-3 D served all week 6-10 Av 3 course alc £15 **Brewery/Company:** Eldridge Pope ☛: Bass, 6X, Tetleys, Bombardier ♟: 10 **Children's Facilities:** Licence Fam room (Changing area, pool table, games machine) Menu/Portions Cutlery Highchair Food warming Baby changing **Notes:** Dogs allowed in bar, in garden **Garden:** Lawn area with benches patio area, seating **Parking:** 65

LEIGH
The Plough ♟

Church Road LEIGH Reigate RH2 8NJ

☎ 01306 611348 🖷 01306 611299

Dir: *Telephone for directions*

A welcoming country pub overlooking the village green and situated opposite St Bartholomew's Church. Varied clientele, good atmosphere and quaint low beams which are conveniently padded! A hearty bar menu offers steak sandwiches, burgers, melts, salads, ploughmans' and jacket potatoes, while the restaurant area menu features tomato and artichoke pasta, smoked haddock fillet mornay, or Mexican style tortilla wraps. **Open:** 11-11 (Sun 12-10.30) **Bar Meals:** L/D served all week all day Av main course £8.95 **Restaurant Meals:** L served all week all Day D served all week all Day Av 3 course alc £20 **Brewery/Company:** Hall & Woodhouse ☛: Badger Best , Tanglefoot, Sussex Bitter ♟: 15 **Children's Facilities:** Menu/Portions Games Highchair Food warming **Nearby:** Gatwick Zoo **Notes:** Dogs allowed in bar, in garden, Water **Garden:** Patio/Paved surrounded by climbing roses **Parking:** 6

NEWDIGATE
The Surrey Oaks ♀
Parkgate Road RH5 5DZ
☎ 01306 631200 📠 01306 631200
Email: ken@surreyoaks.co.uk
Web: www.surreyoaks.co.uk
Dir: *from A24 follow signs to Newdigate, at T-junct turn left, pub 1m on left*
Picturesque oak-beamed pub located one mile outside the village of Newdigate. Parts of the building date back to 1570, and it became an inn around the middle of the 19th century. There are two bars, as well as a restaurant area, patio and beer garden with boule pitch.
Open: 11.30-2.30 5.30-11 (Sat 11.30-3, 6-11, Sun 12-10.30) **Bar Meals:** L served all week 12-2 D served Tue-Sat 7-9 Av main course £8 **Restaurant Meals:** L served all week 12-2 D served Tue-Sat 7-9 🍺: Harveys Sussex Best, Surrey Hills Ranmore Ale and rotating guest beers ♀: 8 **Children's Facilities:** Play area (Outdoor swings, slide, climbing frame) Menu/Portions Cutlery Games Highchair Food warming **Nearby:** Bocketts Farm **Notes:** Dogs allowed in bar, in garden, Water Garden: Large Child area, pond, goat paddock **Parking:** 75

WITLEY
The White Hart ♀
Petworth Road Godalming GU8 5PH
☎ 01428 683695 📠 01428 682554
Dir: *From A3 follow signs to Milford, then A283 towards Petworth. Pub 2m on left*
Dating from the 16th century, The White Hart has an original fireplace, oak beams and a wood fire burning all day. To the rear is an orchard with a large garden, terrace and swings for children. Food is traditionally British, serving the likes of beef and Guinness pie, fillet of salmon, and lasagne, all home-cooked to order.
Open: 11-11 (Sun 11-10.30) **Bar Meals:** L served all week 12-2.30 D served Mon-Sat 7-9.30 (Sun 12-2.30) Av main course £7.50 **Restaurant Meals:** L served all week 12-2.30 D served Mon-Sat 7-9.30 Av 3 course alc £20 **Brewery/Company:** Shepherd Neame 🍺: Shepherd Neame Master Brew, Early Bird, Spitfire & Best ♀: 15 **Children's Facilities:** Play area (Garden with roundabout) Menu/Portions Highchair Food warming **Notes:** Dogs allowed in bar, in garden, Water & Chews Garden: Patio, large grassed area **Parking:** 20

ALFRISTON
George Inn ♀
High Street BN26 5SY
☎ 01323 870319 📠 01323 871384
Email: info@thegeorge-alfriston.com
Web: www.thegeorge-alfriston.com
Dir: *Telephone for directions*
Splendid Grade II-listed flint and half-timbered inn set in a magical South Downs village. The George boasts heavy oak beams, an ancient inglenook fireplace and a network of smugglers' tunnels leading from its cellars. The team of three chefs create delights such as flat mushrooms sautéed in garlic with smoked bacon and goats' cheese; poached cod in red wine with spiced pear; and chicken breast filled with spinach and lentils. There is a good choice of puddings.
Open: 12-11 (Fri-Sat 12-12, Sun 12-10.30) Closed: Dec 25 **Bar Meals:** L served all week 12-2.30 D served all week 7-10 **Restaurant Meals:** L served all week 12-2.30 D served all week 7-10 **Brewery/Company:** Greene King 🍺: Greene King Old Speckled Hen, Abbot Ale, 2 Guests ♀: 12 **Children's Facilities:** Play area (Highchairs) Menu/Portions Highchair Food warming **Notes:** Dogs allowed in bar Garden: Large

SURREY / EAST SUSSEX

EAST CHILTINGTON
The Jolly Sportsman ♟

Chapel Lane BN7 3BA

☎ 01273 890400 📄 01273 890400

Email: thejollysportsman@mistral.co.uk

Web: www.thejollysportsman.com

Dir: *From Lewes take A275, left at Offham onto B2166 towards Plumpton, take Novington Ln, after approx 1m left into Chapel Ln*

An isolated pub with a lovely garden set on a quiet no-through road looking out to the South Downs. The small atmospheric bar, with its stripped wooden floor and mix of comfortable furniture, has been sympathetically upgraded to a character Victorian-style dining inn by respected restaurateur Bruce Wass from Thackerays in Tunbridge Wells. Well-sourced food features on the daily-changing menus, served throughout the bar and smart yet informal restaurant. You'll find plenty of seafood dishes,as well as interesting meat dishes. There's also a short fixed price lunch menu.

Open: 12-2.30 6-11 (Sun 12-4) Closed: 25-26 Dec **Bar Meals:** L served Tue-Sun 12.30-2.15 D served Tue-Sat 7-9 (Sun 12-3, Fri & Sat eve 7-10) Av main course £12 **Restaurant Meals:** L served Tue-Sun 12.30-2.15 D served Tue-Sat 7-9.15 (Sun 12-3, Fri & Sat eve 7-10) Av 3 course alc £28 **Brewery/Company:** Free House 🍺: Changing guest beers ♟: 9 **Children's Facilities:** Licence Play area (Large climbing frame, slide & swings) Menu/Portions Games Highchair Food warming Baby changing **Nearby:** Bluebell Railways & Drusillas Park **Notes:** Dogs allowed in bar, Water Garden: quiet, secluded, view of South Downs **Parking:** 30

FLETCHING
The Griffin Inn ♟

Uckfield TN22 3SS

☎ 01825 722890 📄 01825 722810

Email: thegriffininn@hotmail.com

Web: www.thegriffininn.co.uk

Dir: *M23 junct 10 to East Grinstead then A22 then A275. Village signed on left, 10m from M23*

Reputedly the oldest licensed building in Sussex, this Grade II-listed pub stands in an unspoilt village just a stone's throw from the Ashdown Forest and overlooking the glorious Ouse Valley. It is handy for visiting Bateman's - the home of Rudyard Kipling - Glyndebourne, and the Bluebell Railway. The two-acre, west-facing garden offers impressive views, while inside old beams, wainscoting, open fires and old pews enhance the character of the main bar. Both the bar and restaurant menus change daily, with organic, locally sourced ingredients wherever possible. The emphasis is on modern British food with Mediterranean influences.

Open: 12-3 6-11 (Open afternoons in summer at wknds) Closed: 25 Dec **Bar Meals:** L served all week 12-2.30 D served all week 7-9.30 (Sun 7-9) Av main course £9.50 **Restaurant Meals:** L served all week 12.15-2.30 D served Mon-Sat 7.15-9.30 Av 3 course alc £28.50 **Brewery/Company:** Free House 🍺: Harvey Best, Badger Tanglefoot, Guest Ales ♟: 15 **Children's Facilities:** Fam room Play area Menu/Portions Games Highchair Food warming Baby changing **Nearby:** Bluebell Railway, Drusillas Zoo & Pooh Bridge in Ashdown Forest **Notes:** Garden: 2 large lawns, beautiful views, large terrace **Parking:** 20

GUN HILL
The Gun ♟

Nr Horam Heathfield TN21 0JU

☎ 01825 872361

Web: www.elitepubs.com

Dir: *5m S of Heathfield, 1m off A267 in direction of Gun Hill. 4m off A22 between Uckfield and Hailsham.*

Lovely 17th-century building and former court house set in the heart of East Sussex with country views and a pretty terrace and garden. The interior is beamed with lots of hideaway places to sit and eat. Dishes range from tapas and fish soup to beef bourguignon.

Open: 12-11 (Sun 12-10.30) **Bar Meals:** L served all week 12-3 D served all week 2.30-9.30 Av main course £10 **Restaurant Meals:** L served all week 12-3 D served all week 2.30-9.30 (Sun 12-9) Av 3 course alc £24 **Brewery/Company:** Free House 🍺: Harveys, Guinness, Leffe, Youngs, St Miguel ♟: 13 **Children's Facilities:** Licence Play area (Wooden play area) Cutlery Highchair Food warming **Nearby:** Bentley Wildfowl & Motor Museum, Drusillas Park, Herstmonceux Castle **Notes:** Garden: Large, pretty, mature trees, good views **Parking:** 100

HARTFIELD
Anchor Inn
Church Street TN7 4AG
☎ 01892 770424
Dir: *On B2110*
A 14th-century inn at the heart of Winnie the Pooh country, deep within the scenic Ashdown Forest. Inside are stone floors enhanced by a large inglenook fireplace. Sandwiches and salads are among the bar snacks, while for something more substantial you could try whole Dover sole; grilled pork loin on a bed of spaghetti; or medeallions of beef fillet. Puddings include crème brûlée; ice cream gateaux; and orange marmalade bread and butter pudding.
Open: 11-11 **Bar Meals:** L served all week 12-2 D served all week 6-10 Av main course £7 **Restaurant**

Meals: L served all week 12-2 D served Tue-Sat 7-9.30 Av 3 course alc £21 **Brewery/Company:** Free House
🍺: Fuller's London Pride, Harveys Sussex Best Bitter, Interbrew Flowers IPA, Flowers Original Bitter & Bass, Adnams **Children's Facilities:** Fam room Menu/Portions Food warming **Notes:** Dogs allowed in bar, Water **Parking:** 30

ICKLESHAM
The Queen's Head 🍷
Parsonage Lane Winchelsea TN36 4BL
☎ 01424 814552 📠 01424 814766
Web: www.queenshead.com
Dir: *(Between Hastings & Rye on A259. Pub in village of Icklesham on x-rds near church)*
Distinctive tile-hung pub dating from 1632, an alehouse since the 19th century. It is close to the 12th-century parish church, with glorious views across the Brede Valley. High beamed ceilings, large inglenook fireplaces, church pews and a clutter of old farm implements enhance its atmosphere Hearty home-cooked food includes starters, pies, steaks and grills. Typical examples might be lamb and mint pie, leek and haddock mornay, home-made lasagna, and smoked salmon ploughman's.

Open: 11-11 (Sun 12-10.30) **Bar Meals:** L served all week 12-2.45 D served all week 6.15-9.30 (Sat-Sun 12-9.30) **Restaurant Meals:** L served all week D served all week **Brewery/Company:** Free House 🍺: Rother Valley Level Best, Greene King Abbot Ale, Ringwood Old Thumper, Woodforde Wherry, Grand Union Special 🍷: 10 **Children's Facilities:** Play area (Play area, wendy house) Menu/Portions Games Highchair Food warming **Notes:** Garden: Seating for 60, boules pitch **Parking:** 50

KINGSTON NEAR LEWES
The Juggs 🍷
The Street BN7 3NT
☎ 01273 472523 📠 01273 483274
Email: juggs@shepherd-neame.co.uk
Web: www.shepherd-neame.co.uk
Dir: *E of Brighton on A27*
Named after the women who walked from Brighton with baskets of fish for sale, this rambling, tile-hung 15th-century cottage, tucked beneath the South Downs, offers an interesting selection of freshly-cooked food. The area is ideal for walkers, and families are very welcome. New owners.
Open: 11-11 (Sunday 12-10.30) **Bar Meals:** L served all week 12-2.30 D served Mon-Sat 6-9 (Sun 12-3.30, Wknd snacks 12-9) Av main course £7.50 **Restaurant**

Meals: L served all week 12-2.30 D served Mon-Sat 6-9 (Sun 12-3.30) Av 3 course alc £15.50 **Brewery/Company:** Shepherd Neame 🍺: Shepherd Neame Spitfire, Best & Oranjeboom 🍷: 7 **Children's Facilities:** Fam room Games Highchair Food warming Baby changing **Nearby:** South Downs **Notes:** Dogs allowed on leads, not in restaurant Garden: patio, beer garden **Parking:** 30

LEWES
The Snowdrop ♟
119 South Street BN7 2BU
☎ 01273 471018

In 1836 Britain's biggest ever avalanche fell from the cliff above this pub, hence its deceptively gentle name. The owners provide good-value fresh food (all meat is free range, including tempting ranges of doorstep sandwiches (try Sussex cheese and home-made chutney), pizzas, home-made vegetable burger; and wild boar sausages. Vegetarians are well catered-for. Beer garden with a waterfall and palm tree!
Open: 11-11 (Sun 12-10.30) **Bar Meals:** L served all week 12-9 D served all week 12-9 Av main course £7 **Restaurant Meals:** L served all week 12-9 D served all week 12-9 **Brewery/Company:** Free House 🍺: Harveys

Best, Adnams Broadside plus guests **Children's Facilities:** Menu/Portions Games Highchair Food warming Baby changing **Nearby:** Drusillas Zoo Park, Stamer Park, Bluebell Railway, Lewes Castle **Notes:** Dogs allowed in bar, Water & biscuits **Garden:** Beer patio & enclosed garden area

MAYFIELD
The Middle House ♟
High Street TN20 6AB
☎ 01435 872146 📠 01435 873423
Dir: *E of A267, S of Tunbridge Wells*

Occupying a dominant position in the High Street of this 1000-year-old village, the 16th-century inn is a magnificent example of Elizabethan architecture. A private residence until the 1920s, it retains a fireplace by master carver Grinling Gibbons, and a splendid oak-panelled restaurant, still incorporating a private chapel. An impressive selection of imaginative dishes is served.
Open: 11-11 (Sun 12-10.30) **Bar Meals:** L served all week 12-2 D served all week 7-9.30 (Sun 12-2.30, 7-9) Av main course £10.95 **Restaurant Meals:** L served all week 12-2 D served Tue-Sat 7-9 Av 3 course alc £24

Brewery/Company: Free House 🍺: Harvey Best, Greene King Abbott Ale, Black Sheep Best, Theakston Best, Adnams Bitter ♟: 9 **Children's Facilities:** Play area (Wooden Climbing Frame) Menu/Portions Highchair Food warming **Nearby:** Drusilla's Zoo, Bodiam Castle & Eastbourne **Notes:** Garden: Terraced area with flower beds, good views **Parking:** 25

SHORTBRIDGE
The Peacock Inn ♟
Piltdown TN22 3XA
☎ 01825 762463 📠 01825 762463
Email: enquiries@peacock-inn.co.uk
Web: www.peacock-inn.co.uk
Dir: *Just off Haywards Heath and Lewes*

Mentioned in Samuel Pepys' diary, this traditional inn dates from 1567 and is full of old world charm, both inside and out. Today it is renowned for its food (created by no fewer than three chefs), and also the resident ghost of Mrs Fuller. The large rear patio garden is a delightful spot in summer.
Open: 11-3 6-11 Closed: 25-26 Dec **Bar Meals:** L served all week 12-2.30 D served all week 6-9.30 **Restaurant Meals:** L served all week 12-9.30 D served

all week 7-10 (Sun 7-9) Av 3 course alc £20 **Brewery/Company:** Free House 🍺: Morlands Old Speckled Hen, Harveys Best Bitter, Fullers London Pride ♟: 8 **Children's Facilities:** Play area (Climbing frame) Menu/Portions Highchair Food warming **Nearby:** Bluebell Railway **Notes:** Dogs allowed in bar **Garden:** Patio area, BBQ, lawn **Parking:** 40

THREE LEGGED CROSS
The Bull
Dunster Mill Lane Ticehurst TN5 7HH

☎ 01580 200586 🖺 01580 201289

Email: enquiries@thebullinn.co.uk

Web: www.thebullinn.co.uk

Dir: *From MG25 exit at Sevenoaks toward Hastings, right at x-rds onto B2087, right onto B2099 through Ticehurst, right for Three Legged Cross*

Based around a 14th-century Wealden hall house and set in a peaceful hamlet close to Bewl Water, the Bull features oak beams, inglenook fireplaces and quarry tiled floors. There's a duck pond in the garden, together with a pétanque court and children's play area. Food is an important part of life at the Bull, with delicious home-cooked dishes that range from freshly baked baguettes to a full à la carte selection in the restaurant.

Open: 12-11 Closed: Dec 25, 26 (evening) **Bar Meals:** L served all week 12-2.30 D served all week 6.30-9.30 (Sat/Sun 12-3, summer all day) Av main course £8 **Restaurant Meals:** L served all week 12-2.30 D served all week 6.30-9.30 Av 3 course alc £15 **Brewery/Company:** Free House 🍺: Harveys, Spitfire, Speckled Hen, Stella Artois, Wealdell Bitter **Children's Facilities:** Licence Play area Highchair Food warming Baby changing **Nearby:** Bewl Water Resevoir **Notes:** Dogs allowed in bar, in garden, Water bowls **Garden:** Front garden-pond, rear garden play area **Parking:** 80

UPPER DICKER
The Plough 🍷
Coldharbour Road nr Hailsham BN27 3QJ

☎ 01323 844859

Web: www.theploughupperdicker.co.uk

Dir: *Off A22, W of Hailsham*

17th-century former farmhouse which has been a pub for over 200 years, and now comprises two bars and two restaurants. Excellent wheelchair facilities, a large beer garden and a children's play area add to the appeal, and the Plough is also a handy stop for walkers. Expect such fish dishes as Sussex smokie or prawn, Brie and broccoli bake, while other options include duck breast in spicy plum sauce, veal in lemon cream, or lamb cutlets in redcurrant and rosemary sauce.

Open: 11-11 (Sun 12-3, 7-10.30, Summer wknd 11-11)

Bar Meals: L served all week 12-2.30 D served all week 6-9 (Food all day Sat-Sun) **Restaurant Meals:** L served all week 12-2.30 D served all week 6-9 **Brewery/Company:** Shepherd Neame 🍺: Shepherd Neame Spitfire Premium Ale, Best & Bishop's Finger 🍷: 6 **Children's Facilities:** Fam room Play area (Climbing frame, play area) Menu/Portions Highchair Food warming **Nearby:** Drusillas Zoo Park, Knockhatch Adventure Park, Michelham Priory **Notes:** Dogs allowed in bar, in garden **Garden:** Large open 1 acre, seats 80 **Parking:** 40

WINCHELSEA
The New Inn 🍷
German Street TN36 4EN

☎ 01797 226252

Email: newinnchelsea.co.uk

Web: www.newinnchelsea.co.uk

Elegant Winchelsea has seen much change over the centuries, not least the sea's retreat that ended its days as a thriving seaport. The 18th-century New Inn has witnessed change of a far more beneficial nature and is known today for its comfort, hospitality and excellent cuisine. Chalkboard specials include lobster tails with chips and salad, Rye Bay lemon sole, and chicken Kiev. The lovely walled garden is a delight on a sunny day.

Open: 11.30-midnight- **Bar Meals:** L served all week 12-3 D served all week 6.30-9.30 (Sun 12-9)

Restaurant Meals: L served all week 12-2.30 D served all week 6.30-9.30 (Sun 12-9) **Brewery/Company:** Greene King 🍺: Morlands Original, Abbots Ale, Greene King IPA, Fosters, Old Speckled Hen 🍷: 10 **Children's Facilities:** Fam room Menu/Portions Highchair Food warming **Nearby:** Beach, Museum, Windmill, Ancient Church **Notes:** Dogs allowed in bar, in garden **Garden:** Traditional Old English **Parking:** 20

WEST SUSSEX

AMBERLEY
The Bridge Inn
Houghton Bridge BN18 9LR
☎ 01798 831619
Email: bridgeamberley@aol.com
Dir: *5m N of Arundel on B2139*
The Bridge Inn dates from 1650, and has a Grade II listing. The following year Charles II stopped here to take ale after the Battle of Worcester, and nowadays cyclists and walkers enjoy exploring this delightful part of Sussex. Picturesque Amberley, Arundel Castle and Bignor Roman Villa are all close by. Recent change of management.
Open: 11-11 (Sun 12-10.30) **Bar Meals:** L served all week 12-2.30 D served all week 6.30-9 Av main course £8 **Restaurant Meals:** L served all week 12-2.30 D served all week 6.30-9 (Sun 12-3) Av 3 course alc £18.50 **Brewery/Company:** Free House 🍺: Harveys Sussex, Spitfire, Abbot Ale, Sharps Doom Bar, Shepherd Neame & Masterbrew **Children's Facilities:** Menu/Portions Cutlery Games Highchair Food warming **Nearby:** Arundel Castle, Amberley Chalkpits Museum **Notes:** Dogs allowed in bar, Water **Garden:** Well kept with views of downs **Parking:** 20

CHARLTON
The Fox Goes Free 🍷
nr Goodwood PO18 0HU
☎ 01243 811461 📠 01243 811946
Email: thefoxgoesfree.always@virgin.net
Web: www.thefoxgoesfree.com
Dir: *A286 6m from Chichester, towards Midhurst 1m from Goodwood racecourse*
Built in 1588, the pub was a favoured hunting lodge of William III. It exudes charm and character, and has an amazing five places where diners can eat: the main bar, the main restaurant, the Snug, the Bakery and the Stable.
Open: 11-11 (Sun 12-10.30) **Bar Meals:** L served all week 12-2.30 D served all week 6.30-10 (Sat-Sun 12-10) **Restaurant Meals:** L served all week 12-2.30 D served all week 6-10 (Sat-Sun 12-10.30, 12-10) 🍺: Hampshire Special, Arundel Gauntlet, Ballards Best, Ringwood Special, Horsham Special 🍷: 8 **Children's Facilities:** Menu/Portions Highchair Food warming **Nearby:** Singleton Open Air Museum, Goodwood Racecourse, West Dean Gardens **Notes:** Dogs allowed in bar, in garden, Water **Garden:** Large, with patio & lawn Seats approx 90 **Parking:** 40

CHICHESTER
Crown and Anchor 🍷
Dell Quay Road PO20 7EE
☎ 01243 781712
Email: crown&anchor@thespiritgroup.com
Dir: *Take A286 out of Chichester towards West Wittering, then R for Dell Quay*
Nestling at the foot of the Sussex Downs with panoramic views of Chichester harbour, this unique hostelry dates in parts to the early 18th century when it also served as a custom house for the old port. It has a superb terrace for al fresco dining and enjoys a fine reputation for its fresh fish, which is delivered daily. Menu choices include fish (battered to order) and chips, grilled steaks, and steak and ale pie.
Open: 11-11 (Sun 12-10.30) **Bar Meals:** L served all week 12-3 D served all week 6-9 (Sun 12-9) Av main course £10 **Restaurant Meals:** L served all 12-3 D served all week 6-9 (Sun 12-9) Av 3 course alc £40 **Brewery/Company:** Punch Taverns 🍺: Bombardier, Theakstons, Fosters, Kronenberg & Guinness 🍷: 17 **Children's Facilities:** Licence Menu/Portions Food warming **Nearby:** Seaside & Butterfly Farm **Notes:** Dogs allowed in bar **Garden:** Patio & Terrace **Parking:** 20

CHICHESTER
Royal Oak Inn ★★★★★ INN ◉ 🍷
Pook Lane East Lavant PO18 0AX
☎ 01243 527434 📄 01243 775062
Email: nickroyaloak@aol.com
Web: www.sussexlive.co.uk/royaloakinn
There's a real buzz to this 200-year-old coaching inn, with real beer too, and a resident ghost. It is set in a pretty Downland village with speedy access to both the rolling countryside of Sussex and the Georgian streets and Festival Theatre of Chichester. The brick-lined bar and restaurant achieve an effortless rustic chic, and the same attentiveness can be seen in the inn's simple, contemporary menu.
Open: All day Closed: 25 Dec **Bar Meals:** L served all week 12-2 D served all week 6-9.30 **Restaurant**

Meals: L served all week 12-2 D served all week 6-9.30 🍺: Ballards, HSB, Sussex, Arundel 🍷: 12
Children's Facilities: Menu/Portions Cutlery Highchair Food warming Baby changing **Nearby:** Goodwood, West Dean Gardens, Weald & Downland Open Air Museum
Notes: Garden: Large front patio & rear lawn area
Parking: 24

DUNCTON
The Cricketers 🍷
nr Petworth GU28 0LB
☎ 01798 342473 📄 01799 344753
Email: info@thecricketersinn.com
Web: www.cricketersinn.com
Attractive white-painted pub situated in spectacular walking country at the western end of the South Downs. Delightful and very popular garden with extensive deck seating and weekend barbecues. Regularly changing menus, sometimes four a day! Look out for good hearty meals like beer-battered haddock or ribeye steak, both with hand-cut chips.
Open: 11-3 6-11 (Fri-Sat all day Open all day all wk Etr-Oct) **Bar Meals:** L served all week 12-2.30 D served Mon -Sat7-9.30 (Sun 12-3.30) Av main course £10

Restaurant Meals: L served all week 12-2.30 D served Mon-Sat 7-9.30 (Sun 12-3.30) Av 3 course alc £21
Brewery/Company: Free House 🍺: Youngs Bitter, Archers Golden, Harvey Sussex, Ballards 🍷: 10
Children's Facilities: Play area Menu/Portions Games Highchair Food warming **Notes:** Dogs on leads allowed in bar, Water provided **Parking:** 30

HALNAKER
The Anglesey Arms at Halnaker 🍷
Chichester PO18 0NQ
☎ 01243 773474 📄 01243 530034
Email: angleseyarms@aol.com
Web: www.angleseyarms.co.uk
Dir: *4m E from centre of Chichester on A285 (Petworth Road)*
This Georgian hostelry stands in two acres of landscaped grounds on the Goodwood estate. Fresh local ingredients go into the dishes on the extensive menu.
Open: 11-3 5.30-12 (Open all day Sat-Sun) **Bar Meals:** L served all week 12-2.30 D served all week 7-9.30 (Sun 12-3) Av main course £12.95 **Restaurant Meals:** L served all week 12-2 D served all week 7.30-9.30 (Sun 12-3) Av 3 course alc £21.95 🍺: Young's Bitter,

Adnams Bitter, Deuchars IPA, Hop Back Summer Lightning & Staropramen 🍷: 8 **Children's Facilities:** Menu/Portions Cutlery Highchair Food warming Baby changing **Nearby:** Goodwood, Weald & Downland Musuem, Arundel Castle **Notes:** Dogs allowed in bar, in garden, Water Garden: Courtyard, 2 acres with Boules Terrain **Parking:** 50

HORSHAM
Boars Head ♀
Worthing Road RH13 0AD
☎ 01403 254353 📄 01403 218114
Email: tazzrail@hotmail.com
Web: www.boarsheadtavern.co.uk
Dir: *On B2237 1m from Horsham town centre, follow signs for Christs Hospital*
Built in 1761 as a farm, although late-Victorian additions have substantially altered the original structure. It's known locally as a friendly, traditional bar and restaurant with lots going on, from music evenings to beer festivals. Main dishes in the restaurant include grills; chicken, beef or vegetable fajitas; bangers and mash; fisherman's pie; and a weekly fish special. There's an extensive bar food menu as well. Look out for speciality food weeks, as well as a self-serve deli counter in the summer.
Open: 11.30-3 5-11 (Open all day Fri-Sun) **Bar Meals:** L served all week 12-2.30 D served Mon-Sat 6-9.30 (Sun 12-6) **Restaurant Meals:** L served all week 12-2.15 D served all week 6.30-9 (Sun 12-4) 🍺: Badger, Sussex, Tanglefoot, Hofbrau ♀: 10 **Children's Facilities:** Licence Menu/Portions Cutlery Games Highchair Food warming **Notes:** Dogs allowed in bar, Biscuits, bowls Garden: Two-tiered beer terrace with tables **Parking:** 42

KINGSFOLD
The Dog and Duck
Dorking Road RH12 3SA
☎ 01306 627295
Email: info@thedogandduck.fsnet.co.uk
Dir: *(On A24, 3m N of Horsham)*
Set in a large garden with a pond and 17 acres of fields, this 15th-century pub also boasts an inglenook fireplace for cold winter nights. Once a favourite of Flanagan and Allen's 'Crazy Gang' during the 1920s and 30s, contemporary entertainment includes fortnightly quiz nights and monthly live music. The pub also hosts a local darts team.
Open: 12-3 6-11 (BHs open all day, Fri-Sun 12-11) **Bar Meals:** L served all week 12-2 D served all week 6-9 (Sun 12-3) Av main course £8.50 **Restaurant Meals:** L served all week 12-2 D served all week 6-9 (Sun 12-3) Av 3 course alc £17.50 🍺: King & Barnes Sussex, Badger Best, seasonal variations, guest ales **Children's Facilities:** Menu/Portions Cutlery Games Highchair Food warming **Nearby:** Holmbush Farm, Soutwater Park **Notes:** Dogs allowed in bar Garden: Large grassed area with benches and pond **Parking:** 50

LICKFOLD
The Lickfold Inn ◉♀
Nr Petworth GU28 9EY
☎ 01798 861285
Email: thelickfoldinn@aol.com
Web: www.thelickfoldinn.co.uk
Dir: *From A3 take A283, through Chiddingfold, 2m on right signed 'Lurgashall Winery', pub in 1m*
This delightful free house dates back to 1460. The thriving pub is heavily food oriented, offering seasonal dishes cooked to order. The menu changes every 10 to 12 weeks to take advantage of seasonal availability.
Open: 11-3.30 6-11.30 (BH Mon 12-2.30) Closed: 25-26 Dec **Bar Meals:** L served Tue-Sun 12-2.30 D served Tue-Sat 7-9.30 Av main course £10.75 **Restaurant Meals:** L served Tue-Sun 12-2.30 D served Tue-Sat 7-9.30 Av 3 course alc £26 🍺: Harveys Best Bitter, Youngs, 49er, Hogsback TEA, Guinness, Harveys Best Sussex & Lagers ♀: 12 **Children's Facilities:** Licence Menu/Portions Games Highchair Food warming Baby changing **Nearby:** Devils Punch Bowl **Notes:** Dogs allowed in bar, in garden, Water bowl Garden: Stone terrace with alfresco dining, seats 60 **Parking:** 40

LODSWORTH
The Hollist Arms ♟
The Street Petworth GU28 9BZ

☎ 01798 861310

Email: george@thehollistarms.co.uk

Web: www.thehollistarms.co.uk

Dir: *0.5m between Midhurst & Petworth, 1m N of A272, adjacent to Country Park.*

This 15th-century building has been a pub since 1823. You'll probably need to book to enjoy dishes such as tiger prawns and leek gratin with fresh bread; home-made steak, Guinness and mushroom pie; or hoi sin duck in soy sauce with ginger, mushrooms and spring onions. Bar snacks range from toasties to sausages and mash. **Open:** 11-3 6-12 **Bar Meals:** L served all week 12-2 D served all week 7-9 (Sun 12-2.30) Av main course £11

Restaurant Meals: L served all week 12-2 D served all week 7-9 **Brewery/Company:** Free House 🍺: Youngs, Timothy Taylors Landlord, Horsham Best ♟: 7 **Children's Facilities:** Licence Menu/Portions Cutlery Highchair Food warming Baby changing **Nearby:** Goodwood, Petworth Park & Cowdray Park **Notes:** Dogs allowed in bar Garden: Large and enclosed **Parking:** 20

LURGASHALL
The Noah's Ark
The Green Petworth GU28 9ET

☎ 01428 707346 📠 01428 707742

Email: bernard@noahsarkinn.co.uk

Web: www.noahsarkinn.co.uk

Dir: *Off A283 N of Petworth*

Very much at the centre of village life, this charming 16th-century inn is said to have got its name because customers once had to cross a pond by the door to get in. For the last 30 years it has hosted a theatrical production each summer. An extensive snack menu is backed by more substantial fare, including crayfish tails with sweet chilli, tournedos of venison with onion marmalade, and sticky toffee pudding. **Open:** 11-3 6-11 Closed: 25 Dec **Bar Meals:** L served all week 12-2.30 D served Mon-Sat 7-9.30 **Restaurant Meals:** L served all week 12-2 D served Mon-Sat 7-9.30 **Brewery/Company:** Greene King 🍺: Greene King IPA , Old Speckled Hen & Abbot **Children's Facilities:** Fam room Play area (Large gardens) Menu/Portions Highchair Food warming **Nearby:** Fishers Farm **Notes:** Garden: Large garden, seats over 60 **Parking:** 20

MAPLEHURST
The White Horse
Park Lane RH13 6LL

☎ 01403 891208

Dir: *5m SE of Horsham, between A281& A272*

In the tiny Sussex hamlet of Maplehurst, this traditional pub offers a break from modern life: no music, no fruit machines, no cigarette machines, just hearty pub food and an enticing range of ales. Sip Harvey's Best, Welton's Pride and Joy, or Dark Star Espresso Stout in the bar or whilst admiring the rolling countryside from the quiet, south-facing garden. Village-brewed cider is a speciality. **Open:** 12-2.30 6-11 (Sun 12-3, 7-10.30) **Bar Meals:** L served all week 12-2 D served all week 6-9 (Sun 12-2.30, 7-9) Av main course £5 🍺: Harvey's Best, Welton's Pride & Joy, Dark Star Expresso Stout, King's Red River, Beer Station-Pullman **Children's Facilities:** Licence Fam room Play area (swings, slide, climbing frame) Menu/Portions Games Highchair Food warming **Notes:** Dogs allowed in bar, in garden, dog biscuits Garden: Large, great views, quiet & safe **Parking:** 20

WEST SUSSEX

MIDHURST

The Angel Hotel 🍷
North Street GU29 9DN
☎ 01730 812421 📄 01730 815928
Web: www.theangelmidhurst.co.uk
An imposing and well-proportioned, late-Georgian façade hides the true Tudor origins of this former coaching inn. Its frontage overlooks the town's main street, while at the rear attractive gardens give way to meadowland and the ruins of Cowdray Castle. Bright yellow paintwork on local cottages means they are Cowdray Estate-owned. Gabriel's is the main restaurant, or try The Halo Bar where dishes range from snacks and pasta to sizzlers and steaks, with additional specials.
Open: 11-11 **Bar Meals:** L served all week 12-2.30 D served all week 6-9.30 Av main course £8

Brewery/Company: Free House 🍺: Gale's HSB & Best 🍷: 6 **Children's Facilities:** Licence Menu/Portions Games Highchair Food warming **Nearby:** Petworth Park, Weald & Downland Open Air Museum **Notes:** Dogs allowed in garden, in bedrooms charge for dogs to stay in hotel **Garden:** walled garden, pond, views of Cowdray Ruins **Parking:** 75

NUTHURST

Black Horse Inn
Nuthurst Street Horsham RH13 6LH
☎ 01403 891272 📄 01403 891272
Email: clive.henwood@btinternet.com
Web: www.theblackhorseinn.info
Dir: *4m S of Horsham, off A281 & A24.*
This one-time smugglers' hideout is still appropriately secluded in a quiet backwater. The pub has a reputation for good beers, and on sunny days, visitors can sit out on the terraces at the front and rear, or take their drinks across the stone bridge over a stream into the delightful back garden. All food is prepared on the premises and the meat is free-range and slaughtered locally.
Open: 12-3 6-11 (Sat-Sun, BHs open all day) **Bar Meals:** L served all week 12-2.30 D served all week

6-9.30 (All day wknds & BH's) **Restaurant Meals:** L served all week 12-2.30 D served all week 6-9.30 (All Day wknds & BHs) 🍺: Harveys Sussex, W J King, Timothy Taylor Landlord, London Pride and numerous guest ales 🍷: 6 **Children's Facilities:** Licence Menu/Portions Games Highchair Food warming **Notes:** Dogs allowed in bar, **Garden:** Front & rear **Parking:** 28

OVING

The Gribble Inn 🍷
Nr Chichester PO20 2BP
☎ 01243 786893 📄 01243 788841
Email: brianelderfield@hotmail.com
Dir: *From A27 take A259. After 1m L at roundabout, 1st R to Oving, 1st L in village*
Named after local schoolmistress Rose Gribble, the inn retains all of its 16th-century charm. Large open fire-places, wood burners and low beams set the tone. There's no background music at this peaceful hideaway, which is the ideal spot to enjoy any of the half dozen real ales from the on-site micro-brewery. Liver and bacon; spinach lasagne with red peppers; and special fish dishes are all prepared and cooked on the premises.
Open: 11-3 5.30-11 (Sun 12-4, 7-10.30) **Bar Meals:** L

served all week 12-2.30 D served all week 6-9.30 (Sun 7-9) Av main course £7.95 **Restaurant Meals:** L served all week 12-2.30 D served all week 6-9.30 (Sun 7-9) **Brewery/Company:** Hall And Woodhouse Retail 🍺: Gribble Ale, Reg's Tipple, Slurping Stoat, Plucking Pheasant, Fursty Ferret 🍷: 8 **Children's Facilities:** Fam room Menu/Portions Highchair Food warming **Notes:** Dogs allowed in bar, in garden, Toys & Water **Garden:** Large shaded garden with seating for over 100 **Parking:** 40

PETWORTH
The Black Horse
Byworth GU28 0HL
☎ 01798 342424 📄 01798 342868
Email: blackhorsebyworth@btopenworld.com
An unspoilt pub built on the site of an old priory in a beautiful garden. The three-storey, brick and stone, Georgian frontage hides a much older interior dating back to the 14th century. Wooden floors and furniture, half-panelled walls, portraits of locals and open fires characterise the three rustic rooms. Good ales and traditional home-cooked food includes pheasant calvados, Cajun chicken, lasagne verde, haddock topped with Welsh rarebit, and steak and kidney pudding.
Open: 11.30-11 (Sun 12-10.30) **Bar Meals:** L served all week 12-2 D served all week 7-9 Av main course £9.45 **Restaurant Meals:** L served all week 12-2 D served all week 6-9 Av 3 course alc £16 🍺: Arundel Gold, Cheriton Pots Ale, Hogs Back Brew, London Pride, Betty Stoggs **Children's Facilities:** Menu/Portions Highchair Food warming **Notes:** Dogs allowed in bar, Water, on leads **Garden:** Country garden, views of Shimmings Valley **Parking:** 24

PETWORTH
The Halfway Bridge Inn 🍷
Halfway Bridge GU28 9BP
☎ 01798 861281
Email: hwb@thesussexpub.co.uk
Web: www.thesussexpub.co.uk
Dir: *Between Petworth and Midhurst, next to the Cowdray Estate and golf club on A272.*
Cunningly styled and refurbished to combine a modern ambience with old world charm. An intimate and casual atmosphere pervades the numerous dining rooms, at this 17th-century coaching inn. The emphasis is on local produce along with fresh meats, fish and vegetables from the London markets.
Open: 11-11 Closed: 25 Dec **Bar Meals:** L served all week 12-2 D served all week 7-10 (All day Sun) **Restaurant Meals:** L served all week 12-2 D served all week 7-10 (All Day Sun) 🍺: Cheriton Pots Ale, Sussex Badgers Best 🍷: 14 **Children's Facilities:** Menu/Portions Cutlery Highchair Food warming Baby changing **Nearby:** Petworth Park, Cowday Park, Blue Bell Railway **Notes:** Dogs allowed in bar, in garden **Garden:** Secluded patio at rear; tables in front **Parking:** 30

RUDGWICK
The Fox Inn 🍷
Guildford Road Bucks Green RH12 3JP
☎ 01403 822386 📄 01403 823950
Email: seafood@foxinn.co.uk
Web: www.foxinn.co.uk
Dir: *situated on A281 midway between Horsham and Guildford*
'Famous for Fish!' is the claim of this attractive 16th-century inn, a message borne out by the extensive menu. Food offered includes all-day breakfast and afternoon tea, while the bar menu focuses on seafood, from fish and chips to the huge fruits de mer platter. Dishes include Foxy's famous fish pie; seared tuna loin on Caesar salad; and hand-made Cumberland sausage on Stilton mash. A horse is apparently walked through the pub each Christmas day!
Open: 11-11 (Sun 12-10.30) **Bar Meals:** L/D served all week 12-10 Av main course £13 **Restaurant Meals:** L served 12-10 Av 3 course alc £22 **Brewery/Company:** Hall & Woodhouse 🍺: King & Barnes Sussex, Badger Tanglefoot, Fursty Ferret 🍷: 8 **Children's Facilities:** Play area (Wooden tower, Slide, Climbing frame) Menu/Portions Highchair Food warming **Nearby:** Fish farm at Wisborough Green **Notes:** Dogs allowed, Water **Garden:** Large patio, grassed area **Parking:** 30

STEDHAM
Hamilton Arms/Nava Thai Restaurant 🍷
Hamilton Arms School Lane Nr Midhurst GU29 0NZ
☎ 01730 812555 📄 01730 817459
Email: hamiltonarms@hotmail.com
Web: www.thehamiltonarms.co.uk
Dir: *Off A272 between Midhurst & Petersfield*
This traditional English free house, named after Admiral
Lord Nelson's mistress, is renowned for its authentic Thai
cuisine. The extensive range of over 100 Thai dishes
includes soups, curries and salads.
Open: 11-3 6-11 (Sun 12-3, 7-10.30) **Bar Meals:** L
served Tues-Sun 12-2.30 D served Tues-Sun 6-10.30
(Sun 7-9.30) Av main course £8 **Restaurant Meals:** L
served Tues-Sun 12-2.30 D served Tues-Sun 6-10.30
(Sun 7-9.30) Av 3 course alc £20 **Brewery/Company:**
Free House 🍺: Ballard's Best, Fuller's London Pride,
Everards Tiger Best, Gales HSB, Wadworth 6X, Sussex
King & Barnes 🍷: 8 **Children's Facilities:** Play area
(games room) Menu/Portions Cutlery Games Highchair
Food warming Baby changing **Nearby:** Goodwood,
Birdworld **Notes:** Dogs allowed in bar, in garden, Water
Garden: Lawn with benches and umbrellas **Parking:** 40

WALDERTON
The Barley Mow 🍷
Nr Chichester PO18 9ED
☎ 023 9263 1321 📄 023 9263 1403
Email: mowbarley@aol.co.uk
Dir: *B2146 from Chichester towards Petersfield. Turn
right signed Walderton, pub 100yds on left.*
A pretty, ivy-clad, 18th-century pub in the rolling Sussex
Downs, famous locally for its skittle alley, and used by
the local Home Guard as its HQ in World War II. A value-
for-money menu offers succulent chargrilled steaks;
home-made meat pies and burgers; trout, tuna and
jumbo cod; and vegetarian hot bake. Less filling options
include ploughman's and sandwiches. The secluded,
stream-bordered garden is a real sun-trap perfect for
a pint of Ringwood Old Thumper.
Open: 11-3 6-11.30 (Sun 12-3, 6-10.30) **Bar Meals:** L
served all week 12-2 D served all week 6-9.30 (Sun
12-2.30, 6-9.30) Av main course £8 **Restaurant
Meals:** L served all week 12-2.15 D served all week
6-9.30 (Sun 12-2.30, 6-9.30) **Brewery/Company:** Free
House 🍺: Ringwood Old Thumper & Fortyniner, Fuller's
London Pride, Itchen Valley Godfathers, Scottish Courage
John Smith's & Brakspear 🍷: 8 **Children's Facilities:**
Menu/Portions Highchair Food warming **Nearby:** Gun
Wharf Portsmouth, Goodwood & Marwell Zoo **Notes:**
Dogs allowed in bar, in garden Garden: Mature garden,
tables, seats, stream **Parking:** 50

BEMBRIDGE
The Crab & Lobster Inn 🍷
32 Foreland Field Road PO35 5TR
☎ 01983 872244 📄 01983 873495
Email: allancrab@aol.com
Web: www.crabandlobsterinn.co.uk
Refurbished, award-winning 19th-century pub just yards
from the popular 65-mile coastal path, and including a
newly raised deck and patio area offering superb sea
views. Originally a fisherman's cottage built of island
stone. Locally caught seafood is one of the pub's great
attractions, with lemon sole, sea bass and fresh tuna
among the dishes.
Open: 11-3 6-11 (Summer 11-11) **Bar Meals:** L served
all week 12-2.30 D served all week 6-9.30 Av main
course £8.95 **Restaurant Meals:** L served all week 12-
2.30 D served all week 7-9.30 Av 3 course alc £25
Brewery/Company: Enterprise Inns 🍺: Interbrew
Flowers Original, Goddards Fuggle-Dee-Dum, Greene
King IPA, John Smiths 🍷: 10 **Children's Facilities:**
Licence Menu/Portions Cutlery Games Highchair Food
warming Baby changing **Notes:** Dogs allowed in bar, in
garden Garden: Patio overlooking beach **Parking:** 40

BEMBRIDGE
The Pilot Boat Inn

Station Road Isle of Wight PO35 5NN

☎ 01983 872077 & 874101

Email: michelle@pilotboatinn.com

Web: www.pilotboatinn.com

Dir: *On the corner of the harbour at the bottom of Kings Road*

Just a stone's throw from Bembridge harbour, this strikingly designed free house enjoys a strong local following, whilst being handy for sailors and holidaymakers. New owners Nick and Michelle Jude offer an attractive menu of traditional favourites, including cod in beer batter with chips and peas; and bangers and mash with red wine and onion gravy. There's also a children's menu, together with specials like vegetable balti with rice; and chunky lamb stew and mash. **Open:** 11-11 **Bar Meals:** L served all week 12-2.30 D served all week 6-9 (Wed 6-8.30) Av main course £7.95 **Restaurant Meals:** L served all week 12-2.30 D served all week 6-9 **Brewery/Company:** Free House ☎: London Pride, Guinness, Carling, Grolsch & IPA **Children's Facilities:** Menu/Portions Cutlery Games Highchair Food warming **Nearby:** Dinosaur Museum, Beaches, Sandown Zoo **Notes:** Dogs allowed in bar Garden: Patio at rear **Parking:** 12

BONCHURCH
The Bonchurch Inn

Bonchurch Shute Ventnor PO38 1NU

☎ 01983 852611 📄 01983 856657

Email: bonchurchinn@aol.com

Web: www.bonchurch-inn.co.uk

Dir: *Off A3055 in Bonchurch*

Splendidly preserved pub, built of local stone, hidden away in a secluded continental-style courtyard. Charles Dickens, one of Britain's best-loved authors, wrote part of *David Copperfield* in the village. The menu offers a choice of Italian specialities, fish dishes and popular meat options, such as grilled fillet steak with Bonchurch sauce (mushrooms, onions, pâté, mustard, cream and brandy). **Open:** 11-3.30 6.30-11 Closed: 25 Dec **Bar Meals:** L served all week 11-2.15 D served all week 6.30-9 Av main course £7.50 **Restaurant Meals:** D served all week 6.30-9 **Brewery/Company:** Free House ☎: Scottish Courage Courage Directors & Courage Best **Children's Facilities:** Fam room Highchair Food warming **Notes:** Dogs allowed, Water Garden: Courtyard, patio & fountain **Parking:** 7

COWES
The Folly ♟

Folly Lane PO32 6NB

☎ 01983 297171

Web: www.follyinn.com

Reached by land and water, and very popular with the boating fraternity, the Folly is one of the island's more unusual pubs. Timber from an old sea-going French barge was used in the construction, and wood from the hull can be found in the bar. House specialities include lamb Henry, and ham hock in a honey and mustard glaze. Pasta, a wide range of light bites, sandwiches and jackets also feature on the menu. **Open:** 9-11 **Bar Meals:** L served all week 12-9.30 D served all week 12-9.30 Av main course £8 **Brewery/Company:** Greene King ☎: Greene King IPA, Old Speckled Hen & Goddards Best Bitter ♟: 10 **Children's Facilities:** Menu/Portions Highchair Food warming Baby changing **Nearby:** Robin Hill Adventure Park, Butterfly World & Amazon World **Notes:** Dogs allowed in bar, Water Garden: Overlooking Water **Parking:** 30

ISLE OF WIGHT

ISLE OF WIGHT

NORTHWOOD
Travellers Joy
85 Pallance Road PO31 8LS
☎ 01983 298024
Email: tjoy@slobalnet.co.uk
Ruth and Derek Smith have run this 300-year-old ale-house since 1989, although "at times it feels like 1889!" they say. Older locals remember a mynah bird that so upset a visiting darts team they tried to set it alight! A simple menu lists grills, scampi, battered cod, honey-roast ham with egg and chips, home-made steak and kidney pie, burgers and children's meals. Outside is a pétanque terrain, pets' corner and play area.
s 11-3 5-12 (Sun 11-3, 7-12) **Bar Meals:** L served all week 12-2 D served all week 6-9 (Sun 12-2 7-9)
🍺: Goddardss Special Bitter, Courage Directors, Ventnor Golden Bitter, Deuchars IPA, Hampshire King Alfred **Children's Facilities:** Fam room Play area (Climbing frame) Menu/Portions Games Highchair Food warming **Notes:** Dogs allowed in bar Garden: Large garden with patio and terrace **Parking:** 30

ROOKLEY
The Chequers
Niton Road nr Newport PO38 3NZ
☎ 01983 840314 📄 01983 840820
Email: richard@chequersinn-iow.co.uk
Web: www.chequersinn-iow.co.uk
Horses in the neighbouring riding school keep a watchful eye on comings and goings at this 250-year-old family-friendly free house. In the centre of the island, surrounded by farms, the pub has a reputation for good food at reasonable prices. Fish, naturally, features well, with sea bass, mussels, plaice, salmon and cod usually available. Other favourites are mixed grill, pork medallions, T-bone steak, and chicken supreme with BBQ sauce and cheese.
Open: 11-11 **Bar Meals:** L served all week 12-10 D served all week 12-10 (Sun 12-9.30) Av main course £7.95 **Restaurant Meals:** L served all week 12-10 D served all week (Sun 12-9.30) **Brewery/Company:** Free House 🍺: Scottish Courage John Smiths, Courage Directors, Best, Wadsworth 6X, 3 guest ales **Children's Facilities:** Licence Fam room Play area (Baby changing, highchairs, play area) Menu/Portions Games Highchair Food warming Baby changing **Nearby:** Robin Hill Adventure Park, Blackgang Chine **Notes:** Dogs allowed in bar, Water Garden: Large garden and patio with seating **Parking:** 70

SEAVIEW
The Seaview Hotel & Restaurant
★★★ HL ◉◉
High Street PO34 5EX
☎ 01983 612711 📄 01983 613729
Email: reception@seaviewhotel.co.uk
Web: www.seaviewhotel.co.uk
Dir: *B3330 (Ryde-Seaview rd), turn left via Puckpool along seafront road, hotel on left adjacent to sea.*
Directly facing the sea, this smart, small hotel is bulging with nautical associations. There are ships' wheels, oars, ship models, old pictures, and lots of polished wood and brass, particularly in the two bars. The one at the front is ideal in summer when you can look out at the passing crowds and the yachts at sea. The bar at the back, the Pump Bar, is crowded with the trophies of local sailors. Snacks in the bar include many fish dishes, but also venison sausage from Carisbrooke, as well as a range of doorstep sandwiches. A smart brasserie restaurant can be found in the Regatta Room, where dishes such as hot crab ramekin may be served. For those seeking a more substantial meal, the hotel's main restaurant at the front offers a civilised, relaxed experience.
Open: 11-2.30 6-11 **Bar Meals:** L served all week 12-2 D served all week 7-9.30 **Restaurant Meals:** L served all week 12-1.30 D served all week 7.30-9.30 **Brewery/Company:** Free House 🍺: Goddards, Greene King Abbot Ale, Adnams Ale **Children's Facilities:** Games Highchair Food warming Baby changing **Nearby:** Flamingo Park, Needles Park, Carisbrooke Castle **Notes:** Dogs allowed in bar Garden: Courtyard/patio, Food served outside **Parking:** 12

SHORWELL
The Crown Inn

Walkers Lane nr Newport PO30 3JZ

☎ 01983 740293 📄 01983 740293

Email: sally@crowninn.net

Web: www.crowninn.net

Dir: *Turn left at top of Carrsbrooke High Street, Shorwell is approx 6m*

Traditional, family-run village pub serving home-made favourites, using locally sourced produce. These include game in winter, and lots of fish, especially in summer. **Open:** 10.30-3 6-11 (Open all day during summer holidays, Sun eve 6-10:30) **Bar Meals:** L served all week 12-2.30 D served all week 6-9 **Restaurant Meals:** L served all week 12-2.30 D served all week 6-9 **Brewery/Company:** Enterprise Inns 🍺: Interbrew Boddingtons, Flowers Original, Badger Tanglefoot, Wadworth 6X **Children's Facilities:** Fam room Play area (Swings, slide & wendy house) Menu/Portions Highchair Food warming Baby changing **Nearby:** Dinosaur Farm, Blackgang Chine, Carisbrooke Castle **Notes:** Dogs allowed in bar, in garden, Dogs on lead **Garden:** Large, sheltered, flower beds, stream, ducks **Parking:** 70

West Country

North Cornish Coast

BLISLAND
The Blisland Inn
Bodmin
☎ 01208 850739
Dir: *5m from Bodmin, between Bodmin and Launceston. 2.5 m off A30 signed Blisland. On the village Green*
An award-winning inn in a very picturesque village on the edge of Bodmin Moor. The superb parish church was a favourite of John Betjeman who wrote about it extensively. Most of the traditional pub fare is home cooked, including a variety of puddings. Leek and mushroom bake is a perennial favourite, while lasagne, sausage and mash, and traditional farmhouse ham, egg and chips are also popular.
Open: 11.30-11 (Sun 12-10.30) **Bar Meals:** L served all week 12-2.15 D served all week 6.30-9.30 (Sun 12-2, 6.30-9) Av main course £6.95 **Restaurant Meals:** L served all week 12-2.15 D served 6.30-9.30 Av 3 course alc £15 🍺: A number of guest ales **Children's Facilities:** Fam room Menu/Portions Cutlery Games Highchair Food warming Baby changing **Notes:** Dogs allowed in bar, Water, chews **Garden:** Picnic tables and chairs at front of the pub

BOLVENTOR
Jamaica Inn 🍷
Launceston PL15 7TS
☎ 01566 86250 📠 01566 86177
Email: enquiry@jamaicainn.co.uk
Web: www.jamaicainn.co.uk
The setting for Daphne du Maurier's famous novel of the same name, this 18th-century inn stands high on Bodmin moor. Its Smugglers Museum houses fascinating smuggling artefacts, while the Daphne de Maurier room honours the great writer. The place is big on atmosphere, with a cobbled courtyard, beamed ceilings and roaring fires. Lunch includes Cornish pasties; a daily roast; and jacket potatoes. Typical restaurant dishes are steaks; curry of the day; and home-made vegetable lasagne.
Open: 9-11 **Bar Meals:** L served all week 12-2.30 D served all week 2.45-9 **Restaurant Meals:** L served all week 2.30-9 D served all week 2.45-9 🍺: Doombar, Tribute, Budweiser & Jamaica Inn Ale 🍷: 8 **Children's Facilities:** Licence Play area (Pirate boat with rope, swings, slide) Highchair Food warming Baby changing **Nearby:** Flambards, Trethorn Farm & Eden Project **Notes:** Garden: Lawn area with tables **Parking:** 40

BOSCASTLE
The Wellington Hotel ★★ HL ❀❀
The Harbour PL35 0AQ
☎ 01840 250202 📠 01840 250621
Email: info@boscastle-wellington.com
Web: www.boscastle-wellington.com
Dir: *In Boscastle, follow signs to harbour, turn into Old Rd, hotel ahead.*
Listed 16th-century coaching inn located in a glorious wooded valley. Bar meals are available, and restaurant offers treats such as seared Michaelstow fillet steak on dauphinoise potatoes with red wine jus, and seared tronçon of Cornish monkfish with creamed leeks.
Open: 11-11 **Bar Meals:** L served all week 12-3 D served all week 6-10 (Sun 12-9) Av main course £6 **Restaurant Meals:** D served Fri-Wed 7-9 Av 3 course alc £25 **Brewery/Company:** Free House 🍺: St Austell HSD, St Austell-HSD, Skinners Ales-Spriggan, Wooden Hand Brewery & Cornish Blonde **Children's Facilities:** Menu/Portions Cutlery Games Highchair Food warming Baby changing **Nearby:** Trethorne Leisure Farm, Goonhilly Satellite Earth Station & bike hire on Camel Trail **Parking:** 20

CALLINGTON
The Coachmakers Arms ♟
6 Newport Square PL17 7AS
☎ 01579 382567 📄 01579 384679
Dir: *Between Plymouth and Launceston on A388*
Traditional stone-built pub on the A388 between
Plymouth and Launceston. Clocks, plates, pictures of
local scenes, old cars and antique trade advertisements
contribute to the atmosphere, as do the fish tank and
aviary. There's plenty of choice on the menu, from
chargrilled steaks, steak and kidney pie or hot-pot, to
oven-baked plaice, vegetable balti or salads. Wednesday
there's a charity quiz night, and Thursday is steak night.
Open: 11-11.30 (Sun 12-10.30) **Bar Meals:** L served
all week 12-2 D served all week 7-9.30 Av main course
£4.95 **Restaurant Meals:** L served all week 12-2 D

served all week 7-9.30 Av 3 course alc £15
Brewery/Company: Enterprise Inns 🍺: Doombar,
Worthing Best Bitter, Abbot Ale, Tetley, Sharps Special
♟: 7 **Children's Facilities:** Menu/Portions Cutlery
Highchair Food warming **Nearby:** Donkey Sanctuary,
Cothele House, Morwellam Quay **Notes:** Dogs allowed
in bar, Water **Parking:** 10

CONSTANTINE
Trengilly Wartha Inn ♟
Nancenoy TR11 5RP
☎ 01326 340332 📄 01326 340332
Email: reception@trengilly.co.uk
Web: www.trengilly.co.uk
Dir: *SW of Falmouth*
A long-established residential inn, whose name means
'settlement above the trees'. The trees in question are
those in the valley of Polpenwith Creek, an offshoot of the
Helford River. The inn, now owned by William and Lisa
Lea, lies within an Area of Outstanding Natural Beauty,
surrounded by six acres of gardens and meadows. Pub
grub, including steak sandwiches and lasagne, is usually
available, but it's the Trengilly Classics that may catch the
eye, including tagliolini Cipriani (spinach pasta, crab meat

in olive oil, garlic and chilli); and pad Thai, a dish of spicy
pork, prawns, chicken, dried shrimp and egg noodles.
The river yields the oysters and mussels that appear on
the menu, while the sea supplies pollock, hake, haddock
and other fishy treats.
Open: 11-3 6.30-11 **Bar Meals:** L served all week
12-2.15 D served all week (ex 25 Dec) 6.30-9.30 (Sun
12-2, 7-9.30) **Restaurant Meals:** D served all week
7.30-9.30 **Brewery/Company:** Free House 🍺: Sharps
Cornish Coaster, Skinners, Lizard Ales, Cotleigh brewery
♟: 15 **Children's Facilities:** Fam room (Toys)
Menu/Portions Highchair Food warming Baby changing
Nearby: National Seal Sanctuary, Flambards, Trebah
Gardens **Notes:** Dogs allowed in bar, Water bowls
Garden: Walled garden, benches, pergola, terrace
Parking: 40

CUBERT
The Smuggler's Den Inn ♟
Trebellan Nr Newquay TR8 5PY
☎ 01637 830209 📄 01637 830580
Email: hankers@aol.com
Web: www.thesmugglersden.co.uk
Dir: *From Newquay take A3075 to Cubert crossroads,
then right, then left signed Trebellan, 0.5m*
Thatched 16th-century pub located two miles from the
coast in a pretty valley. The pub is well known for its real
ales served alongside a selection of snacks and meals.
Open: 11-3 6-11 (Winter 12-2) **Bar Meals:** L served all
week 12-2 D served all week 6-9.30 **Restaurant
Meals:** L served all week 12-2 D served all week 6-
9.30 **Brewery/Company:** Free House 🍺: Skinner's
Smugglers Ale, Betty Stogs Bitter, Sharp's Doom Bar,

Trebellan Tipple, St Austell Tribute & HSD ♟: 8
Children's Facilities: Fam room Play area (climbing
frames, rope nets, slide,seesaw) Menu/Portions Games
Highchair Food warming **Nearby:** Holywell Bay Fun Park,
Dairyland, Newquay Zoo **Notes:** Dogs allowed in bar, in
garden, Water Garden: Large fenced beer garden, tables
& chairs **Parking:** 50

DUNMERE
The Borough Arms
Bodmin PL31 2RD
☎ 01208 73118
Email: borougharms@aol.com
Web: www.borougharms.ukpub.net
Dir: *From A30 take A389 to Wadebridge, pub approx 1m from Bodmin*
Built in the 1850s for train crews taking china clay from the moors down to the port at Padstow, but it seems much older. Walkers, cyclists and horseriders drop in for refreshment as they follow the disused railway line, now the 17-mile Camel Trail. The menus include steak and ale pie, fish and chips, and tender meats from the carvery.
Open: 11-11 (Sun 12-10.30) **Bar Meals:** L served all week 12-9 D served all week 12-9 Av main course

£6.95 **Restaurant Meals:** L served all week 12-9 D served all week 12-9 **Brewery/Company:** Spirit Group
🍺: Sharp's Bitter, Skinner's, John Smith's Smooth
Children's Facilities: Fam room Play area Menu/Portions Cutlery Games Highchair Food warming Baby changing
Notes: Dogs allowed in bar, in garden, Water Garden: Large with kids play area **Parking:** 150

FEOCK
The Punch Bowl & Ladle 🍷
Penelewey TR3 6QY
☎ 01872 862237 📠 01872 870401
Dir: *Off Truro to Falmouth rd, after shell garage at 'playing place' rdbt follow signs for King Harry Ferry to the right continue for 0.5m & pub is on the right.*
This is a traditional thatched pub of picturesque cob construction. Small, cosy rooms and a large restaurant add to the atmosphere at this former custom house, and there is even a resident ghost! There are delightful rural views from the inn's patio, and in warmer weather you can even enjoy a drink in the walled garden. The owners offer daily fish and seafood specials, while meat dishes might include pan-fried supreme of chicken, pork tenderloin, or Punch Bowl mixed grill.

Open: 11.30-11 (Fri & Sat 11.30-12, Sun 12-10.30, Sun Summer 12-11) **Bar Meals:** L served all week 12-2.30 D served all week 6-9.15 Av main course £7.95
Restaurant Meals: L served all week 12-2.30 D served all week 6-9.15 Av 3 course alc £20.50 🍺: IPA Tribute, HSD & Cornish Cream 🍷: 8 **Children's Facilities:** Menu/Portions Cutlery Highchair Baby changing **Nearby:** Trelissick Gardens **Notes:** Dogs allowed in bar, Water bowls Garden: lovely views **Parking:** 60

GOLDSITHNEY
The Trevelyan Arms ★★★ INN 🍷
Fore Street TR20 9JU
☎ 01736 710453
Email: georgecusick@hotmail.com
Web: www.trevelyanarms.com
Dir: *5 miles from Penzance. A394 signed to Goldsithney*
The former manor house for Lord Trevelyan, this 17th-century property stands at the centre of the picturesque village just a mile from the sea. It has also been a coaching inn and a bank/post office in its time, but these days is very much the traditional family-run Cornish pub, newly refurbished. Food is fresh and locally sourced, offering good value for money.
Open: 12-12 **Bar Meals:** L served all week 12-2 D served all week 6-9 (Sun 12-2.30) **Restaurant Meals:**

L served all week 12-2 D served all week 6-9
Brewery/Company: Punch Taverns 🍺: Morland Speckled Hen, Sharps Doombar, Flowers IPA, Guinness, Carlsberg **Children's Facilities:** Menu/Portions Cutlery Games Highchair Food warming **Nearby:** Cheney Mill Farm, Flambards, Paradise Park **Notes:** Dogs allowed in bar, Water Garden: Front patio **Parking:** 5

GWEEK
The Gweek Inn
Helston TR12 6TU
☎ 01326 221502 📠 01326 221502
Email: info@gweekinn.co.uk
Web: www.gweekinn.co.uk
Dir: *2m E of Helston near Seal Sanctuary*
The lovely location of this traditional family-run village pub at the mouth of the pretty Helford River makes booking a table a wise precaution. A reputation for odd goings-on was recently given further credence by a Paranormal Society investigation. It is also known for value-for-money food, typically steak, kidney and ale pie; tagliatelle con pollo; filled jacket potatoes; and a range of salads. The chalkboard lists locally caught seafood.
Open: 12-2.30 6.30-11 **Bar Meals:** L served all week 12-2 D served all week 6.30-9 **Restaurant Meals:** L served all week 12-2 D served all week 6.30-9 **Brewery/Company:** Punch Taverns 🍺: Interbrew Flowers IPA, Old Speckled Hen, Sharps Doom Bar, 3 guest beers **Children's Facilities:** Play area (Screened garden area) Highchair Food warming Baby changing **Nearby:** Flambards, National Seal Sanctuary **Notes:** Dogs allowed in bar, in garden, Dogs on lead **Garden:** BBQ, food served outdoors **Parking:** 70

HAYLE
The Watermill
Old Coach Road Lelant Downs TR27 6LQ
☎ 01736 757912
Email: watermill@btconnect.com
Dir: *Exit A30 at junct for St Ives, left at 2nd mini rdbt.*
Built in the 1700s to mill grain for the local estate, the watermill was converted into a pub/restaurant in the 1970s. Old mill machinery is still in place and the iron waterwheel still turns, gravity fed by the mill stream. It is a family friendly establishment, with extensive gardens and fantastic views up the valley towards Trencrom Hill. Bar meals are served, and there is a separate restaurant where local fish and steaks are specialities.
Open: 12-11 **Bar Meals:** L served all week 12-2 D served all week 6-9 Av main course £6.50 **Restaurant Meals:** D served all week 6-9 Av 3 course alc £16.50 **Brewery/Company:** Free House 🍺: Sharp's Doombar, Ring 'o' Bells Dreckly, Skinners Betty Stogs, Carling & Stella Artois **Children's Facilities:** Play area (swings) Highchair Baby changing **Nearby:** Porthmere, St. Ives, Hayle & Carbis Bay beaches **Notes:** Garden: 15-acres with waterwheel & mill stream **Parking:** 35

KINGSAND
The Halfway House Inn 🍷
Fore Street Torpoint PL10 1NA
☎ 01752 822279 📠 01752 823146
Email: info@halfwayinn.biz
Web: www.halfwayinn.biz
Dir: *From Torpoint Ferry or Tamar Bridge follow signs to Mount Edgcumbe*
Set among the narrow lanes and colour-washed houses of a quaint fishing village, this family-run inn has been licensed since 1850, and has a pleasant stone-walled bar with low-beamed ceilings. The Halfway House is between the conservation villages of Kingsand and Cawsand and stands on the coastal path by Mount Edgecumbe Country Park. Locally caught seafood is a feature, and there is a good selection of bar snacks.
Open: 12-3 7-11 (All day in summer) **Bar Meals:** L served all week 12-2 D served all week 7-9 (Winter 12-2, 7-9) Av main course £10.50 **Restaurant Meals:** L served all week 12-2 D served all week 7-9 (Sun 12-2, 7-9) Av 3 course alc £17 **Brewery/Company:** Free House 🍺: Sharp's Doom Bar Bitter, Sharps Own, Marstons Pedigree, Guinness, John Smith's Smooth 🍷: 10 **Children's Facilities:** Menu/Portions Games Highchair Food warming Baby changing **Notes:** Dogs allowed in bar, in bedrooms, water, dog chews

1001 Great Family Pubs

LANLIVERY
The Crown Inn ★★★ INN ♟
Bodmin PL30 5BT
☎ 01208 872707 📄 01208 871208
Email: thecrown@wagtailinns.com
Web: www.wagtailinns.com
Dir: *Signed off A390 via brown sign about 1.5m W of Lostwithiel*
This historic pub has a long history dating from the 12th century. It stands on the old Saint's Way, an enjoyable walk past chapels, standing stones and holy wells. Local produce features strongly on the menu,
Open: 12-3 6-11 (All day during summer) Bar Meals: L served all week 12-2.15 D served all week 7-9.15 (Summer 12-3, 5.30-9.15) Av main course £8.50
Restaurant Meals: L served all week 12-2.15 D served all week 7-9.15 (Summer 12-3, 5.30-9.15) Av 3 course alc £18 🍺: Sharp's Doom Bar, Skinners Betty Stogs, Skinners Cornish Knocker ♟: 7 Children's Facilities: Menu/Portions Highchair Food warming Baby changing Nearby: Eden Project, Charlestown Harbour, Lanhydrock House Notes: Dogs allowed in bar, in garden Garden: Cottage style, wrought iron furniture, plants Parking: 40

LOSTWITHIEL
Ship Inn ★★★ INN ♟
Lerryn PL22 0PT
☎ 01208 872374 📄 01208 872614
Email: shiplerryn@aol.com
Web: www.cornwall-online-co.uk/shipinn-lerryn
Dir: *3m S of A390 at Lostwithiel*
The Ship dates from the 16th century and is the sole pub in the idyllic riverside village of Lerryn. The River Lerryn joins the Fowey River a mile or so further down stream, and the wooded banks inspired Kenneth Grahame to write *The Wind in the Willows*. It's still a great area for walkers. Typical dishes include local plaice cooked with cheddar and cider; vegetarian tagliatelle; venison, pheasant and rabbit pie; and for dessert: Cornish nog.
Open: 11-11 (Sun 12-3, 6-10.30) Bar Meals: L served all week 12-3 D served all week 6.30-9.30 Av main course £10 Restaurant Meals: L served all week 12-3 D served all week 6.30-9.30 Av 3 course alc £16 Brewery/Company: Free House 🍺: Interbrew Bass, Sharp's, Skinner's ♟: 9 Children's Facilities: Play area Games Highchair Food warming Baby changing Nearby: Eden Project Notes: Dogs allowed in bar Parking: 36

LOSTWITHIEL
The Royal Oak ♟
Duke Street PL22 0AG
☎ 01208 872552 📄 01208 872922
Email: mail@royaloakrestaurant.co.uk
Web: www.royaloakrestaurant.co.uk
Dir: *A30 from Exeter to Bodmin then onto Lostwithiel. Or A38 from Plymouth towards Bodmin then left onto A390 to Lostwithiel*
There is believed to be a secret tunnel connecting this 13th-century inn to Restormel Castle a short way up the River Fowey. Quality Cornish produce is used wherever possible in a menu of largely traditional fare.
Open: 11-12 (Fri-Sat 11am-1am, Sun 12pm-11.30pm) Bar Meals: L served all week 12-2 D served all week 6.30-9 Av main course £8.50 Restaurant Meals: L served all week 12-2 D served all week 6.30-9 Av 3 course alc £20 🍺: Interbrew Bass, Fuller's London Pride, Sharp's Own, Doom Bar, Old Speckled Hen, Abbot's Ale ♟: 8 Children's Facilities: Fam room Menu/Portions Highchair Food warming Nearby: Dobwalls Theme Park, Eden, Dairyland Notes: Dogs allowed in bar Garden: Patio, palm trees Parking: 15

MALPAS
The Heron Inn 🍷
Trenhaile Terrace Truro TR1 1SL
☎ 01872 272773 📄 01872 272773
Set in an Area of Outstanding Natural Beauty, this Cornish inn overlooks the river Fal where you might spot herons from the riverside patio. Choose from a range of seafood dishes and specials to enjoy as you birdwatch: fresh Cornish crab, cod mornay, smoked haddock and more. Real ales to wash it down include Duchy and I.P.A.
Open: 11-3 6-11 **Bar Meals:** L served all week 12-2 D served all week 6-9 (Sun 12-2, 7-9) Av main course £7.50 **Restaurant Meals:** L served all week 12-2 D served all week 7-9 **Brewery/Company:** St Austell Brewery 🍺: HSD, Tribute, IPA, Duchy & Carlsberg 🍷: 8 **Children's Facilities:** Licence Menu/Portions Highchair Food warming **Notes:** Dogs allowed outside only, Water provided **Garden:** Patio area overlooking river with seating **Parking:** 13

MANACCAN
The New Inn 🍷
TR12 6HA
☎ 01326 231323
Email: penny@macace.net
Web: www.thenewinnmanaccan.co.uk
Dir: *7m from Helston*
Thatched village pub, deep in Daphne du Maurier country, dating back to Cromwellian times, although obviously Cromwell forbade his men from drinking here. Attractions include the homely bars and a large, natural garden full of flowers. At lunchtime you might try a locally made pasty or moules marinière, and in the evening perhaps sea bass and chive fishcakes with tomato coulis.
Open: 12-3 6-11 (Sat-Sun all day in summer) **Bar Meals:** L served all week 12-2.30 D served all week 6-9.30 (Sun 12-2, 7-9) Av main course £8 **Brewery/Company:** Pubmaster 🍺: Flowers IPA, Sharps Doom Bar 🍷: 10 **Children's Facilities:** Menu/Portions Cutlery Games Highchair Food warming **Nearby:** St Anthony Beach, Goonhilly **Notes:** Dogs allowed in bar, Water **Garden:** Courtyard, natural, flowers, BBQ **Parking:** 20

MEVAGISSEY
The Ship Inn ★★★ INN 🍷
Fore Street St Austell PL26 6UQ
☎ 01726 843324 📄 01726 844368
Email: reservations@smallandfriendly.co.uk
With Mevagissey's picturesque fishing harbour mere yards away, you can understand why there's a separate fish and seafood menu here. Beer-battered cod, oven-baked mackerel with cracked black pepper, and half pints of prawns are served all day, alongside home-made steak and ale pie, trio of speciality sausages, home-cured honey roast lamb, and home-made lasagne. Doorstep sandwiches at lunchtime are served on thick crusty white or brown bread.
Open: 11-11 **Bar Meals:** L served all week 12-3 D served all week 6-9 (Summer 12-9) Av main course £7.95 **Restaurant Meals:** L served all week 12-2.30 D served all week 6-8.30 **Brewery/Company:** St Austell Brewery 🍺: St Austell Ales 🍷: 8 **Children's Facilities:** Fam room Menu/Portions Highchair Food warming Baby changing **Nearby:** Eden Project, Beaches & Heligan Gardens **Notes:** Dogs allowed in bar

CORNWALL & ISLES OF SCILLY

MITCHELL
The Plume of Feathers
Truro TR8 5AX
☎ 01872 510387 📠 01637 839401
Email: enquiries@theplume.info
Web: www.theplume.info
Since its establishment in the 16th century, the Plume of Feathers has accommodated various historical figures - John Wesley preached Methodism from the pillared entrance, and Sir Walter Raleigh used to live locally. The present owners took over the inn some years ago and have turned it into a successful destination pub restaurant; the imaginative kitchen has an excellent reputation for its food, based on a fusion of modern European and classical British dishes, with an emphasis on fresh fish and the best Cornish ingredients. There is always a daytime specials board, which changes at 6pm to include an extensive choice of 'on the night' creations. Dinner could start with chicken liver parfait with spiced pear chutney, or salmon and cod fishcake. Mains choices include grilled Angus rib-eye steak with tomato and onion salad; and penne pasta in a wild mushroom sauce. Specials include dishes such as roasted whole sea bass. **Open:** 9-11 **Bar Meals:** L served all week 12-5 D served all week 6-10 Av main course £9 **Restaurant Meals:** L served all week 12-5 D served all week 6-10 **Brewery/Company:** Free House 🍺: Doom Bar, John Smiths Smooth & Stella **Children's Facilities:** Play area (Slides & climbing frame) Menu/Portions Cutlery Games Highchair Food warming Baby changing **Nearby:** Dairyland, Eden Project, Lappa Valley Railway **Notes:** Garden: Exotic trees & bushes, seating **Parking:** 50

MORWENSTOW
The Bush Inn
Bude EX23 9SR
☎ 01288 331242 📠 01288 331630
Email: info@bushinn-morwenstow.co.uk
Web: www.bushinn-morwenstow.co.uk
Dir: *10m from Bude. Turn off 3m N of Kilkhampton, take 2nd right into village of Shop. Continue 1.5m to hamlet of Crosstown. Bush Inn on left on far side of the green.*
Originally built as a chapel in 950 for pilgrims from Wales en route to Spain, The Bush is reputedly one of Britain's oldest pubs. Set in an isolated cliff-top hamlet close to bracing coastal path walks, it is open all day every day. **Open:** 11-12 **Bar Meals:** L served all week 12-6 D served all week 6-9 Av main course £10 **Restaurant Meals:** L served all week 12-3 D served all week 6-9 (Sun 12-4.30) **Brewery/Company:** Free House 🍺: St Austell HSD, Sharps Doombar & Dartmoor Best **Children's Facilities:** Play area (Climbing frame, swings, bridge & playhouse) Menu/Portions Cutlery Food warming **Nearby:** Killarney Spings, Harlequins Playzone & Brocklands Adventure Park **Notes:** Dogs allowed in bar Garden: Beer garden, tables, good views **Parking:** 30

MYLOR BRIDGE
The Pandora Inn 🍷
Restronguet Creek Falmouth TR11 5ST
☎ 01326 372678 📠 01326 378958
Web: www.pandorainn.com
Dir: *From Truro/Falmouth follow A39, turn left at Carclew and follow signs to pub.*
This thatched, white-painted building is one of Cornwall's best-known waterside inns. Parts date back to the 13th century, and its flagstone floors, low-beamed ceilings and thatched roof suggest little can have changed since. It is named after the good ship *Pandora*, sent to Tahiti to capture the Bounty mutineers. Unfortunately it was wrecked, and its captain was court-martialled. Forced into early retirement, he bought the inn. Lunchtime offers sandwiches, jacket potatoes and mains such as Cornish crab cakes with rocket, orange and asparagus salad. In the evening make a meal of seared local scallops with belly pork and white onion sauce; or veal escalopines with fried egg and anchovies. There's seating outside, and also at the end of the pontoon, where boats moor. **Open:** 10-12 (Winter 10.30-11) **Bar Meals:** L served all week 12-3 D served all week 6.30-9 (Fri-Sat 6.30-9.30) Av main course £11 **Restaurant Meals:** L served all week 12-3 D served all week 7-9 (Fri-Sat 7-9.30) Av 3 course alc £24 🍺: St Austell Tinners Ale, HSD, Bass, Tribute, Dutchy Bitter, Cornish Cream 🍷: 9 **Children's Facilities:** Menu/Portions Games Highchair Food warming Baby changing **Nearby:** National Maritime Museum, Trelissick Gardens, Eden Project **Notes:** Dogs allowed in bar, Water Garden: Seated waterside terrace extending into river **Parking:** 30

PENZANCE
Dolphin Tavern
Quay Street TR18 4BD

☎ 01736 364106 📄 01736 364194

A 600-year-old harbourside pub overlooking Mounts Bay and St Michael's Mount. In this building, apparently, Sir Walter Raleigh first smoked tobacco on English soil and, the following century, Judge Jeffreys held court. Haunted by not one but several ghosts. A good choice of seafish is among the options on the menu offered by new tenants.

Open: 10-12 **Bar Meals:** L served all week 11-9.30 D served all week 11-9.30 Av main course £6.95 **Brewery/Company:** St Austell Brewery ◀: St Austell HSD, Tinners Tribute, Cornish Cream **Children's Facilities:** Fam room Menu/Portions Cutlery Highchair

Food warming **Notes:** Dogs allowed in bar, Water provided **Garden:** Pavement patio area

PENZANCE
The Turks Head Inn 🍷
Chapel St TR18 4AF

☎ 01736 363093 📄 01736 360215

Email: turkshead@gibbards9476.fsworld.co.uk

Web: www.turksheadpenzance.co.uk

Dating from around 1233, making it Penzance's oldest pub, it was the first in the country to be given the Turks Head name. Sadly, a Spanish raiding party destroyed much of the original building in the 16th century, but an old smugglers' tunnel leading directly to the harbour and priest holes still exist. Typically available are mussels, sea bass, John Dory, lemon sole, tandoori monkfish, pan-fried venison, chicken stir-fry, pork tenderloin, steaks, mixed grill and salads. A sunny flower-filled garden lies at the rear.

Open: 11-3 5.30-12 (Sun 12-3, 5.30-10.30) **Bar Meals:** L served all week 11-2.30 D served all week 6-10 (Sun 12-2.30, 6-10) **Restaurant Meals:** L served all week 11-2.30 D served all week 6-10

Brewery/Company: Punch Taverns ◀: Adnams Bitter, Sharp's Doom Bar Bitter & Guest Ale 🍷: 14 **Children's Facilities:** Fam room Menu/Portions Games Highchair Food warming **Notes:** Dogs allowed in bar, in garden **Garden:** Walled garden

PERRANUTHNOE
The Victoria Inn ★★★ INN 🍷
TR20 9NP

☎ 01736 710309 📄 01736 719284

Web: www.victoriainn-penzance.co.uk

Dir: *Off the A394 Penzance to Helston road, signed Perranuthoe*

Queen Victoria stares sternly from the sign outside this pink-washed, 12th-century inn, reputedly Cornwall's oldest, and first used as a hostelry by masons building the village church. Fresh seafood is its forte, the selection changing daily according to the local catch. Among the possibilities are megrim sole stuffed with Newlyn crab and baby bay prawns, and halibut steak with avocado salsa and Moroccan orange dressing. In the garden imagine you're by the Med.

Open: 11.30-2.30 6.30-11 (July & Aug open at 6pm) **Bar Meals:** L served all week (exc 25 Dec) 12-2 D served all week (exc 25 Dec) 6.30-9 (Sun 7-9) **Restaurant Meals:** L served all week 12-2 D served all week 6.30-9 (Sun 7-9) Av 3 course alc £18 ◀: Bass, Doom Bar, Abbot Ale 🍷: 8 **Children's Facilities:** Cutlery Games Highchair Food warming **Nearby:** Flambards, Seal Sanctuary, Paradise Park **Notes:** Dogs allowed in bar, in garden, Water **Garden:** Paved Mediterranean style **Parking:** 10

POLKERRIS

The Rashleigh Inn

Par PL24 2TL

01726 813991 01726 815619

Email: jonspode@aol.com

Web: www.rashleighinnpolkerris.co.uk

Dir: *Off A3082 outside Fowey*

A 300-year-old, stone-built pub on the beach, once a boathouse and coastguard station. Panoramic views across St Austell Bay can be enjoyed from the multi-level sun terrace. The pub specialises in freshly caught fish and offers sandwiches, steaks and specials like fish pie.

Open: 11-11 (Sun 12-10.30) **Bar Meals:** L served all week 12-2 D served all week 6-9 (Snacks 3-5 daily) Av main course £8 **Restaurant Meals:** L served all week 12-2 D served all week 6-9 Av 3 course alc £25 **Brewery/Company:** Free House : Sharp's Doom Bar, Cotleigh Tawny , Blue Anchor Spingo, Timothy Taylor Landlord, Rashleigh Bitter : 8 **Children's Facilities:** Menu/Portions Highchair Food warming Baby changing **Nearby:** The Eden Project, Lost Gardens of Heligan, Dobwalls **Notes:** Garden: Multi-level terrace, overlooks Polkerris **Parking:** 22

PORTHLEVEN

The Ship Inn

Helston TR13 9JS

01326 564204 01326 564204

This 17th-century smuggling inn is built into the cliffs and approached by a flight of stone steps. The terraced garden has wonderful views over the harbour; inside, you'll find log fires in the bar, and a family room converted from a former smithy. A selection of Sharp's ales accompanies the extensive menu, which ranges from toasties and jacket potatoes to main meals like home-made chilli; grilled goats' cheese on pesto croutons; and Cornish fish pie.

Open: 11.30-11 Closed: 25 Dec **Bar Meals:** L served all week 12-2 D served all week 7-9 Av main course £10 **Brewery/Company:** Free House : Scottish Courage Courage Best, Sharp's Doom Bar, Old Speckled Hen, Sharps Special, Sharps Atlantic IPA **Children's Facilities:** Fam room (Toys available) Games Highchair Food warming **Nearby:** Flambards Theme Park, beaches **Notes:** Dogs allowed in bar, in garden, Water Garden: Terraced Overlooks the harbour

---

PORTREATH

Basset Arms

Tregea Terrace Redruth TR16 4NG

01209 842077 01209 843936

Email: bas.bookings@ccinns.com

Web: www.ccinns.com

Dir: *From Redruth take B3300 to Portreath*

Typical Cornish stone cottage, built as a pub in the early 19th century to serve the harbour workers, with plenty of tin mining and shipwreck memorabilia adorning the low-beamed interior. As you'd expect, seafood dominates the menu. Look out for grilled seabass fillet, tuna steak with sweet chili sauce, turbot stuffed with prawns and mushrooms, large grilled fillet of plaice Veronique, and whole trout with almonds.

Open: 11.30-3 6-11 (all day in summer) **Bar Meals:** L served all week 12-2 D served all week 6-9 Av main course £6 **Restaurant Meals:** L served all week 12-2 D served all week 6-9 **Brewery/Company:** Free House : Sharps Doom Bar, Worthington 6X, Courage & John Smith's Smooth : 6 **Children's Facilities:** Licence Play area (Fenced play area with soft surface) Menu/Portions Cutlery Games Highchair Food warming **Nearby:** Beach **Notes:** Dogs on leads allowed in bar Garden: Paved seating area, barbecue **Parking:** 25

SALTASH
The Crooked Inn ★★★ INN

Stoketon Cottage Trematon PL12 4RZ

☎ 01752 848177 🖶 01752 843203

Email: info@crooked-inn.co.uk

Web: www.crookedinn.co.uk

Overlooking the lush Lyher Valley, a family-run inn that once housed staff from Stoketon Manor, whose ruins lie the other side the courtyard. Traditional, home-made dishes include pie, pasta or curry of the day. Boards list specials and there's a special Little Horrors menu.
Open: 11-11 (Sun 11-10.30) Closed: 25 Dec **Bar Meals:** L served all week 12-2.30 D served all week 6-9.30 Av main course £6.95 **Restaurant Meals:** L served all week 12-2.30 D served all week 6-9.30 **Brewery/Company:** Free House 🍺: Hicks Special

Draught, Sharp's Own Ale, Skinner's Cornish Knocker Ale **Children's Facilities:** Licence Play area (Trampoline, animals, treehouse, slide, swings) Menu/Portions Highchair Food warming **Nearby:** Plymouth National Aquarium, Eden Project, Looe Monkey Sanctuary **Notes:** Dogs allowed in bar, in garden, Garden: 10 acres, enclosed courtyard, seats, decking **Parking:** 60

SALTASH
The Weary Friar Inn ★★★★ INN

Pillaton PL12 6QS

☎ 01579 350238 🖶 01579 350238

Email: info@wearyfriar.co.uk

Web: www.wearyfriar.co.uk

Dir: *2m W of A388 between Callington & Saltash*

This whitewashed 12th-century inn with oak-beamed ceilings, an abundance of brass, and blazing fires lies next to the Church of St Adolphus, tucked away in a small Cornish village. Varied menu includes venison pie, spit roasted chicken, fillet steak with wild mushroom sauce, and Cornish crab cakes. Salads, sandwiches, afternoon cream teas and ploughman's also available.
Open: 11-11 (Sun 12-10.30) **Bar Meals:** L served all week 11-3 D served all week 5-9 (Sun 12-3, 5-9)

Av main course £8.95 **Restaurant Meals:** L served all week 11-3 D served all week 5-9 Av 3 course alc £15 **Brewery/Company:** Free House 🍺: St Austell Tribute, Tinners, Interbrew Bass, Fullers London Pride, Sharp's Doom Bar **Children's Facilities:** Fam room Menu/Portions Cutlery Highchair Food warming **Notes:** Garden: sun trap, seating, illuminated fountain **Parking:** 30

SENNEN
The Old Success Inn ★★ HL

Sennen Cove Penzance TR19 7DG

☎ 01736 871232 🖶 01736 871457

Email: oldsuccess@sennencove.fsbusiness.co.uk

Web: www.oldsuccess.com

Once the haunt of smugglers and now a focal point for the Sennen Lifeboat crew, this 17th-century inn enjoys a glorious location overlooking Cape Cornwall. Its name comes from the days when fishermen gathered here to count their catch and share out their 'successes'. Fresh local seafood is to the fore, and favourites include cod in Doom Bar batter, steaks, chilli, and vegetable lasagne. Live music every Saturday night in the bar.
Open: 11-11 **Bar Meals:** L served all week 12-2.30 D served all week 6.15-9.30 **Restaurant Meals:** L served

Sun 12-2.15 D served all week 7-9.30 Av 3 course alc £18.50 **Brewery/Company:** Free House 🍺: Doom Bar, Skinners, Heligan Honey, Headlaunch Special **Children's Facilities:** Menu/Portions Highchair Food warming **Nearby:** Beach, Land's End, Flambards **Notes:** Dogs allowed in bar Garden: Beer terrace, stunning views of Whitesand Bay **Parking:** 16

ST AGNES
Driftwood Spars Hotel ★★★★ GA 🍷
Trevaunancc Cove TR5 0RT
☎ 01872 552428 & 553323 📠 01872 553701
Email: driftwoodsparshotel@aol.com
Web: www.driftwoodspars.com
Dir: *A30 onto B3285, through St Agnes, down steep hill, left at Peterville Inn, onto road signed Trevaunance Cove*
Previously a tin miners' store, a chandlery and a sail loft, this 300-year-old building has an old smugglers' tunnel in the back bar. Sit by the fire and try ales from its micro-brewery, or dine on moules marinière; roasted stuffed sea bass ; or chargrilled fillet of beef with a mushroom gratin.
Open: 11-12 (Fri-Sat 11-12, Sun 12-10.30) **Bar Meals:** L served all week 12-2.30 D served all week 6.30-9.30 (All day Aug) Av main course £8 **Restaurant Meals:** L served all week 12-2.30 D served all week 6.30-9.30
Brewery/Company: Free House 🍺: Carlsberg-Tetley Bitter, Sharp's Own, St Austell HSD, Cuckoo Ale, Sharps Doom Bar 🍷: 15 **Children's Facilities:** Menu/Portions Highchair Food warming **Nearby:** Beaches, Blue Hills Tin Streams, St Agnes Craft Trail **Notes:** Dogs allowed in bar, in garden **Garden:** Patio opposite pub **Parking:** 80

ST BREWARD
The Old Inn & Restaurant 🍷
Churchtown Bodmin Moor PL30 4PP
☎ 01208 850711 📠 01208 851671
Email: darren@theoldinn.fsnet.co.uk
Web: www.theoldinnandrestaurant.co.uk
Dir: *A30 to Bodmin. Continue for 16m just after Temple turn R and follow signs to St Breward. B3266 Bodmin to Camelford road take turning to St Breward as indicated on brown signs.*
High up on Bodmin Moor, one of Cornwall's oldest inns is well-known throughout this glorious area for its wholesome home-cooked food.
Open: 11-11 **Bar Meals:** L served all week 11-2 D served all week 6-9 (Sun 12-2, 6-9) Av main course £7.95 **Restaurant Meals:** L served all week 11-2 D served all week 6-9 (Sun 12-2, 6-9) Av 3 course alc £25 **Brewery/Company:** Free House 🍺: Sharp's Doom Bar Bitter, Sharps Special, Guest Ales 🍷: 20 **Children's Facilities:** Fam room Menu/Portions Games Highchair Food warming Baby changing **Nearby:** North Cornwall Avaries, Eden Project, Colliford Lake Park **Notes:** Dogs allowed in bar, in garden **Parking:** 35

ST EWE
The Crown Inn
Nr Mevagissey St Austell PL26 6EY
☎ 01726 843322 📠 01726 844720
Email: linda@thecrowninn737.fsnet.co.uk
Dir: *From St Austell take B3273. At Tregiskey x-rds turn right. St Ewe signed on right*
Hanging baskets add plenty of brightness and colour to this delightful 16th-century inn, just a mile from the famous 'Lost Gardens of Heligan', which Crown chef John Nelson co-founded and helped to restore. Well-kept St Austell ales complement an extensive menu and daily specials. Expect cod in beer batter, local steaks, rack of lamb, and liver and bacon among other favourites.
Open: 12-3 5-11 **Bar Meals:** L served all week 12-2 D served all week 6-9 Av main course £7.50 **Restaurant Meals:** L served all week 12-2 D served all week 6-9
Brewery/Company: St Austell Brewery 🍺: Tribute, Hicks Special, Tinners, plus guest ale **Children's Facilities:** Fam room Play area Cutlery Highchair Food warming **Notes:** Dogs allowed in bar, in garden, Water **Garden:** fenced and well lit **Parking:** 60

ST MAWES
The Victory Inn
Victory Hill TR2 5PQ

☎ 01326 270324 📄 01326 270238

Email: info@roseland-inn.co.uk

Web: www.victory-inn.co.uk

Dir: *Take A3078 to St Mawes, located up the Victory Steps adjacent to the Harbour*

Close to St Mawes Harbour on the Roseland Peninsula, this friendly fishermen's local is a modern dining pub, offering the freshest of local seafood. There is a heated and covered sea view terrace. The blackboard specials change daily and there's a choice of pub grub dishes.

Open: 11-11 (Fri/Sat 11-12) **Bar Meals:** L served all week 12-2.15 D served all week 6.30-9 Av main course £10 **Restaurant Meals:** L served Mon-Sun 12-2.15 D served Mon-Sun 6.30-9 Av 3 course alc £24 🍺: Sharps, Bass, Ringwood, IPA, Tetley Smooth, Speckled Hen 🍷: 6 **Children's Facilities:** Play area (Various board games) Menu/Portions Cutlery Games Highchair Food warming **Nearby:** Eden Project, Falmouth Maritime Museum & Flambards **Notes:** Dogs allowed in bar, Biscuits, water and toys Garden: Seaview terrace

ST MAWGAN
The Falcon Inn ★★★★ INN 🍷
Nr Newquay TR8 4EP

☎ 01637 860225 📄 01637 860884

Email: enquiries@thefalconinn-newquay.co.uk

Web: www.thefalconinn-newquay.co.uk

Dir: *From A30 8m W of Bodmin, follow signs to Newquay/St Mawgan Airport. After 2m turn right into village, pub at bottom of hill*

This 16th-century inn in the sleepy village of St Mawgan, nestling in the sheltered Vale of Lanherne, has a large, attractive garden with a lovely magnolia tree and walls covered with wisteria, plus a cobbled courtyard.

Open: 11-3 6-12 (Sun 12-5, 7-11) **Bar Meals:** L served all week 12-2 D served all week 6-9 (Summer 12-2.30, 6-9.30) **Restaurant Meals:** L served all week 12-2 D served all week 6-9 **Brewery/Company:** St Austell Brewery 🍺: St Austell HSD, Tinners Ale & Tribute 🍷: 7 **Children's Facilities:** Fam room Play area (Childrens Playroom in garden) Menu/Portions Games Highchair Food warming Baby changing **Nearby:** Dairyland, Shire Adventure Park **Notes:** Dogs allowed in bar, in garden Garden: Large garden, sheltered, safe **Parking:** 25

ST NEOT
The London Inn ★★★ INN 🍷
Liskeard PL14 6NG

☎ 01579 320263 📄 01579 321642

Email: lon.manager@ccinns.com

Web: www.ccinns.com

Dating back to the 18th century, this pub was the first coaching inn on the route from Penzance to London. The bar and dining areas have old beamed ceilings and polished flagstone floors. Seafood platter, salmon, and halibut are among the fish dishes, while other main courses include lamb shank in a spiced port sauce. Lighter fare ranges from ciabatta bread with a variety of fillings, including roast beef, chicken, bacon and cheese, to a choice of ploughman's lunches.

Open: 12-3 6.30-11 **Bar Meals:** L served all week 12-2 D served all week 7-9 Av main course £9.95 **Restaurant Meals:** L served all week 12-2 D served all week 7-9 Av 3 course alc £25 **Brewery/Company:** Coast & Country Inns 🍺: Doom Bar, Courage Best, John Smiths & Guest Ales 🍷: 16 **Children's Facilities:** Menu/Portions Cutlery Games Highchair Food warming Baby changing **Notes:** Dogs allowed, Water **Parking:** 15

TINTAGEL
The Port William ★★★ INN ♟

Trebarwith Strand PL34 0HB
☎ 01840 770230 📄 01840 770936
Email: theportwilliam@btinternet.com
Web: www.theportwilliam.com
Dir: *Off B3263 between Camelford & Tintagel, pub signed*

Occupying one of the best locations in Cornwall, this former harbourmaster's house lies directly on the coastal path, 50 yards from the sea. There is an entrance to a smugglers' tunnel at the rear of the ladies' toilet! Offers a daily-changing specials board.
Open: 11-11 (Sun 12-10.30, 12 opening in winter) **Bar Meals:** L served all week 12-2.30 D served all week 6.30-9.30 Av main course £8.50 **Restaurant Meals:** L

served all week 12-2.30 D served all week 6-9.30
Av 3 course alc £15 **Brewery/Company:** Free House
🍺: St Austell Tinners Ale & Hicks, Interbrew Bass ♟: 8
Children's Facilities: Fam room (Beach) Menu/Portions Highchair Food warming Baby changing **Nearby:** Beach
Notes: Dogs allowed in bar, Water Garden: Patio overlooking sea, food served outside **Parking:** 75

TORPOINT
The Edgcumbe Arms ★★★★ INN ♟

Cremyll PL10 1HX
☎ 01752 822294 📄 01752 822014
Email: edgcumbe-arms@btconnect.com
Web: www.smallandfriendlyinns.co.uk
Dir: *Please phone for directions*

The inn dates from the 15th century and is located right on the Tamar estuary, next to the National Trust Park, close to the foot ferry from Plymouth. Views from the bow window seats and waterside terrace are glorious, taking in Drakes Island, the Royal William Yard and the marina. Real ales from St Austell like Cornish Cream, Tribute HS, and Tinners, and quality home-cooked food are served in a series of rooms, which are full of character with American oak panelling and stone flagged floors. A good choice of bar snacks is also offered. The inn has a first floor function room with sea views, and a courtyard garden; it also holds a civil wedding license. A bridal suite is included in the range of pretty bedrooms.
Open: 11-11 (Sun 12-10.30) **Bar Meals:** L served all week 12-6 D served all week 6-9.30 **Restaurant Meals:** L served all week 12-6 D served all week 6-9.30 **Brewery/Company:** St Austell Brewery 🍺: St Austell HSD, Tribute HS, IPA, Cornish Cream, Tinners ♟: 10 **Children's Facilities:** Menu/Portions Highchair Food warming Baby changing **Nearby:** Plymouth Aquarium, Mount Edgcumbe Country Park , Dobwell Theme Park **Notes:** Dogs allowed in bar, in garden, Water and treats Garden: Large picnic area with tables **Parking:** 12

TREBARWITH
The Mill House Inn

Tintagel PL34 0HD
☎ 01840 770200 📄 01840 770647
Email: management@themillhouseinn.co.uk
Web: www.themillhouseinn.co.uk
Dir: *From Tintagel take B3263 S, turn right after Trewarmett to Trebarwith Strand, pub is 0.5m down valley on right.*

The 18th-century Mill House stands on the north Cornish coast in seven acres of wooded gardens, with King Arthur's legendary castle of Camelot in the next valley. It provides first-class food in a charming stone building.
Open: 12-11 Closed: 25 Dec **Bar Meals:** L served all week 12-2.30 (Sun 12-3) Av main course £7
Restaurant Meals: D served all week 6.30-9 (Sun 12-3)

Av 3 course alc £25 🍺: Sharps Doom Bar, Sharps Special, Red Stripe, Carlsberg, Sharps & Wills Resolve
Children's Facilities: Licence Fam room Play area (Enclosed play area on front terrace) Menu/Portions Cutlery Games Highchair Food warming Baby changing
Nearby: Tintagel Castle, Trebarwith Strand & Camel Trail
Notes: Dogs allowed in bar Garden **Parking:** 60

The Mill House

TREBURLEY
The Springer Spaniel 🍷
Nr Launceston PL15 9NS
☎ 01579 370424 📄 01579 370113
Email: thespringer@wagtailinns.com
Web: www.wagtailinns.com
Dir: *On the A388 halfway between Launceston & Callington*
This unassuming-looking roadside hostelry may not look very different from many other pubs, but it's a different story inside. It dates from the 18th century, and the old creeper-covered walls conceal a cosy bar with two high-backed wooden settles, farmhouse-style chairs, and a wood-burning stove. It was once part of a farm, and remains homely and welcoming, though these days it is the terrific food that provides the biggest draw.

Blackboards in the bar list the lighter snack options - freshly filled sandwiches and rolls, decent soups and daily specials - as well as the more serious choices that are also served in the separate beamed dining room where the setting is slightly more formal. Dishes vary according to the seasons.
Open: 11-3 6-11 **Bar Meals:** L served all week 12-2 D served all week 6.30-9 Av main course £8.95
Restaurant Meals: L served all week 12-2 D served all week 6.30-9 Av 3 course alc £20 **Brewery/Company:** Free House 🍺: Sharp's Doom Bar, Eden Ale, Springer Ale, Cornish Coaster 🍷: 7 **Children's Facilities:** Fam room Menu/Portions Cutlery Food warming Baby changing
Nearby: Hidden Valley, Tamar Otter, Launceston Castle
Notes: Dogs allowed in bar, Water & Biscuits **Garden:** Landscaped with seating, heated, umbrella **Parking:** 30

TREGADILLETT
Eliot Arms (Square & Compass) 🍷
PL15 7EU
☎ 01566 772051
Email: eli.bookings@ccinns.com
Web: www.ccinns.com
Dir: *From Launceston take A30 towards Bodmin. Then follow brown signs to Tregadillett*
This old coaching inn is built from Cornish stone and boasts a huge collection of clocks, Masonic regalia and horse brasses. It was believed to have been a Masonic lodge for Napoleonic prisoners, and even has its own friendly ghost! Customers can enjoy real fires in winter and lovely hanging baskets in summer. Fish features strongly, with delicacies such as moules marinière and grilled sardines. Other options include Cajun-style

chicken, and home-made vegetable curry.
Open: 11.30-3 6-11 (Fri-Sun all day) **Bar Meals:** L served all week 12-2 D served all week 7-9 Av main course £11 **Restaurant Meals:** L served all week 12-2 D served all week 7-9 Av 3 course alc £20
Brewery/Company: Free House 🍺: Doom Bar, Scottish Courage Courage Best 🍷: 9 **Children's Facilities:** Fam room (Changing mat) Menu/Portions Cutlery Highchair Baby changing **Nearby:** Trethorne Leisure Farm, Railway, Otterpark **Notes:** Dogs allowed in bar, in bedrooms **Garden:** Seating areas around pub **Parking:** 20

TRESCO
The New Inn ★★ HL 🌐🌐 🍷
New Grimsby Isles of Scilly TR24 0QQ
☎ 01720 422844 📄 01720 423200
Email: newinn@tresco.co.uk
Web: www.tresco.co.uk/holidays/new_inn.asp
Dir: *By New Grimsby Quay*
The New Inn is on most visitors' itineraries, being the only pub in Tresco. It is open all year, and in the evenings it becomes the island's social centre. New Grimsby Harbour, Tresco Stores, the Island Hotel and Abbey Garden are all nearby. Maritime artefacts abound: walls are panelled with exotic woods jettisoned by a freighter, the mahogany bar top is from a French wreck, and the pub's signboard was salvaged from the *Award*, wrecked in 1861. Lunchtime dishes include moules marinière;

garlic crevettes; imaginative sandwiches; fish and chips; and Tresco beef and ale pie. Dinner might include seared marlin steak with tarragon mash and sun-dried tomato sauce; corn-fed chicken breast with bacon lardons, Swiss rösti potato and green peppercorn sauce; and asparagus risotto. Look out for ales from Britain's most south-westerly brewery, Ales of Scilly.
Open: 11-11 **Bar Meals:** L served all week 12-2 D served all week 6-9 (Limited menu Apr-Sep) Av main course £12.25 **Restaurant Meals:** D served all week 7-9 Av 3 course alc £30 **Brewery/Company:** Free House 🍺: Skinner's Betty Stogs Bitter, Tresco Tipple, Ales of Scilly Maiden Voyage, St Austell IPA, Ales of Scilly Natural Beauty 🍷: 8 **Children's Facilities:** Cutlery Games Highchair Food warming Baby changing **Notes:** Garden: Patio area with sub-tropical plants

CORNWALL & ISLES OF SCILLY / DEVON

WADEBRIDGE
Swan Hotel ★★★★ INN ♟
9 Molesworth Street PL27 7DD
☎ 01208 812526 📄 01208 812526
Email: reservations@smallandfriendly.co.uk
Web: www.staustellbrewery.co.uk
Dir: *In centre of Wadebridge on corner of Molesworth St and The Platt*

A town centre hotel that is family friendly, it was originally called the Commercial Hotel, and sits alongside the old Padstow Railway Branch Line. Typical pub food includes doorstep sandwiches and baguettes, light snacks like cheesy chips, salads, chargrill dishes, full Cornish breakfast and main courses like Tribute beer-battered cod, or curry of the day. Children's dishes include chicken nuggets made of 100% chicken breast; pizza or pork sausage.
Open: 10-11 **Bar Meals:** L served all week 12-3 D served all week 6-9 Av main course £6.50
Brewery/Company: St Austell Brewery ◀: HSD, Tribute, Carlsberg, Guinness & Carling ♟: 13 **Children's Facilities:** Licence Fam room Menu/Portions Cutlery Games Highchair Food warming Baby changing **Nearby:** Crealy, Landhyndrock, Dobwalls **Notes:** Dogs allowed in bar Garden: Beer garden with parasols and seating

ASHBURTON
The Rising Sun ★★★★ INN ♟
Woodland TQ13 7JT
☎ 01364 652544
Web: www.risingsunwoodland.co.uk
Dir: *E of Ashburton from A38 take lane signed Woodland/Denbury. Pub on left approx 1.5m*

Once a drovers' inn, where animals were rested on their way to Newton Abbot market from Dartmoor, the Rising Sun was largely rebuilt following a fire in 1989. There's a good choice of fish, along with home-made pies, Devon chicken, and home-cooked ham.
Open: 11.45-3 6-12 (Sun 12-3, 7-10.30) Closed: 25 Dec **Bar Meals:** L served Tue-Sun 12-2.15 D served Tue-Sun 6-9.15 (Sun 12-3, 7-9.15) Av main course £10.25 **Restaurant Meals:** L served Tue-Sun 12-2.15 D served Tue-Sun 6-9.15 (Sun 12-3, 7-9.15) Av 3 course alc £17 **Children's Facilities:** Fam room Play area (Toys, books, swings, old tractor) Menu/Portions Cutlery Games Highchair Food warming Baby changing **Nearby:** Otter Sanctuary & Butterfly Farm, Pennywell Farm, S Devon Steam Railway **Notes:** Dogs allowed in bar, in garden Garden: Seating **Parking:** 30

AXMOUTH
The Ship Inn ♟
EX12 4AF
☎ 01297 21838
Dir: *1m S of A3052 between Lyme and Sidmouth*

Creeper-clad family-run inn built soon after the original Ship burnt down on Christmas Day 1879, and able to trace its landlords back to 1769; the current ones have been there for 40 years. There are long views over the Axe estuary from the beer garden. Well kept real ales complement an extensive menu including daily black-board specials where local fish and game feature, cooked with home-grown herbs.
Open: 11-3 6-11 (Winter 11.30-2.30, 6.30-11) **Bar Meals:** L served all week 12-2 D served all week 6-9.30 Av main course £7 **Restaurant Meals:** L served all week 12-2 D served all week 6-9 Av 3 course alc £15 **Brewery/Company:** Pubmaster ◀: Otter Bitter, Guinness, 6X, Carling & Stowford Press ♟: 10 **Children's Facilities:** Fam room Play area (Climbing frame) Menu/Portions Cutlery Highchair Food warming **Nearby:** Beaches, Donkey Sanctuary & Model Railways **Notes:** Dogs allowed in bar, Dogs on leads Garden: Lawn/patio area with panoramic views **Parking:** 25

BERE FERRERS
Olde Plough Inn
Yelverton PL20 7JL
☎ 01822 840358
Email: oldeplough@btinternet.com
Dir: *A386 from Plymouth, A390 from Tavistock*
Originally three cottages, dating from the 16th century, this inn has bags of character, with its old timbers and flagstones, which on closer inspection are revealed to be headstones. To the rear is a fine patio overlooking the River Tavey, and there are lovely walks in the Bere Valley on the doorstep. The area is ideal for birdwatchers. Dishes on offer range through fresh fish, crab, local pies, curries and stir-fries.
Open: 12-3 7-11.30 **Bar Meals:** L served all week 12-2 D served all week 7-9 Av main course £7 **Restaurant**

Meals: L served all week 12-2 D served all week 7-9 Av 3 course alc £16 **Brewery/Company:** Free House ◖: Sharp's Doom Bar & Sharp's Own, Interbrew Flowers, weekly guest ale **Children's Facilities:** Fam room Menu/Portions Highchair Food warming **Notes:** Dogs allowed in bar, Water Garden: Safe beer garden with river views

BRAUNTON
The Williams Arms
Wrafton EX33 2DE
☎ 01271 812360 🖷 01271 816595
Web: www.williams-arms.co.uk
Dir: *On A361 between Barnstaple and Braunton*
Spacious thatched pub dating back to the 16th century, and adjacent to the popular Tarka Trail, named after the much-loved otter created by author Henry Williamson. The restaurant has a carvery serving fresh locally-sourced meat and various vegetable dishes. Try the North Devon lamb steak marinated in dark rum, oranges and spices.
Open: 11-11 **Bar Meals:** L served all week 12-2 D served all week 6-10 (Sun 12-2.30) **Restaurant Meals:** L served all week 12-2 D served all week 6.30-10 (Sun 12-2.30) Av 3 course alc £18 ◖: Draught Bass, Worthington Creamflow, Tetleys Creamflow, Carling & Stella **Children's Facilities:** Licence Play area (Wooden fort, large garden) Menu/Portions Highchair Food warming Baby changing **Nearby:** The Big Sheep, Milky Way & Beaches **Notes:** Garden: Large lawned area with picnic tables **Parking:** 90

BRENDON
Rockford Inn
nr Lynton EX35 6PT
☎ 01598 741214 🖷 01598 741265
Email: enquiries@therockfordinn.com
Web: www.therockfordinn.com
Dir: *A39 through Minehead follow signs to Lynmouth. Turn left off A39 to Brendon approx 5m before Lynmouth*
Set within the magnificent Exmoor National Park, on the banks of the East Lyn River at Brendon, this traditional West Country pub is the perfect place for exploring Devon and Somerset on foot or by car. The atmospheric Doone Valley, made famous by R D Blackmore's classic 19th-century novel *Lorna Doone*, lies close by. Home-made Lancashire hot pot, steak and kidney pie, sirloin steak, and scampi and chips typify the popular menu.

Open: 12-3 6.30-10.30 **Bar Meals:** L served all week 12-2.30 D served all week 7-9 Av main course £8 **Brewery/Company:** Free House ◖: Rockford, Barn Owl, Golden Arrow, Archers, Tribute **Children's Facilities:** Licence Fam room Highchair Food warming Baby changing **Notes:** Dogs allowed in bar, Water Garden: Small beer garden overlooking East Lyn River

DEVON

BROADHEMPSTON
The Monks Retreat Inn
The Square TQ9 6BN
☎ 01803 812203
Dir: *Exit Newton Abbot to Totnes rd at Ipplepen, follow signs for Broadhempston for 3.5m.*
Apparently a friendly ghost inhabits this inn - certainly it's the sort of place you'd want to linger in: the building (listed as of outstanding architectural interest) is full of fascinating features, including a panelled oak screen typical of ancient Devon houses. Sit by one of the cosy log fires and enjoy a pint of Skinner's Cornish Knocker or other decent real ales from Butcombe.
Open: 12-2.30 6-11 (Sun 12-3, 7-10.30) **Bar Meals:** L served Tue-Sun 12-2 D served Tue-Sun 6.30-9.30 (Sun 12-2.30 7-9) Av main course £9.50 **Restaurant**

Meals: L served Tue-Sun 12-2 D served Tue-Sun 6.30-9.30 Av 3 course alc £18 **Brewery/Company:** Enterprise Inns ▰: Buttcombe, Fosters, Kronenbourg, Guinness & Cornish Knocker **Children's Facilities:** Licence Menu/Portions Cutlery Food warming **Notes:** Dogs allowed

BUCKFASTLEIGH
Dartbridge Inn ♇
Totnes Road TQ11 0JR
☎ 01364 642214 ▤ 01364 643839
Email: dartbridge.buckfastleigh@oldenglishinns.co.uk
Web: www.dartbridgeinn.com
Dir: *From Exeter A38, take 1st Buckfastleigh turn, turn right to Totnes and hotel is on the left.*
Standing close to the River Dart, this 19th-century building was originally a simple dwelling, then a teashop before becoming a pub. Well known for its eye-catching floral displays, inside are open fires and oak beams. The lunch/bar menu includes slow-cooked Welsh lamb, and spinach and ricotta girasole, while dinner mains are typically baked rainbow trout with pan-fried tiger prawns, gammon and other steaks, sausages and

mash, and chicken Caesar salad.
Open: 11-11 **Bar Meals:** L served all week 12-5 D served all week 5-9.30 (Sun 11-9) Av main course £8.95 **Restaurant Meals:** L served all week 12-2 D served all week 7-9.30 **Brewery/Company:** Old English Inns & Hotels ▰: Scottish Courage, Abbot Ale, IPA, Otter Ale ♇: 12 **Children's Facilities:** Menu/Portions Highchair Food warming **Nearby:** South Devon Steam Railway, Otters, Butterfly Farm & Pennywell Farm **Notes:** Garden: Terrace overlooking front of building **Parking:** 100

BUCKLAND MONACHORUM
Drake Manor Inn ♇
The Village Yelverton PL20 7NA
☎ 01822 853892 ▤ 01822 853892
Web: www.drakemanorinn.co.uk
Dir: *Off A386 near Yelverton*
Prettily located between the village church and the stream, this welcoming 16th-century inn takes its name from one-time local resident Sir Francis Drake. Award-winning hanging baskets and summer floral displays add a touch of brightness outside, while inside customers enjoy good quality food in congenial surroundings. Pub fare includes freshly baked baguettes and ploughman's, while more substantial options range from grilled whole lemon sole and rib-eye steak to guinea fowl supreme and baked fillet of cod.

Open: 11.30-2.30 6.30-11 (Sat 11.30-3) **Bar Meals:** L served all week 12-2 D served all week 7-10 (Sun 12-2, 7-9.30) Av main course £7.50 **Restaurant Meals:** L served all week 12-2 D served all week 7-10 (Sun 12-2, 7-9.30) Av 3 course alc £14 **Brewery/Company:** Punch Taverns ▰: Scottish Courage John Smiths & Courage Best, Greene King Abbott Ale, Sharp's Doom Bar ♇: 9 **Children's Facilities:** Fam room Menu/Portions Cutlery Highchair Food warming **Nearby:** Buckland Abbey, The Garden House, Morwellham Quay **Notes:** Dogs allowed in bar, in garden, Water Garden: Pretty cottage garden next to stream **Parking:** 4

CHAGFORD
Ring o'Bells ♇
44 The Square TQ13 8AH
☎ 01647 432466 📠 01647 432466
Email: info@ringobellschagford.co.uk
Web: www.ringobellschagford.co.uk
Dir: *From Exeter take A30 to Whiddon Down rdbt, take 1st left onto A382 to Mortonhampstead. After 3.5m to Easton Cross turn right signed to Chagford*
You won't find a juke box, games machines or television at this traditional West Country free house, but you can count on some lively conversation amid the open winter fires, beams and hand-carved bar. On warmer days, the exotic trees in the sun-drenched walled garden make a great backdrop to a drink and a bite to eat. Dishes include pan-fried trout with citrus butter; chicken Wellington; and spinach, mozzarella and cherry tomato pudding.
Open: 9.30-3 5-11 (Sat 10-3, 6-11, Sun 12-3, 6-10.30) **Bar Meals:** L served all week 12-2 D served all week 6-9 Av main course £9 **Restaurant Meals:** L served all week 12-2 D served all week 6-9 **Brewery/Company:** Free House 🍺: Butcombe Bitter, Dartmoor Ale, Reel Ale, Tetley ♇: 8 **Children's Facilities:** Licence (Coloured pencils and paper) Games Highchair Food warming **Nearby:** Minature Pony Centre, Castle Drogo, Outdoor swimming pool **Notes:** Dogs allowed in bar, in garden Garden: Walled courtyard with lawn & covered area

CHAGFORD
Three Crowns Hotel ★★ HL
High Street TQ13 8AJ
☎ 01647 433444 & 433441 📠 01647 433117
Email: threecrowns@msn.com
Web: www.chagford-accom.co.uk
An impressive, 13th-century, granite-built inn with a wealth of historical associations to investigate. Take young poet and Cavalier Sydney Godolphin, for example, who was shot in the hotel doorway in 1643 and who continues to 'appear', making him the hotel's oldest resident. Period features include mullioned windows, sturdy oak beams and a massive open fireplace. Among the chef's specialities are sautéed fillet of pork with mango salsa; roasted breast of duck with plum sauce; and lemon sole poached in white wine with mixed seafood sauce.
Open: 8-12.30 **Bar Meals:** L served all week 12-3 D served all week 6-9.30 Av main course £6 **Restaurant Meals:** L served all week (booking essential) D served all week 6-9.30 Av 3 course alc £28.50 **Brewery/Company:** Free House 🍺: Flowers Original, Boddingtons, Bass, Whitbread, Jail Ales, guest ales **Children's Facilities:** Licence Menu/Portions Cutlery Highchair Food warming **Nearby:** Eden Project, Castle Drogo, Lydford Gorge **Notes:** Dogs allowed in bar **Parking:** 20

CHAWLEIGH
The Earl of Portsmouth
The Square Nr Chulmleigh EX18 7HJ
☎ 01769 580204
Email: grahamlev@901.com
Web: www.earlofportsmouth-pub.co.uk
A former coaching inn on the old road from Barnstaple to London. Until it burnt down in 1869, it was the London Inn, but when the estate owner, the Earl of Portsmouth, rebuilt it no-one dared oppose the new name. Much of the food, and most of the real ales, are locally sourced. Baked pork tenderloin is served with stilton and broccoli; flaked salmon comes in pesto sauce on fresh penne pasta.
Open: 11-3.30 5.30-11 (Fri-Sat 12-2am) **Bar Meals:** L served Tue, Wed, Fri-Sun 12.30-2.30 D served Tue, Wed, Fri-Sun Av main course £10 **Restaurant Meals:** L served Tue-Sun 12.30-2.30 D served Tue-Sun Av 3 course alc £25 🍺: Rail Ale, Firing Squad **Children's Facilities:** Licence Fam room Menu/Portions Cutlery Games Highchair Food warming Baby changing **Notes:** Dogs allowed in bar Garden: Large lawn with tables and parasols **Parking:** 20

DEVON

CHERITON BISHOP
The Old Thatch Inn ♥
Nr Exeter EX6 6HJ
☎ 01647 24204 📄 01647 24584
Email: mail@theoldthatchinn.f9.co.uk
Web: www.theoldthatchinn.com
Dir: *0.5m off A30, 7m SW of Exeter*
This charming free house dates from the 16th century, when it welcomed stagecoaches on the London to Penzance run. Local brews accompany the extensive menu, which ranges from ploughman's and light snacks to dishes like braised West Country lamb shank with rosemary and garlic jus.
Open: 11.30-3 6-11 Closed: 25-26 Dec **Bar Meals:** L served all week 12-2 D served all week 6.30-9 **Restaurant Meals:** L served all week 12-2 D served all week 6.30-9 Av 3 course alc £23 🍺: Sharp's Doom Bar, Otter Ale, Princetown's Jail Ale, Port Stout, O'Hanlon's Royal Oak ♥: 9 **Children's Facilities:** Fam room Menu/Portions Cutlery Highchair Food warming **Nearby:** Crealy Adventure Park, Woodlands Venture Centre, Country Life World **Notes:** Dogs allowed in bar area only **Garden:** South facing **Parking:** 30

CLOVELLY
Red Lion Hotel ★★ HL
The Quay EX39 5TF
☎ 01237 431237 📄 01237 431044
Email: redlion@clovelly.co.uk
Web: www.redlion-clovelly.co.uk/redlionindex.html
Dir: *From Bideford rdbt, follow A39 to Bude for 10m. At Clovelly Cross rdbt turn right, follow past Clovelly E, bear to left. Located at bottom of hill on seafront.*
An idyllic location, right on the 14th-century harbour wall in a picture-perfect village. Guests staying in the bedrooms can fall asleep to the sound of the sea on the shingle. Seafood is a priority on the modern menu, which could include mussel soup, or pan-fried crevettes with garlic and butter to start, followed by sautéed pork loin with a creamy thyme sauce, or a roulade of bream and mullet with a swirl of crab mousse.
Open: 10-12 **Bar Meals:** L served all week 11-6.30 D served all week 6.30-9 Av main course £5 **Restaurant Meals:** L served all week 12-3 D served all week 7.30-9 Av 3 course alc £25 **Brewery/Company:** Free House 🍺: Doom Bar, Old Appledore, Guinness & Carlsberg Export **Children's Facilities:** Licence Fam room Menu/Portions Cutlery Games Highchair Baby changing **Nearby:** Milky Way, Brocklands & Big Sheep

CLYST HYDON
The Five Bells Inn ♥
Cullompton EX15 2NT
☎ 01884 277288
Email: info@fivebellsclysthydon.co.uk
Web: www.fivebellsclysthydon.co.uk
Dir: *10m from Exeter. B3181 towards Cullompton, turn right at Hele Cross towards Clyst Hydon. Continue 2m turn right to Clyst Hydon*
Originally a thatched farmhouse, this attractive country pub began life as a farm as long ago as the 16th century. It has a reputation for good food. Light meals are eaten in the bar, or in the garden which enjoys marvellous views.
Open: 11.30-3 6.30-11 (Winter 11.30-3, 7-11 Sun 12-3, 7-10.30) **Bar Meals:** L served all week 11.30-2 D served all week 7-9 (Sun 12-2) Av main course £9 **Restaurant Meals:** L served all week 11.30-2 D served all week 7-9 (Sun 12-2, 7-9) **Brewery/Company:** Free House 🍺: Cotleigh Tawny Ale, Otter Bitter, O'Hanlon's ♥: 8 **Children's Facilities:** Fam room Play area (Ropes, climbing frame) Cutlery Games Highchair Food warming **Nearby:** Sidmouth Coast, Cullompton Quad Bikes, Crealy Park **Notes:** Garden: Large **Parking:** 40

COLEFORD

The New Inn ★★★★ INN ⚲

Crediton EX17 5BZ

☎ 01363 84242 📄 01363 85044

Email: enquiries@thenewinncoleford.co.uk

Web: www.thenewinncoleford.co.uk

Dir: *From Exeter take A377, 1.5m after Crediton turn left for Coleford, continue for 1.5m.*

A pretty, thatched, cob-built freehouse beside the Cole Brook in a sleepy, mid-Devon conservation village. There is a restaurant, a central bar servery, and a bar around the fireplace. Three chefs create a changing selection of locally sourced fresh fish, meat and vegetarian dishes. **Open:** 12-3 6-11 (Sun 7-10.30) Closed: 25-26 Dec **Bar Meals:** L served all week 12-2 D served all week 7-10 (Sun 12-2, 7-9.30) **Restaurant Meals:** L served all week 12-2 D served all week 7-10 (Sun 12-2, 7-9.30) **Brewery/Company:** Free House 🍺: Doom Bar, Otter Ale, Badger Bitter, Wells Bombardier & Tanglefoot ⚲: 8 **Children's Facilities:** Menu/Portions Highchair Food warming **Nearby:** Amazing Maize Maze, Clearly Adventure Park **Notes:** Garden: Terraced, paved, decked area, stream **Parking:** 50

CORNWORTHY

Hunters Lodge Inn ⚲

Nr Totnes TQ9 7ES

☎ 01803 732204

Email: gill.rees@virgin.net

Web: www.hunterslodgeinnn.com

Dir: *Off A381 S of Totnes*

Built in 1740, this country local is at the hub of village life, sponsoring a football team, charity events and a dog show (it's a dog friendly pub). There's even a Christmas party for children. Other notable features are the real log fire and resident ghost. An extensive menu offers dishes from the sea (Dartmouth dressed crab salad), and from the land (rump of Devon lamb) as well as a selection of pasta dishes (wild mushroom tagliatelle). **Open:** 11.30-2.30 6.30-11 **Bar Meals:** L served all week 12-2 D served all week 7-9 **Restaurant Meals:** L served all week 12-2 D served all week 7-9 **Brewery/Company:** Free House 🍺: Teignworthy Reel Ale & Springtide, Guest Ales ⚲: 14 **Children's Facilities:** Play area (Games) Menu/Portions Cutlery Food warming **Notes:** Dogs allowed in bar, in garden, Water Garden: Lrg paddock with shaded seating areas **Parking:** 18

DITTISHAM

The Ferry Boat ⚲

Manor Street nr Dartmouth TQ6 0EX

☎ 01803 722368

This quiet traditional pub is the only riverside inn on the River Dart, and continues to prove popular with sailors, walkers and their dogs, and families. There are tables by the waterfront with views across the river to Greenway House and Gardens, a National Trust property that was once Agatha Christie's home. In the winter months, open log fires crackle in the grates, making it a snug place to go for a pint of Hobgoblin. Cider too is popular here, there's a good selection of malt whiskies, and plenty of wines by the glass to accompany the menus of home-cooked food. Dishes served both at lunchtime and in the evening are based on local produce and include fish pies and crab cakes in season, along with occasional locally caught fresh fish. A children's menu is also provided, or smaller portions from the main menu can be served. **Open:** 11-11 (Sun 12-10.30) **Bar Meals:** L served all week 12-2.30 D served all week 7-9 Av main course £9 **Brewery/Company:** Punch Taverns 🍺: Bass, Stella Artois, Youngs & Hobgoblin ⚲: 9 **Children's Facilities:** Licence Fam room (Books, games, toys) Menu/Portions Games Food warming **Nearby:** Woodlands Holiday Park **Notes:** Dogs allowed in bar, water, dog chews Garden: Riverside with tables

DOLTON
The Union Inn
Fore Street Nr Winkleigh EX19 8QH
☎ 01805 804633 📠 01805 804633
Email: theunioninn@dolton.wanadoo.co.uk
Dir: *From A361 take B3227 to S Moulton, then Atherington. Left onto B3217 then 6m to Dalton. Pub on right*
A 17th-century free house built as a Devon longhouse. Traditionally constructed of cob, the building was converted to a hotel in the mid-19th century to serve the local cattle markets, and it remains a traditional village pub with a cosy atmosphere. There's a homely beamed bar, oak settles and sturdy wooden tables, plus good home cooking, especially Sunday roasts and traditional dishes washed down with West Country ales.

Open: 12-3 6-11 Closed: 1st 2 wks Feb **Bar Meals:** L served Thu-Tue 12-2 D served Thu-Tue 7-10 (Sun 12-2.30, 7-9) Av main course £6.95 **Restaurant Meals:** L served Sun 12-2.30 D served Thu-Tue 7-9 (Sun 12-2.30, 7-9) **Brewery/Company:** Free House 🍺: Sharp's Doom Bar, Jollyboat Freebooter, Clearwater Cavalier, St Austell Tribute, Jollyboat Grenvilles Renown **Children's Facilities:** Licence Menu/Portions Cutlery Games Highchair Food warming **Nearby:** The Big Sheep, The Milky Way, Wildlife and Dinosaur Park **Notes:** Dogs allowed in bar, in garden, in bedrooms Dog bed and toys Garden: Small area with three tables **Parking:** 15

DREWSTEIGNTON
The Drewe Arms
The Square EX6 6QN
☎ 01647 281224
Dir: *W of Exeter on A30 for 12m. Left at Woodleigh junct follow signs for 3m to Drewsteignton*
Quintessentially English thatched inn tucked away in a sleepy village square close to the National Trust's Castle Drogo, and plenty of outstanding country walks on and around Dartmoor. Built in 1646, the Drewe Arms is a rare find these days. Formerly run by Mabel Mudge for 75 years, until her retirement in 1996, the pub has changed hands only twice during the last century. The unique interior - virtually unchanged - and timeless atmosphere both in the pub and the village are undoubtedly the key to its success. Traditional ales are drawn direct from the cask, housed in the original 'tap bar' and served through two hatchways. The chef provides first class food, native favourites and international dishes prepared from fresh produce sourced from local independent suppliers. Expect half crispy roast duck, braised lamb shank, Mediterranean chicken bake, and Thai-style red snapper, as well as sandwiches and ploughman's lunches.
Open: 11-3 6-12 (11-12 Summer) **Bar Meals:** L served all week 12-3 D served all week 6-9.30 Av main course £6.95 **Restaurant Meals:** L served all week 12-3 D served all week 6.30-9 **Brewery/Company:** Whitbread 🍺: Bass, Otter Bright, Princetowns Jail Ale **Children's Facilities:** Menu/Portions Cutlery Highchair Food warming **Nearby:** Castle Drogo, Dartmoor National Park, Crealy Adventure Park **Notes:** Dogs allowed in bar, Water Garden: beer garden, patio, outdoor eating **Parking:** 20

EXETER
Red Lion Inn 🍷
Broadclyst EX5 3EL
☎ 01392 461271
Dir: *on the B3181 Exeter to Culompton.*
A 16th-century inn which has been transformed by the landlady's builder husband. It is set at the heart of a delightful National Trust village, next to the church. Typical examples of the restaurant menu include monkfish medallions with bacon and tomato jus; seafood gratin; pan-fried pigeon; roast pheasant with redcurrant and red onion jus; and a range of steaks. In the bar expect ham, egg and chips; venison sausages with colcannon; and Thai curry.
Open: 11-3 5.30-11 (Sun 12-3, 7-10.30) **Bar Meals:** L served all week 12-2.30 D served all week 6-9.30 (Sun 12-2.30, 7-9) **Restaurant Meals:** L served all week 12-2.30 D served Mon-Sat 6-9.30 (Sun 12-2.30, 7-9) **Brewery/Company:** Free House 🍺: Bass, Fullers London Pride, O'Hanlons Local Blakelys Red, Speckled Hen 🍷: 7 **Children's Facilities:** Menu/Portions Cutlery Games Highchair Food warming Baby changing **Notes:** Garden: Small garden with three tables **Parking:** 70

EXMINSTER

Swans Nest ♀

Station Road EX6 8DZ

☎ 01392 832371

Web: www.swans-nest.co.uk

Dir: *From M5 follow A379 Dawlish Rd*

A much extended pub in a pleasant rural location whose facilities, unusually, extend to a ballroom, dance floor and stage. The carvery is a popular option for diners, with a choice of meats served with freshly prepared vegetables, though the salad bar is a tempting alternative, with pies, quiches and home-smoked chicken. A carte of home-cooked fare includes grilled lamb steak, Devon pork chop, and five-bean vegetable curry. Interested diners might like to sample 'Plant Pot Pudding', as well as take a look at a jukebox that once belonged to Sir Elton John.

Open: 10.30-2.30 6-11 (Sun 12.2.30, Sun 7-10.30) **Closed:** 26 Dec **Bar Meals:** L served all week 12-2 D served all week 6-9.45 **Restaurant Meals:** L served all week 12-2 D served all week 6-9.30 **Brewery/Company:** Free House 🍺: Otter Bitter **Children's Facilities:** Fam room Highchair Baby changing **Parking:** 102

EXTON

The Puffing Billy ♀

Station Road EX3 0PR

☎ 01392 877888 📠 01392 876232

Email: food@thepuffingbilly.com

Web: www.thepuffingbilly.com

Dir: *3m from junct 30 of M5. Take A376 signed Exmouth, pass through Ebford and follow signs for Puffing Billy which is a right turn into Exton*

Named for its proximity to the Exeter-Exmouth branch line, the 16th-century Puffing Billy enjoys views of the Exe estuary. The previous owner spent a small fortune installing some superb equipment in the kitchen, and on giving the restaurant and bar a modern, light makeover. Diners can see the serious approach to food expressed pictorially in the original artwork on display. Enjoy mackerel rillette with marinated aubergine, pink fir potato and tapenade salad; caramelised scallops with truffled baby leek terrine; confit duck leg and fennel risotto; or twice-baked Cornish Blue soufflé with walnuts and French bean salad.

Open: 11.30-3 6-11 (Sun 12-2.30, 6.30-10.30) **Closed:** selected days over Christmas **Bar Meals:** L served all week 12-2.30 D served Mon-Sat 6.30-9.30 (Sun 12-2.30) Av main course £8.50 **Restaurant Meals:** L served all week 12-2.30 D served Mon-Sat 6.30-9.30 (Sun 12-2.30) Av 3 course alc £29 🍺: Otter, Bass, Laffe ♀: 12 **Children's Facilities:** Licence (Public playground opposite) Menu/Portions Games Highchair Food warming **Nearby:** Exmouth beach, Crealy Park Adventure Park **Notes:** Garden: Sun terrace, small garden, 48 seats **Parking:** 30

HARBERTON

The Church House Inn

Totnes TQ9 7SF

☎ 01803 863707 📠 1803 864661

Email: churchhouseinn@btconnect.com

Dir: *From Totnes take A381 S. Take turn for Harberton on right, pub adjacent to church in centre of village*

Built to house masons working on the church next door (around 1100), the inn has some fascinating historic features, including a Tudor window frame and latticed window with 13th-century glass; there's even a resident ghost. The extensive menu is supplemented by daily specials and a traditional roast on Sundays. There's plenty of seafood/fish, and a family room is provided. **Open:** 11-2.30 6-11 (Sat 11-3, 6-11, Sun 12-3, 7-10.30) **Bar Meals:** L served all week 12-2 D served all week 6.30-9 Av main course £10.95 **Brewery/Company:** Free House 🍺: Skinners, Abbots, Dartmoor IPA, Church House Bitter & guest ales **Children's Facilities:** Fam room (Games room) Menu/Portions Games Highchair Food warming **Notes:** Dogs allowed in bar

DEVON

HAYTOR VALE
The Rock Inn ★★ HL ◉ �

Newton Abbot TQ13 9XP
☎ 01364 661305 📄 01364 661242
Email: inn@rock-inn.co.uk
Web: www.rock-inn.co.uk
Dir: *A38 from Exeter, at Drum Bridges rdbt take A382 for Bovey Tracey, 1st exit at 2nd rdbt (B3387), 3m left to Haytor Vale.*

Old-fashioned values are as important as ever at this cheerful 18th-century coaching inn, and the old stables recall the pub's strategic position on the road between Widecombe-in-the-Moor and Newton Abbot. Modern-day travellers will find nine comfortable en-suite bedrooms, all named after Grand National winners. Open fires, antique tables and sturdy furnishings lend a traditional feel to the rambling bars, but the cooking style is unashamedly modern British, using excellent produce in nicely presented dishes. Lunchtime might bring River Teign mussels in white wine and garlic to start, followed by local pheasant served with bacon and shallot sauce. Dinner might include a main of shank of Devon lamb on puréed potato with mustard sauce. The children's menu offers the likes of cottage pie and fish and chips. **Open:** 11-11 Closed: Dec 25-26 **Bar Meals:** L served all week 12-2.30 D served all week 6.30-9.30 **Restaurant Meals:** L served all week 12-2.30 D served all week 7-9 Av 3 course alc £27.50 **Brewery /Company:** Free House 🍺: Old Speckled Hen, St Austell Dartmoor Best, Interbrew Bass **Children's Facilities:** Fam room Menu/Portions Highchair Food warming Baby changing **Notes:** Garden: Large well kept **Parking:** 35

HOLBETON
The Mildmay Colours Inn

Plymouth PL8 1NA
☎ 01752 830248 📄 01752 830432
Email: mildmaycolours@btconnect.com
Web: www.mildmay-colours.co.uk
Dir: *S from Exeter on A38, Yealmpton/Ermington, S past Ugborough & Ermington right onto A379. After 1.5m, turn left, signed Mildmay Colours/Holbeton*

A 17th-century pub, which derives its unusual name from a famous jockey, Lord Anthony Mildmay, whose portrait and silks are hung in the pub. There are simple bar snacks and children's meals, along with daily specials such as nut roast with a sherry cream sauce; Dartmouth smoked chicken salad; local mackerel and salsa sauce; Mildmay Colours beer batter cod; and whole Torbay sole.

Open: 11-3 6-11 (Sun 12-3, 7-10.30) **Bar Meals:** L served all week 12-2.15 D served all week 6-9 (Sun 12-2.30) **Brewery/Company:** Free House 🍺: Mildmay Colours Bitter & Mildmay SP, Hellican Honey, Keel Over, Betty Stogs **Children's Facilities:** Fam room Menu/Portions Highchair Food warming **Notes:** Dogs allowed in bar, in garden Water Garden: 10 picnic benches **Parking:** 20

HONITON
The Otter Inn

Weston EX14 3NZ
☎ 01404 42594
Dir: *Just off A30 W of Honiton*

On the banks of the idyllic River Otter, this ancient 14th-century inn is set in over two acres of grounds and was once a cider house. Enjoy one of the traditional real ales, try your hand at scrabble, dominoes or cards, or peruse the inn's extensive book collection. A wide-ranging menu caters for all tastes and includes fresh fish, game, steak, vegetarian dishes, bar meals and Sunday lunch. **Open:** 10-11 (Sun 12-10.30) **Bar Meals:** L served all week 12-3 D served all week 6-10 (Snacks/bar meals all day. Sun 12-8) **Restaurant Meals:** L served all week 12 D served all week 6-9 **Brewery/Company:** Free House 🍺: Otter Ale, London Pride, Guest Ales **Children's Facilities:** Licence Fam room (Changing Room) Menu/Portions Cutlery Games Highchair Food warming **Notes:** Dogs allowed, Water Garden: Large with river **Parking:** 50

HORNS CROSS

The Hoops Inn and Country Hotel ★★★ HL ⊜ ♟

Clovelly Bideford EX39 5DL
☎ 01237 451222 ▤ 01237 451247
Email: sales@hoopsinn.co.uk
Web: www.hoopsinn.co.uk
Dir: *On the A39 between Bideford & Clovelly*

Having made their way along tortuous footpaths to evade the revenue men, smugglers would share out their spoils in this thatched, cob-walled, 13th-century inn. Set in 16 acres of gardens and meadows, it offers menus are based on the freshest produce Devon can offer.
Open: 8-11 **Bar Meals:** L served all week 12-9.30
D served all week 6-9.30 Av main course £12.50
Restaurant Meals: L served all week 12-3 D served

all week 6-9.30 (Sat-Sun all Day) Av 3 course alc £25
🍺: Hoops Old Ale, Hoops Special Ale, Sharps IPA, Sharps Doombar & Old Appledore ♟: 20 **Children's Facilities:**
Licence Games Highchair Food warming Baby changing
Nearby: Milky Way Adventure Park & The Big Sheep
Notes: Dogs allowed in bar, in garden Garden: outdoor eating, BBQ **Parking:** 100

ILFRACOMBE

The George & Dragon ♟

5 Fore Street EX34 9ED
☎ 01271 863851
Email: linda.quinn5@btinternet.com
Dir: *Please telephone for directions*

Trading since 1360, making it the oldest pub in town. The food is of the simple, no-nonsense variety - prawn cocktail, garlic mushrooms and minestrone soup as starters; fiery chicken, boozy beef, and vegetable curry as main courses. Vegetarians have a good choice, with leek and mushroom crumble, and aubergine and apricot medley on offer. No fruit machines or pool table, but a little home-produced background music.
Open: 10-12 (10am-1pm Jul-Aug) **Bar Meals:** L served all week 12-3 D served all week 6.30-9 Av main course

£7.50 🍺: Courage Directors, Courage Best, Brakespear
♟: 7 **Children's Facilities:** Licence Menu/Portions
Cutlery Games Highchair Food warming Baby changing
Nearby: Beach, Watermouth Castle, Dinosaur Park
Notes: Dogs allowed in bar, Water

IVYBRIDGE

The Anchor Inn ♟

Lutterburn Street Ugborough PL21 0NG
☎ 01752 892283 ▤ 01752 690534
Email: theanchorinn@btinternet.com
Web: www.anchor-ugborough.co.uk

A village inn whose origins can be traced back to the 16th century. Food is served in the bar and the à la carte restaurant, with locally farmed, organic produce used wherever possible. Tiger prawns cooked in chilli, garlic and white wine is a likely offering among the fish dishes. The Anchor is ideally located for exploring the South Hams region of Devon.
Open: 11.30-3 5-11 (Fri-Sat 11.30-11, Sun 12-10.30)
Bar Meals: L served all week 12-2.30 D served all week 7-10 (Sat-Sun 12-10) Av main course £7

Restaurant Meals: L served all week 12-2.30 D served all week 7-10 Av 3 course alc £22.50 **Brewery/ Company:** Free House 🍺: Bass, Courage, Directors, local ales ♟: 8 **Children's Facilities:** Menu/Portions Cutlery Games Highchair Food warming **Nearby:** Dartmoor National Park, Plymouth National Marine Museum, Paignton Zoo **Notes:** Dogs allowed in bar **Parking:** 15

DEVON

KENTON
Devon Arms
Fore Street Nr Exeter EX6 8LD
☎ 01626 890213 📠 01626 891678
Email: devon.arms@ukgateway.net
Dir: *On A379 between Exeter & Dawlish 7m from Exeter, 5m from Dawlish, adjacent to Powderham Castle*
Renamed in the 1830s, this 16th-century whitewashed coaching house was first licensed in 1822 as the Exeter Inn. The Devon Arms is now a comfortable free house offering a garden with patio, barbecue, pets' corner and children's play area, as well as six en suite bedrooms. Lunchtime fare includes traditional ploughman's and jacket potatoes, whilst ham, egg and chips; chicken in white wine and mushroom sauce; and vegetable lasagne are main menu options.

Open: 11-2.30 6-11 (Sun 12-3, 7-10.30) **Bar Meals:** L served all week 12-2.15 D served all week 6.30-8.30 (Sun 7-8.30) Av main course £8 **Restaurant Meals:** L served all week 12-2.15 D served all week 6.30-8.30 (Sun 7-8.30) **Brewery/Company:** Free House 🍺: Teign Valley Tipple, Whitbread Best, Sharps Doom Bar
Children's Facilities: Fam room Menu/Portions Highchai Food warming Baby changing **Nearby:** Powderham Castle, Dawlish Warren, Paignton Zoo **Notes:** Dogs allowed in bar, in garden **Garden:** Grassed area and patie with picnic tables **Parking:** 20

KINGSBRIDGE
The Crabshell Inn
Embankment Road TQ7 1JZ
☎ 01548 852345 📠 01548 852262
Dir: *A38 towards Plymouth, follow signs for Kingsbridge*
A traditional sailors' watering hole on the Kingsbridge estuary quayside (arrive by boat and you may moor free). As you would expect, the views from the outside tables and from the first-floor Waters Edge Restaurant are wonderful. The extensive menu and specials board range through grills, pies, pasta, jacket potatoes, salads and sandwiches, but the house speciality is fresh fish, with dishes such as monkfish provençale, and scallop and smoked bacon gratin always available.
Open: 11-11 (Sun 12-10.30) **Bar Meals:** L served all week 12-2.30 D served all week 6-9.30 (Winter 6-9)

Av main course £6 **Restaurant Meals:** L served all week 12-2.30 D served all week 6-9.30 (Winter 6-9) Av 3 course alc £15 **Brewery/Company:** Free House 🍺: Bass Bitter, Crabshell Bitter, Old Speckled Hen, Flowers IPA, Worthington Cream Flow **Children's Facilities:** Fam room Play area (Games room, game machines, pool table) Menu/Portions Cutlery Games Highchair Food warming **Nearby:** Crab catching on Quayside, Adventureland Parks, Beaches **Notes:** Dogs allowed in bar, in garden, Water, dog biscuits **Garden:** Patio area with tables & seats **Parking:** 40

KINGSKERSWELL
Barn Owl Inn 🍷
Aller Mills Nr Torquay TQ12 5AN
☎ 01803 872130 📠 01803 875279
Email: barnowl@oldridge-pope.co.uk
Web: www.pubswithrooms.co.uk/barnowl.html
Handy for Dartmoor and the English Riviera towns, this 16th-century former farmhouse has many charming features, including flagged floors, a black leaded range, and oak beams in a high-vaulted converted barn with a minstrels' gallery. Lunchtime snacks include toasties, wraps and baguettes, while the main menu features lots of traditional pub favourites plus an extensive tapas selection - perhaps crispy duck spring rolls, Greek lamb skewers, or chilli prawn bruschetta.
Open: 11-11 (Sun 12-10.30) **Bar Meals:** L served all

week 12-2.30 D served all week 6-9.30 **Restaurant Meals:** L served 12-2.30 D served all week 6-9.30 **Brewery/Company:** Eldridge Pope 🍺: 6X & Guest Ales 🍷: 14 **Children's Facilities:** Play area (Colouring books) Cutlery Games Highchair Food warming Baby changing **Nearby:** Paignton Zoo **Notes: Garden:** Small secluded garden **Parking:** 30

KINGSTON
The Dolphin Inn
Nr Bigbury TQ7 4QE
☎ 01548 810314 📄 01548 810314
Email: info@dolphininn.eclipse.co.uk
Web: www.dolphininn.co.uk
Dir: From A379 Plymouth to Kingsbridge Rd take B3233 for Bigbury-on-Sea. Follow brown signs for pub.
Built as accommodation for stonemasons constructing the neighbouring church, this 16th-century inn retains all the beams, inglenooks and exposed stonework you'd hope to find. It stands off the beaten track, a mile from the sea, and only a few miles from Bigbury Bay where Burgh Island can be reached by foot at low tide. Home-made dishes make good use of locally caught fish, with crab, lobster and mussels in season.

Open: 11-3 6-11 (Sun 12-3, 7-10.30) **Bar Meals:** L served all week 12-2 D served all week 6-9.30 (Sun 7-9, closed Mon in winter) Av main course £8.95 **Brewery/Company:** Punch Taverns 🍺: Teignworthy Spring Tide, Four Seasons Ale, Courage Best, Sharps Doom Bar & Wadworth 6X **Children's Facilities:** Fam room Play area (Swings and climbing frame) Menu/Portions Cutlery Games Highchair Food warming Baby changing **Nearby:** Woodlands Adventure Park, Plymouth Marine Aquarium & sandy beaches **Notes:** Garden: Small patio area, large garden & seating **Parking:** 40

KINGSWEAR
The Ship
Higher Street TQ6 0AG
☎ 01803 752348
Dir: Telephone for directions
Historic village pub overlooking the scenic River Dart towards Dartmouth and Dittisham. Located in one of South Devon's most picturesque corners, this tall, character inn is very much a village local with a friendly, welcoming atmosphere inside. Well-prepared fresh food is the hallmark of the menu. Sandwiches, baguettes and pies are available in the bar, while the restaurant menu offers crispy duck with stir-fried vegetables on egg noodles, or oven-baked cod with lemon and lime crust.
Open: 12-3 6-11 (All day in Summer) **Bar Meals:** L served all week 12.30-2 D served all week 7-9.30

Restaurant Meals: L served all week 12.30-2 D served all week 7-9.30 **Brewery/Company:** Heavitree 🍺: Greene King IPA, Otter, Adnams, Timothy Taylor **Children's Facilities:** Fam room Menu/Portions Food warming **Notes:** Dogs allowed in bar, in garden, Water Garden: Patio with several garden tables

LEWDOWN
The Harris Arms 🍷
Portgate EX20 4PZ
☎ 01566 783331 📄 01566 783359
Email: whiteman@powernet.co.uk
Web: www.theharrisarms.co.uk
Dir: From A30 take Lifton turning, halfway between Lifton and Lewdown
The Harris Arms is a 16th-century inn located on the old A30 close to the boundary between Devon and Cornwall, with lovely views to Brent Tor. The pub has established a reputation as an eating place for discerning diners.
Open: 12-3 6-11 (Winter 12-3, 6-11) **Bar Meals:** L served all week 12-2 D served all week 6.30-9 (Sun 12-2, 7-9) Av main course £8.25 **Restaurant Meals:** L served all week 12-2 D served all week 6.30-9 (Sun 12-2, 7-9) Av 3 course alc £25 **Brewery/Company:** Free House 🍺: Ring O'Bells, Sharps Doom Bar, Guinness Extra Cold, Peroni Nastro Azzuro 🍷: 18 **Children's Facilities:** Menu/Portions Games Highchair Food warming **Nearby:** Dingle Steam Village, Roadford Lake & Lydford Gorge **Notes:** Dogs allowed in bar, in garden Garden: Lawned area, decking & garden tables **Parking:** 30

LIFTON

The Arundell Arms ★★★ HL 🏵🏵 🍷

PL16 0AA

☎ 01566 784666 📠 01566 784494

Email: reservations@arundellarms.com

Web: www.arundellarms.com

Dir: *1m off the A30 dual carriageway, 3m E of Launceston*

This creeper-clad, 18th-century coaching inn is in a delightful village on the edge of Dartmoor. It has two bars, one serving food and the other offering minimal food but good beers. The hotel restaurant serves award-winning cuisine from fixed-price menus at lunch and dinner. **Open:** 11-11 (Fri/Sat 11-12, Sun 12-11) **Bar Meals:** L served all week 12-2.30 D served all week 6-10 Av main course £13 **Restaurant Meals:** L served all week 12.30-2 D served all week 7.30-9.30 Av 3 course alc £36 **Brewery/Company:** Free House 🍺: Guest beers 🍷: 9 **Children's Facilities:** Menu/Portions Games Highchair Food warming Baby changing **Nearby:** Trethorne Leisure Park, Otter Park **Notes:** Dogs allowed in bar, in garden, in bedrooms Garden: Terraced garden with fountain **Parking:** 70

LYDFORD

Dartmoor Inn 🏵🏵 🍷

Okehampton EX20 4AY

☎ 01822 820221 📠 01822 820494

Email: karen@dartmoorinn.co.uk

Web: www.dartmoorinn.com

Dir: *On A386 S of Okehampton*

Set in the pretty village of Lydford on the western side of Dartmoor National Park, the inn was almost certainly described in Charles Kingsley's novel *Westward Ho!* The current interior with its Swedish and New England influenced décor provides a rather more contemporary atmosphere. The inn even has its own boutique with attractive homeware, sourced by the co-owner. An easy dining menu is served in the bars. The restaurant, comprising a series of dining rooms, offers a carte and a good-value, no-choice set meal. **Open:** 11.30-3 6.30-11 (6-11 in Summer) **Bar Meals:** L served Tue-Sun 12-2.15 D served Tue-Sat 6.30-9.15 (Sun 12-2.30) Av main course £9.50 **Restaurant Meals:** L served Tue-Sun 12-2.15 D served Tue-Sat 6.30-9.15 (Sun 12-2.30) Av 3 course alc £26.50 🍺: Otter Ale, Austell Hicks Special & Dartmoor Best 🍷: 6 **Children's Facilities:** Menu/Portions Games Highchair Food warming **Nearby:** Morwellham Quay, Trethorne Leisure Park **Notes:** Dogs allowed in bar, in garden Garden: Paved area with umbrellas **Parking:** 35

LYNTON

The Bridge Inn

Lynbridge Hill EX35 6NR

☎ 01598 753425 📠 01598 753225

Email: bridgeinnlynton@hotmail.co.uk

Web: www.bridgeinnlynton.co.uk

Dir: *Turn off the A39 at Barbrook onto the B3234. Continue for 1m and pub is located on the right just after the Sunny Lyn camp site.*

This attractive 17th-century riverside inn is overlooked by National Trust woodlands. In the cellars the remains of 12th-century salmon fishermen's cottages are visible, and the unusually shaped windows at the front originally belonged to Charles I's hunting lodge at Coombe House. **Open:** 12-3 6-11 (Sun 7-10.30-winter) **Bar Meals:** L served all week 12-2.30 D served all week 6-9.30 (Sun 7-10.30 Winter) Av main course £8.50 **Restaurant Meals:** L served all week 12-2.30 D served all week 6-9.30 🍺: St. Austell Tribute, Sharps Doombar, Exmoor Fox **Children's Facilities:** Licence Menu/Portions Highchair Food warming **Nearby:** Exmoor Zoo, Woodybay Steam Railway **Notes:** Dogs allowed in bar Garden: Patio with picnic tables, benches **Parking:** 14

DEVON

MODBURY
California Country Inn
California Cross Ivybridge PL21 0SG
☎ 01548 821449 📄 01548 821566
Email: california@bellinns.entadsl.com
Web: www.californiacountryinn.co.uk
Oak beams and exposed stonework set the scene at this whitewashed 14th-century free house. Brass, copper and old photographs decorate the interior, and there's a landscaped garden for warmer days. Ingredients from local suppliers are the inspiration for dishes in the bar and restaurant: expect choices like Devon beef Wellington with red wine sauce; and seafood pie with cheesy mash. **Open:** 11-11 **Bar Meals:** L served all week 12-2 D served all week 6-9 (Sun 6-8.30) Av main course £7.85 **Restaurant Meals:** L served Sun 12-2 D served Wed-

Sun 6-9 (Sun Eve 6-8.30) Av 3 course alc £23.85 **Brewery/Company:** Free House 🍺: Guinness, Speckled Hen, Carling, Grolsch **Children's Facilities:** Licence Fam room Cutlery Highchair Baby changing **Nearby:** Pennywell Farm, Woodlands Leisure Park & Sorley Farm Adventures **Notes:** Dogs allowed in bar **Garden:** Patio, lawn & decked areas with seating **Parking:** 40

MOLLAND
The London Inn
South Molton EX36 3NG
☎ 01769 550269
Just below Exmoor lies peaceful Molland, and to find its church is to find this 15th-century inn. Historic features abound, but try and picture today's spacious dining room as the original inn, and the bar as the brewhouse. The frequently-changing menu features savoury pancakes, Welsh rarebit, mixed grill, as well as ploughman's, jackets and sandwiches. No credit cards. **Open:** 11.30-2.30 6-11 (Sun 12-3, 7-10.30) **Bar Meals:** L served all week 12-2 D served all week 7-9 Av main course £8 **Restaurant Meals:** L served all week D served all week Av 3 course alc £19.50 **Brewery/Company:** Free House 🍺: Exmoor Ale, Cotleigh

Tawny Bitter **Children's Facilities:** Fam room (Box of toys in family room) Menu/Portions Cutlery Games Highchair Food warming **Nearby:** Exmoor National Park **Notes:** Dogs allowed in bar, in garden, in bedrooms, Water **Garden:** 5 tables, seats 30 **Parking:** 15

MORETONHAMPSTEAD
White Hart Hotel ★★★ HL ♟
The Square TQ13 8NF
☎ 01647 441340 📄 01647 441341
Email: whitehart1600@aol.com
Web: www.whitehartdartmoor.co.uk
Dir: In Dartmoor National Park, 16m from Exeter
This Grade II listed building was a meeting place for French officers on parole from Dartmoor's nearby prison during the Napoleonic Wars. Today's stylish hotel provides both a well-stocked bar offering lunch and a brasserie serving up a contemporary combination of dishes: chargrilled aubergine and brie; pan fried calves' liver with red onion marmalade; or roast loin of venison with butter beans. **Open:** 8-12 **Bar Meals:** L served all week 12.30-2.30

D served all week (Sun 12-2.30) Av main course £6.50 **Restaurant Meals:** L served Sun 12-2 D served all week 6.30-9 Av 3 course alc £21 **Brewery/Company:** Warm Welcome Hotels 🍺: Tribute, Otter Fursty Ferret ♟: 16 **Children's Facilities:** Licence Menu/Portions Cutlery Highchair Food warming **Notes:** Dogs allowed in bar **Garden:** Courtyard with tables **Parking:** 7

RATTERY
Church House Inn ♀
South Brent TQ10 9LD
☎ 01364 642220 📠 01364 642220
Email: ray12@onetel.com
Web: www.thechurchhouseinn.co.uk
Dir: *1m from A38 Exeter to Plymouth Rd & 0.75m from A385 Totnes to South Brent Rd*
This historic 11th-century inn is not only Devon's oldest, but one of England's too. Featuring large open fireplaces, sturdy oak beams and loads of nooks and crannies, it offers a good selection of fish, as well as pheasant, game pie, rabbit, steak and ale pie, duck and guinea fowl.
Open: 11-3 6-11 (Winter 11-2.30, 6.30-10.30) **Bar Meals:** L served all week 12-2 D served all week 7-9 **Restaurant Meals:** L served all week 12-2 D served all

week 7-9 **Brewery/Company:** Free House 🍺: St Austell Dartmoor Best, Greene King Abbot Ale, Princetown Jail Ale & Otter Ale ♀: 8 **Children's Facilities:** Licence Menu/Portions Cutlery Highchair Food warming **Nearby:** Pennywell Farm, River Dart Country Park, Dare Devils Adventure Park **Notes:** Dogs allowed in bar, Water Garden: Large lawn, seating, benches **Parking:** 30

ROCKBEARE
Jack in the Green Inn ◎◎ ♀
London Road Nr Exeter EX5 2EE
☎ 01404 822240 📠 01404 823445
Email: info@jackinthegreen.uk.com
Web: www.jackinthegreen.uk.com
Dir: *From M5 take old A30 towards Honiton, signed Rockbeare*
Paul Parnell at this attractive, whitewashed pub has a simple philosophy: to serve real food to real people who want to eat and drink in comfortable surroundings and be served by nice people.
Open: 11-2.30 6-11 (Sun 12-10.30) Closed: Dec 25-Jan 5 **Bar Meals:** L served all week 11-2 D served all week 6-9.30 (Sun 12-9.30) Av main course £13.50 **Restaurant Meals:** L served all week 11-2 D served all

week 6-9.30 Av 3 course alc £25 🍺: Cotleigh Tawny Ale, Thomas Hardy Hardy Country, Otter Ale, Royal Oak, Branscombe Vale JIG ♀: 12 **Children's Facilities:** Fam room (Baby changing) Menu/Portions Games Food warming Baby changing **Nearby:** Crealy Adventure Park, Bicton Park & Escot Park **Notes:** Garden: Courtyard area, herb garden & hanging baskets **Parking:** 120

SALCOMBE
The Victoria Inn ♀
Fore Street TQ8 8BU
☎ 01548 842604 📠 01548 844201
Email: info@victoriainnsalcombe.co.uk
Web: www.victoriainnsalcombe.co.uk
Dir: *centre of Salcombe, overlooking estuary. 12m from Totnes railway station*
When owner Andy Cannon introduced a menu focusing on locally sourced ingredients, his trade dramatically increased. The achievement won him a competition run by St Austell Brewery, the pub's owner, which has since announced a commitment to using local produce throughout its 156-pub estate. From the restaurant there are stunning views of the pretty harbour and the fishing boats bringing in the catch for the kitchen. Deciding

which fresh fish dish to choose could be difficult, although one in particular merits attention - Andy's signature dish. This is a delicious chowder starter of handpicked Salcombe white crabmeat, prawns and other shellfish, white wine, fresh dill and Devon double cream.
Open: 11-11 (may close 3-6 during Winter) **Bar Meals:** L served all week 12-2.30 D served all week 6-9 Av main course £9.95 **Restaurant Meals:** D served all week 7-9 **Brewery/Company:** St Austell Brewery 🍺: St Austell Tribute, Dartmoor Best, St Austell HSD, Black Prince & Tinners Tribute ♀: 9 **Children's Facilities:** Play area (Fully enclosed children's activity area) Menu/Portions Cutlery Games Highchair Food warming Baby changing **Nearby:** Sorley Tunnel Adventure Park, Woodlands Leisure Park, Paignton Zoo **Notes:** Dogs allowed in bar Garden: Large beer garden with play area

SLAPTON

The Tower Inn 🍷

Church Road Kingsbridge TQ7 2PN

☎ 01548 580216

Email: towerinn@slapton.org

Web: www.thetowerinn.com

Dir: *Off A379 S of Dartmouth, turn left at Slapton Sands*

A unique 14th-century inn within the historic village of Slapton in the delightful South Hams. It is approached down a narrow lane, and entered through a rustic porch. The interior is a fascinating series of low-ceilinged rooms. **Open:** 12-3 6-11 (Sun 7-10.30, Closed Sun & Mon eve in winter) Closed: 25 Dec **Bar Meals:** L served all week 12-2.30 D served all week 6-9.30 Av main course £6 **Restaurant Meals:** L served all week 12-2.30 D served all week 7-9.30 Av 3 course alc £20 **Brewery/Company:** Free House 🍺: Butcombe Bitter, Badger Tanglefoot, St Austell, Tower, Guest 🍷: 8 **Children's Facilities:** Fam room Menu/Portions Games Highchair Food warming **Nearby:** Woodlands Activity Centre, Slapton Sands Beach, Dart Valley Steam Railway **Notes:** Dogs allowed in bar, Water & biscuits Garden: Beautiful walled garden **Parking:** 6

SOUTH POOL

The Millbrook Inn 🍷

nr Kingsbridge TQ7 2RW

☎ 01548 531581

Email: cjstarkey@hotmail.com

Dir: *Take A379 from Kingsbridge to Frogmore then E*

This quaint 16th-century village pub is cosy and unspoilt inside, with open fires, fresh flowers, cushioned wheel-back chairs, and beams adorned with old banknotes and clay pipes. Fish is a speciality, and there's a peaceful sunny rear terrace overlooking a stream with ducks. **Open:** 12-3 6-11 (open all day Aug, Sun 12-3, 6-10.30) **Bar Meals:** L served all week 12-2 D served all week 7-9 Av main course £7.95 **Brewery/Company:** Free House 🍺: Bass, Sharps Doom Bar, Otter Ale, Teignworthy Reel, Palmers IPA 🍷: 12 **Children's Facilities:** Fam room Menu/Portions Cutlery Highchair Food warming **Nearby:** Sorley Tunnel Equine & Adventure Centre, Woodlands Leisure Park **Notes:** Dogs allowed in bar, Water Bowls Garden: Paved area with canopy available

SOUTH ZEAL

Oxenham Arms ★★ HL

Okehampton EX20 2JT

☎ 01837 840244 📠 01837 840791

Email: theoxenhamarms@aol.com

Web: www.theoxenhamarms.co.uk

Dir: *Just off A30 4m E of Okehampton in the centre of the village*

Probably built by monks in the 12th century, this building is scheduled as an Ancient Monument. In the lounge is a stone shaped by prehistoric man, which archaeologists believe the monks built around. First licensed in 1477, the pub retains a historical feel, with beams and blazing fires. Traditional and international dishes are available in the bar and dining room, from sausage and mash to lobster thermidor. The garden overlooks Cosdon Hill and Cawsand Beacon.

Open: 11-2.30 5-11 (Sun 12-2.30, Sun 7-10.30) **Bar Meals:** L served all week 12-1.45 D served all week 6.30-8.45 (Summer food all day Sat) **Restaurant Meals:** L served all week 12-1.45 D served all week 6.30-8.45 (Summer 6-8.45) **Brewery/Company:** Free House 🍺: Sharp's Doom Bar Bitter, Sharps Special Ale, Archers Golden, Sharps Own, Sharps Eden **Children's Facilities:** Fam room Menu/Portions Cutlery Highchair Food warming **Notes:** Dogs allowed in bar, Water Garden: Overlooking Cosdon Hill, Cawsand Beacon **Parking:** 8

DEVON

SPREYTON
The Tom Cobley Tavern
EX17 5AL
☎ 01647 231314
Dir: *From Merrymeet rdbt take A3124 N. Right at Post Inn, then 1st right over bridge.*
From this pub one day in 1802 a certain Thomas Cobley and his companions set forth for Widecombe Fair, recorded and remembered in the famous song. Today, this traditional village local offers a good selection of bar snacks, lighter fare and home-made main meals, including pies, salads, duck and fish dishes, as well as a good vegetarian selection.
Open: 12-2 6-11 (Mon open Summer, BHs) **Bar Meals:** L served Tue-Sat 12-2 D served Tue-Sun 7-9 Av main course £8 **Restaurant Meals:** L served Sun 12-2 D served Wed-Sat 7-8.45 **Brewery/Company:** Free House 🍺: Cotleigh Tawny Ale, Interbrew Bass, Tom Cobley Bitter, Doom Bar Tribute & Real Ales **Children's Facilities:** Menu/Portions Games Highchair Food warming Baby changing **Nearby:** Miniature Pony Centre & Creley Farm **Notes:** Garden: Wooden seated area, approx 8 benches **Parking:** 8

STOCKLAND
The Kings Arms Inn 🍷
Nr Honiton EX14 9BS
☎ 01404 881361 📠 01404 881732
Email: info@kingsarms.net
Web: www.kingsarms.net
Dir: *Off A30 to Chard, 6m NE of Honiton*
A traditional 16th-century coaching inn tucked away in the Blackdown Hills, where real ales and good food are served in a lively atmosphere. The Grade II-listed inn boasts an impressive flagstoned walkway entrance, a medieval oak screen and an original bread oven. It offers a wide-ranging menu.
Open: 12-3 6.30-11.30 Closed: Dec 25 **Bar Meals:** L served Mon-Sat 12-2 D served all week 6.30-9 Av main course £7.50 **Restaurant Meals:** L served all week 12-2 D served all week 6.30-9 Av 3 course alc £25 **Brewery/Company:** Free House 🍺: Otter Ale, Exmoor Ale, O'Hanlon's Yellowhammer, Firefly & Port Stout 🍷: 15 **Children's Facilities:** Menu/Portions Highchair Food warming **Nearby:** Crealy Park, Lyme Regis, Donkey Sanctuary **Notes:** Dogs allowed in bar, in garden Garden: Lawn & patio, Seating 30 **Parking:** 45

STOKE FLEMING
The Green Dragon Inn 🍷
Church Road nr Dartmouth TQ6 0PX
☎ 01803 770238 📠 01803 770238
Email: pcrowther@btconnect.com
Web: www.green-dragon-pub.co.uk
Dating back to the 12th century and built by the masons who constructed the church opposite, the Green Dragon supposedly has a smugglers' tunnel running to the sea at Blackpool Sands. The first recorded landlord, William Lidstone, was here in 1607. Records refer to him as a 'licenced tippler.' Lunchtime snacks include baguettes and beefburgers, while the dinner menu may include venison steak, red mullet fillets, and leek and stilton-stuffed chicken breast.
Open: 11-3 5.30-11 **Bar Meals:** L served all week 12-2.30 D served all week 6.30-9 **Restaurant Meals:** L served all week 12-2.30 D served all week 6.30-9 **Brewery/Company:** Heavitree 🍺: Otter, Flowers IPA, Bass, 6x 🍷: 9 **Children's Facilities:** Play area (Garden, climbing frame, swing) Menu/Portions Games Highchair Food warming **Nearby:** Blackpool Sands, Woodlands Leisure Park, Dart Steam Railway **Notes:** Dogs allowed in bar, in garden Garden: Small at rear, covered patio at front **Parking:** 6

TEDBURN ST MARY
Kings Arms Inn ♟

Exeter EX6 6EG

☎ 01647 61224 📠 01647 61324

Email: info@kingsarmsinn.co.uk

Web: www.kingsarmsinn.co.uk

Dir: *A30 W to Okehampton, 1st exit right signed Tedburn St Mary*

Expect log fires and exposed beams in this delightful 14th-century thatched inn, which sits just off Dartmoor's northern flanks. Food is local and organic where possible. **Open:** 11-3 6-12 (Open all day Sat and Sun) **Bar Meals:** L served all week 11-2.30 D served all week 6-9.30 (Sat/Sun all day) Av main course £12 **Restaurant Meals:** L served all week 11-2.30 D served all week 6-9.30 (Sat/Sun all Day) **Brewery/Company:** Free House

🍺: Interbrew Bass & Worthington Best, Sharps Cornish Coaster, Whitbread Best, ♟: 8 **Children's Facilities:** Play area (Wendy House) Highchair Food warming Baby changing **Nearby:** Donkey Sanctuary, Crealy Adventure Park **Notes:** Garden: Large lawned gardens, large covered courtyard **Parking:** 40

TORCROSS
Start Bay Inn ♟

Nr Kingsbridge TQ7 2TQ

☎ 01548 580553 📠 01548 581285

Email: cstubbs@freeuk.com

Web: www.startbayinn.co.uk

Dir: *between Dartmouth & Kingsbridge on the A379*

Start Bay Inn dates back to the 14th century when local fishermen frequented it. Everything including the crisps is sourced locally. The landlord takes great delight in scuba diving in Start Bay for plaice and scallops, and catching bass by rod and line for his customers. Arrive soon after opening, especially in the summer, to sample the catch of the day; which may include monkfish, lemon sole, Dover sole, bass, brill, skate, plaice, John Dory or shellfish like crab and lobster. Alternatives include prime cut steaks or a few meat dishes like freshly roasted chicken. Vegetarian options might be a lasagne or curry. Lighter choices include ploughman's; sandwiches; burgers and jacket potatoes.
Open: 11.30-2.30 6-11 (Summer 11.30-11) **Bar Meals:** L served all week 11.30-2 D served all week 6-10 (Sun 12-2.15, winter 6-9.30) Av main course £5.50 **Brewery/Company:** Heavitree 🍺: Interbrew Flowers Original & Bass, Otter Ale ♟: 8 **Children's Facilities:** Fam room Games Highchair Food warming Baby changing **Nearby:** Woodlands Leisue Park, Sorely Tunnel, Pennywell Farm, Paignton Zoo **Notes:** Garden: Patio area overlooks Slapton Sands **Parking:** 18

TOTNES
The Durant Arms ★★★★ INN ♟

Ashprington TQ9 7UP

☎ 01803 732240

Email: info@thedurantarms.com

Web: www.thedurantarms.com

Dir: *Leave A38 at Totnes Junct, proceed to Dartington & Totnes, at 1st set of lights right for Knightsbridge on A381, after 1m left for Ashprington*

An 18th-century, locally renowned dining pub delightfully situated in the picturesque village of Ashprington, just outside the Elizabethan town of Totnes. The bar is fitted out in traditional style and displays work by local artists. All dishes are cooked to order, with a wide variety of meat and fish, as much as possible supplied locally. **Open:** 11.30-2.30 6.30-11 **Bar Meals:** L served all week 12-2.30 D served all week 7-9.15 **Restaurant Meals:** L served all week 12-2 D served all week 7-9.15 **Brewery/Company:** Free House 🍺: Dartmoor Bitter, Tetley, Tribute ♟: 8 **Children's Facilities:** Fam room Menu/Portions Highchair Food warming **Nearby:** Woodland Leisure Park **Notes:** Garden: Terraced garden with rosewood furniture **Parking:** 8

DEVON

TOTNES

The Steam Packet Inn ★★★★ INN ♟

St Peter's Quay TQ9 5EW

☎ 01803 863880   ▤ 01803 862754

Email: steampacket@bucaneer.co.uk

Web: www.steampacketinn.co.uk

Dir: *Exit A38 towards Plymouth 18m. Take A384 to Totnes 6m. Turn left at mini-rdbt, pass Morrisons on left, over mini-rdbt, 400yds on left.*

A delightful riverside setting with river views. The menu features traditional recipes re-worked with flair using herbs from the garden and fish from local fishermen.

Open: 11-11 (Sun 12-10.30) **Bar Meals:** L served all week 12-2.30 D served all week 6-9.30 (Sun 12-2.30, 6-9) Av main course £12 **Restaurant Meals:** L served all week 12-2.30 D served all week 6-9.30 (Sun 12-2.30, 6-9) Av 3 course alc £23 **Brewery/Company:** Free House ▥: Courage Best, Butcombe, Otter Bright & 1 Guest Ale ♟: 8 **Children's Facilities:** Licence (Board games) Menu/Portions Highchair Food warming Baby changing **Nearby:** Woodlands Adventure Park, Paignton Zoo & Pennywell Farm **Notes:** Garden: Riverside quay, raised terrace, heaters **Parking:** 16

TUCKENHAY

The Maltsters Arms ♟

Totnes TQ9 7EQ

☎ 01803 732350   ▤ 01803 732823

Email: pub@tuckenhay.demon.co.uk

Web: www.tuckenhay.com

This 18th-century pub is accessible only through high-banked Devon lanes, or by boat for about three hours either side of high tide. It is noted for its charcoal barbecues and cream teas in summer, and live music events. The daily changing menu may feature winter casserole of rabbit in red wine, or perhaps grilled fillet of sea trout with a white wine and parsley sauce. There is a children's menu offering proper food like pan-fried chicken breast.

Open: 11-11 **Bar Meals:** L served all week 12-3 D served all week 7-9.30 Av main course £14.1 **Restaurant Meals:** L served all week 12-3 D served all week 7-9.30 Av 3 course alc £20 **Brewery/Company:** Free House ▥: Princetown Dartmoor IPA, Young's Special, Teignworthy Maltsters Ale, Southams Eddystone, Sharos Doom Bar ♟: 18 **Children's Facilities:** Fam room (Comics, games) Menu/Portions Cutlery Games Highchair Food warming **Nearby:** Pennywell Farm, Paignton Zoo, Woodlands Adventure Park **Notes:** Dogs allowed in bar, in garden Garden: On quayside **Parking:** 40

TYTHERLEIGH

Tytherleigh Arms Hotel ♟

EX13 7BE

☎ 01460 220400 & 220214   ▤ 01460 220406

Email: tytherleigharms@aol.com

Web: www.tytherleighsarmshotel.com

Beamed ceilings and huge roaring fires are notable features of this family-run, 17th-century former coaching inn. It is a food-led establishment, situated on the Devon, Somerset and Dorset borders. Fresh home-cooked dishes, using local ingredients, include lamb shank with honey and cider, steaks and fresh seafood such as West Country cod and Lyme Bay scallops. Comprehensive bar snack menu also available.

Open: 11-2.30 6.30-11 **Bar Meals:** L served all week 12-2.30 D served all week 6.30-9 Av main course £8.95 **Restaurant Meals:** L served all week 12-2.30 D served all week 6.30-9 Av 3 course alc £16.95 **Brewery/Company:** Free House ▥: Butcombe Bitter, Exmoor Fox, Murphy's, Boddingtons **Children's Facilities:** Licence Menu/Portions Highchair Food warming **Notes:** Garden: Courtyard, very pretty **Parking:** 60

UMBERLEIGH
The Rising Sun Inn 🍷
EX37 9DU

☎ 01769 560447 📠 01769 560764

Email: risingsuninn@btopenworld.com

Web: www.risingsuninn.com

Dir: *on A377, Exeter/Barnstaple road, at junct with B3227*

Idyllically set beside the River Taw and with a very strong fly fishing tradition, the Rising Sun dates back in part to the 13th century. Outside is a sunny raised terrace with beautiful rural views of the valley, and the riverside walk is equally enjoyable before or after a meal. This inn is an excellent base for the touring motorist with several National Trust properties nearby. A choice of à la carte restaurant or regularly updated bar menus feature the best of West Country produce, with seasonal delights like seafood from the North Devon coast, salmon and sea trout from the Taw, game from Exmoor, and local cheeses. The daily changing specials board is often the best place to start looking.

Open: 12-3 6-11 (Open all day May-Sep) **Bar Meals:** L served all week 12-2 D served all week 6.30-9 (Sun separate carvery) **Restaurant Meals:** L served all week 12-2 D served all week 6.30-9 (Sun 6.30-8.30)

Brewery/Company: Free House 🍺: Cotleigh Tawny Bitter, Barn Owl, Guinness, Speckled Hen 🍷: 9

Children's Facilities: Licence (High chairs, changing facilities) Menu/Portions Games Highchair Food warming Baby changing **Nearby:** Big Sheep **Notes:** Dogs allowed in bar, in garden **Garden:** Patio garden overlooking the river **Parking:** 30

WINKLEIGH
The Kings Arms
Fore Street EX19 8HQ

☎ 01837 83384

Dir: *The village is signed off the B3220, Crediton to Torrington road.*

Scrubbed pine tables and traditional wooden settles set the scene at this ancient thatched country inn in Winkleigh's central square. Wood-burning stoves keep the beamed bar and dining rooms warm in chilly weather, and traditional pub games are encouraged. Generous servings of freshly-made food include sandwiches and hot snacks, as well as roasted vegetables with goats' cheese; Lucy's fish pie; and lamb's liver with bacon. Booking is recommended at weekends.

Open: 11-11 **Bar Meals:** L/D served all week 11-9.30 (Sun 12-9) Av main course £8.50 **Restaurant Meals:** L served all week 11-9.30 D served all week (Sun 12-9)

Brewery/Company: Enterprise Inns 🍺: Butcombe Bitter, Sharps Doom Bar & Cornish Coaster **Children's Facilities:** Licence Menu/Portions Games Highchair Food warming Baby changing **Notes:** Dogs allowed in bar Garden: Small courtyard to side of property

ABBOTSBURY
Ilchester Arms 🍷
Market Street Weymouth DT3 4JR

☎ 01305 871243 📠 01305 871225

Rambling 16th-century coaching inn set in the heart of one of Dorset's most picturesque villages. Abbotsbury is home to many crafts including woodwork and pottery. A good area for walkers, and handy for the Tropical Gardens and Swannery.

Open: 11-11 (Sun 12-10.30) **Bar Meals:** L served all week 12-2 D served all week 7-9 (Sun 12-2.30) Av main course £10 **Restaurant Meals:** L served all week 12-2.30 D served all week 7-9.30 (Sun 12-2.30, 7-9) Av 3 course alc £20 🍺: Gales HSB, Courage Best, Tribute, Speckled Hen, Abbot 🍷: 12 **Children's Facilities:** Licence Menu/Portions Cutlery Games Highchair Food warming **Notes:** Dogs allowed in bar, bar only Garden: Patio/beer garden **Parking:** 50

DEVON / DORSET

DORSET

BOURTON
The White Lion Inn

High Street Nr Gillingham SP8 5AT
☎ 01747 840866 🖹 01747 840191
Email: enquiries@whitelionbourton.com
Dir: *Off A303, opposite B3092 to Gillingham*
A quintessentially English pub, built from stone in 1723 and packed with beams and flagstones, not to mention a log fire and a good choice of real ales. New owners are now at the helm, and food options are divided between light bites (baguettes; ham, egg and chips; Catalan style meatballs) and the Shoals restaurant menu. There's also a daily selection of fish specials.
Open: 12-3 5-11 Closed: 26 Dec **Bar Meals:** L served all week 12-2 D served all week 7-9 (Sun 12-3) Av main course £6.95 **Restaurant Meals:** L served all

week 12-2 D served Mon-Sat 7-9 (Sun 12-3)
Brewery/Company: Admiral Taverns 🍺: Fullers London Pride, Greene King IPA & Guest Beer **Children's Facilities:** Menu/Portions Highchair Food warming
Nearby: Longleat, Stourhead Gardens **Notes:** Dogs allowed in bar, in garden, Water **Garden:** Grassed with trees, patio area **Parking:** 30

BRIDPORT
Shave Cross Inn 🍷

Shave Cross Marshwood Vale DT6 6HW
☎ 01308 868358 🖹 01308 867064
Email: roy.warburton@virgin.net
Web: www.theshavecrossinn.co.uk
Dir: *From Bridport take B3162, 2m turn left signed 'Broadoak/Shave Cross' then Marshwood*
This 13th-century pub with a thatched roof and cob and flint walls is one of Dorset's hidden treasures. Owners Roy and Mel Warburton spent a long time in Tobago, returning in 2003 with their head chef, creator of the authentic Caribbean cooking on the menu.
Open: 11-3 6-11 (All day Tue-Sun in Summer, BH Mons)
Bar Meals: L served Tue-Sun 12-2.30 D served Tue-Sun 5-9.30 (Sun 12-3, 6-8 Summer) **Restaurant**

Meals: L served Tue-Sun 12-2.30 D served Tue-Sat 7-9.30 (Sun 6-8 Summer) Av 3 course alc £26
Brewery/Company: Free House 🍺: Local guest beers, Branoc (Branscombe Valley), Quay Brewery Weymouth 🍷: 8 **Children's Facilities:** Licence Play area Menu/Portions Cutlery Games Highchair Food warming **Notes:** Dogs allowed on leads in bar, in garden **Parking:** 30

BURTON BRADSTOCK
The Anchor Inn 🍷

High Street DT6 4QF
☎ 01308 897228 🖹 01308 897228
Email: aex013@dialpipex.xom
Web: www.dorset-seafood-restaurant.co.uk
Dir: *2m SE of Bridport on B3157 in the centre of the village of Burton Bradstock*
The Anchor Inn is a 300-year-old coaching inn just inland from a stretch of the Jurassic Coast World Heritage Site, and near Chesil Beach. In keeping with its name, the pub is full of marine memorabilia. The speciality is seafood, and with twenty different main fish courses on the menu, plus Catch of the Day specials, choosing might be hard.
Open: 11-11 (Sun 12-10.30) **Bar Meals:** L served all week 12-2 D served all week 6.30-9 **Restaurant**

Meals: L served all week 12-2 D served all week 6.30-9 **Brewery/Company:** Innspired 🍺: Ushers Best, Flowers IPA, Hobgoblin 🍷: 8 **Children's Facilities:** Licence Fam room Play area Menu/Portions Cutlery Highchair Food warming **Nearby:** Fresh Water Caravan Park, Abbotsbury Swannery, Jurassic Coastline **Notes:** Dogs allowed in bar Patio/courtyard **Parking:** 24

CATTISTOCK
Fox & Hounds Inn ◆◆◆◆

Duck Street Dorchester DT2 0JH

☎ 01300 320444 🖷 01300 320444

Email: info@foxandhoundsinn.com

Web: www.foxandhoundsinn.com

An attractive 16th-century inn set in the beautiful village of Cattistock. Original features include bare beams and huge inglenooks, one with an original bread oven. It's a fascinating building, full of curiosities such as the 'hidden cupboard', reached by a staircase that winds around the chimney. Meals are traditional and home made: typical examples include cottage pie, fresh cod fillet in 'secret batter', pork in cider and apple sauce, lamb shank on mash, and haddock mornay.

Open: 12-2.30 7-11 **Bar Meals:** L served Tue-Sun 12-1.45 D served all week 7-8.45 Av main course £8 **Restaurant Meals:** L served Tue-Sun 12-1.45 D served all week 7-8.45 🍺: Palmers IPA, Copper Ale, Gold **Children's Facilities:** Menu/Portions Highchair Food warming **Nearby:** Sealife Centre Weymouth, Swannery at Abbotsbury **Notes:** Dogs allowed in bar, in garden Garden: Front patio serving food & drinks **Parking:** 12

CHRISTCHURCH
The Ship In Distress

56 Stanpit BH23 3NA

☎ 01202 485123 🖷 01202 483997

Email: enquires@theshipindistress.com

Web: www.theshipindistress.com

Once a haunt of famous Christchurch smugglers, this 300-year-old pub featured in a recent documentary film about the history of smuggling. It is located close to Mudeford Quay and has an award-winning seafood and dessert restaurant.

Open: 11-11 Closed: Dec 25 **Bar Meals:** L served all week 12-2 D served all week 7-9.30 (Sun 12-3) Av main course £10 **Restaurant Meals:** L served all week 12-2 D served all week 7-9.30 Av 3 course alc £30 **Brewery/Company:** Punch Taverns 🍺: Ringwood Best, Fortyniner, Interbrew Bass, Courage Directors, Adnams Broadside **Children's Facilities:** Menu/Portions Cutlery Games Highchair Food warming **Nearby:** Maze-Christchurch, Alice in Wonderland, Paultons Park **Notes:** Dogs allowed in bar, Water, Biscuits **Garden:** Patio with awning and parasols **Parking:** 40

CORFE CASTLE
The Greyhound Inn

The Square BH20 5EZ

☎ 01929 480205 🖷 01929 480205

Email: mjml@greyhound-inn.fsnet.co.uk

Web: www.greyhoundcorfe.com

Dir: *W from Bournemouth, take A35, after 5m left onto A4351, 10m to Corfe Castle*

This classic old coaching inn has a lively atmosphere, encouraged by special events such as three beer festivals on bank holidays, a sausage and cider festival in September and regular live music, karaoke and entertainment. Alongside real ales you'll find scrumpy ciders and home-made mulled wine. Sandwiches, salads, baguettes, baskets, chargrills, vegetarian options and light bites are served alongside a huge range of fresh seafood including the famous Purbeck seafood platter.

Open: 11-12.30 **Bar Meals:** L served all week 12-3 D served all week 6-9 (Jul-Sep food all day) Av main course £9.95 **Restaurant Meals:** L served all week 12-3 D served all week 6-9 (Jul-Sep food all day) Av 3 course alc £24 **Brewery/Company:** Enterprise Inns 🍺: Fuller's London Pride, Timothy Taylor Landlord, Black Sheep, Ringwood Best, Purbeck Brewery Fossil Fuel & Marsdens Pedigree 🍷: 6 **Children's Facilities:** Fam room Play area (Games, colouring books & mini football) Menu/Portions Games Highchair Food warming **Nearby:** Monkey World, Farmer Palmers, Putlake Adventure Farm & Swanage Steam Train **Notes:** Dogs allowed in bar, in garden, in bedrooms, Water/Bowls **Garden:** Suntrap, castle view, BBQ/Hog roast in summer

DORSET

CORFE MULLEN

The Coventry Arms

Mill Street BH21 3RH

☎ 01258 857284 FAXLINE

Dir: *On A31 (Wimborne-Dorchester Road)*

A 13th-century pub, formerly a watermill with its own island, offering beer served direct from the cask. The inn specialises in fish and game from local estates, and most of the produce is sourced from within the area. An annual spring seafood festival is an attraction here. Expect oven-roasted whole gurnard, pan-fried fillet of monkfish, honey-glazed duck breast, and chargrilled Cumberland sausages among the varied specials. Fish and seafood menu Wednesday and Thursday lunchtime.

Open: 11-3 5.30-11 **Bar Meals:** L served all week12-2.30 D served all week 6-9.30 (All day Sun) Av main course £12.50 **Restaurant Meals:** L served all12-2.30 D served all week 6-9.30 (All Day Sun) Av 3 course alc £22.50 **Brewery/Company:** Free House: HSB, Timothy Taylor Landlord, Gales Best: 17 **Children's Facilities:** Menu/Portions Cutlery Food warming **Nearby:** Monkey World, Tank Museum **Notes:** Dogs allowed in bar Garden: By river, seating for 150 **Parking:** 50

EAST CHALDON

The Sailors Return

Dorchester DT2 8DN

☎ 01305 853847 01305 851677

Web: www.sailorsreturn.com

Dir: *1m S of A352 between Dorchester & Wool*

A splendid 18th-century thatched country pub in the village of East Chaldon (or Chaldon Herring - take your pick), tucked away in rolling downland near Lulworth Cove. Seafood includes whole local plaice, scallop and mussel Stroganoff, and wok-fried king prawns. Alternatives include half a big duck, local faggots, whole gammon hock, and vegetarian dishes. Choose from the blackboard in the beamed and flagstoned bar and eat inside or in a grassy area outside.

Open: 11-11 (Sun 12-10.30) **Bar Meals:** L served all week 12-2 D served all week 6-9 **Restaurant Meals:** L served all week 12-2 D served all week 6-9 (Summer 12-9) **Brewery/Company:** Free House: Ringwood Best, Hampshire Strongs Best Bitter, Badger Tanglefoot **Children's Facilities:** Fam room Play area **Notes:** Garden: Grassed area with wooden tables and benches **Parking:** 100

GILLINGHAM

The Kings Arms Inn

East Stour Common SP8 5NB

☎ 01747 838325

Dir: *4m W of Shaftesbury on A30*

This family-run country free house dates back 200 years, and offers a large car park and beer garden. It makes an excellent base for exploring the delights of Dorset's countryside and coast, with plenty of well-loved attractions within reach, including nearby Shaftesbury and the famous Golden Hill.

Open: 12-3 5.30-11 (Sat-Sun 12-11) **Bar Meals:** L served all week 12-2.30 D served all week 5.30-9.15 (Sat-Sun 12-9.15) Av main course £9 **Restaurant Meals:** L served all week 12-2.30 D served all week 5.30-9.15 Av 3 course alc £22 **Brewery/Company:** Free House: London Pride, Copper Ale, IPA **Children's Facilities:** Fam room Play area (Grassed area, no climbing) Menu/Portions Cutlery Games Highchair Food warming Baby changing **Nearby:** Bison Farm, Stour Head, Longleat **Notes:** Garden: Patio & Sitting area, grassed area **Parking:** 60

IWERNE COURTNEY OR SHROTON

The Cricketers ★★★★★ INN ⚲

Blandford Forum DT11 8QD

☎ 01258 860421 📠 01258 861800

Dir: *Off the A350 Shaftesbury to Blandford, signed from Shroton.*

The Cricketers nestles under Hambledon Hill, which is renowned for its Iron-Age hill-forts. A classically English pub, built at the turn of the 20th century, it is above all a welcoming local. A main bar, sports bar and den, all light and airy rooms, lead to the restaurant. This in turn overlooks a lovely garden. Expect an extensive food selection that ranges from traditional to modern and international. **Open:** 11.30-2.30 6.30-11 (Winter Sun eve 7-11) **Bar Meals:** L served all week 12-2 D served all week 6.30- Av main course £8.95 **Restaurant Meals:** L served all week 12-2 D served all week 6.30-9 Av 3 course alc £17.50 **Brewery/Company:** Free House 🍺: Ringwood 49er, Greene King IPA, Tanglefoot Marstons Pedigree, Wadworth 6X ⚲: 10 **Children's Facilities:** Menu/Portions Cutlery Games Highchair Food warming Baby changing **Notes:** Garden: Bordered by trees and hedges, herb garden **Parking:** 19

MARSHWOOD

The Bottle Inn ⚲

Bridport DT6 5QJ

☎ 01297 678254 📠 01297 678739

Email: thebottleinn@msn.com

Web: www.thebottleinn.co.uk

Dir: *On the B3165 Crewkerne to Lyme Regis road.*

The thatched Bottle Inn was first mentioned as an ale house back in the 17th century, and was the first pub in the area during the 18th century to serve bottled beer rather than beer from the jug - hence the name. Proprietor Shane Pym loves introducing new dishes onto the menu, and recent additions have included local pork tenderloin with a cream and Stilton sauce; Highland chicken stuffed with smoked salmon and served with a whisky and mustard sauce.

Open: 12-3 6.30-11 **Bar Meals:** L served all week 12-2 D served all week 6.30-9 Av main course £8.50 **Restaurant Meals:** L served all week D served all week **Brewery/Company:** Free House 🍺: Otter Ale & 3 Guest Ales ⚲: 7 **Children's Facilities:** Fam room Play area (baby changing facilities, high chairs, toys) Highchair **Notes:** Garden: Play area, beer garden **Parking:** 40

MOTCOMBE

The Coppleridge Inn ⚲

Shaftesbury SP7 9HW

☎ 01747 851980 📠 01747 851858

Email: thecoppleridgeinn@btinternet.com

Web: www.coppleridge.com

Converted from an 18th-century dairy farm in the 1980s, the former farmhouse is now the bar and restaurant. The menus offer everything from jacket potatoes and filled ciabattas to a full meal. Coppleridge is surrounded by 15 acres of grounds.

Open: 11-3 5-11 (All day Sat & Sun) **Bar Meals:** L served all week 12-2.30 D served all week 6-9.30 Av main course £8.50 **Restaurant Meals:** L served all week 12-2.30 D served all week 6-9.30 Av 3 course alc £19 **Brewery/Company:** Free House 🍺: Butcombe Bitter, Greene King IPA, Wadworth 6X, Fuller's London Pride ⚲: 8 **Children's Facilities:** Fam room Play area (garden, swings & slide) Menu/Portions Cutlery Games Highchair Food warming **Nearby:** Haynes Motor Museum, Stourhead Gardens, Longleat **Notes:** Dogs allowed in bar, in garden Garden: 15 acres including lawns, wood, pond area **Parking:** 60

DORSET

NETTLECOMBE
Marquis of Lorne ♟
Nr Bridport DT6 3SY
☎ 01308 485236 🖹 01308 485666
Email: enquiries@marquisoflorne.com
Web: www.marquisoflorne.com
Dir: *B3066 Bridport-Beaminster rd, turn off E approx*
1.5m N of Bridport. N of Gorecross Business Park, rdbt,
thru West Norton, continue for 1m straight over junct to
Nettlecombe, inn at top of hill, 300yds on left
A 16th-century farmhouse converted into a pub in 1871.
Membership of the Campaign for Real Food means that
much local produce is used in the dishes.
Open: 12-3 6.30-11 (Sun all day) **Bar Meals:** L served
all week 12-2 D served all week 7-9.30 Av main course
£10 **Restaurant Meals:** L served all week 12-2 D

served all week 7-9.30 Av 3 course alc £20 🍺: Palmers
Copper, IPA, 200 Premium Ale ♟: 12 **Children's**
Facilities: Play area Menu/Portions Cutlery Games
Highchair Food warming Baby changing **Nearby:** The
Swannery Abbotsbury, Fossil Hinting Charmouth **Notes:**
Dogs allowed in bar, in garden, Water Garden: Well kept
gardens with good views & play area **Parking:** 50

NORTH WOOTTON
The Three Elms ♟
Nr Sherborne DT9 5JW
☎ 01935 812881 🖹 01935 812881
Dir: *From Sherborne take A352 towards Dorchester then*
A3030. Pub 1m on right
Real ales and locally produced ciders await you at this
family-run free house overlooking scenic Blackmore Vale.
Stunning views can be enjoyed from the pub garden, and
the landlord prides himself on his impressive collection of
about 1,600 model cars, as well as number plates from
every state in America. Wide-ranging menu includes
dishes like rosemary-crusted trout fillet, minted lamb
shank, chicken Kiev and mixed grill. Extensive range of
starters, snacks and sandwiches.
Open: 11-2.30 6.30-11 (Sun 12-3, 7-10.30) Closed:

25-26 Dec **Bar Meals:** L served all week 12-2 D
served all week 6.30-10 (Sun 7-10) **Restaurant Meals:**
L served all week 12-2 D served all week 6.30-10
Brewery/Company: Free House 🍺: Fuller's London
Pride, Butcombe Bitter, Otter Ale ♟: 10 **Children's**
Facilities: Play area Menu/Portions Highchair Food
warming **Notes:** Dogs allowed **Parking:** 50

OSMINGTON MILLS
The Smugglers Inn ♟
nr Weymouth DT3 6HF
☎ 01305 833125 🖹 01305 832219
Email: smugglers.weymouth@hall-woodhouse.co.uk
Web: www.innforanight.co.uk
Dir: *7m E of Weymouth, towards Wareham, pub is signed*
Set on the cliffs at Osmington Mill with the South Coast
Footpath running through the garden, the inn has
beautiful views across Weymouth Bay. In the late 18th
century it was the base of infamous smuggler Pierre
Latour who fell in love with the publican's daughter,
Arabella Carless, who was shot dead while helping him
to escape during a raid. Typical dishes are chicken and
bacon salad, chargrilled rump steak, and Sussex smokey
(fish pie).

Open: 11-11 (Sun 12-10.30) **Bar Meals:** L served all
week 11-6 D served all week 12-9 Av main course £7
Restaurant Meals: L served all week 11-6 D served all
week 12-9 **Brewery/Company:** Hall And Woodhouse
Retail 🍺: ♟: 12 **Children's Facilities:** Licence Play area
(Swings, slide & climbing frame) Menu/Portions Games
Highchair Food warming Baby changing **Nearby:**
Monkey World, Bovington Tank Museum **Notes:** Dogs
allowed in garden, In garden Garden: Large patio,
stream, landscaped gardens **Parking:** 40

PIDDLEHINTON
The Thimble Inn
Dorchester DT2 7TD
☎ 01300 348270
Dir: *A35 westbound, right onto B3143, Piddlehinton 4m.*
Friendly village local with open fires, traditional pub games and good food cooked to order. The pub stands in a pretty valley on the banks of the River Piddle, and the riverside patio is popular in summer. The extensive menu ranges from sandwiches and jacket potatoes to specials such as rabbit, mushroom and tarragon pie, or poached rolled sole filled with shrimps and garlic and topped with seafood sauce.
Open: 12-2.30 7-11 (Sun 12-2.30 7-10.30) Closed: 25 Dec **Bar Meals:** L served all week 12-2 D served all week 7-9 Av main course £7 **Restaurant Meals:** L served all week 12-2 D served all week 7-9
Brewery/Company: Free House 🍺: Badger Best & Tanglefoot, Palmer Copper Ale & Palmer IPA, Ringwood Old Thumper **Children's Facilities:** Menu/Portions Cutlery Highchair Food warming Baby changing **Notes:** Dogs allowed in bar, in garden Garden: Riverside with plenty of wildlife **Parking:** 50

PIDDLETRENTHIDE
The Piddle Inn 🍷
Dorchester DT2 7QF
☎ 01300 348468 🖷 01300 348102
Email: piddleinn@aol.com
Web: www.piddleinn.co.uk
Dir: *7m N of Dorchester on B3143 in middle of Piddletrenthide*
This friendly village free house has been a pub since the 1760s, and was originally a stopover for prisoners in transit between the jails at Dorchester and Sherborne. Traditional pub games and real ales accompany pub favourites like jacket potatoes; home-made chilli con carne; and Cumberland sausage and mash.
Open: 12-3 6-11 **Bar Meals:** L served Tue-Sun 12-2 D served Mon-Fri 6.30-9 (Sat-Sun 12-9) **Restaurant Meals:** L served Tue-Sun 12-2 D served Mon-Sun 6.30-9 **Brewery/Company:** Free House 🍺: Greene King IPA, Ringwood Best, Ringwood 49er 🍷: 8 **Children's Facilities:** Licence Menu/Portions Highchair Food warming Baby changing **Notes:** Dogs allowed in bar, in garden, Water Garden: 48 seater patio area, riverside **Parking:** 15

PIDDLETRENTHIDE
The Poachers Inn 🍷
DT2 7QX
☎ 01300 348358 🖷 01300 348153
Email: thepoachersinn@piddletrenthide.fsbusiness.co.uk
Web: www.thepoachersinn.co.uk
Dir: *6m N from Dorchester on B3143. At the church end of Piddletrenthide*
This family-run inn beside the River Piddle continues to provide real ales, good food, fires and traditional pub games right in the heart of Thomas Hardy country. The riverside patio is especially popular in summer. There's an extensive menu, supported by daily specials that may include home-made spaghetti bolognese; seafood salad with lemon and dill; or pork and leek sausages with mustard mash. Leave room for traditional red and blackcurrant crumble!
Open: 11-12 **Bar Meals:** L served all week 12-9.30 D served all week 12-9.30 Av main course £11
Restaurant Meals: L served all week 12-9.30 D served all week 12-9.30 Av 3 course alc £16
Brewery/Company: Free House 🍺: **Children's Facilities:** Cutlery Highchair Baby changing **Nearby:** Farmer Palmers, Bovington Tank Museum & Monkey World **Notes:** Dogs allowed in bar, in garden Garden: Overlooking beautiful Piddle Valley **Parking:** 57

DORSET

POOLE
The Guildhall Tavern Ltd 🍷
15 Market Street BH15 1NB
☎ 01202 671717 📄 01202 242346
Email: sewerynsevfred@aol.com
Dir: *Near Poole Quay*
In the Old Town, just two minutes from Poole Quay, is this former cider house, owned by Severine and Frederic Grande, whose French influence is evident throughout the bi-lingual menu. Here, we'll stick to English, and quote typical dishes such as fresh crab, mussel and prawn gratin with white wine sauce; pan-fried fillet of halibut with hollandaise; and duck breast with pepper sauce.
Open: 11-3.30 6.15-11 Closed: 1st & 2nd wk in Nov
Bar Meals: L served all week 11-2.30 **Restaurant Meals:** L served all week 12-2.30 D served all week

6.30-9.30 Av 3 course alc £27.50 **Brewery/Company:** Punch Taverns 🍺: Ringwood Best 🍷: 7 **Children's Facilities:** Menu/Portions Cutlery Games Highchair **Parking:** 8

POWERSTOCK
Three Horseshoes Inn ★★★★ INN 🍷
Bridport DT6 3TF
☎ 01308 485328
Email: info@threehorseshoesinn.com
Web: www.threehorseshoesinn.com
Dir: *3m out of Bridport off A5066 Beaminster Rd.*
Popularly known as the Shoes, this pretty, rural Victorian inn is surrounded by some of Dorset's finest scenery. In the restaurant, fresh local produce is used wherever possible; even the herbs, for example, are picked each day from the garden.
Open: 11-3 6.30-11 (Sun 12-3 6.30-10.30) **Bar Meals:** L served all week 12-2.30 D served all week 7-9 (Summer 7-9.30, Sun 12-3, 7-8.30) **Restaurant Meals:** L served all week 12-2.30 D served all week 7-

9 (Sun 7-8.30) **Brewery/Company:** Palmers 🍺: Palmer's IPA, Copper Ale 🍷: 7 **Children's Facilities:** Fam room Play area (Climbing frame) Menu/Portions Games Highchair Food warming **Nearby:** Jurassic coastline, Dinosaur Museum, Cricket St. Thomas **Notes:** Dogs allowed in bar, in garden **Garden:** Large terrace with good views of countryside **Parking:** 30

PUNCKNOWLE
The Crown Inn 🍷
Church Street Dorchester DT2 9BN
☎ 01308 897711 📄 01308 898282
Dir: *From A35, into Bridevally, through Litton Cheney. From B3157, inland at Swyre.*
There's a traditional atmosphere within the rambling, low-beamed bars at this picturesque 16th-century thatched inn, which was once the haunt of smugglers on their way from nearby Chesil Beach to visit prosperous customers in Bath. Food ranges from light snacks and sandwiches to home-made dishes like lamb chops with mint sauce; and tuna steak with basil and tomato sauce.
Open: 11-3 7-11 (Sun 12-3, 7-10.30, Summer 6.30 opening) Closed: 25 Dec **Bar Meals:** L served all week 12-2 D served all week 7-9 (Summer weekdays from

6.30pm) Av main course £7.60 **Brewery/Company:** Palmers 🍺: Palmers IPA, 200 Premium Ale, Copper, Tally Ho! 🍷: 10 **Children's Facilities:** Fam room Menu/Portions Highchair Food warming **Nearby:** Abbotsbury Swannery, Weymouth Sealife Centre, Monkey World **Notes:** Dogs allowed in bar, in garden **Garden:** Large garden with raised patio area **Parking:** 12

SHERBORNE
Half Moon Inn ☺
Half Moon Street DT9 3LN
☎ 01935 812017 🖺 01935 818130
Email: halfmoon@eldridge-pope.co.uk
Web: www.roomattheinn.info
Standing opposite Sherborne Abbey in the heart of this charming Dorset town, the Half Moon is at the centre of local life. There's a choice of real ales, 11 wines served by the glass, and great food is served all day. Daily specials supplement the wide-ranging themed menus; typical choices include roast pork hock; chilli prawn bruschetta; Mediterranean stuffed peppers; and fisherman's crumble. Sunday roasts, desserts and children's menus are also offered.
Open: 11-11 **Bar Meals:** L served all week 11-6

D served all week 6-9.15 **Restaurant Meals:** L served all week 11-3 D served all week 6-9.30 Av 3 course alc £17.50 **Brewery/Company:** Eldridge Pope
🍺: Wadworth 6X, Ringwood Best, Otter 3.6, Ringwood 49er 🍷: 11 **Children's Facilities:** Games Highchair Food warming Baby changing **Notes:** Garden: Front patio area, seating and flowers **Parking:** 40

SHERBORNE
Queen's Head
High Street Milborne Port DT9 5DQ
☎ 01963 250314 🖺 01963 250339
Dir: *On A30*
Milborne Port has no facilities for shipping, the suffix being Old English for 'borough', a status it acquired in 1249. The building came much later, in Elizabethan times, although no mention is made of it as a hostelry until 1738. Charming and friendly bars, restaurant, beer garden and skittle alley combine to make it a popular free house in these parts.
Open: 12-2.30 5.30-11 (Sunday 12-10.30) **Bar Meals:** L served Sat-Sun 12-1.4 D served all week 7-9.30 (Mon-Tue 7-8.40, Wed-Fri 7-9.10) Av main course £8 **Restaurant Meals:** L served Sat-Sun 12-2 D served all

week 7-9.30 (Mon-Tue 7-8.40, Wed-Fri 7-9.10) Av 3 course alc £16 **Brewery/Company:** Enterprise Inns
🍺: Butcombe Bitters, Fullers London Pride, Hopback Summer Lightning **Children's Facilities:** Licence Menu/Portions Highchair Food warming **Notes:** Dogs allowed, Water Garden: Terrace, food served outside **Parking:** 15

SHERBORNE
White Hart
Bishops Caundle DT9 5ND
☎ 01963 23301 🖺 01963 23301 (by arrangement)
Dir: *On A3030 between Sherborne & Sturminster Newton*
Located in the heart of the Blackmore Vale, the 16th-century White Hart was reputedly used as a courthouse by the infamous Judge Jeffries. The large enclosed family garden offers beautiful views of the wonderful Bullbarrow Hill, as well as play equipment and an adventure trail for children. The extensive menu starts with baguettes, jacket potatoes and ploughman's, whilst hot dishes include pork steak Valentine; spinach and mushroom tagliatelle; and poached salmon supreme.
Open: 11.30-3 6.30-11 (Sun 12-3, 7-10.30) **Bar Meals:** L served all week 12-2 D served all week 6.45-

9.30 **Restaurant Meals:** L served all week 12-2 D served all week 6.30-9.30 **Brewery/Company:** Hall & Woodhouse 🍺: Badger Best, Tanglefoot, Golden Champion, Sussex Golden Glory **Children's Facilities:** Fam room Play area (Activity play trail, 2 trampolines) Menu/Portions Highchair Food warming **Notes:** Dogs allowed, Water Garden: Patio area and large grass area with benches **Parking:** 32

DORSET

STOKE ABBOTT
The New Inn
DT8 3JW
☎ 01308 868333
A welcoming 17th-century farmhouse turned village inn, with thatched roof, log fires and a beautiful garden. It offers three real ales, and an extensive menu of light meals such as grilled black pudding with caramelised apples, and cold smoked duck breast with plum chutney, plus a good choice of baguettes, sandwiches and vegetarian dishes. Specials might include pork schnitzel with sweet chili dip, scallops wrapped in bacon, and beef and mushroom pie. Listen out for the singing chef! **Open:** 11.30-3 7-11 (Sun 12-3, 7-10.30) **Bar Meals:** L served all week 12-2 D served all week 7-9.30 **Restaurant Meals:** L served all week 12-2 D served all week 7-9.30 **Brewery/Company:** Palmers ◧: Palmers IPA & 200 Premium Ale, Tally Ho **Children's Facilities:** Menu/Portions Games Highchair Food warming **Nearby:** Abbotsbury Swannery, Monkey World, Crealey **Notes:** Dogs allowed in bar **Garden:** Large, comfortable, beautiful views **Parking:** 25

STOURPAINE
The White Horse Inn ♟
Shaston Road Blandford DT11 8TA
☎ 01258 453535 📠 01258 453535
Dir: *A350 towards Shaftesbury in village of Stourpaine*
Typical village pub dating back to the early 18th century, sympathetically refurbished and extended. Inside, are an inglenook fireplace and two dining rooms, one opening on to the patio. The menu offers home-baked ham, eggs and chips; pan-fried duck breast with black cherries and brandy sauce; wholetail deep-fried scampi and chips; and mixed vegetable, pasta and blue cheese bake. Hod Hill Roman fort and the River Stour are within easy reach. **Open:** 12-3 6-11 (Fri/Sat 6-12) **Bar Meals:** L served all week 12-2 D served Tue-Sun 6-9 Av main course £8.75 **Restaurant Meals:** L served all week 12-2 D served Tue-Sun 6-9 Av 3 course alc £18 ◧: Badgers Best, Festive Pheasant, Fursty Ferret, Sussex, Tanglefoot ♟: 8 **Children's Facilities:** Licence Menu/Portions Cutlery Games Highchair Food warming **Nearby:** Monkey World. Bovington Camp, Farmer Palmers, Rare Breed Centre **Notes:** Dogs allowed in bar **Garden:** Decked courtyard **Parking:** 25

TARRANT MONKTON
The Langton Arms ★★★★ INN ⊛
nr Blandford DT11 8RX
☎ 01258 830225 📠 01258 830053
Email: info@thelangtonarms.co.uk
Web: www.thelangtonarms.co.uk
Dir: *A31 from Ringwood, or A357 from Shaftesbury, or A35 from Bournemouth*
Well known for its excellent food and an ever-changing range of real ales, this attractive 17th-century thatched inn occupies a peaceful spot in the village centre close to the church. Expect interesting dishes featuring produce from local farmers wherever possible. The main menu includes game, traditional pub favourites, and a good choice of fish and vegetarian dishes, plus rare breed beef steaks. A meal could begin with Dorset Country farmhouse pâté and home-made Cumberland sauce, followed by the likes of wild rabbit braised on the bone. In the Stables restaurant things shift up a gear with starters such as king prawn and crayfish remoulade, followed perhaps by roast breast of Barbary duck with home-made chutney and ginger, lemon and honey sauce **Open:** 11.30-11 (Sun 12-10.30) **Bar Meals:** L served all week 11.30-2.30 D served all week 6-9.30 (Sat-Sun all day) Av main course £9.25 **Restaurant Meals:** L served Sun 12-2 D served Wed-Sat 7-9 ◧: Ringwood Best Bitter, Hop Back Odyssey, Hidden Pleasure Guest Beers ♟: 6 **Children's Facilities:** Fam room Play area (Adventure playground) Menu/Portions Highchair Baby changing **Nearby:** Monkey World, Moors Valley Country Park & Banbury Rings **Notes:** Garden: Large beer garden **Parking:** 100

TOLPUDDLE
The Martyrs Inn ▾
Nr Dorchester DT2 7ES
☎ 01305 848249
Email: scottz@freezone.co.uk
Web: www.martyrsinn.co.uk
Dir: *Off A35 between Bere Regis (A31/A35 Junction)*
Tolpuddle is the somewhat unlikely birthplace of the Trades Union Congress, after six impoverished farm labourers tried to bargain with local landowners for better conditions in 1834. Home-made starters include chicken liver and wild mushroom pâté, and garlic mushrooms en croûte; with main courses like Tolpuddle sausages with mash and onion gravy, country vegetable pasta bake, and red mullet and mash. There is a play area to keep the children amused.

Open: 11-11 **Bar Meals:** L served all week 12-3 D served all week 6.30-9 **Restaurant Meals:** L served all week D served all week **Brewery/Company:** Hall & Woodhouse ▣: Badger Dorset Best & Tanglefoot ▾: 10 **Children's Facilities:** Play area Menu/Portions Cutlery Games Highchair Food warming Baby changing **Nearby:** Monkey World, Beaches, Tank Museum **Notes:** Dogs allowed in bar Garden: south facing **Parking:** 25

WEST BEXINGTON
The Manor Hotel ★★ HL ▾
Nr Dorchester DT2 9DF
☎ 01308 897616 ▤ 01308 897704
Email: themanorhotel@btconnect.com
Web: www.themanorhotel.com
Dir: *On B3157, 5m E of Bridport*
The 500-year-old Manor Hotel, mentioned in the Domesday Book, has a cosy cellar bar with a log fire and a conservatory with wonderful sea views. Local real ales, organic cider and soft drinks are served alongside the freshest fish and quality meat that Dorset has to offer, including an organic children's menu. Muddy boots, dogs and children are all welcome. Organic hog roasts and barbecues are held in the landscaped garden overlooking the sea.

Open: 11-11 **Bar Meals:** L served all week 12-2 D served all week 6.30-9.30 **Restaurant Meals:** L served all week 12-2 D served all week 7-9.30 **Brewery/Company:** Free House ▣: Butcombe Gold, Harbour Master ▾: 8 **Children's Facilities:** Fam room Play area (Playing field) Menu/Portions Cutlery Games Highchair Food warming **Nearby:** Chesil Beach, Abbotsbury Swannery, Abbotsbury Tythe Barn **Notes:** Dogs allowed in bar, Water bowls **Garden:** Large garden with sea views & picnic area **Parking:** 55

WEST LULWORTH
The Castle Inn ▾
Main Road BH20 5RN
☎ 01929 400311 ▤ 01929 400415
Web: www.thecastleinn-lulworthcove.co.uk
Dir: *On Wareham to Dorchester Rd, approx 1m from Wareham*
In a delightful setting near Lulworth Cove, this family-run thatched village inn lies close to plenty of good walks. The friendly bars offer a traditional atmosphere; outside, you'll find large tiered gardens. The wide-ranging menu includes grills, poultry, fish and steak dishes and flambéed dishes cooked at the table.

Open: 11-3 6-11 (Winter 12-2.30, 7-11) Closed: 25 Dec **Bar Meals:** L served all week 11-2.30 D served all week 6-10.30 **Restaurant Meals:** L served all week D served Fri & Sat 7-9.30 **Brewery/Company:** Free House ▣: Ringwood Best, Gales, Courage, John Smiths ▾: 8 **Children's Facilities:** Licence Fam room (Outside chess/draughts, board games) Menu/Portions Cutlery Games Highchair Food warming Baby changing **Nearby:** Monkey World, Poole Park & Tank Museum **Notes:** Dogs allowed in bar, in garden Large garden **Parking:** 30

DORSET

WEYMOUTH
The Old Ship Inn 🍷

7 The Ridgeway DT3 5QQ

☎ 01305 812522 📄 01305 816533

Dir: *3m from Weymouth town centre, at bottom of The Ridgeway.*

Copper pans, old clocks and a beamed open fire create just the right atmosphere at this historic pub, while outside the terrace offers views over Weymouth. Thomas Hardy refers to it in his novels *Under the Greenwood Tree* and *The Trumpet Major*. A good range of jacket potatoes, baguettes and salads is supplemented by traditional pub favourites, and there are fish dishes among the daily specials.

Open: 12-12 (Sun 12-10.30) **Bar Meals:** L served all week 12-2.30 D served all week 6-9.30 (Sun 12-4) Av main course £10.95 **Restaurant Meals:** L served Mon-Sat 12-2 D served all week 6-9.30 (Sun 12-4) Av 3 course alc £11.45 **Brewery/Company:** Punch Taverns 🍺: Greene King, Old Speckled Hen, Ringwood Best & Guest Ales 🍷: 7 **Children's Facilities:** Licence Menu/Portions Highchair Food warming **Nearby:** Sealife Centre & Deep Sea Adventure **Notes:** Dogs allowed in bar, in garden, Water **Garden:** Patio garden with enclosed grass area **Parking:** 12

WINTERBORNE ZELSTON
Botany Bay Inne 🍷

Blandford Forum DT11 9ET

☎ 01929 459227

Web: www.botanybay-inne.co.uk

Dir: *A31 between Bere Regis & Wimborne Minster*

An obvious question: how did the pub get its name? Built in the 1920s as The General Allenby, it was changed about 17 years ago in belated recognition of prisoners from Dorchester jail who were required to spend a night nearby before transportation to Australia. Since no such fate awaits anyone these days, meals to enjoy at leisure include bacon-wrapped chicken breast; steak and kidney pudding; roasted Mediterranean vegetable Wellington; and fish catch of the day. Real ales are locally brewed.

Open: 11.30-3 6-11 (Mon-Sat summer open 10) **Bar Meals:** L served all week 12-2.15 D served all week 6.30-9.30 Av main course £7 **Restaurant Meals:** L served all week 12-2.15 D served all week 6.30-9.30 Av 3 course alc £17 🍺: Badger Best Bitter, Tanglefoot, Botany Bay Bitter, Fursty Ferret, Badger Smooth 🍷: 7 **Children's Facilities:** Licence Fam room Menu/Portions Games Highchair **Nearby:** Monkey World, Sealife Centre **Notes:** Dogs allowed in bar, In bar only, Water **Garden:** Paved area with flowers overlooking fields **Parking:** 60

ALMONDSBURY
The Bowl ★★ HL 🍷

16 Church Road BS32 4DT

☎ 01454 612757 📄 01454 619910

Email: reception@thebowlinn.co.uk

Web: www.thebowlinn.co.uk

A whitewashed stone inn first licensed in 1550, but with much older parts that housed the men building the village church. A good choice of meals is available in the bar. The smart Lilies Restaurant offers pan-fried Barbary duck with Puy lentil mash, roasted fillet of salmon on creamed baby spinach, and penne pasta with wild mushrooms.

Open: 11-3 5-11 (Sun 12-10.30) **Bar Meals:** L served all week 12-2.30 D served all week 6-10 (Sun 12-8) Av main course £9.95 **Restaurant Meals:** L served all week 12-2.30 D served all week 7-10 Av 3 course alc £25 **Brewery/Company:** Free House 🍺: Scottish Courage Courage Best, Smiles Best, Wickwar BOB, Mole Best, Interbrew Bass, guest ales 🍷: 9 **Children's Facilities:** Menu/Portions Cutlery Games Highchair Food warming **Nearby:** Slimbridge Wildlife, Hollywood Bowl, Bristol Zoo **Notes:** Dogs allowed in bar, in garden **Garden:** Patio at rear; seating at front **Parking:** 50

AMPNEY CRUCIS
The Crown of Crucis ★★★ HL ♟

Ampney Crucis Cirencester GL7 5RS

☎ 01285 851806 🖨 01285 851735

Email: info@thecrownofcrucis.co.uk

Web: www.thecrownofcrucis.co.uk

Dir: On A417 to Lechlade, 2m E of Cirencester

This classic 16th-century inn stands beside the Ampney
Brook at the gateway to the glorious Cotswolds. The
hotel, which takes its name from the Latin cross or
'crucis' in the nearby village churchyard, provides modern
comforts while still retaining the original character. Food
is served all day in the bar.

Open: 10.30-11 Closed: Dec 25 **Bar Meals:** L served all
week 12-10 D served all week 12-10 Av main course
£7.50 **Restaurant Meals:** L served all week 12-2.30 D

served all week 7-9.30 Av 3 course alc £22.50
Brewery/Company: Free House 🍺: Wadworth 6X,
Archers Village, Scottish Courage John Smith's ♟: 10
Children's Facilities: Menu/Portions Highchair Food
warming **Nearby:** Cotswold Water & Wildlife Park &
Magicland **Notes:** Dogs allowed in bar, in garden
Garden: Riverside Setting **Parking:** 70

ANDOVERSFORD
The Royal Oak Inn ♟

Old Gloucester Road Cheltenham GL54 4HR

☎ 01242 820335

Email: bleninns@clara.net

Web: www.cotswoldinns.co.uk

Dir: 200metres from A40, 4m E of Cheltenham

The Royal Oak stands on the banks of the River Coln,
one of a small chain of popular food-oriented pubs in
the area. Originally a coaching inn, its main dining room,
galleried on two levels, occupies the converted former
stables. Lunchtime bar fare of various sandwiches,
lasagne and ham, egg and chips (for example), extends
in the evening to Chinese crispy duck with lime and soy
noodles or roast pork fillet with rosti potato and creamy
cider sauce.

Open: 11-2.30 5.30-11 **Bar Meals:** L served all week
12-2.30 D served all week 7-9.30 Av main course
£6.50 **Restaurant Meals:** L served all week 12-2.30
D served all week 7-9.30 Av 3 course alc £15
Brewery/Company: Free House 🍺: Hook Norton Best,
Tetleys Bitter, Draught Bass ♟: 8 **Children's Facilities:**
Menu/Portions Highchair Food warming **Nearby:**
Cotswold Wild Life Park & Folly Farm **Notes:** Dogs
allowed in bar, in garden, Water **Garden:** Patio area with
tables on banks of the river **Parking:** 44

AWRE
The Red Hart Inn at Awre ♟

nr Newnham-on-Severn GL14 1EW

☎ 01594 510220

Dir: E of A48 between Gloucester & Chepstow, access is
from Blakeney or Newnham villages

The history of this cosy traditional free house goes back
to 1483, when it was built to house workmen renovating
the nearby 10th-century church. Close to the River
Severn, the setting is ideal for hikers - and there's a map
by the front door for inspiration! The charming interior
includes flagstone floors, stone fireplaces, lots of exposed
old beams, and an original working well, now attractively
illuminated. Food is taken so seriously that a list of all
local growers and suppliers is provided on each table.
Vegetables are organic where possible, and the Awre

family supply the inn with beef, lamb and pork, the latter
cooked with Severn Sider cider on Sundays.
Open: 12-3 6.30-11 Closed: 23 Jan-5 Feb **Bar Meals:**
L served all week 12-2 D served all week 6-9.30 (Sun
12-2.30, 6-9) Av main course £7.45 **Restaurant
Meals:** L served all week 12-2 D served all week
6-9.30 (Sun 12-2.30, 6-9) Av 3 course alc £19.95
Brewery/Company: Free House 🍺: Wye Valley Butty
Bach, Guest Ales, Whttingtons, Archers, Freeminer,
Wickwar ♟: 11 **Children's Facilities:** Menu/Portions
Games Highchair **Nearby:** Mallards Pike, Clearwell
Caves, Dean Forest Railway, Go Ape **Notes:** Dogs
allowed in bar, Water & treats **Garden:** Tranquil country
garden with seating **Parking:** 40

GLOUCESTERSHIRE

BARNSLEY
The Village Pub ☺ ♇
Cirencester GL7 5EF
☎ 01285 740421 📄 01285 740929
Email: reservations@thevillagepub.co.uk
Web: www.thevillagepub.co.uk
Dir: *On B4425 4m NE of Cirencester*
Despite its mellow-stoned country pub setting, this distinctive dining venue is light years away from the average local. The beautifully restored dining rooms with their eclectic mix of furniture, rug-strewn floors and open fires provide an atmospheric background to a busy free house that enjoys a reputation as one of the best local eating places. The daily-changing menus are founded on quality ingredients that include locally sourced produce, traceable or organic meats, and fresh seasonal fish from Cornwall. Lunchtime fare ranges from curried parsnip soup with crackling; or farmhouse terrine with home-made chutney; to cottage pie and greens; or lemon sole with kale and creamed leeks. In the evening, main course choices include tagliatelle with wild mushrooms, garlic and parsley; and roast duck with lentils and purple sprouting broccoli.
Open: 11-3.30 6-11 **Bar Meals:** L served all week 12-3 D served all week 7-10 Av main course £13
Restaurant Meals: L served all week 12-3 D served all week 7-10 Av 3 course alc £24.50
Brewery/Company: Free House 🍺: Hook Norton Bitter, Wadworth 6X ♇: 17 **Children's Facilities:** Licence Menu/Portions Cutlery Highchair Food warming **Notes:** Dogs allowed in bar, in garden **Garden:** Walled terrace **Parking:** 35

BERKELEY
The Malt House ★★★ INN
Marybrook St GL13 9BA
☎ 01453 511177 📄 01453 810257
Email: the-malthouse@btconnect.com
Web: www.themalthouse.uk.com
Dir: *From A38 towards Bristol from M5 junct 13/14, after approx 8m Berkeley is signposted, the Malthouse is situated on the main road heading towards Sharpness*
Within walking distance of Berkeley Castle and its deer park, this family-run free house is also handy for the Edward Jenner museum, dedicated to the life of the founding father of immunology. Inside the heavily beamed pub you'll find a varied selection of lunchtime bar food, as well as weekly home-made specials.
Open: 12-11 **Bar Meals:** L served all week 12-2 D served Mon-Sat 6-9 (Sun 12-2) **Restaurant Meals:** L served all week 12-2 D served Mon-Sat 6-9 (Sun 12-2)
Brewery/Company: Free House 🍺: Courage Directors & Theakstons **Children's Facilities:** Menu/Portions Cutlery Highchair Food warming **Nearby:** Berkeley Castle & Slimbridge Wildfowl & Wetlands Trust **Notes:** Garden: Food served outside in summer **Parking:** 40

BIBURY
Catherine Wheel
Arlington GL7 5ND
☎ 01285 740250 📄 01285 740779
Email: catherinewheel.bibury@eldridge-pope.co.uk
Low-beamed 15th-century pub situated in a Cotswold village described by William Morris as 'the most beautiful in England'. Inside is an original ship's timber beam, as well as various prints and photographs of Old Bibury, and blazing log fires in winter. Traditional pub food includes the likes of fresh Bibury trout, salmon and prawns, and tuna steak.
Open: 11-11 (Sun 12-10.30) **Bar Meals:** L served all week 12-2 D served all week 6-9.30 Av main course £10 **Restaurant Meals:** L served all week 12-2 D served all week 6-9 Av 3 course alc £20
Brewery/Company: Eldridge Pope 🍺: Wadworth 6X, Hook Norton **Children's Facilities:** Play area Games Highchair Food warming Baby changing **Nearby:** Cotswold Wildlife Park **Notes:** Dogs allowed, Water provided **Garden:** Food served outside, vintage orchard **Parking:** 20

BIRDLIP
The Golden Heart ♟
Nettleton Bottom GL4 8LA
☎ 01242 870261 📄 01242 870599
Email: cathstevensgh@aol.com
Dir: *on A417 Gloucester to Cirencester*
There are glorious country views from the terraced gardens of this Cotswold stone inn, while inside you'll find real fires, real ales and a wide selection of wines. The regular menu is supplemented by a daily blackboard choice. Starters might include prawn dim sum; Indian meatballs with mango and chilli sauce; or asparagus with hollandaise sauce. Follow with anything from ostrich and black cherry casserole to grilled marlin steak with lemon and herb butter.
Open: 11-3 5.30-11 (Fri-Sat 11-11, Sun 12-10.30)

Closed: 25 Dec **Bar Meals:** L served all week 12-3 D served all week 6-10 (Sun 12-10) Av main course £10.50 **Restaurant Meals:** L served all week 12-3 D served all week 6-10 (Sun 12-10) **Brewery/Company:** Free House 🍺: Pedigree, Timothy Taylor Landlord & Golden Best, Archers Golden, Young's Special ♟: 10 **Children's Facilities:** Fam room (Garden) Menu/Portions Games Highchair Food warming **Nearby:** Crickley Hill Park, Prinknash Abbey **Notes:** Dogs allowed in bar, in garden, in bedrooms, Water Garden: Terrace, 3 levels, large patio area, seating **Parking:** 60

CHEDWORTH
Hare & Hounds ★★★★ INN ⊛ ♟
Foss Cross Cheltenham GL54 4NN
☎ 01285 720288 📄 01285 720488
Email: stay@hareandhoundsinn.com
Web: www.hareandhoundsinn.com
Dir: *On A429 (Fosse Way), 6m from Cirencester*
A 14th-century inn with various interconnecting dining areas often described as a rabbit warren. Open fires, beams and stone and polished wood floors add to the charm. There is a daily changing blackboard, along with a menu typically listing breast of Gressingham duck; baked fillet of cod; and Burmese vegetable tofu curry.
Open: 11-3 6-12 **Bar Meals:** L served all week 12-2.30 D served all week 7-9.45 (Sun 12-3, 7-9) Av main course £12.95 **Restaurant Meals:** L served all week

11-2.30 D served all week 6.30-9.45 (Sun 12-3, 7-9) Av 3 course alc £15.95 **Brewery/Company:** Arkells 🍺: Arkells 3B & JRA 2B ♟: 10 **Children's Facilities:** Fam room Menu/Portions Cutlery Games Highchair Food warming Baby changing **Nearby:** Cotswold Wildlife Park, Water Park, Birdland & Trout Farm **Notes:** Dogs allowed in bar, in garden Garden: Large, colourful **Parking:** 80

CHEDWORTH
Seven Tuns ♟
Queen Street GL54 4AE
☎ 01285 720242 📄 01285 720242
Email: theseventuns@clara.co.uk
Dir: *Exit A429, turn off at the junct to Chedworth. Approx half way between Northleach & Cirencester, follow signs to pub.*
A 17th-century village inn, unmistakeably Cotswold in character. The lunch menu offers nothing too heavy - sandwiches, ploughman's, jacket potatoes, and ham, egg and chips. You can have the same in the evening, but there are more sophisticated choices too.
Open: 11-12 (Fri-Sat 11am-2am, Nov-Mar 11-3, 6-12, Sun 12-10.30) **Bar Meals:** L served all week 12-3 D served all week 6.30-10 **Restaurant Meals:** L served

all week 12-3 D served all week 6.30-10 🍺: Young's Bitter, Youngs Special, Winter Warmer, Waggledance, St Georges ♟: 12 **Children's Facilities:** Fam room (Skittle alley) Menu/Portions Cutlery Games Highchair Food warming Baby changing **Nearby:** Cotswold Water Park, Roman Villa **Notes:** Dogs allowed in bar Garden: 60 seater terrace, heaters, SA BBQ **Parking:** 40

GLOUCESTERSHIRE

CHIPPING CAMPDEN
Eight Bells Inn ♀
Church Street GL55 6JG
☎ 01386 840371   📠 01386 841669
Email: neilhargreaves@bellinn.fsnet.co.uk
Web: www.eightbellsinn.co.uk
Built in the 14th century to house stonemasons working
on the nearby church and to store the eight church bells,
the Eight Bells is now a tiny free house. Freshly prepared
local food is offered from a daily-changing seasonal
menu, featuring fresh fish in summer and game in winter.
Open: 12-3 5.30-11 (all day May-Oct) Closed: 25 Dec
Bar Meals: L served all week 12-2.30 D served all
week 6.30-9.30 (Mon-Thu 6.30-9) Av main course £11
Restaurant Meals: L served all week 12-2.30 D served
all week 6.30-9.30 (Mon-Thu 6.30-9) Av 3 course alc

£22   🍺: Hook Norton Best & Guest Beers, Goff's
Jouster, Marston Pedigree, Purity UBU ♀: 8 **Children's
Facilities:** Fam room (Colouring competition on menus)
Menu/Portions Cutlery Highchair Food warming **Nearby:**
Warwick Castle, Shakespeare's Birthplace, Cotswold
Water Park **Notes:** Dogs on leads allowed in bar, in
garden **Garden:** Terrace, courtyard, views of almshouses

CHIPPING CAMPDEN
King's Arms ★★★★ INN
The Square GL55 6AW
☎ 01386 840256   📠 01386 841598
Email: info@kingscampden.co.uk
Web: www.kingscampden.co.uk
Set in the square of a pretty Cotswold town, this smart
17th-century inn has an air of relaxed elegance. There
are plenty of snacks, but the full menu offers some
imaginative delights: pan-fried squid and chorizo with
soy and honey dressing perhaps; or local pork and leek
sausages with creamed mash and onion gravy. Have a
look at the specials board for more choices, and take
in some lovely artwork by a local painter.
Open: 9-11 Closed: 25 Dec **Bar Meals:** L served all
week 12-2.30 D served all week 6.30-9.30 (Sat-Sun

12-3) Av main course £8 **Restaurant Meals:** L served
all week 12-2.30 D served all week 6.30-9.30 (Sat-Sun
12-3) Av 3 course alc £30 **Brewery/Company:** Free
House 🍺: Hook Norton Best **Children's Facilities:**
Menu/Portions Games Highchair Food warming **Nearby:**
Stratford, Museums, Falconry **Notes:** Dogs allowed in
bar **Parking:** 8

CHIPPING CAMPDEN
The Bakers Arms
Broad Campden GL55 6UR
☎ 01386 840515
Small Cotswold inn with a great atmosphere, where
visitors are welcomed and regulars are involved with the
quiz, darts and crib teams. Good meals at reasonable
prices are served, with a choice of four or five real ales.
You can go for a light bite, like warm baguette, or giant
Yorkshire pudding filled with, perhaps, cottage pie mince,
or chicken curry. Specials include lamb shank, and pork
chop cooked in cider.
Open: 11.30-2.30 4.45-11 (Sun 12-10.30, Summer
11.30-11) Closed: 25 Dec **Bar Meals:** L served all week
12-2 D served all week 6-9 (Apr-Oct 12-9) Av main
course £7 **Restaurant Meals:** L served all week 12-2

D served all week 6-9 **Brewery/Company:** Free House
🍺: Stanway Bitter, Bombardier, Timothy Taylor Landlord,
Donnington BB **Children's Facilities:** Play area (Swings)
Menu/Portions Cutlery Highchair Food warming **Notes:**
Dogs allowed in garden, Water provided **Garden:** Large
grassed area and patios **Parking:** 30

CHIPPING CAMPDEN
The Noel Arms Hotel ★★★ HL ♟

High Street GL55 6AT

☎ 01386 840317 📠 01386 841136

Email: reception@noelarmshotel.com

Web: www.noelarmshotel.com

Dir: *On High St, opposite Town Hall*

Combining the very best of the past and present, this 16th-century coaching inn has a great atmosphere. Original oak beams, and an open fire warm the Dover's Bar, where guests can enjoy local and European beers and wines. Bar meals feature produce exclusively from the Cotswolds, look out for Moreton-in-Marsh smoked bacon and cabbage broth; or grilled whole Donnington trout with a warm watercress dressing and herbed new potatoes. The Gainsborough restaurant offers modern British cuisine or an Oriental fusion menu, with flavours from all over the Far East. You might try salmon pavé, stir-fried mange-tout and carrot with lime dressing; tempura vegetables with sweet chilli and tartar sauces; seafood coconut curry; and prawns, squid, cod, tuna and salmon in a mild Sri Lankan sauce with yellow rice. **Open:** 11-11 (Sun 12-10.30) **Bar Meals:** L served all week 12-2.30 D served all week 6-9.30 Av main course £12.50 **Restaurant Meals:** L served all week 12-2.30 D served all week 7-9.30 Av 3 course alc £25 **Brewery/Company:** Free House 🍺: Hook Norton Best Bitter, Carling, Guinness ♟: 10 **Children's Facilities:** Menu/Portions Games Highchair Food warming **Nearby:** Cotswold Water Park, Cotswold Farm Park, Birdland **Notes:** Dogs allowed Garden: Courtyard with cast iron & ceramic furniture **Parking:** 25

CHIPPING CAMPDEN
The Volunteer Inn ♟

Lower High Street GL55 6DY

☎ 01386 840688 📠 01386 840543

Email: saravol@aol.com

Web: www.thevolunteerinn.com

A 300-year-old inn where, in the mid-19th-century, the able-bodied used to sign up for the militia. Ramblers can set off from here to walk the Cotswold Way. Unusually, there is a takeaway food menu, featuring home-made burger with coleslaw and fries; and spinach, ricotta and basil lasagne with a herby tomato sauce. The in-house menus, supplemented by daily specials, feature the likes of honey and ginger beef with stir-fried vegetables and crispy noodles. **Open:** 11-11 (Nov-Mar 12-3, 5-11 weekdays) **Bar Meals:** L served all week 12-2.30 D served all week 12-2.30 (Sun 12-3) Av main course £8 **Restaurant Meals:** L served all week 12-2.30 D served all week 12-2.30 (Sun 12-3) Av 3 course alc £16 **Brewery/Company:** Free House 🍺: Hook Norton, London Pride, Archers, Goffs & Carling ♟: 12 **Children's Facilities:** Fam room Play area (Swings, slide & tower in enclosed area) Menu/Portions Games Highchair Food warming **Notes:** Dogs allowed in bar Garden: Grassed with tables

CLIFFORD'S MESNE
The Yew Tree ♟

Clifford Mesne Newent GL18 1JS

☎ 01531 820719 📠 01531 820912

Email: cass@yewtreeinn.com

Web: www.yewtreeinn.com

Dir: *From Newent High Street, S following signs to Cliffords Mesne. Pub is at far end of village on road to Glasshouse.*

Clifford's Mesne is a lovely old village, and the Yew Tree is a lovely old pub. A cider house in the 16th century, it stands in five acres on the slopes of the National Trust's May Hill, from whose 971ft summit you can see the Welsh Mountains, Malvern Hills and the River Severn. After 21 years running a pub in Buckinghamshire, Caroline Todd came here in 2004 for what she hoped would be 'a quieter life'. Traditional bars are floored with quarry tiles, pleasantly furnished and log-fire heated. The simple menu offers chargrilled meats and fish, light lunches and seasonal specialities which, depending on when you visit, might include beef Wellington; pan-fried, bacon-wrapped chicken supreme stuffed with cream cheese; or roasted garlic and gorgonzola tart. **Open:** 12-2.30 6-11 (Sun 12-4) **Bar Meals:** L served Wed-Sun 12-2 D served Tue-Sun 6-9 (Sun 12-4) Av main course £10 **Brewery/Company:** Free House 🍺: Wye Valley Butty Bach, Fuller's London Pride, Wye Valley Best, Adnams Broadside, Guests ♟: 8 **Children's Facilities:** Play area (Swing, slide) Menu/Portions Food warming **Nearby:** Birds of Prey Centre, Mayhill **Notes:** Dogs allowed in bar, in garden Garden: Spacious garden, patio, furniture, parasols **Parking:** 30

GLOUCESTERSHIRE

GLOUCESTERSHIRE

COATES
The Tunnel House Inn
Cirencester GL7 6PW
☎ 01285 770280 🖺 01285 770120
Email: info@tunnelhouse.com
Web: www.tunnelhouse.com
Dir: *Leave Cirencester on A433 towards Tetbury, after 2m turn right towards Coates, follow signs to Canal Tunnel and Inn.*
The Tunnel House sits in a glorious rural location, between the Cotswold villages of Coates and Tarlton. In warm weather the garden is an ideal place for relaxing with a drink or a meal, and enjoying the views. The menu, updated monthly, boasts a range of good home cooking using fresh and local produce wherever possible.
Open: 11-3 6-11 (Open all day Fri-Sun) **Bar Meals:** L

served all week 12-2.15 D served all week 6.45-9.15 Av main course £8.50 🍺: Uley Old Spot, Uley Bitter, Wye Valley Bitter, Archers Village **Children's Facilities:** Licence Play area Cutlery Highchair Food warming **Nearby:** Westonbirt Aboretum, Cotswold Water Park & Longleat **Notes:** Dogs allowed in bar, Water Garden: Large area at rear of pub **Parking:** 50

COLESBOURNE
The Colesbourne Inn 🍷
Cheltenham GL53 9NP
☎ 01242 870376
Email: info@thecolesbourneinn.co.uk
Web: www.thecolesbourneinn.co.uk
Dir: *Located midway between Cirencester & Cheltenham on the A435.*
A handsome 17th-century stone pub situated within the Colesbourne estate at the heart of the Cotswolds. It has a reputation for excellent quality menus.
Open: 11-3 6-11 (Sat/Sun 11-11, Nov-Feb noon opening) **Bar Meals:** L served all week 12-1.45 D served all week 6-8.45 (Sat/Sun 12-2.30, Fri/Sat 6-9.30) Av main course £11 **Restaurant Meals:** L served all week 12-1.45 D served all week 6-8.45 (Sat/Sun 12-2.30, Fri/Sat

6-9.30) Av 3 course alc £21 🍺: Wadworth 6X, Henrys IPA, Bishops Tipple/Summersault 🍷: 20 **Children's Facilities:** Play area Menu/Portions Cutlery Games Highchair Food warming Baby changing **Nearby:** Magicland, Cotswold Water Park, Cotswold Motor Museum & Toy Collection **Notes:** Dogs in bar and garden Garden: Lawn, terrace with views **Parking:** 100

COWLEY
The Green Dragon Inn 🍷
Cockleford Cheltenham GL53 9NW
☎ 01242 870271 🖺 01242 870171
Web: www.buccaneer.co.uk
A handsome stone-built inn dating from the 17th century and located in the Cotswold hamlet of Cockleford. The fittings and furniture are the work of the 'Mouse Man of Kilburn' (so-called for his trademark mouse) who lends his name to the popular Mouse Bar, with its stone-flagged floors, beamed ceilings and crackling log fires. The wide-ranging weekly menu includes sandwiches at lunchtime, children's favourites, and a choice of starters/light meals such as smoked haddock chowder or Caesar salad.
Open: 11-11 (Sun 12-10.30) **Bar Meals:** L served all

week 12-2.30 D served all week 6-10.30 (Sat 12-3, 6-10 Sun 12-3.30, 6-9) Av main course £12.50 **Brewery/Company:** Free House 🍺: Hook Norton, Directors Butcombe, guest ale 🍷: 9 **Children's Facilities:** Licence Menu/Portions Highchair Food warming **Notes:** Dogs allowed in bar, in garden Water **Parking:** 100

FORD
Plough Inn ★★★★ INN ♈
Nr Temple Guiting GL54 5RU
☎ 01386 584215 📄 01386 584042
Email: info@theploughinnatford.co.uk
Web: www.theploughinnatford.co.uk
Dir: *4m from Stow-on-the-Wold on Tewkesbury rd*
This 16th-century inn, steeped in history and character, provides all that one associates with a traditional English pub: flagstone floors, log fires, sturdy pine furnishings and lively conversation. Meals made from local produce are cooked to order, and include half a slow roasted shoulder of lamb, luxury fish pie, and braised beef.
Open: 11-12 (Fri-Sat 11am-1am) Closed: 25 Dec **Bar Meals:** L served all week 12-2 D served all week 6.30-9 (Wknds 12-9) Av main course £9.95 **Restaurant**

Meals: L served all week 11.30-2 D served all week 6.30-9 (Wknds 11.30-9) **Brewery/Company:** Donnington 🍺: Donnington BB, SBA & XXX (summer only) ♈: 7 **Children's Facilities:** Play area (Play fort in garden) Menu/Portions Cutlery Games Highchair Food warming
Nearby: Cotswold Farm Park, Model Village, Birdland
Notes: Garden: Lrg court, beer garden **Parking:** 50

FOSSEBRIDGE
The Inn at Fossebridge ♈
Nr Cheltenham GL54 3JS
☎ 01285 720721 📄 01285 720793
Email: info@fossebridgeinn.co.uk
Web: www.fossebridgeinn.co.uk
Dir: *From M4 junct 15, A419 towards Cirencester, then A429 towards Stow. Pub approx 7m on left*
This attractive family-run free house in the heart of the Coln Valley is ideal for touring Bibury, Northleach and Chedworth. The atmospheric Bridge bar and restaurant is located in the oldest part of the building dating back to the 15th century. Offers varied bar and restaurant menus.
Open: 12-12 (Sun 12-11.30) **Bar Meals:** L served all week 12-3 D served all week 6-10 (Sun 6-9.30) Av main course £11.50 **Restaurant Meals:** L served all

week 12-3 D served all week 6-10 (Sun 6-9.30) Av 3 course alc £2.50 **Brewery/Company:** Free House 🍺: Youngs, Hooky, Old Hooky & 6X ♈: 8 **Children's Facilities:** Menu/Portions Highchair Food warming
Nearby: Cotswold Water, Wildlife & Rare Breeds Parks
Notes: Dogs allowed in bar, Biscuits Garden: 35 acres, food served outside **Parking:** 40

GREAT RISSINGTON
The Lamb Inn ♈
Nr Bourton-on-the-Water Cheltenham GL54 2LP
☎ 01451 820388 📄 01451 820724
Email: enquiries@thelambinn.com
Web: www.thelambinn.com
Dir: *Between Oxford & Cheltenham off A40*
Make this delightful former farmhouse your base for exploring the picturesque Cotswold countryside on foot and touring the region's famous old towns by car. Among the attractions at this inn, parts of which date back 300 years, are part of a Wellington bomber which crashed in the garden in 1943. Serves home-cooked pub food.
Open: 11.30-2.30 6.30-11 **Bar Meals:** L served all week 12-2 D served all week 7-9.30 (Sat-Sun 12-2.30) Av main course £8.95 **Restaurant Meals:** L served all

week 12-2 D served all week 7-9.30 **Brewery/Company:** Free House 🍺: Hook Norton, John Smiths & guest ale ♈: 9 **Children's Facilities:** Play area (Slide) Cutlery Games Highchair Food warming Baby changing
Nearby: Birdland, Model Village **Notes:** Dogs allowed in bar, Water Garden: Food served outside, seats 60 **Parking:** 15

GLOUCESTERSHIRE

GLOUCESTERSHIRE

GREET
The Harvest Home ☐
Evesham Road nr Winchcombe GL54 5BH
☎ 01242 602430
Dir: *M5 junct 9 take A435 towards Evesham, then B4077 & B4078 towards Winchcombe, 200yds from station.*
Set in the beautiful Cotswold countryside, this traditional country inn draws steam train enthusiasts aplenty, as a restored stretch of the Great Western Railway runs past the end of the garden. Built around 1903 for railway workers, the pub is handy for Cheltenham Racecourse and Sudeley Castle. Expect a good range of snacks and mains, including locally-reared beef and tempting seafood dishes.
Open: 12-3 6-11 (Sun 6-10.30) **Bar Meals:** L served all week 12-2 D served all week 6-9 Av main course £8

Restaurant Meals: L served all week 12-2 D served all week 6-9 Av 3 course alc £16.50 **Brewery/Company:** Enterprise Inns ☐: Old Speckled Hen, Goffs Jouster, Deuchars IPA, Carling & Strongbow ☐: 11 **Children's Facilities:** Licence Menu/Portions Cutlery Highchair Food warming **Nearby:** GWR Steam Railway, Sudeley Castle **Notes:** Dogs allowed in bar, in garden, Water **Garden:** Grass area, picnic tables, countryside views **Parking:** 30

GUITING POWER
The Hollow Bottom ★★★ INN ☐
Cheltenham GL54 5UX
☎ 01451 850392 ☐ 01451 850945
Email: hello@hollowbottom.com
Web: www.hollowbottom.com
There's a horse-racing theme at this 18th-century Cotswold free house, often frequented by the Cheltenham racing fraternity. Its nooks and crannies lend themselves to an intimate drink or meal, and there's also a separate dining room, plus outside tables for fine weather. Specials include prawn cocktail on seasonal leaves with a spicy tomato sauce; and grilled salmon.
Open: 11-12.30- **Bar Meals:** L/D served all week 12-9.30 Av main course £10 **Restaurant Meals:** L served all week 12-9.30 **Brewery/Company:** Free House ☐:

Hollow Bottom Best Bitter, Goff's Jouster, Timothy Taylor Landlord, Fullers London Pride, Caledonian IPA ☐: 7 **Children's Facilities:** Licence (High chairs and cots) Menu/Portions Cutlery Games Highchair Food warming Baby changing **Nearby:** Cotswold Farm Park, Sudeley Castle, Cotswold Water Park **Notes:** Dogs allowed in bar, in garden **Garden:** Bench, table, heaters **Parking:** 15

HINTON
The Bull Inn ☐
nr Chippenham SN14 8HG
☎ 0117 9372332
Dir: *From M4 junct 18, A46 to Bath for 1m then right, 1m down hill, Bull on right*
Dating from the 17th century, The Bull has been an inn, a farm and a dairy over the years. Original dishes are prepared from locally sourced suppliers, with home-grown seasonal fruit and vegetables wherever possible. The extensive menu is served in the restaurant and bar.
Open: 12-3 6-11 (Sun 7.30-10.30) **Bar Meals:** L served Tue-Sun 12-2 D served Mon-Sat 6-9 (Fri-Sat 9.30) Av main course £10 **Restaurant Meals:** L served Tue-Sun 12-2 D served Mon-Sat 6-9 (Fri-Sat 9.30) Av 3 course alc £20 **Brewery/Company:** Wadworth ☐:

Wadworth 6X & Henrys IPA, Wadworth Bishops Tipple, Wadworth Summersault plus monthly guest ale ☐: 12 **Children's Facilities:** Play area (Swings, climbing frames, obstacle course) Highchair Food warming **Nearby:** Bristol Zoo, Avon Wild Life Park & Dynham Park House & Gardens **Notes:** Dogs allowed in bar, in garden Garden: Very large **Parking:** 50

LECHLADE ON THAMES
The Trout Inn 🍷

St Johns Bridge GL7 3HA

☎ 01367 252313 📠 01367 252313

Email: chefpjw@aol.com

Web: www.thetroutinn.com

Dir: *From A40 take A361 then A417. From M4 to Lechlade then A417 to Inn*

Dating from around 1220, a former almshouse with a large garden on the banks of the Thames. The interior is all flagstone floors and beams in a bar that overflows into the old boat-house. Appetising small snacks, and dishes like pork fillet in a stilton and bacon sauce are on offer. **Open:** 10-3 6-11 (Open all day summer) Closed: 25 Dec **Bar Meals:** L served all week 12-2 D served all week 7-10 (Sun 7-9.30) Av main course £10.50

Brewery/Company: Unique 🍺: Courage Best, John Smiths, Doom Bar, Bombardier & Guest 🍷: 16 **Children's Facilities:** Fam room Play area Menu/Portions Cutlery Games Highchair Food warming **Nearby:** Buscot House & Gardens & Boat hire on Thames **Notes:** Dogs allowed in bar, Water **Garden:** Food served outside, overlooking Weir Pool **Parking:** 30

LITTLE WASHBOURNE
The Hobnails Inn 🍷

Tewkesbury GL20 8NQ

☎ 01242 620237 📠 01242 620458

Dir: *From M5 junct 9 take A46 towards Evesham then B4077 to Stow-on-the-Wold. Inn 1.5 m on L*

Established in 1473, the Hobnails is one of the oldest inns in the county. Inside you'll find winter log fires, and you can tuck yourself into a private corner, or relax with a pint of ale on one of the leather sofas. A good range of bar snacks is supplemented by a lunchtime carvery and a new fresh fish range. Outside is a lovely large garden for warmer days with views over surrounding countryside. **Open:** 12-2.30 6-11 **Bar Meals:** L served all week 12-2 D served all week 6-9 (Sun 7-9) Av main course £9.95 **Restaurant Meals:** L served Mon-Sun 12-2 D served Mon-Sun 6-9 (Sun 7-9) **Brewery/Company:** Enterprise Inns 🍺: London Pride, Flowers IPA, Hook Norton Best, Deuchars IPA, Tetleys 🍷: 6 **Children's Facilities:** Licence Menu/Portions Cutlery Highchair Food warming **Nearby:** Toddington Steam Railway, Sudeley Castle, Rosley Hall **Notes:** Dogs allowed in bar **Garden:** Large patio area with tables, country views **Parking:** 80

MARSHFIELD
The Lord Nelson Inn 🍷

& 2 High Street Chippenham SN14 8LP

☎ 01225 891820 & 891981

Email: clair.vezey@btopenworld.com

Web: www.thelordnelsoninn.info

Family-run 17th-century coaching inn located in the Cotswolds, in a village on the outskirts of Bath. A friendly atmosphere, various real ales and cosy open fires add to its appeal and character. The Cotswolds are also a haven for hikers and countryside lovers. The menu features medallions of monkfish with a lemon and herb sauce; home-made steak and kidney pudding; and mushroom and goats' cheese filo parcel. **Open:** 12-2.30 5.30-11 (all day Sun) **Bar Meals:** L served all week 12-2 D served all week 6.30-9 (Sun 12-3, 6-9) Av main course £10.95 **Restaurant Meals:** L served all week 12-2 D served all week 6.30-9 (Sun 12-3, 6-9) Av 3 course alc £18.95 **Brewery/Company:** Enterprise Inns 🍺: Courage Best, Bath Gem 🍷: 7 **Children's Facilities:** Menu/Portions Cutlery Games Highchair Food warming **Nearby:** Bowood House, Bristol Zoo, Bath Park **Notes:** Dogs allowed in bar **Garden:** small patio area with seating

MINCHINHAMPTON
The Weighbridge Inn ♀
GL6 9AL
☎ 01453 832520 📄 01453 835903
Email: enquiries@2in1pub.co.uk
Web: www.2in1pub.co.uk
Dir: *Situated between Nailsworth and Avening on the B4014*
Located on the original London to Bristol packhorse trail, this historic 17th-century free house is full of period charm. Inside, the drinking areas are cosy while, outside, the patios and arbours offer good views of the Cotswolds. **Open:** 12-11 (Sun 12-10.30) Closed: 25 Dec & 10 days in Jan **Bar Meals:** L served all week 12-9.30 D served all week 12-9.30 Av main course £9.95 **Restaurant Meals:** L served all week 12-9.30 D served all week 12-9.30 Av 3 course alc £18 🍺: Wadworth 6X, Uley Old Spot & Laurie Lee ♀: 16 **Children's Facilities:** Fam room Menu/Portions Highchair Food warming Baby changing **Nearby:** Westonbirt Arboretum, Minchinhampton Common & Slimbridge Wildfowl Trust **Notes:** Dogs allowed in bar, in garden, Water Garden: Two large patios, heaters, awnings, arbors **Parking:** 50

NAILSWORTH
Egypt Mill ★★ HL ◉ ♀
GL6 0AE
☎ 01453 833449 📄 01453 836098
Email: reception@egyptmill.com
Web: www.egyptmill.com
Dir: *M4 junct 18, A46 N to Stoud. M5 junct 13, A46 to Nailsworth*
Situated in the charming Cotswold town of Nailsworth, this converted corn mill contains many features of great character, including the original millstones and lifting equipment. The refurbished ground floor bar and bistro enjoy a picturesque setting, and its views over the pretty water gardens complete the scene. There is a choice of eating in the bistro or restaurant.
Open: 7-11 **Bar Meals:** L served all week 12-2 D served all week 6.30-9 Av main course £10 **Restaurant Meals:** L served all week 12-2 D served all week 7-9 (Sun food all day) Av 3 course alc £22 **Children's Facilities:** Menu/Portions Cutlery Games Highchair Food warming **Nearby:** Slimbridge Wildfowl & Wetlands Trust, Westonbirt Arboretum, Berkeley Castle **Notes:** Garden: Mill Garden, waterside **Parking:** 100

NAILSWORTH
The Britannia ♀
Cossack Square GL6 0DG
☎ 01453 832501 📄 01453 832010
Email: pheasantpluckers2003@yahoo.co.uk
Web: www.foodclub-uk.com
Dir: *in town centre*
A 17th-century former manor house occupying a position on the south side of Nailsworth's Cossack Square. The interior is bright and uncluttered. Outside there's a pretty garden with plenty of tables, chairs and umbrellas. The brasserie-style menu is an interesting blend of modern British and continental food, with ingredients bought from local suppliers and from Smithfield Market.
Open: 11-11 Closed: 25 Dec **Bar Meals:** L served all week 11-2.45 D served all week 5.30-10 (All day Sun) Av main course £9.95 **Restaurant Meals:** L served all week 11-2.45 D served all week 5.30-10 (Sun all day) **Brewery/Company:** Free House 🍺: Greene King Abbot Ale, Fuller's London pride, Bass, Deuchars IPA ♀: 12 **Children's Facilities:** Menu/Portions Cutlery Games Highchair Food warming **Notes:** Dogs allowed in bar, Water Garden: Heated terrace & lawns **Parking:** 100

NORTH CERNEY
Bathurst Arms 🍷

North Cerney nr Cirencester GL7 7BZ

☎ 01285 831281 📠 01285 831887

Email: chefpilgrim@aol.com

Web: www.thebathurstarms.co.uk

Dir: *5m N of Cirencester on A435*

Former coaching inn, set in a pretty village, with antique settles, flagstone floors, stone fireplaces, beams and panelled walls. The garden stretches down to the River Churn and includes its own boules pitch. A special wine room offers over 100 wines, 10 available by the glass. Fresh fish, local and organic produce feature in dishes such as roast cod fillet, wilted rocket and new potato and chorizo hash; and old spot sausages with mustard mash.

Open: 12-3 6-11 (Sun Eve 7-10.30) **Bar Meals:** L served all week 12-2 D served all week 6-9 (Sun 7-9) Av main course £10 **Restaurant Meals:** L served all week 12-2 D served all week 6-9 (Sun 12-2.30, 7-9 Fri/Sat 6-9.30) Av 3 course alc £20 **Brewery/Company:** Free House 🍺: Hook Norton, Cotswold Way, rotating guest beers 🍷: 10 **Children's Facilities:** Menu/Portions Cutlery Games Highchair Food warming Baby changing **Nearby:** Chedworth Roman Villa, Cotswold Wildlife Park, Cotswold Water Park **Notes:** Dogs allowed in bar, Dog bowl Garden: Riverside with boules pitch **Parking:** 40

OAKRIDGE LYNCH
The Butcher's Arms

Nr Stroud GL6 7NZ

☎ 01285 760371 📠 01285 760602

Dir: *From Stroud take A419, left for Eastcombe. Then follow Bisley signs. Just before Bisley turn right to Oakridge, follow brown signs for pub*

Traditional Cotswold country pub with stone walls, old beams and log fires in the renowned Golden Valley. It was once a slaughterhouse and butcher's shop. A full and varied restaurant menu offers steak, fish and chicken dishes, while the bar menu ranges from ploughman's lunches to home-cooked daily specials.

Open: 11-3 6-11 Closed: 25-26 Dec, 1 Jan **Bar Meals:** L served Tue-Sun 12-2 D served Tue-Sat 6.30-9.30 **Restaurant Meals:** L served Sun 12-3 D served Tue-Sat 7-9 **Brewery/Company:** Free House 🍺: Greene King Abbot Ale, Wickwar BOB, Archers Best, Buttcombe Bitter **Children's Facilities:** Fam room Menu/Portions Highchair Food warming Baby changing **Notes:** Dogs allowed in bar, in garden, No dogs in restaurant Garden: Food served outside, overlooks Golden Valley **Parking:** 50

PAINSWICK
The Falcon Inn 🍷

New Street GL6 6UN

☎ 01452 814222 📠 01452 813377

Email: bleninns@clara.net

Web: www.falconinn.com

Dir: *On A46 in centre of Painswick*

Boasting the world's oldest known bowling green in its grounds, the Falcon dates from 1554 and stands at the heart of a conservation village. For three centuries it was a courthouse, but today its friendly service extends to a drying room for walkers' gear. A sampling of dishes from the menu includes whole trout and almonds; gammon and egg; sirloin steak; chilli crust beef fillet; duck leg confit on a bed of sherry and puy lentils with Madeira sauce; penne pasta arrabiatta; stuffed pork loin with apricot and pistachios; steamed seabass fillet with scallop mousseline; and minted lamb chop with fennel, asparagus and Jerusalem artichoke garnish.

Open: 11-11 (Sun 12-10.30) **Bar Meals:** L served all week 12-2.30 D served all week 7-9.30 Av main course £22 **Restaurant Meals:** L served all week 12-2.30 D served all week 7-9.30 **Brewery/Company:** Free House 🍺: Greene King IPA, Otters Ale, Wye Valley 🍷: 10 **Children's Facilities:** Licence Menu/Portions Highchair Food warming **Nearby:** Painswick Rococo Gardens, Cotswold Wildlife Park **Notes:** Dogs allowed in garden, in bedrooms, Water Garden: Courtyard and large bowling green to rear **Parking:** 35

PAINSWICK
The Royal Oak Inn ♟
St Mary's Street GL6 6QG
☎ 01452 813129
Email: bleninns@clara.net
Web: www.cotswoldinns.co.uk
Dir: *In the centre of Painswick on the A46 between Stroud & Cheltenham*
Tucked away behind the church of this conservation village, the Royal Oak features very low ceilings, old paintings and artefacts, and a huge, open fire. In the summer, a sun-trap rear courtyard contributes to its atmosphere. Food is a mixture of old favourites (Cumberland sausage and mash; cauliflower cheese; beef curry); specials (lamb and apricot casserole; rabbit and leek pie); grills and vegetarian choices.

Open: 11-3 6-11 (Wed-Sun all day (trial basis)) **Bar Meals:** L served all week 12-2.30 D served all week 7-9.30 Av main course £6.50 **Restaurant Meals:** L served all week 12-2.30 D served all week 7-9.30 **Brewery/Company:** Free House 🍺: Black Sheep Bitter, Spitfire, Moles plus Guest Ales ♟: 8 **Children's Facilities:** Menu/Portions Highchair Food warming **Nearby:** Rococo Gardens **Notes:** Dogs allowed in bar, in garden, Water **Garden:** Patio and courtyard, seats 50

SHEEPSCOMBE
The Butchers Arms ♟
Nr Painswick GL6 7RH
☎ 01452 812113 📠 01452 814358
Email: bleninns@clara.net
Web: www.cotswoldinns.co.uk
Dir: *1.5m S of A46 (Cheltenham to Stroud road), N of Painswick*
Originally used to hang and butcher deer hunted by Henry VIII from his royal deer park, this welcoming hostelry benefits from a sun-filled terrace and far-reaching views of the surrounding countryside. Well-known writer Laurie Lee was once a regular customer. A varied menu includes home-made beer-battered cod fillet, and tenderloin of pork among the lunchtime options, while breast of chicken, and medley of fish

kebabs might feature in the evening.
Open: 11.30-2.30 6-11.30 **Bar Meals:** L served all week 12-2.30 D served all week 7-9.30 (Sun 12-9.30) **Restaurant Meals:** L served all week 12-2.30 D served all week 7-9.30 (Sun 12-9.30) **Brewery/Company:** Free House 🍺: Otter Ale, Moles, Wye Valley, Dorothy Goodbodys Summer Ale ♟: 10 **Children's Facilities:** Licence Menu/Portions Highchair Food warming **Nearby** Rococo Gardens, Country Park **Notes:** Dogs allowed in garden, Water **Garden:** Beer garden, food served outdoors, patio **Parking:** 16

SOMERFORD KEYNES
The Bakers Arms ♟
Cirencester GL7 6DN
☎ 01285 861298 📠 01453 832010
Email: pheasantpluckers2003@yahoo.co.uk
Web: www.foodclub-uk.com
Dir: *From Cirencester follow the signs to the Cotswold Water Park. Somerford Keynes is 2m from Cirencester.*
A beautiful chocolate box pub built from Cotswold stone. Somerford Keynes is in the Cotswold Water Park, and the Keynes Park beach is within easy walking distance. The pub offers a balanced, imaginative selection of meals.
Open: 11-12pm **Bar Meals:** L served all week 11-3 D served all week 6-10 (Sun 11-10) Av main course £10
Restaurant Meals: L served all week 11-3 D served all week 6-10 (Sun all Day) Av 3 course alc £19 🍺: Green

King IPA, Abbot Ale, Speckled Hen, Fireside & Brakspear ♟: 12 **Children's Facilities:** Fam room Play area (Outside equipment) Menu/Portions Cutlery Games Highchair Food warming **Nearby:** Keynes Beach, Cotswold Way Walk, Thames Path & Cotswold Water Park **Notes:** Dogs allowed in bar, Water bowl **Garden:** Large mature, terrace with heaters & lighting **Parking:** 60

SOUTHROP
The Swan at Southrop ♟
Nr Lechlade GL7 3NU

☎ 01367 850205 📠 01367 850555

Dir: *Off A361 between Lechlade and Burford*

The Swan is a creeper clad, early 17th-century Cotswold inn with a classic location on the village green at Southrop. This is an area of Gloucestershire, close to the borders of Oxfordshire and Wiltshire, which is renowned for gentle strolls and picturesque country rambles. The inn has recently changed hands and is now run by Graham Williams with Bob Parkinson as chef, both of them formerly of Bibendum in London. Their aim is to provide food of excellent quality at village inn prices. **Open:** 11.30-3.30 6.30-11 **Bar Meals:** L served all week 12-2 D served all week 7-9 **Restaurant Meals:** L served all week 12-2.30 D served all week 7-10 (Closed Sun pm in winter) Av 3 course alc £28 **Brewery/Company:** Free House 🍺: Hook Norton, Wadworth 6X, Timothy Taylor Landlord, Marstons, Adnams Best, guest ale ♟: 10 **Children's Facilities:** Menu/Portions Games Food warming **Nearby:** Cotswold Wildlife Park, Cotswold Farm Park **Notes:** Dogs allowed in bar

STONEHOUSE
The George Inn ★★★ INN
Bath Road Frocester GL10 3TQ

☎ 01453 822302 📠 01453 791612

Email: enquiries@georgeinn.fsnet.co.uk

Web: www.georgeinn.co.uk

Dir: *M5 junct 13, take A419 at 1st rdbt - 3rd exit Eastington, left at next rdbt Frocester. Continue for approx 2m. Inn on left in centre of the village.*

An award-winning 18th-century coaching inn, unspoiled by music or games machines. Instead, cosy log fires and a sunny courtyard garden give the place all-year-round appeal. The Cotswold Way and a network of leafy paths and lanes are on the doorstep. Home-cooked food includes rack of lamb with a red wine and tarragon sauce; tuna steak with lemon vinaigrette; and beef and ale pie, plus a good range of starters and snacks. **Open:** 11.30-2.30 5-11 (Sat-Sun open all day) **Bar Meals:** L served all week 12-2 D served Mon-Sat 6.30-9.30 (Sun carvery 12.30-3) Av main course £8 **Restaurant Meals:** L served all week 12-2 D served Mon-Sat 6.30-9.30 (Sun 12.30-3) **Brewery/Company:** Enterprise Inns 🍺: Blacksheep, Deuchars IPA, Blacksheep & 3 Guest Beers **Children's Facilities:** Menu/Portions Highchair Food warming **Nearby:** Slimbridge Wildfowl and Wetland Trust, Berkeley Castle, Westonbirt Arboretum **Notes:** Garden: Courtyard, boules pitch **Parking:** 25

STOW-ON-THE-WOLD
The Eagle and Child ★★★ HL ◉◉ ♟
GL54 1HY

☎ 01451 830670 📠 01451 870048

Email: enquiries@theroyalisthotel.com

Web: www.theroyalisthotel.co.uk

Dir: *From the A40 take the A429 towards Stow on the Wold turn into town and pub by the green on the left.*

The Eagle and Child, the oldest inn in England, is part of the Royalist Hotel. The site is said to date back to 947AD and was once a hospice to shelter lepers. Historic finds include a 10th-century Saxon shoe, a leper hole, witches' marks in the rooms, a bear pit, thousand-year-old timbers and an ancient frieze. The Eagle and Child is said to come from the crest of the Earl of Derby (16th century), and the last battle of the English Civil War (1646) was in Stow, hence the hotel's name. Digbeth Street is thought to derive from 'duck bath'. The ducks were said to be running down the street bathed in blood from the Royalist casualties. There's a regularly changing choice of beers on offer as well as a good range of snacks and meals. **Open:** 11-11 **Bar Meals:** L served all week 12-2.30 D served all week 6-9.30 (Sat 6-10) Av main course £9.95 **Restaurant Meals:** L served Wed-Sat 12-2.30 D served Wed-Sat 7-9.30 Av 3 course alc £35.95 **Brewery/Company:** Free House 🍺: ♟: 8 **Children's Facilities:** Menu/Portions Cutlery Games Highchair Food warming **Notes:** Dogs allowed in bar, in garden Garden: Small patio area **Parking:** 8

STROUD

Bear of Rodborough Hotel ★★★ HL ◉ ♀

Rodborough Common GL5 5DE

☎ 01453 878522 📄 01453 872523

Email: bookings@cotswold-inns-hotels.co.uk

Web: www.cotswold-inns-hotels.co.uk/index.aspx

Dir: *From M5 junct 13 follow signs for Stonehouse then Rodborough*

Built in the 17th century, this former alehouse stands 600ft above sea level, surrounded by 300 acres of National Trust land. Its name comes from the bear-baiting that used to take place nearby. The restaurant offers a contemporary British menu, so one might start with baby toad-in-the-hole with red wine jus and redcurrant jelly; or poached salmon and citrus salad; continue with Bibury trout; faggots with buttered mash; or wild mushroom risotto; and finish with a dessert from the daily specials. Sandwiches include Single Gloucester cheese with Uley's Old Spot ale and apple chutney. There are two wine lists, one containing a short, modestly priced selection, the other running to the full 60 bins. Outside is a croquet lawn created in the 1920s by a former resident called Edmunds, a partner in a well-known firm of proud Stroud nurserymen.

Open: 10.30-11 **Bar Meals:** L served all week 12-2.30 D served all week 6.30-10 (Sun 12-2, 6.30-9.30) Av main course £9.95 **Restaurant Meals:** D served all week 7-9.30 (Sun 7-9) **Brewery/Company:** Free House 🍺: Uley Bitter, Bob from Wickwar Brewery, Guest ale ♀: 6 **Children's Facilities:** Play area Games Highchair Food warming **Notes:** Dogs allowed in bar, Water Garden: Patio area, next to croquet lawn **Parking:** 175

STROUD

Rose & Crown Inn ♀

The Cross Nympsfield GL10 3TU

☎ 01453 860240 📄 01453 861564

Email: gadros@aol.com

Web: www.roseandcrown-nympsfield.com

Dir: *M5 junct 13 off B4066, SW of Stroud*

An imposing, 400-year-old coaching inn of honey-coloured local stone in the heart of the village close to the Cotswold Way. Inside, the inn's character is preserved with natural stone, wood panelling, a lovely open fire and some local real ales. In the galleried restaurant, main courses include faggots cooked in onion gravy, enchiladas, and salmon en croûte.

Open: 12-11 **Bar Meals:** L served all week 12-9.30 D served all week 6-9.30 **Restaurant Meals:** L served all week 12-9.30 D served all week 6-9.30 **Brewery/Company:** Free House 🍺: Uley, Pigs Ear & Otter ♀: 7 **Children's Facilities:** Licence Play area (Playground, swings, slides, climbing bridge) Highchair Food warming **Notes:** Dogs allowed in bar, in garden, in bedrooms, Water provided Garden: Large, shady, stunning views, safe **Parking:** 20

STROUD

The Ram Inn

South Woodchester GL5 5EL

☎ 01453 873329 📄 01453 873329

Email: jewantsum@aol.com

Dir: *A46 from Stroud to Nailsworth, right after 2m into S.Woodchester (brown tourist signs)*

From the terrace of the 17th-century Cotswold stone Ram there are splendid views over five valleys, although proximity to the huge fireplace may prove more appealing in winter. Rib-eye steak, at least two fish dishes, home-made lasagne and Sunday roasts can be expected, washed down by regularly changing real ales such as Uley Old Spot, Wickwar BOB and Archer's Golden. The Stroud Morris Men regularly perform here.

Open: 11-11 (Sun 12-10.30) **Bar Meals:** L served all week 12-2.30 D served all week 6-9.30 (Sun 12-2.30, 6-8.30) Av main course £7 **Restaurant Meals:** L served all week 12-2.30 D served all week 6-9.30 (Sun 12-2.30, 6-8.30) **Brewery/Company:** Free House 🍺: Uley Old Spot, Otter Brewery, Archers Village, Whittingtons Cats Whiskers & Nine Lives **Children's Facilities:** Fam room Menu/Portions Cutlery Highchair Food warming Baby changing **Nearby:** Westonbirt Aboretum, Slimbridge Bird Sanctuary, Owlpen Manor **Notes:** Dogs allowed in bar, in garden, Water Garden: 2 large Patio areas, seats approx 120 people **Parking:** 60

TETBURY

Gumstool Inn ♜

Calcot Manor GL8 8YJ

☎ 01666 890391 📄 01666 890394

Email: reception@calcotmanor.co.uk

Web: www.calcotmanor.co.uk

Dir: *3m W of Tetbury*

The Calcot Manor Hotel, of which the Gumstool forms part, is a charmingly converted 14th-century English farmhouse built of Cotswold stone by Cistercian monks. Of the two places to eat, the Conservatory Restaurant is truly stylish, while the Gumstool itself, although making a similar impact, is arguably cosier. The varied menu changes monthly.
Open: 11.30-2.30 5.30-11 (Sat 11.30-11, Sun 12-10.30) **Bar Meals:** L served all week 12-2 D served all week 7-9.30 **Restaurant Meals:** L served all week 12-2 D served all week 7-9.30 **Brewery/Company:** Free House 🍺: Wickwar BOB, Sharps Doom Bar, Fullers London Pride, Butcombe ♜: 12 **Children's Facilities:** Fam room (Ofsted registered playzone) Cutlery Games Highchair Food warming **Nearby:** Slimbridge, Bowood, Cotswold Wildlife Park **Parking:** 100

TEWKESBURY

The Fleet Inn ♜

Twyning GL20 6FL

☎ 01684 274310 📄 01684 291612

Email: enquiries@fleet-inn.co.uk

Web: www.fleet-inn.co.uk

Idyllically located on the banks of the River Avon, this 15th-century pub with restaurant has lawns and large patios. The traditional bars and themed areas provide a wide range of dishes. Produce is locally sourced, and all meats come from a local Master Butcher. Dishes include lamb shank, gourmet sausages, traditional battered cod, and Admiral's fish pie. Boules court for teens and older, and pets' corner for the little ones.
Open: 11-11 **Bar Meals:** L served all week 12-2.30 D served all week 6-9.30 Av main course £8.50 **Restaurant Meals:** L served 12-2.30 D served 6-9 Av 3 course alc £20 **Brewery/Company:** Enterprise Inns 🍺: Boddingtons, Greene King Abbot Ale & Old Speckled Hen, Wells Bombardier , Fullers London Pride, Banks Bitter ♜: 7 **Children's Facilities:** Play area (Changing room, swings and pets corner) Menu/Portions Games Highchair Food warming Baby changing **Notes:** Garden: Patios and water front garden **Parking:** 50

TODENHAM

The Farriers Arms ♜

Main Street Moreton-in-Marsh GL56 9PF

☎ 01608 650901 📄 01608 650403

Email: louise@farriersarms.com

Web: www.farriersarms.com

Dir: *3m from Moreton-in-Marsh, turn right to Todenham at N end of Moreton-in-Marsh*

Set in the very heart of the Cotswolds, adjacent to the old village smithy and just three miles from Moreton-in-Marsh, this cheery traditional pub has all the features you'd associate with the country local. There are plenty of books, games and colouring materials for younger visitors. The pub prides itself on its food. Lunch and evening bar snacks include olives, houmous and crusty bread; goats' cheese and red onion tart; and filled baguettes. A full meal could include dishes such as home-cured gravadlax with horseradish and mustard cream, followed by roasted pork tenderloin wrapped in Parma ham and served on Lyonnaise potatoes with stilton and cider sauce.
Open: 12-3 6.30-11.20 (Sun open at 7) **Bar Meals:** L served all week 12-2 D served all week 7-9 (Fri-Sat 7-9.30) Av main course £10 **Restaurant Meals:** L served all week 12-2 D served all week 7-9 (Fri-Sat 7-9.30) **Brewery/Company:** Free House 🍺: Hook Norton Best, Archers Golden, Wye Valley Butty Bach, Timothy Taylor Landlord, Black Sheep ♜: 11 **Children's Facilities:** Fam room Cutlery Games Highchair Food warming **Nearby:** Batsford Arboretum, Cotswold Farm Park **Notes:** Dogs allowed in bar, Water bowl Garden: Landscaped garden with seating **Parking:** 18

TORMARTON

Compass Inn ★★ HL 🍷

Nr Badminton GL9 1JB

☎ 01454 218242 📠 01454 218741

Email: info@compass-inn.co.uk

Web: www.compass-inn.co.uk

Dir: *From M4 junct 18 take A46 N towards Stroud. After 200mtrs take first right then turn towards Tormarton village, continue for 300mtrs*

A traditional pub - in the same family for 45 years - with extensive facilities including an orangery, 26 bedrooms and space for functions. It is set in five and a half acres of beautiful grounds right on the Cotswold Way. Light bites include jacket potatoes and sandwiches, while the bar menu offers home-cooked dishes (lamb curry, spinach and ricotta ravioli) and specials from the blackboard. There is also a daily carte in the restaurant.

Open: 7-11 Closed: 25-26 Dec **Bar Meals:** L served all week 11-10 D served all week 7-10 Av main course £11.50 **Restaurant Meals:** L served all week D served all week 7-10 Av 3 course alc £22.50 **Brewery/Company:** Free House 🍺: Interbrew Bass & Butcombe, Butcombe Gold 🍷: 7 **Children's Facilities:** Menu/Portions Highchair Food warming Baby changing **Nearby:** Bowood House, Dyrham House, Bristol Zoo **Notes:** Dogs allowed in bar, in garden, in bedrooms, Water Garden: Beer garden & 55 acres of grounds **Parking:** 200

WINCHCOMBE

The White Hart Inn and Restaurant 🍷

High Street Cheltenham GL54 5LJ

☎ 01242 602359 📠 01242 602703

Email: enquiries@the-white-hart-inn.com

Web: www.the-white-hart-inn.com

Dir: *in centre of Winchcombe on B4632*

A traditional 16th-century coaching inn with a Swedish twist, the White Hart has been refurbished to offer a beamed bar and Swedish-style restaurant. Enjoy snacks (antipasti, olives), a pizza or a Swedish hotdog at the bar - followed by an Italian ice-cream dessert. Dinner in the restaurant could be Scandinavian seafood platter; or pan-fried cod with red caviar mashed potato.

Open: 8-midnight Closed: 25 Dec **Bar Meals:** L served all week 11-10 D served all week 6-10 **Restaurant Meals:** L served all week 11-10 D served all week 6-10 Av 3 course alc £25 🍺: Archers Golden, Uley Old Spot, Whittingtons Cats Whiskers, Greene King IPA, Wadworth 6X, Old Speckled Hen 🍷: 8 **Children's Facilities:** Licence Menu/Portions Cutlery Games Highchair Food warming Baby changing **Nearby:** Sudeley Castle, Cotswold Farm Park, Gloucestershire Steam Railway **Notes:** Dogs allowed in bar, Bowls, towels Garden: Patio area **Parking:** 12

WITHINGTON

The Mill Inn

GL54 4BE

☎ 01242 890204 📠 01242 890195

Dir: *3m from the A40 between Cheltenham & Oxford*

This traditional inn has been serving travellers for over 400 years from its position beside the River Coln in a deep Cotswold valley. Inside are stone-flagged floors, oak panelling and log fires, whilst outside is a lawned garden with 40 tables, providing a peaceful setting for a drink or meal. The menu has a good fish content, including seafood medley, battered cod, and stuffed plaice.

Open: 11.30-3 6.30-11 (Open all day high season, Sun 12-3, 6.30-10.30) **Bar Meals:** L served all week 12-2 D served all week 6-9 Av main course £8 **Brewery/Company:** Samuel Smith 🍺: Samuel Smith Old Brewery Bitter, Samuel Smith Sovereign **Children's Facilities:** Fam room (Baby changing facilities) Highchair Food warming Baby changing **Nearby:** Cotswold Farm Park, Magic Land, Cotswold Wildlife Park **Notes:** Dogs allowed in garden, in bedrooms, water, biscuits Garden: Lawned with 60 tables, trees and river **Parking:** 65

WOODCHESTER
The Old Fleece ♀

Bath Road Rooksmoor GL5 5NB

☎ 01453 872582 📠 01453 832010

Email: pheasantpluckers2003@yahoo.co.uk

Web: www.foodclub-uk.com

Dir: *2m S of Stroud on the A46*

Delightful coaching inn dating back to the 18th century and built of Cotswold stone with a traditional stone roof. Owners Nick and Christophe are passionate about their pub and are well-known for fine fresh food and customer comforts. Predominantly French chefs prepare quality, freshly produced dishes seven days a week and ingredients are sourced locally or directly - London for meat and Bristol and Birmingham for vegetables and fish.

Open: 11-11 Closed: 25 Dec **Bar Meals:** L served all week 11-2.45 D served all week 5.30-10 (Sat-Sun all day) **Restaurant Meals:** L served all week 11-2.45 D served all week 5.30-10 (Sat-Sun all day) 🍺: Interbrew Boddington & Bass, Greene King Abbot Ale ♀: 12

Children's Facilities: Menu/Portions Cutlery Games Highchair Food warming **Notes:** Dogs allowed in bar, in garden **Garden:** Heated terrace **Parking:** 40

APPLEY
The Globe Inn

Nr Wellington TA21 0HJ

☎ 01823 672327

Web: www.theglobeinnappley.co.uk

Dir: *From M5 junct 26 take A38 towards Exeter. Village signed in 5m*

This quirky slate and cob-built pub on the Somerset-Devon border is 500 years old, and is known for its large collection of Corgi and Dinky cars, Titanic memorabilia, and old advertising posters and enamel signs from the 20s, 30s and 40s. As far as the food goes, you might be offered duck in Madeira sauce, venison pie with bacon, mushrooms and shallots; Moroccan lamb; or sea bass with chive and lime butter.

Open: 11-3 6.30-12 **Bar Meals:** L served Tue-Sun 12-2 D served Tue-Sun 7-9.30 Av main course £10 **Restaurant Meals:** L served Tue-Sun D served Tue-Sun 7-9.30 **Brewery/Company:** Free House 🍺: Palmers Copper Ale, Palmers 200, Exmoor Ales, Sharps & Butcombe Ales **Children's Facilities:** Play area (Climbing frame) Menu/Portions Cutlery Highchair Food warming Baby changing **Notes:** Garden: Large garden overlooking countryside **Parking:** 30

ASHCOTT
Ring O'Bells ♀

High Street Bridgwater TA7 9PZ

☎ 01458 210232

Email: info@ringobells.com

Web: www.ringobells.com

Dir: *From M5 follow signs A39 & Glastonbury. N off A39 at post office follow signs to church and village hall*

The oldest parts of this traditional village pub date from 1750, with beams and an old fireplace to prove it. It is run by three partners as a real family concern, and has won many awards for its quality ales, good food and friendly service. All dishes are made on the premises, with a daily specials board to supplement the menu. Options might include chicken and coriander pie, Moroccan lamb with couscous, pork chop with chilli and apricot stuffing. Look out for the collection of bells and horse brasses

Open: 12-3 7-11 (Sun 7-10.30) Closed: 25 Dec **Bar Meals:** L served all week 12-2 D served all week 7-10 Av main course £7.50 **Restaurant Meals:** L served all week 12-2 D served all week 7-10 Av 3 course alc £16 **Brewery/Company:** Free House 🍺: Guest beers ♀: 7 **Children's Facilities:** Play area (swings, slide, climbing frame, boxed games) Menu/Portions Cutlery Games Highchair Food warming **Nearby:** Clarks Village, Peat Moors Visitor Centre, Glastonbury **Notes:** Garden: Large, enclosed garden, grass, patio **Parking:** 25

SOMERSET

ASHILL
Square & Compass

Windmill Hill Nr Ilminster TA19 9NX

☎ 01823 480467

Web: www.squareandcompasspub.com

Dir: *Turn off A358 at Stewley Cross service station (Ashill) 1m along Wood Road, behind service station*

There's a warm, friendly atmosphere at this traditional free house, beautifully located overlooking the Blackdown Hills in the heart of rural Somerset. Lovely gardens make the most of the views, and the refurbished bar area features hand-made settles and tables. A good choice of home-cooked food, including beef casserole with cheesy dumplings; tasty shortcrust game pie; and duck breast with port and orange sauce. The barn next door is regularly used as a music venue.

Open: 12-2.30 6.30-11 (Sun 7-11) **Closed:** 25-26 Dec **Bar Meals:** L served all week 12-2 D served all week 7-10 Av main course £6.95 **Brewery/Company:** Free House ◧: Exmoor Ale & Gold Moor Withy Cutter, Wadworth 6X, Branscombe Bitter, Exmoor Ale, WHB, HSD **Children's Facilities:** Menu/Portions Cutlery Highchair Food warming Baby changing **Nearby:** Yeovilton Aircraft Museum, Haynes Motor Museum & Cricket St Thomas Wildlife Park **Notes:** Dogs allowed in bar Garden: Very large garden, patio area, amazing views **Parking:** 30

BECKINGTON
Woolpack Inn ♀

Bath BA11 6SP

☎ 01373 831244 🖹 01373 831223

Email: 6534@grenneking.co.uk

Dir: *Just off A36 near junction with A361*

Standing on a corner in the middle of the village, this charming, stone-built coaching inn dates back to the 1500s. Inside there's an attractive, flagstoned bar and outside at the back, a delightful terraced garden. The lunch menu offers soup and sandwich platters, and larger dishes such as home-made sausages and mash; fresh herb and tomato omelette; steak and ale pie; and beer-battered cod and chips. Some of these are also listed on the evening bar menu.

Open: 11-11 (Sun 12-10.30) **Bar Meals:** L served all week 12-2.30 D served all week 6.30-9.30 (Sun 6.30-9) Av main course £10.95 **Restaurant Meals:** L served Sun 12-2.30 D served all week 6.30-9.30 Av 3 course alc £20 **Brewery/Company:** Old English Inns & Hotels ◧: Greene King IPA, Abbot Ale, guest beer ♀: 8 **Children's Facilities:** Menu/Portions Cutlery Games Highchair Food warming **Notes:** Dogs allowed in bar Garden: Terrace garden **Parking:** 12

BLUE ANCHOR
The Smugglers

Minehead TA24 6JS

☎ 01984 640385 🖹 01984 641697

Email: simonandsuzie@aol.com

Web: www.take2chefs.co.uk

Dir: *Off A3191, midway between Minehead and Watchet*

Reputedly linked to the local abbey by an underground tunnel, this 300-year-old inn stands just yards from Blue Anchor's sandy bay. Winter fires warm the eating areas and, in fine weather, diners spill out into the large walled garden. The Cellar Bar menu features a range of sandwiches, fish dishes and grills, as well as salads with hot buttered new potatoes. There's comfort food, too: English lamb with smoked bacon and thyme-scented mash is typical.

Open: 12-11 (Closed from 1 Nov-Etr, Open 3-6 on w/days) **Bar Meals:** L served all week 12-11 D served all week 12-11 Av main course £8.50 **Restaurant Meals:** L served Sun 12-3 D served Thu-Sun 7-10 Av 3 course alc £23.95 **Brewery/Company:** Free House ◧: Smuggled Otter, Otter Ale ♀: 6 **Children's Facilities:** Licence Play area (Bouncy castle) Menu/Portions Cutlery Highchair Food warming **Nearby:** Home Farm, West Somerset Steam Railway **Notes:** Dogs allowed in bar, Water Garden: Large, well maintained walled garden, benches **Parking:** 30

BUTLEIGH

The Rose & Portcullis ♇
Sub Road nr Glastonbury BA6 8TQ
☎ 01458 850287 📠 01458 850120
Web: www.roseandportcullis.com

This stone built 16th-century free house takes its name from the coat of arms granted to the local lord of the manor. Thatched bars and an inglenook fireplace are prominent features of the cosy interior; there's also a skittle alley, garden, and children's play area. Grills and traditional pub favourites like ham, egg and chips rub shoulders on the menu with more adventurous fare: oriental duck with ginger and honey; and lentil moussaka are typical choices.

Open: 12-3 6-11 **Bar Meals:** L served all week 12-2 D served all week 7-9 **Restaurant Meals:** L served all week 12-2 D served all week 7-9 **Brewery/Company:** Free House 🍺: Interbrew Flowers IPA, Butcombe Bitter, Archers Best ♇: 7 **Children's Facilities:** Play area Highchair Food warming **Notes:** Dogs allowed in bar **Parking:** 50

CLUTTON

The Hunters Rest ★★★★ INN ♇
King Lane Clutton Hill BS39 5QL
☎ 01761 452303 📠 01761 453308
Email: info@huntersrest.co.uk
Web: www.huntersrest.co.uk
Dir: *Follow signs for Wells A37 through village of Pensford, at large rdbt turn left towards Bath, after 100mtrs right into country lane, pub 1m up hill*

The views from the Hunters Rest over the Cam Valley to the Mendip Hills and across the Chew Valley to Bristol are breathtaking. The pub offers good home-made food.

Open: 11.30-3 6-11 (All day Sun) **Bar Meals:** L served all week 12-2 D served all week 6.30-9.45 (Sun 12-9) Av main course £8 **Restaurant Meals:** L served all week 12-2 D served all week 6.30-9.45 (Sun 12-9) **Brewery/Company:** Free House 🍺: Interbrew Bass, Otter Ale, Sharps Own, Hidden Quest & Butcombe ♇: 14 **Children's Facilities:** Fam room Play area (Play area with swing, slides etc) Menu/Portions Cutlery Games Highchair Food warming Baby changing **Notes:** Dogs allowed in bar, in garden, Water **Garden:** Large landscaped areas with country views **Parking:** 80

COMBE HAY

The Wheatsheaf ♇
Bath BA2 7EG
☎ 01225 833504 📠 01225 833504
Email: pauldolan@btinternet.com
Web: www.wheatsheafcombehay.co.uk
Dir: *From Bath take A369 (Exeter road) to Odd Down, left at park towards Combe Hay. Follow for 2m to thatched cottage & turn left*

Just south of Bath, this pretty black and white timbered free house nestles on a peaceful hillside close to the route of the former Somerset Coal Canal.

Open: 10.30-3 6-11 (Fri-Sat 11-11, Sun 12-10.30) **Closed:** 25-26 Dec and first two weeks in January **Bar Meals:** L served all week 12-2.30 D served all week 6.30-9.30 Av main course £10 **Restaurant Meals:** L served all week 12-2 D served all week 6.30-9.30 **Brewery/Company:** Free House 🍺: Speckled Hen, Barnstormer, Doom Bar, Tunnel Vision ♇: 6 **Children's Facilities:** Play area (Large area in pub field) Menu/Portions Highchair Food warming **Notes:** Dogs allowed in bar, Dogs on leads **Garden:** Large south facing garden & 50 tables **Parking:** 100

CORTON DENHAM
The Queens Arms ♀

DT9 4LR
☎ 01963 220317
Email: relax@thequeensarms.com
Web: www.thequeensarms.com
Dir: *A303 take Chapel Cross turn-off signed Sutton Montis. Follow signs for South Cadbury continue on road for 25m. Left turn signed Sherborne & Corton Denham. Left at top of hill. Pub at end of village on right*
Drink is taken seriously in this smart, ivy-covered pub, where locally brewed ales and Somerset ciders sit alongside a good selection of tapped and bottled beers and an imaginative range of wines and whiskies. Corton Denham is an ancient village surrounded by beautiful countryside just three miles from the historic town of Sherborne, whose castles, abbey and boutiques are well worth a visit. The pub is an ideal base for walkers and holidaymakers, and children are well catered for with giant sized games and a fun, healthy menu. For adults, there is an imaginative, well-priced selection of British greats.
Open: 11-3 6-11 (Open all day Sat/Sun & BHs) **Bar Meals:** L served all week 12-3 D served all week 6-10 (Sun 12-3.30, 6-9.30) **Restaurant Meals:** L served all week 12-3 D served all week 6-10 (Sun 12-3.30, 6-9.30) Av 3 course alc £18 **Brewery/Company:** Free House ◔: Artois Bock, Butcombe, Tim Taylor, Bath Spa & Bath Organic Lager ♀: 10 **Children's Facilities:** Play area (Children's games) Menu/Portions Cutlery Games Highchair Food warming **Nearby:** Yeovilton Air Museum & Haynes Motor Museum **Notes:** Dogs allowed in bar, Water bowl **Parking:** 12

CREWKERNE
The Manor Arms ★★★ INN ♀

North Perrott TA18 7SG
☎ 01460 72901 📄 01460 74055
Email: bookings@manorarmshotel.co.uk
Web: www.manorarmshotel.co.uk
Dir: *From A30 (Yeovil/Honiton) take A3066 towards Bridport. North Perrott 1.5m*
On the Dorset-Somerset border, this 16th-century Grade II listed pub and its neighbouring hamstone cottages overlook the village green. The popular River Parrett trail runs by the door. The inn has been lovingly restored and an inglenook fireplace, flagstone floors and oak beams are among the charming features inside. Bar food includes fillet steak medallions, pan-fried whole plaice, shank of lamb, and chicken supreme.
Open: 11-11 (Sun 12-10.30) **Bar Meals:** L served all week 12-2 D served all week 7-9.30 Av main course £6 **Restaurant Meals:** L served all week 12-2 D served all week 7-9.30 **Brewery/Company:** Free House ◔: Butcombe, Otter, Fullers London Pride, 5 guest ales ♀: 8 **Children's Facilities:** Fam room Menu/Portions Cutlery Games Highchair Food warming **Nearby:** Cricket St Thomas, Fern Animal Farm, **Notes:** Garden: Secluded lawn, Large wooden tables **Parking:** 30

CROWCOMBE
Carew Arms ♀

Taunton TA4 4AD
☎ 01984 618631 📄 01984 618428
Email: info@thecarewarms.co.uk
Web: www.thecarewarms.co.uk
Dir: *10m from both Taunton and Minehead, off A358.*
Situated in The Quantock Hills, the Carew Arms has been welcoming travellers since the 16th century. The pub owes its name to the Carew family, who became lords of the manor in Queen Elizabeth I's reign. Backed up by a strong team, chef/proprietor Reg Ambrose devises creative menus that suit all.
Open: 11-3 6-11 (Apr-Sep phone for details) **Bar Meals:** L served all week 12-2 D served all week 7-9.30 Av main course £10 **Restaurant Meals:** L served all week 12-2.30 D served Mon-Sat 7-10 Av 3 course alc £22 ◔: Exmoor Ale, Otter Ale, Cotleigh Ales ♀: 8 **Children's Facilities:** Menu/Portions Highchair Food warming Baby changing **Nearby:** Tropiquaria, Butlins Minehead **Notes:** Dogs allowed in bar, in garden, in bedrooms Garden: Beautiful garden with countryside views **Parking:** 40

DINNINGTON
Dinnington Docks
TA17 8SX

☎ 01460 52397 🖹 01460 52397

Email: hilary@dinningtondocks.co.uk

Dir: *On A303 between South Petherton & Ilminster*

This welcoming and traditional village pub on the old Fosse Way has been licensed for over 250 years. Rail or maritime enthusiasts will enjoy the large collection of memorabilia, and it's an ideal location for cycling and walking. The pub is well known for the quality of its cask ales, and farmhouse cider is also available. A varied selection of freshly prepared food is available every lunchtime and evening, made using local produce wherever possible.

Open: 11.30-3.30 6-12 **Bar Meals:** L served all week 12-2.30 D served all week 6-9.30 (Sun 7-9.30) Av main course £5 **Restaurant Meals:** L served all week 12-2.30 D served all week 6-9.30 (Sun 7-9.30) Av 3 course alc £12.50 **Brewery/Company:** Free House 🍺: Butcombe Bitter, Wadworth 6X, Guest Ales **Children's Facilities:** Fam room Play area (climbing frame, swings) Menu/Portions Cutlery Highchair Food warming **Nearby:** Cricket St Thomas Wildlife Park, Fleet Air Arm Museum, Haynes Motor Museum **Notes:** Dogs allowed in bar, in garden, Water provided Garden: Large garden **Parking:** 30

EAST COKER
The Helyar Arms ★★★★ INN ◉ ♉
Moor Lane BA22 9JR

☎ 01935 862332 🖹 01935 864129

Email: info@helyar-arms.co.uk

Web: www.helyar-arms.co.uk

Dir: *3m from Yeovil. Take A57 or A30 and follow signs for East Coker*

This charmingly 15th-century inn was reputedly named after Archdeacon Helyar, a chaplain to Queen Elizabeth I. A Grade II listed building, it dates back in part to 1468. Log fires warm the old world bar, and the restaurant has been restored from an original apple loft. The kitchen makes full use of local produce, especially cheeses, beef and bread. Bar snacks include speciality sandwiches and ploughman's lunches, while starters on the main menu could include a smoked fish platter. Follow with the likes of roast chicken breast with apricot stuffing, green beans, Lyonnaise potatoes and tarragon cream sauce;

Open: 11-3 6-11 (Sun 12-10.30) **Bar Meals:** L served all week 12-2.30 D served all week 6.30-9.30 (Sun 12-4.30, 6.30-9) Av main course £10 **Restaurant Meals:** L served all week 12-2.30 D served all week 6.30-9.30 (Sun 12-4.30, 6.30-9) Av 3 course alc £24 **Brewery/Company:** Punch Taverns 🍺: Butcombe Bitter, Doom Bar Bitter, Greene King IPA ♉: 30 **Children's Facilities:** Fam room (Basket of toys/books) Menu/Portions Cutlery Games Highchair Food warming **Nearby:** Cricket St Thomas, Yeovilton Fleet Air Museum, Haynes Motor Museum **Notes:** Dogs allowed in bar, in garden, in bedrooms Garden: Grassed area seats 40 **Parking:** 40

EXFORD
The Crown Hotel ★★★ HL ◉◉ ♉
Exmoor National Park TA24 7PP

☎ 01643 831554 🖹 01643 831665

Email: info@crownhotelexmoor.co.uk

Web: www.crownhotelexmoor.co.uk

Dir: *From M5 junct 25 follow Taunton signs. Take A358 then B3224 via Wheddon Cross to Exford*

This 17th-century pub, reputedly Exmoor's oldest, is set in three acres of water gardens and woodland. The characterful bar with its log fire is very much the hub of village life. Bar food includes lunchtime sandwiches and baguettes or soup. The smart dining room is the setting for serious dining from a gourmet menu, using quality ingredients, sourced locally where possible

Open: 11-3 6-11 (Apr-Sep 11-11) **Bar Meals:** L served all week 12-2 D served all week 6.30-9.30 Av main course £7.50 **Restaurant Meals:** D served all week 7-9 Av 3 course alc £25 **Brewery/Company:** Free House 🍺: Exmoor Ale, Ansells, Worthingtons & Wild Cat ♉: 8 **Children's Facilities:** Menu/Portions Cutlery Highchair Food warming **Nearby:** Falcon Centre & Coast **Notes:** Dogs allowed in bar, in garden **Parking:** 20

SOMERSET

FRESHFORD
The Inn at Freshford 🍷
Bath BA2 6EG
☎ 01225 722250 📠 01225 723887
Dir: *1m from A36 between Beckington & Limpley Stoke*
With its 15th-century origins, and log fires adding to its warm and friendly atmosphere, this popular inn in the Limpley Valley is an ideal base for walking, especially along the Kennet & Avon Canal. Extensive gardens. The à la carte menu changes weekly to show the range of food available, and a daily specials board and large children's menu complete the variety. Typical home-made dishes are pâtés, steak and ale pie, lasagne and desserts; a nice selection of fish dishes includes fresh local trout.
Open: 11-3 6-11 (Sun 7-11) **Bar Meals:** L served all week 12-2 D served all week 6-9 Av main course £10 **Restaurant Meals:** L served all week 12-2 D served all week 6-9 Av 3 course alc £20 **Brewery/Company:** Latona Leisure Ltd 🍺: Butcombe Bitter, Courage Best & Guest ale 🍷: 12 **Children's Facilities:** Menu/Portions Highchair Food warming Baby changing **Nearby:** Country Park, Leisure Centre **Notes:** Dogs allowed in bar, in garden, Water **Garden:** Large terraced **Parking:** 60

HINTON BLEWETT
Ring O'Bells 🍷
BS39 5AN
☎ 01761 452239 📠 01761 451245
Email: jonjenssen@btinternet.com
Web: www.ringobells.net
Dir: *11m S of Bristol on A37 toward Wells, small road signed in Clutton & Temple Cloud*
On the edge of the Mendips, this 200-year-old pub offers good views of the Chew Valley. An all-year-round cosy atmosphere is boosted by a log fire in winter, and a wide choice of real ales. The bar-loving shove ha'penny players attract a good following. Good value dishes include beef in Guinness served in a giant Yorkshire pudding, and chicken breast with stilton and bacon. Baguettes, sandwiches and ploughman's also available.
Open: 11-3.30 5-11 (Sat 11-4 6-11, Sun 12-4 7-10.30) **Bar Meals:** L served all week 12-2 D served all week 6.30-10 **Restaurant Meals:** L served all week 12-2 D served all week 7-10 (Sat 12-2.30, 12-2.30) **Brewery/Company:** Free House 🍺: Butcombe, Fuller's London Pride, Badger Tanglefoot, Gem **Children's Facilities:** Play area (Enclosed garden with 'Little Tykes' playhouse) Menu/Portions Highchair Food warming **Nearby:** Cheddar Gorge, Chew Valley Lake, Roman Baths **Notes:** Dogs allowed in bar, Water **Garden:** Enclosed garden with lovely views **Parking:** 20

HINTON ST GEORGE
The Lord Poulett Arms ★★★★ INN 🍷
High Street TA17 8SE ☎ 01460 73149
Email: steveandmichelle@lordpoulettarms.com
Web: www.lordpoulettarms.com
Dir: *2m N of Crewkerne, 1.5m S of A303*
Fronting the street in one of Somerset's most beautiful and peaceful villages, is this stone-built, thatched pub. Built in 1680, it has been excellently restored by owners, Michelle Paynton and Steve Hill. Menus are inventive. You can dine in the wild flower meadow, admire the ancient fives wall or play boules on the lavender-edged piste. Somerset ales are served straight from the barrel, and ciders direct from the jug.
Open: 12-3 6.30-11 **Bar Meals:** L served all week 12-2 D served all week 7-9 Av main course £12 **Restaurant Meals:** L served all week 12-2 D served all week 7-9 Av 3 course alc £22 🍺: Hopback, Branscombe, Cotleigh, Archers, Sharps & Changing Guest Beers 🍷: 7 **Children's Facilities:** Menu/Portions Highchair Food warming **Notes:** Dogs allowed in bar, in garden **Garden:** Garden with fruit trees and Poleta wall **Parking:** 10

LCHESTER

lchester Arms ★★★★ INN

The Square BA22 8LN

01935 840220 01935 841353

Email: ilchester@yahoo.co.uk

Web: www.ilchester-arms-hotel.co.uk

Dir: *From A303 take A37 to Ilchester/Yeovil, left towards Ilchester at 2nd sign marked Ilchester. Hotel 100yds on right*

First licensed in 1686, this elegant Georgian building was owned between 1962 and 1985 by the man who developed Ilchester cheese. Brendan McGee, the head chef, and his wife Lucy are well settled in now, enabling Brendan to create an extensive bistro menu offering pan-fried fillet of red snapper, rich lamb casserole, and vegetable moussaka. A selection of sandwiches, paninis, salads, the house burger, and beef and ale pie are available at the bar.

Open: 11-11 Closed: 26 Dec **Bar Meals:** L served all week 12-2.30 D served Mon-Sat 7-9.30 (Sun 12-2.30) Av main course £11.50 **Restaurant Meals:** L served all week 12-2.30 D served Mon-Sat 7-9.30 (Sun 12-2.30) Av 3 course alc £21.50 **Brewery/Company:** Free House : Carling, Stella Artois, Butcombe, Flowers IPA, London Pride & regularly changing ales from local breweries : 12 **Children's Facilities:** Licence Fam room Play area (Wendy house in garden with toys) Menu/Portions Cutlery Games Highchair Food warming Baby changing **Nearby:** Air Fleet Museum, Wookey Hole, Haynes Motor Museum **Notes:** Garden: Paved & terraced enclosed garden **Parking:** 15

LMINSTER

New Inn

Dowlish Wake TA19 0NZ

01460 52413

Web: www.newinn-somerset.co.uk

Dir: *From Ilminster follow signs for Kingstone then Dowlish Wake*

A 350-year-old stone-built pub tucked away in a quiet village close to Perry's thatched cider mill. There are two bars with woodburning stoves, and a games room with bar billiards and a dart board. In the garden is a water feature, shady trees and a skittle alley. The menu features local produce and West Country specialities, including fish, steaks and home-made pies. There's a good vegetarian choice, along with ploughmans' and light bites.

Open: 11-3 6-11 **Bar Meals:** L served all week 12-2.30 D served Mon-Sat 6-9.30 Av main course £7 **Restaurant Meals:** L served all week 12-2.30 D served Mon-Sat 6-9.30 Av 3 course alc £20 **Brewery/Company:** Enterprise Inns : Butcombe Bitter, Otter & Speckled Hen **Children's Facilities:** Licence Fam room Menu/Portions Cutlery Highchair Food warming **Notes:** Dogs allowed in bar Garden: Picturesque, secluded & food served outside **Parking:** 50

KILVE

The Hood Arms ★★★★ INN

Nr Williton TA5 1EA

01278 741210 01278 741477

Email: easonhood@aol.com

Web: www.thehoodarms.co.uk

Dir: *From M5 junct 23/24 follow A39 to Kilve. Located between Bridgwater & Minehead on edge of Exmoor.*

This traditional, friendly 17th-century coaching inn is set among the Quantock Hills and provides thirsty walkers with traditional ales and a good range of dishes.

Open: 11-3 6-11 (Winter Sun-Mon 6-10) **Bar Meals:** L served all week 12-2.30 D served all week 6.15-9 (Winter 7-8.30) Av main course £7.95 **Restaurant Meals:** L served all week 12-2 D served all week 7-9 (Winter 7-8.30) Av 3 course alc £19.95 **Brewery/Company:** Free House : Sharps Doom Bar, Cotleigh Tawney Ale, Tribute, St Austell, Newmans Wolvers & Tetley : 8 **Children's Facilities:** Fam room Play area (Large, walled rear garden, climbing frame) Menu/Portions Highchair Food warming **Nearby:** Beachs, Tropiquaria, Dunster Castle **Notes:** Dogs allowed in bar, Water Garden: Large, patios **Parking:** 40

LANGPORT
Rose & Crown

Huish Episcopi TA10 9QT

☎ 01458 250494

A traditional thatched inn, in the same family for four generations, with Gothic-style windows and a stone-flagged cellar which doubles as the bar. It is handy for good walks, including the popular River Parrett Trail, and for visiting the Somerset Wetlands. Somerset farm cider and real ales are always available, while a typical menu offers vegetable curry, steak and ale pie, beef lasagne, and chicken breast.

Open: 11.30-2.30 5.30-11 (Fri-Sat 11.30-11, Sun 12-10.30) **Bar Meals:** L served all week 12-2 D served Mon-Sat 6-7.30 **Brewery/Company:** Free House
🍺: Teignworthy Reel Ale, Mystery Tor, Hop Back Summer

Lightning, Butcombe Bitter, Summathat **Children's Facilities:** Fam room Play area (Outside play area with sand pit & slide) Games Food warming **Notes:** Dogs allowed in bar, in garden, Water Garden: Mainly lawns, seating, play area **Parking:** 50

LANGPORT
The Old Pound Inn

Aller TA10 0RA

☎ 01458 250469 🖷 01458 250469

Web: www.infotel.co.uk

Built as a cider house, the Old Pound Inn dates from 1571 and retains plenty of historic character with oak beams, open fires and a garden that used to be the village pound. It's a friendly pub with a good reputation for its real ale and home-cooked food, but also provides function facilities for 200 with its own bar. Whimsically named dishes include portly venison, horsy wild boar, and fruit 'n' nut trout.

Open: 11-11 **Bar Meals:** L served all week 12-1.45 D served all week 6-9.45 **Restaurant Meals:** L served all week 12-1.45 D served all week 6-9.45

🍺: Butcombe,Butcombe Gold, Yorkshire Bitter, Courage Best **Children's Facilities:** Menu/Portions Cutlery Highchair Food warming Baby changing **Nearby:** Fleet Air Museum **Notes:** Dogs allowed in bar **Parking:** 30

LEIGH UPON MENDIP
The Bell Inn 🍷

BA3 5QQ

☎ 01373 812316 🖷 01373 812434

Email: rodcambourne@aol.com

Dir: *Follow the Frome Rd towards Radstock, turn right towards Mells and then Leigh upon Mendip*

The Bell is a 17th-century inn in the village centre on the edge of the Mendip Hills. Pilgrims on their way to Glastonbury used to stop here. A three-mile walk around the lanes starts and finishes at the pub.

Open: 12-3 6-12 **Bar Meals:** L served all week 12-2 D served all week 6.30-9.30 (Sun 12-2.30) Av main course £8.50 **Restaurant Meals:** L served all week 12-2 D served all week 6.30-9.30 (Sun 12-2.30)
🍺: Wadworth 6X, Butcombe Bitter, Wadworths JCB,

Henrys IPA, Bishops Tipple 🍷: 11 **Children's Facilities:** Fam room Play area (Slide, swings, swingball & climbing ropes) Menu/Portions Cutlery Games Highchair Food warming Baby changing **Nearby:** Cheddar Caves, Longleat House/Park, Steam Railway **Notes:** Dogs allowed in bar, in skittle alley, in garden Garden: Patio area, grassed area with flower borders **Parking:** 30

LONG SUTTON
The Devonshire Arms 🍷
Langport TA10 9LP
☎ 01458 241271 📠 01458 241037
Email: mail@thedevonshirearms.com
Web: www.thedevonshirearms.com
Dir: *Exit A303 at the Podimore rdbt onto the A372. Continue for 4m before turning left onto B3165.*
A Grade II listed former hunting lodge set on the village green. Inside you'll find unexpectedly contemporary styling that nevertheless complements original features such as a large open fire. The pub is renowned locally for its food, which is made with the best local produce wherever possible. Lunch might feature bangers and mash; Caesar salad; or a smoked salmon sandwich with rocket salad. The evening menu offers starters likes pan-fried squid with red pepper, chilli and Puy lentils, and sweet potato and cumin soup, followed perhaps by fillet of beef with red onion and parsley potato cake and cep sauce. The pub is ideally located for exploring local countryside.
Open: 12-3 6-11 Closed: 25 Dec **Bar Meals:** L served all week 12-2.30 D served Mon-Sat 7-9.30 Av main course £8 **Restaurant Meals:** L served all week 12-2.30 D served Mon-Sat 7-9.30 Av 3 course alc £22.50 **Brewery/Company:** Free House 🍺: Teignworthy 'Real Ale', Hopback 'Crop Circle', Amstel, Warsteiner & Leffe Blonde 🍷: 8 **Children's Facilities:** Licence Play area (Play equipment in secure garden) Menu/Portions Games Highchair Food warming **Nearby:** Fllet Air Arm Museum, Haynes Motor Museum & Willow & Wetlands Visitor Centre **Notes:** Garden: Courtyard garden & large walled garden **Parking:** 6

LOVINGTON
The Pilgrims 🍷
Castle Cary BA7 7PT
☎ 01963 240597
Email: thejools@btinternet.com
Web: www.thepilgrims@lovington.co.uk
Dir: *From A303 take A37 to Lyford, right at lights, 1.5m to The Pilgrims on B3153.*
The award-winning Pilgrims bills itself as 'the pub that thinks it's a restaurant', serving restaurant-quality food in the informal atmosphere of a pub. Emphasis is on local produce cooked at home: fish is delivered from Brixham and Bridport; meat from local farms; cheeses from the West Country. Bread is home made using locally milled organic flour. Even the beer is made round the corner.
Open: 12-3 7-11 Closed: Oct **Bar Meals:** L served Wed-Sun 12-2 D served Wed-Sat 7-9 Av main course £17 **Restaurant Meals:** L served Wed-Sun 12-2 D served Wed-Sat 7-9 Av 3 course alc £30 **Children's Facilities:** Licence Menu/Portions Cutlery Games Highchair Food warming Baby changing **Nearby:** Yeovilton Air Museum, Haynes Motor Museum, Glastonbury Abbey **Notes:** Dogs in bar **Parking:** 30

LOWER VOBSTER
Vobster Inn 🍷
Bath BA3 5RJ
☎ 01373 812920 📠 01373 812920
Email: info@vobsterinn.co.uk
Dir: *4m W of Frome*
Rafael and Peta Davila are the new owners at this stone-built inn, which can be found in the hamlet of Lower Vobster. Both bar and restaurant menus heavily feature seafood and West Country meats, but with a distinctive Galician flavour, as Rafael is a native of the rugged north Spanish coast. Children are particularly welcome and have their own menu as well as being encouraged to try smaller portions from the main menus.
Open: 12-3 7-11 (Apr-Sep 12-3 6.30-11) **Bar Meals:** L served all week 12-2 D served all week 7-9 (Fri/Sat 9.30 last orders) **Restaurant Meals:** L served all week 12-2 D served Mon-Sat 7-11 Av 3 course alc £22.50 🍺: Butcombe & John Smiths 🍷: 8 **Children's Facilities:** Fam room (Play area) Menu/Portions Cutlery Games Highchair Food warming **Nearby:** Longleat House, Cheddar Caves & Wookey Hole **Notes:** Garden: Boule court, 10 tables **Parking:** 45

SOMERSET

MARTOCK
The Nag's Head Inn
East Street TA12 6NF
☎ 01935 823432
Dir: *Telephone for directions*
A 200-year-old former cider house set in a picturesque village in rural south Somerset. Alfresco eating and drinking is encouraged in both the landscaped garden and a huge orchard area, with the home-made food being much sought after locally. Lamb shanks, venison casserole, various Thai and other oriental dishes, and delicious steaks are also available in the bar and restaurant.
Open: 12-2.30 6-11 (Open all day Sat-Sun) **Bar Meals:** L served Mon-Sun 12-2 D served Mon-Sat 6-9
Restaurant Meals: L served Mon-Sun 12-2 D served Mon-Sat 6-8.30 ■: Tanglefoot, Worthington, Stella Artois, Carling, Toby **Children's Facilities:** Fam room Menu/Portions Food warming **Notes:** Dogs allowed in bar, in garden, Water, Biscuits **Garden:** Landscaped garden with flower beds **Parking:** 25

MONTACUTE
The Phelips Arms ♟
The Borough TA15 6XB
☎ 01935 822557 📄 01935 822557
Email: infophelipsarms@aol.com
Web: www.phelipsarms.co.uk
Dir: *From Cartgate rdbt on A303 follow signs for Montacute*
A 17th-century listed hamstone building overlooking the village square and close to historic Montacute House (National Trust). The emphasis is on the quality of the food, and everything is prepared on the premises using the best local and West Country produce. The menu features an eclectic selection of dishes cooked in a robust style, and there is a small but delicious pudding menu, and an extensive wine list. New proprietors may make changes - please ring for details.
Open: 11.30-2.30 6-11 Closed: 25 Dec **Bar Meals:** L served all week 12-2 D served Tue-Sat 7-9 Av main course £12 **Restaurant Meals:** L served all week 12-2 D served Tue-Sat 6-9 (Sun 12-2.30) Av 3 course alc £21 **Brewery/Company:** Palmers ■: Palmers IPA & 200 Premium Ale, Copper Ale ♟: 35 **Children's Facilities:** Menu/Portions Cutlery Games Food warming **Notes:** Dogs allowed in bar, in garden, in bedrooms, Water **Garden:** Secluded, sheltered & beautiful walled garden **Parking:** 40

NUNNEY
The George at Nunney ★★ HL ♟
Church Street Nr Frome BA11 4LW
☎ 01373 836458 📄 01373 836565
Email: enquiries@georgeatnunneyhotel.wanadoo.co.uk
Web: www.georgenunneyhotel.co.uk
Dir: *0.5m N off A361, Frome/Shepton Mallet*
The garden was used in the Middle Ages as a place of execution, but this rambling old coaching inn is deservedly popular. Set in a historic conservation village, It serves a wide choice of food. Big steaks, mixed grill, steak and ale pie, and double chicken breasts with choice of sauces, plus a separate fish menu including brill, sea bass, hake, red mullet and fresh dressed crabs.
Open: 12-3 5-11 **Bar Meals:** L served all week 12-2 D served all week 7-9 Av main course £8 **Restaurant Meals:** L served all week 12-2 D served all week 7-9 Av 3 course alc £18 **Brewery/Company:** Free House ■: Highgate Brewery Saddlers Best Bitter, Wadworth 6X, Interbrew Bass and Guest Ales ♟: 8 **Children's Facilities:** Fam room Menu/Portions Games Highchair Food warming **Nearby:** Longleat, Nunney Castle, Nunney Brook **Notes:** **Garden:** Walled cottage-type garden with seating **Parking:** 30

OVER STRATTON
The Royal Oak
nr South Petherton TA13 5LQ

☎ 01460 240906 📠 01460 242421

Email: chris&jill@the-royal-oak.net

Web: www.the-royal-oak.net

Dir: *A3088 from Yeovil, left onto A303, Over Stratton on right after South Petherton*

Blackened beams, flagstones, log fires, pews and settles set the scene in this welcoming old thatched inn built from warm hamstone, which has the added attraction of a garden, children's play area and barbecue. Expect real ales, including Tanglefoot from the Badger brewery in Blandford Forum, and dishes ranging from beer-battered haddock and chips with home-made tartare sauce to supreme of chicken in an apricot, ginger and wine sauce.

Open: 11-3 6-11 (Wkds all day) **Bar Meals:** L served all week 12-2.30 D served all week 6.30-9.30 Av main course £9 **Restaurant Meals:** L served all week 12-2.30 D served all week 6.30-9.30 **Brewery/Company:** Hall And Woodhouse Retail 🍺: Badger Best, Tanglefoot, Sussex Best Bitter **Children's Facilities:** Fam room Play area Highchair **Nearby:** Cricket St. Thomas, Yeovilton Air Museum **Notes:** Dogs allowed in bar, in garden, Water **Parking:** 70

PORLOCK
The Ship Inn
High Street TA24 8QD

☎ 01643 862507 📠 01643 863224

Email: mail@shipinnporlock.co.uk

Web: www.shipinnporlock.co.uk

Dir: *A358 to Williton, then A39 to Porlock*

Many travellers have been welcomed to this 13th-century inn, including Wordsworth, Coleridge and even Nelson's press gang. Nestling at the foot of Porlock's notorious hill, where Exmoor tumbles into the sea, its thatched roof and traditional interior provide an evocative setting for a meal or a drink.

Open: 11-11 (Sun 12-11) **Bar Meals:** L served all week 12-2 D served all week 6.30-9 (Sundays 12.30-2.30) **Restaurant Meals:** L served Sun 12-2 D served all week 7-9 (Sun 12.30-2.30, 7-9) **Brewery/Company:** Free House 🍺: Cotleigh Barn Owl, Bass, Courage Best, Regular Guest Ales, 15 Moor Ales **Children's Facilities:** Play area (swings, climbing frame) Menu/Portions Cutlery Games Highchair Food warming **Nearby:** Horse Riding, Falconary Museum **Notes:** Dogs allowed in bar, Water provided **Parking:** 40

PRIDDY
New Inn
Priddy Green nr Wells BA5 3BB

☎ 01749 676465

Web: www.newinnpriddy.co.uk

Dir: *From M4 junct 18 take A39 right to Priddy 3m before Wells. From junct 19 through Bristol onto A39. From M5 junct 21 take A371 to Cheddar, then B3371*

Overlooking the village green high up in the Mendip Hills, this old, former farmhouse is popular with walkers, riders and cavers. A typical dinner menu features liver and bacon, chargrilled steaks, Brixham plaice, and fillet of pork with braised red cabbage. Plus New Inn pies, jacket potatoes, omelettes and toasties.

Open: 12-3 7-11 **Bar Meals:** L served all week 12-2 D served all week 7-9.30 Av main course £6.50 **Restaurant Meals:** L served all week 12-2 D served all week 7-9.30 Av 3 course alc £12 **Brewery/Company:** Free House 🍺: Interbrew Bass, Fuller's London Pride, Wadworth 6X, New Inn Priddy, 5 Real Ales **Children's Facilities:** Fam room Play area (Slide, see-saw, play equipment) Games **Notes:** Dogs allowed in bar, Water Garden: Large garden with skittle alley **Parking:** 30

SOMERSET

SOMERSET

RODE
The Mill at Rode 🍷
Frome BA11 6AG
☎ 01373 831100 📄 01373 831144
Email: info@themillatrode.co.uk
Web: www.themillatrode.co.uk
Dir: *6m from Bath*
This once-prosperous grist mill has been sympathetically modernised throughout, while retaining its original water-wheel, powered by the River Frome, which runs through the gardens. Lunchtime and evening menus offer plenty of choice, such as avocado, stilton and celery crumble; smoked haddock, cod and prawn fishcakes; minted lamb burger in a split ciabatta; and casserole of the day. In addition to the children's menu, there's a microwave where mums and dads can heat baby food.

Open: 12-11 **Bar Meals:** L/D served all week 12-10 **Restaurant Meals:** L served all week D served all week 🍺: Butcombe Bitter, Erdinger, Guinness, guest beers 🍷: 30 **Children's Facilities:** Fam room Play area (playstations etc,climbing frame/castle) Menu/Portions Cutlery Games Highchair Food warming Baby changing **Nearby:** Longleat, Brokerswood Country Park **Notes:** Garden: Riverside garden with adult-only island **Parking:** 72

SHEPTON MALLET
The Three Horseshoes Inn 🍷
Batcombe BA4 6HE
☎ 01749 850359 📄 01749 850615
Dir: *Take A359 from Frome to Bruton. Batcombe signed on right.*
A 16th-century, honey-coloured stone pub where the converted stables used to house cider-makers and a Blacksmith's workshop, but now serve as a dining room seating 40. Terracotta walls, stripped beams, and a fine stone inglenook are to be found in the long, low main bar. A Grade II listed red-brick chimney rises from the kitchens and the lovely rear garden overlooks the 15th-century tower of the parish church. Food is mainly sourced from local organic and soil association certified growers' or farmers' markets. The owner and head chef cook and plan the menus. Daily specials might feature Fowey mussels marinières with crusty bread and a large pot of fries. The carte offers the likes of pan fried organic chicken livers en croûte with a bacon, brandy and parsley cream sauce to start. Main courses feature the likes of Gilcombe farm bangers and mash with onion gravy.
Open: 12-3 6.30-11 **Bar Meals:** L served all week 12-2 D served all week 7-9 Av main course £12.50 **Restaurant Meals:** L served all week 12-2 D served all week 7-9 **Brewery/Company:** Free House 🍺: Butcombe Bitter, Bats in the Belfry & Wadworths 6x 🍷: 8 **Children's Facilities:** Menu/Portions Cutlery Highchair Food warming Baby changing **Nearby:** Wookey Hole, Imax Theatre, East Somerset Railway **Notes:** Dogs allowed in bar Garden: Pretty garden, patio with heaters & pond **Parking:** 25

SHEPTON MALLET
The Waggon and Horses 🍷
Frome Road Doulting Beacon BA4 4LA
☎ 01749 880302 📄 01749 880602
Email: portsmouthpnni@hotmail.com
Web: www.the-waggon-and-horses.co.uk
Dir: *1.5m N of Shepton Mallet at x-rds with Old Wells-Frome road, 1m off A37*
This rural coaching inn is very much at the heart of artistic life in the local community and customers travel quite a distance for the home-cooked food, everything from traditional pub fare to spicy international dishes.
Open: 11.30-3 6-11 (All day Fri-Sun in summer) **Bar Meals:** L served all week 11.30-2.30 D served all week 6-9.30 (All day Sat-Sun in summer) **Restaurant Meals:** L served all week 11.30-2.30 D served all week 6-9.30 (All Day Sat-Sun in summer) 🍺: Wadworth 6X, Greene King IPA, Butcombe 🍷: 12 **Children's Facilities:** Licence (Wooden climbing frame, swing, petting zoo) Menu/Portions Cutlery Games Highchair Food warming **Nearby:** Wookey Hole, Longleat Safari Park, Cheddar Caves **Notes:** Dogs allowed in bar, in garden Garden: Large, 20 tables, lots of special flowers **Parking:** 35

SPARKFORD
The Sparkford Inn

High Street Yeovil BA22 7JH
☎ 01963 440218 📄 01963 440358
Email: sparkfordinn@sparkford.fsbusiness.co.uk
Dir: *just off A303, 400yds from rdbt at Sparkford*

A 15th-century former coaching inn with beamed bars and a fascinating display of old prints and photographs. It is set in an attractive garden just off the A303 between Wincanton and Yeovil. The restaurant offers a popular lunchtime carvery, light meals and a full evening menu, featuring steaks from the grill. Dishes include marinated Cajun chicken breast; smoked haddock and bacon au gratin; and bean, celery and coriander chilli.
Open: 11-3 5.30-11 (Summer 11-11) **Bar Meals:** L served all week 12-2 D served all week 7-9.30

Restaurant Meals: L served all week 12-2 D served all week 7-9.30 **Brewery/Company:** Free House
🍺: Marstons Pedigree, Banks Bitter & Guest Ales
Children's Facilities: Play area Menu/Portions Highchair Food warming Baby changing **Nearby:** Haynes Motor Museum **Notes:** Dogs allowed in bar, in garden
Parking: 50

STAPLE FITZPAINE
The Greyhound Inn 🍷

Taunton TA3 5SP
☎ 01823 480227 📄 01823 481117
Email: info@thegreyhoundinn.fsbusiness.co.uk
Web: www.thegreyhoundinn.fsbusiness.co.uk
Dir: *From M5, take A358 E, signed Yeovil, after 1m turn right, signed Staple Fitzpaine, at T-junct take left, pub is on right at x-rds.*

There's a warm welcome for everyone at this attractive and award-winning 16th-century free house. The menu features a variety of dishes using the finest Somerset ingredients, including local cheeses, pork, beef and lamb. Fish is freshly delivered each morning from Brixham.
Open: 12-2.30 6-11 (Sun open all day, Fri 5.30-11) **Bar Meals:** L served all week 12-2 D served all week 7-9

(Fri-Sat 7-9.30) Av main course £10.45 **Restaurant Meals:** D served 7-9 **Brewery/Company:** Free House
🍺: Otter, Adnams Broadside, London Pride, Sharps Doom Bar, Hanlocks HB, Abbot Ale 🍷: 7 **Children's Facilities:** Fam room Menu/Portions Games Highchair Food warming **Notes:** Dogs allowed on leads in bar, in garden, Water Garden: Split level **Parking:** 60

STOKE ST GREGORY
Rose & Crown 🍷

Woodhill Taunton TA3 6EW
☎ 01823 490296 📄 01823 490996
Email: info@browningpubs.com
Web: www.browningpubs.com
Dir: *M5 junct 25, follow A358 towards Langport, bear left at Thornfalcon, then left again, follow signs to Stoke St Gregory*

The pub has been in the same family for over 25 years and is proud of its reputation for good food, local produce and a warm reception. Built in the 18th century, it became a pub in 1867, and is set in the Somerset Levels at the heart of the willow industry. The interior is cluttered and cosy, full of nooks and crannies with a well in the middle of the bar. Expect fillet of haddock with Somerset

rarebit, scrumpy chicken, or three-cheese tagliatelle.
Open: 11-3 7-11 **Bar Meals:** L served all week 12.30-2 D served all week 7-9.30 (Sun 12-2) **Restaurant Meals:** L served all week 12.30-2 D served all week 7-10 Av 3 course alc £22.50 **Brewery/Company:** Free House 🍺: Exmoor Fox, Stag, Guest Ales, Butcombe
🍷: 8 **Children's Facilities:** Menu/Portions Cutlery Highchair Food warming **Notes:** Garden: Pretty patio area with tables **Parking:** 20

WAMBROOK
The Cotley Inn ♚
nr Chard TA20 3EN
☎ 01460 62348 📄 01460 68833
Email: sue-cotley@ticali.co.uk
Web: www.thecotleyinn.co.uk
Dir: *Take A30 from Chard, then take the Wambrook rd at the toll house.*
Located in an area popular with country walkers and handy for the Devon border and the Lyme Bay coastline, this traditional stone-built inn has a cosy bar and an adjoining dining room both of which offer a choice of appetising meals, light snacks and specials.
Open: 11-3 6.30-12 **Bar Meals:** L served all week 12-2 D served all week 7-10 (Sun 7-9) Av main course £9.25 **Restaurant Meals:** L served all week 12-2 D served all

week 7-10 (Sun D 7-9) Av 3 course alc £18 🍺: Otter Ale, Interbrew Boddingtons Bitter, Otter Bitter, Stella, Castlemaine ♚: 8 **Children's Facilities:** Licence Menu/Portions Highchair Food warming **Nearby:** Cricket St Thomas Wildlife Park, Crealy Donkey Sanctuary **Notes:** Dogs allowed in bar, in garden Garden: Patio area, tables & chairs; beer garden **Parking:** 30

WASHFORD
The Washford Inn
TA23 0PP
☎ 01984 640256
Email: washfordinn@freedomnames.co.uk
A pleasant family inn located beside Washford Station, a stop on the West Somerset Railway between Minehead and Bishop's Lydeard - the longest privately-owned line in Britain. A service runs all year, using both diesel and nostalgic old steam locos. A good range of beers and a simple menu of proven pub favourites such as omelette and chips, grilled steaks, and all-day breakfast. Chicken nuggets, sausages or pizzas for young trainspotters.
Open: 12-11 **Bar Meals:** L/D served all week 12-8.30 Av main course £7.50 **Restaurant Meals:** L served all week 12-2.30 D served all week 5-9

Brewery/Company: Scottish & Newcastle 🍺: Adnams Broadside, Theakstons Best Mild, Ringwood **Children's Facilities:** Fam room Play area (Garden with slide and swing) Cutlery Games Highchair Food warming Baby changing **Notes:** Dogs allowed in bar, in garden Garden: Seating area with good view of steam railway **Parking:** 40

WATERROW
The Rock Inn ★★★★ INN ♚
Nr Taunton TA4 2AX
☎ 01984 623293 📄 01984 623293
Web: www.rockinn.co.uk
Dir: *From Taunton take B3227. Waterrow approx 14m W*
A third of this half-timbered former smithy and coaching inn is carved out of the rock face, with parts of it visible in the bar next to the open fire. The inn dates back over 400 years. Award-winning ales and home-made food are served, including fresh fish daily from Brixham, and Aberdeen Angus beef from their own farm.
Open: 12-3 6-11 **Bar Meals:** L served all week 12-2.30 D served all week 6.30-9.30 (Sun 7-9) Av main course £8.50 **Restaurant Meals:** L served all week 12-2.30 D served all week 6.30-9.30 (Sun 7-9) Av 3 course alc £20 **Brewery/Company:** Free House 🍺: Cotleigh Tawny, Exmoor Gold, Otter Ale, London Pride Cotleigh Barn Owl ♚: 11 **Children's Facilities:** Licence Menu/Portions Cutlery Games Highchair Food warming Baby changing **Nearby:** West Somerset Steam Railway, Wookey Hole Caves, Diggerland **Notes:** Dogs allowed in bar **Parking:** 25

WELLS
The City Arms ♍
59 High Street BA5 2AG
☎ 01749 673916 🖷 01749 672901
Email: query@thecityarmsatwells.co.uk
Web: www.thecityarmsatwells.co.uk
One of the historic sights of Wells, by 1591 this early 16th-century building had become a jail, hence the small barred windows. On the menu expect to find dishes like smoked haddock, spinach and cream bake; stuffed field mushrooms; chargrilled chicken Caesar; and fine Aberdeen Angus steaks. Weekly changing specials include cottage pie, and macaroni and broccoli cheese bake. As one of only two free houses in the city it serves seven real ales.
Open: 8-11 (Fri & Sat 8am-12am, Sun 9am-11pm) **Bar**

Meals: L/D served all week 9-10 Av main course £6.95 **Restaurant Meals:** L served all week 12 D served all week 6-9 Av 3 course alc £19.50 🍺: Butcombe, Greene King, Sharps ♍: 16 **Children's Facilities:** Licence Fam room Menu/Portions Games Food warming **Nearby:** Wookey Hole Caves, Longleat, Cheddar Gorge **Notes:** Dogs allowed in bar Garden: Cobbled courtyard with terrace & seating

WELLS
The Fountain Inn & Boxer's Restaurant ♍
1 Saint Thomas Street BA5 2UU
☎ 01749 672317 🖷 01749 670825
Email: eat@fountaininn.co.uk
Web: www.fountaininn.co.uk
Dir: City centre, at A371 & B3139 junct. Follow The Harringtons signs. Inn on junct of Tor St & St Thomas St
Dating back to the 16th century and built to house builders working on nearby Wells Cathedral, the award-winning Fountain Inn & Boxer's Restaurant has a well-earned reputation for good food. Chef manager Julie Pearce uses the finest local produce to create quality home-cooked food, served in both bar and restaurant. Bar specials may include lasagne bolognaise with dressed side salad; or cod in beer batter with chips and

home-made tartare sauce. Among restaurant mains are fillet steak stuffed with haggis and wrapped in smoked bacon, blackberry and red wine jus, gratin dauphinoise and fresh vegetables; and oven-baked wild salmon escalope topped with fresh asparagus, balsamic, pepper and red onion dressing, new potatoes and vegetables.
Open: 10.30-2.30 6-11 (Sun 12-3, 7-10.30) Closed: 25-26 Dec **Bar Meals:** L served all week 12-2 D served all week 6-10 (Sun 12-2.30, 7-9.30) **Restaurant Meals:** L served all week 12-2.30 D served all week 6-10 (Sun 12-2.30, 7-9.30) **Brewery/Company:** Innspired 🍺: Butcombe Bitter, Interbrew Bass, Scottish Courage Courage Best ♍: 23 **Children's Facilities:** Menu/Portions Games Highchair Food warming Baby changing **Nearby:** Wookey Hole, Cheddar Gorge & Wells Museum **Parking:** 24

WELLS
The Pheasant Inn ♍
North Wookey BA5 1LQ
☎ 01749 672355
Email: pheasant@dsl.pipex.com
Dir: W of Wells on the B3139 towards Wedmore
Popular country pub at the foot of the Mendips, where you can enjoy some impressive views and relax with a pint of real ale beside a welcoming log fire. The menu ranges through light bites, a pasta and pizza section, and dishes such as slow roast lamb shank with minty Somerset sauce, and escalope of pork with cider and sage cream sauce. Friday night is fish night, and there are some great home-made puddings.
Open: 11.30-2.30 6-11 (Sat 11.30-11, Sun 12-10.30) **Bar Meals:** L served all week 12-2 D served all week

6.30-9.30 (Sun 12-2, 7-9) **Restaurant Meals:** L served all week 12-2 D served all week 6.30-9.30 (Sun 7-9) **Brewery/Company:** Enterprise Inns 🍺: Butcombe, Greene King Old Speckled Hen, Pedigree, Butcombe Blond, John Smiths Cream Flow ♍: 6 **Children's Facilities:** Licence Menu/Portions Cutlery Games Highchair **Nearby:** Wookey Hole Caves **Notes:** Dogs allowed in bar Garden: Garden with tables and umbrellas **Parking:** 28

SOMERSET

WEST HUNTSPILL
Crossways Inn 🍷
Withy Rd Highbridge TA9 3RA
☎ 01278 783756 📠 01278 781899
Email: crossways.inn@virgin.net
Web: www.crossways-inn.com
Dir: *On A38 3.5m from M5*
This 17th-century coaching inn is an integral part of village life. Fresh ingredients are used for a wide range of dishes, from traditional/local to more exotic items. **Open:** 12-3 5.30-11 (Sun 12-4.30, 7-10.30) Closed: 25 Dec **Bar Meals:** L served all week 12-2 D served all week 6.30-9 (Sun roast served 12-2.30, full menu 12-2, 7-9) Av main course £7.50 **Restaurant Meals:** L served all week 12-2 D served all week 6.30-9 Av 3 course alc £14.50 🍺: Interbrew Bass, Flowers IPA, Fuller's London Pride, Exmoor Stag, Cotleigh Snowy, Butcombe Gold, Branscombe Bitter 🍷: 8 **Children's Facilities:** Fam room (Indoor games & skittles) Menu/Portions Highchair Food warming Baby changing **Nearby:** Secret World, Burnham-on-Sea, Apex Park & Alstone Wildlife Park **Notes:** Dogs allowed in bar, Water Garden: Seating, food served outside **Parking:** 60

WHEDDON CROSS
The Rest and Be Thankful Inn
Exmoor TA24 7DR
☎ 01643 841222 📠 01643 841813
Email: enquiries@restandbethankful.co.uk
Web: www.restandbethankful.co.uk
Dir: *5m S of Dunster*
Log fires in winter and decent refreshments at any time of the year make this an ideal place to stop in the heart of Exmoor National Park. Years ago, coachmen, passengers and their horses would have been grateful for a break at this old coaching inn, nearly 1000 feet up in Exmoor's highest village. Old world charm blends with friendly hospitality in the cosy bar and spacious restaurant, where both traditional and contemporary food is served. **Open:** 10-2.30 6.30-11 (Winter open at 7) **Bar Meals:** L served all week 12-2 D served all week 7-9 Av main course £7.50 **Restaurant Meals:** L served all week 12-2 D served all week 7-9 **Brewery/Company:** Free House 🍺: Worthington Bitter, Tribute, Guinness & Exmoor **Children's Facilities:** Fam room Highchair Food warming **Notes:** Garden: Paved Patio **Parking:** 50

ALVEDISTON
The Crown
Nr Salisbury SP5 5JY
☎ 01722 780335 📠 01722 780836
Dir: *2.5m off A30 approx half-way between Salisbury and Shaftesbury*
Tucked away in the Ebble Valley between Salisbury and Shaftesbury, the Crown is a well-known landmark. The inn serves entirely home-made food, with particular emphasis on fresh local produce whenever possible. The cosy bar sets the scene for anything from a simple sandwich to fresh fish and rib-eye steaks. There's a wide range of starters and main choices on the specials board. **Open:** 12-3 6.30-11 (Sun 12-3, 7-10.30) **Bar Meals:** L served all week 12-2.30 D served all week 6.30-9 (Sun 12-2.30) Av main course £9.75 **Restaurant Meals:** L served all week 12-2 D served all week 6.30-9.30 (Sun 12-2.30) Av 3 course alc £18 **Brewery/Company:** Free House 🍺: Ringwood Best, Timothy Taylor Lanlord, Youngs Special Bitter 🍷: 10 **Children's Facilities:** Play area (swings, slide) Menu/Portions Cutlery Games Highchair Food warming **Notes:** Dogs allowed, Water Garden: Food served outdoors, patio **Parking:** 40

AXFORD
Red Lion Inn ♟

Marlborough SN8 2HA

☎ 01672 520271 📠 01672 521011

Email: info@redlionaxford.com

Web: www.redlionaxford.com

Dir: *M4 junct 15, A246 Marlborough centre. Follow Ramsbury signs. Inn 3m*

A pretty, award-winning, 17th-century brick and flint pub with fine views over the Kennet Valley. The bar, with large inglenook, has a pleasing mix of sofas and more solid seating. A stand-alone fish menu proposes grilled Torbay sole Véronique; Cornish mussels in white wine and coconut milk; and grilled sardine fillets with chilli and garlic oil. An alternative is venison, wood pigeon, wild mushroom and blackberry pie.

Open: 12-3 6.30-11 (Sun 7-10.30) **Bar Meals:** L served all week 12-2 D served all week 7-9 (Sat 7-9.30) Av main course £11.25 **Restaurant Meals:** L served all week 12-2 D served all week 7-9 (Sat 7-9.30) Av 3 course alc £25 **Brewery/Company:** Free House 🍺: Hook Norton Best, Ramsbury Gold & Guest Beers ♟: 16 **Children's Facilities:** Play area (Secure garden) Menu/Portions Cutlery Highchair Food warming **Notes:** Garden: Garden at rear of pub, patio area at front **Parking:** 30

BERWICK ST JAMES
The Boot Inn

High Street Salisbury SP3 4TN

☎ 01722 790243 📠 01722 790243

Email: kathieduval@aol.com

Dir: *Telephone for directions*

Half of this attractive, 16th-century stone and flint inn was once a cobbler's - hence the name. Tucked away in picturesque countryside, the building is surrounded by gardens. There is an award winning menu of quality home-cooked food. Fresh local produce, including herbs and vegetables from the garden, appear in the daily changing dishes.

Open: 12-3 6-11 (Closed Mon lunch, Sun 7-10.30) **Closed:** 25-26 Dec **Bar Meals:** L served Tue-Sun 12-2.30 D served Tue-Sat 6.30-9.30 Av main course £9.95 **Restaurant Meals:** L served Tue-Sun D served Tue-Sat **Brewery/Company:** Wadworth 🍺: Wadworth 6X, Henrys IPA, guest beers **Children's Facilities:** Fam room (Changing facilities) Menu/Portions Games Highchair Food warming Baby changing **Notes:** Dogs allowed in bar, Water Garden: Large award-winning garden **Parking:** 18

BOX
The Quarrymans Arms ♟

Box Hill Nr Corsham SN13 8HN

☎ 01225 743569

Email: John@quarrymans-arms.co.uk

Web: www.quarrymans-arms.co.uk

Dir: *Please phone pub for accurate directions*

Tucked away up a narrow hillside lane, this 300-year-old miners' pub enjoys fantastic views over the Box Valley. It's also on the long-distance Macmillan Way, and offers luggage transfer for walkers. The interior is packed with mining memorabilia and, by arrangement, you can now take trips down the stone mines. There's a substantial snack menu, plus daily-changing blackboards; calves' liver on mustard mash; fish risotto; and mixed sausage casserole are typical choices.

Open: 11-3.30 6-11 (all day Fri-Sun) **Bar Meals:** L served all week 11-3 D served all week 6.30-10.30 Av main course £10 **Restaurant Meals:** L served all week 11-3 D served all week 6.30-10.30 Av 3 course alc £18.50 **Brewery/Company:** Free House 🍺: Butcombe Bitter, Wadworth 6X, Moles Best ♟: 7 **Children's Facilities:** Fam room Menu/Portions Cutlery Games Highchair Food warming Baby changing **Nearby:** Bowood Country Estate & Park, Bath, Castle Coombe, Laycock Village **Notes:** Dogs allowed in bar, in garden Garden: Small, traditional, views over Box Valley **Parking:** 25

BRADFORD-ON-AVON
The Dandy Lion ♟
35 Market Street BA15 1LL
☎ 01225 863433 📄 01225 869169
Well-kept Wadworth and Butcombe ales supplement an extensive wine list at this 17th-century town centre pub. Formerly a traditional grocery, and handy for exploring Bradford-on-Avon's hilly streets, the internal décor reflects the town's flourishing antiques trade. Typical lunch dishes are baked flat mushrooms, tagliatelle carbonara, and smoked chicken and avocado salad. Thai chicken curry, whole baked lemon sole and medallions of pork tenderloin might feature on the varied and imaginative evening menu.
Open: 10.30-3 6-11 (Sat 10.30-11, Fri 10.30-4, 6-11.30) **Bar Meals:** L served all week 12-2.15 D served all week 7-9.30 (Sun 12-3) Av main course £6.50
Restaurant Meals: L served Sun 12-2.15 D served all week 7-9.30 (Sun 12-3) Av 3 course alc £20
Brewery/Company: Wadworth 🍺: Butcombe, Wadworth 6X, Henrys IPA, Wadworth Seasonal Ales ♟: 11
Children's Facilities: Play area Menu/Portions Cutlery Highchair Food warming **Nearby:** Longleat Safari Park, Lacock National Trust Village, Center Parcs

BRADFORD-ON-AVON
The Kings Arms ♟
Monkton Farleigh BA15 2QH
☎ 01225 858705 📄 01225 858999
Email: enquiries@kingsarms-bath.co.uk
Web: www.kingsarms-bath.co.uk
Dir: *Off the A363 Bath to Bradford-on-Avon road, follow brown tourist signs to Kings Arms*
Dating back to the 11th century, this historic Bath stone building is situated in an attractive village just outside Bradford-on-Avon. Conversion into an alehouse took place in the 17th century, but original features remain, including the mullioned windows, flagged floors and a vast inglenook - said to be the largest in Wiltshire - in the medieval-style Chancel restaurant, which is hung with tapestries and pewter plates.
Open: 12-11 (Sun 12-10.30) **Bar Meals:** L/D served all week 12-10.30 Av main course £10 **Brewery/Company:** Innspired 🍺: Wadworth 6X, Buttcombe Bitter,Wychwood Hobgoblin, Shepherd Neame Spitfire ♟: 8 **Children's Facilities:** Games Highchair Baby changing **Notes:** Dogs allowed in bar, in garden Garden overlooking countryside & courtyard **Parking:** 45

BRINKWORTH
The Three Crowns ♟
Chippenham SN15 5AF
☎ 01666 510366
Web: www.threecrowns.co.uk
Dir: *A3102 to Wootton Bassett, then B4042, 5m to Brinkworth*
The Three Crowns stands on the village green facing the church in the longest village in England. The building extends into a large, bright conservatory and garden room, and then out onto a heated patio and garden. In winter, an open log fire provides a warm welcome in the bars. All the dishes are home made, and main courses are cooked to order and served with at least six fresh vegetables. Options range from prime Scotch beef steaks to a rather more exotic dish of marinated crocodile with a Thai-style sauce presented in a filo pastry basket with a timbale of savoury rice. There's also a good choice of fish.
Open: 11-3 6-11 Closed: 25-26 Dec **Bar Meals:** L served all week 12-2 D served all week 6-9.30 Av main course £16 **Restaurant Meals:** L served all week 12-2 D served all week 6-9.30 **Brewery/Company:** Enterprise Inns 🍺: Wadworth 6X, Archers Village Ale, Castle Eden, Fullers London Pride, Guest Ales ♟: 20
Children's Facilities: Play area (Outdoor obstacle/climbing frame) Menu/Portions Games Highchair Food warming Baby changing **Nearby:** Ashton Keynes Water Park, Bowood House and Gardens, Lydiard Country Park
Notes: Dogs allowed in bar, in garden Garden: Sheltered patio with heaters, well maintained **Parking:** 40

BURCOMBE

The Ship Inn ♌

Burcombe Lane SP2 0EJ

☎ 01722 743182 🗎 01722 743182

Email: theshipburcombe@mail.com

Web: www.theshipburcombe.co.uk

Dir: *In the village of Burcombe, off the A30, 1m out of Wilton & 5m W of Salisbury*

The beautiful river garden at this tranquil 17th-century Nadder Valley pub is just the spot for alfresco summer dining. Seasonal menus and daily changing specials, with lunchtime sandwiches and a variety of main courses. **Open:** 11-3 6-11 (Sun 11-3, 6.30-10.30) Closed: 1st two weeks in Jan **Bar Meals:** L served all week 11-2.30 D served all week 6-10 (Sun 12-2.30, 7-9.30) Av main course £10 **Restaurant Meals:** L served all week 11-2.30 D served all week 6-10 (Sun 12-2.30, 7-9.30) Av 3 course alc £20 🍺: Flowers IPA, Wadworth 6X, Courage Best, Guinness & Kronenbourg ♌: 8 **Children's Facilities:** Licence Menu/Portions Cutlery Games Highchair Food warming **Nearby:** Stonehenge, Farmer Giles & Wilton House **Notes:** Dogs allowed in bar Garden: Beautiful river garden **Parking:** 30

DEVIZES

The Bear Hotel ★★★ HL ♌

The Market Place SN10 1HS

☎ 0845 456 5334 🗎 01380 722450

Email: info@thebearhotel.net

Web: www.thebearhotel.net

Right in the centre of Devizes, home of Wadworth's Brewery, this old coaching inn dates from at least 1559 and lists Judge Jeffreys, George III, and Harold Macmillan amongst its notable former guests. You'll find old beams, log fires, fresh flowers, three bars and two restaurants. The menu offers pot-roasted partridge perhaps, and broccoli and mushroom strudel. Music fans, check out the weekly jazz sessions in the cellar. **Open:** 9.30-11 Closed: 25-26 Dec **Bar Meals:** L served all week 11.30-2.30 D served all week 7-9.30 (Sun 7-9) Av main course £5 **Restaurant Meals:** L served Sun 12.15-1.45 D served Mon-Sat 7-9.30 **Brewery/Company:** Wadworth 🍺: Wadworth 6X, Wadworth IPA, Wadworth JCB, Old Timer, Malt & Hops, Summersault & Seasonal Beers ♌: 18 **Children's Facilities:** Menu/Portions Highchair Food warming Baby changing **Nearby:** Stonehenge, Avebury Stone Circle, Longleat **Notes:** Dogs allowed in bar, in garden Garden: Courtyard **Parking:** 14

DONHEAD ST ANDREW

The Forester Inn ♌

Lower Street SP7 9EE

☎ 01747 828038 🗎 01747 828714

Email: enquiries@foresterinndonheadstandrew.co.uk

Web: www.foresterinndonheadstandrew.co.uk

Dir: *4.5m from Shaftsbury on A30 towards Salisbury.*

A traditional 16th-century inn close to the Dorset and Wiltshire border, the Forester has warm stone walls, a thatched roof, original beams and an inglenook fireplace. In recent years the inn has been extended to include a restaurant and a restaurant/meeting room, which has double doors opening on to the lower patio area. The garden and large patio area are pleasant for eating and drinking outside. The restaurant has a growing reputation for its freshly cooked food and interesting choice of dishes, with starters such as Gran Reserva Parma ham with fresh figs, gorgonzola and honey dressing. Mains take in poussin, poached and chargrilled with black-eye bean cassoulet, and broucette of lambs' kidney with black pudding, swede and a sherry and shallot vinegar. **Open:** 12-3 6.30-11 (Sun 7-10.30) **Bar Meals:** L served all week 12-2 D served all week 6-9 (Sun 12-3, 7-9, Fri-Sat 6-9.30) Av main course £12 **Restaurant Meals:** L served all week 12-2 D served all week 7-9 (Sun 12-3, Fri-Sat 6-9.30) Av 3 course alc £22 **Brewery/Company:** Free House 🍺: 6X, Ringwood, Sharps Doom Bar & Donhead Bitter ♌: 17 **Children's Facilities:** Menu/Portions Highchair Food warming Baby changing **Nearby:** Farmer Giles, Wardor Castle, The Bison Farm **Notes:** Dogs allowed in bar, in garden, Water Garden: Large patio area and garden **Parking:** 30

GRITTLETON
The Neeld Arms
The Street Chippenham SN14 6AP
☎ 01249 782470 📠 01249 782168
Email: neeldarms@zeronet.co.uk
Web: www.neeldarms.co.uk
Dir: *Telephone for directions*
This 17th-century Cotswold stone pub stands at the centre of a pretty village in lush Wiltshire countryside. Its half dozen bedrooms are highly commended for comfort. Quality real ales and freshly prepared food are an equal draw to diners who will eagerly tuck in to lamb shanks, homemade steak and kidney pie or sausage and mash. Children are welcome and the small garden is especially popular for alfresco eating in fine weather.
Open: 12-3 5.30-11 **Bar Meals:** L served all week 12-2 D served all week 7-9.30 Av main course £5 **Restaurant Meals:** L served all week 12-2 D served all week 7-9.30 Av 3 course alc £19 **Brewery/Company:** Free House 🍺: Wadworth 6X, Buckleys Best, Brakspear Bitter & IPA **Children's Facilities:** Menu/Portions Games Highchair Food warming **Nearby:** Village playground **Notes:** Dogs allowed in bar, Water **Garden:** Patio, seats 30 **Parking:** 6

HANNINGTON
The Jolly Tar 🍷
Queens Road SN6 7RP
☎ 01793 762245 📠 01793 765159
Email: jolly.ajc@btinternet.com
Dir: *Leave M4 at junct 15 and take A419 Cirencester. Leave A419 at signs for Bunsdon/Highworth. Follow B4019 Highworth, left at Freke Arms, follow sign for Hannington and Jolly Tar Pub. The Jolly Tar is in the centre of the village.*
Although it's a fair old trek to the sea, there is a connection - the marriage of a lady from a local land-owning family to a 19th-century battleship captain. Inside are old timbers, a log fire and locally brewed Arkells' ales. On the menu, chicken, olive and prosciutto ribbon pasta; home-made lamb burger; Gloucester Old Spot sausages; and Jolly Fantastic fish pie. Specials may include tuna, prawn and red pepper chowder; and shepherd's pie.
Open: 12-3 6-11 **Bar Meals:** L served all week 12-2.30 D served all week 6-9.30 (Sun 7-9.30) Av main course £9 **Restaurant Meals:** L served all week 12-2.30 D served all week 6-9.30 (Sun 7-9.30) Av 3 course alc £17.50 **Brewery/Company:** Arkells 🍺: Arkells 3B, Noel Ale & Kingsdown 🍷: 9 **Children's Facilities:** Licence Fam room Play area (Open grassed area with climbing frame & slide) Menu/Portions Games Highchair Food warming Baby changing **Nearby:** Cotswold Wildlife Park, Roves Farm, Shrivenham GWR Steam Railway Museum **Notes:** Dogs allowed in bar, garden, Water Bowls, Biscuits **Garden:** Sun terrace patio grass play area **Parking:** 50

HINDON
Angel Inn 🍷
High Street Hindon SP3 6DJ
☎ 01747 820696 📠 01747 820054
Email: info@theangelathindon.com
Web: www.theangelathindon.com
Dir: *1.5m from A303, on B3089 towards Salisbury*
Elegant gastro pub in a delightful village setting. Rustic charm meets urbane sophistication in this elegant Georgian coaching inn with a brasserie menu. The Angel has established a reputation for its modern British food. Visitors can eat in the Gallery Restaurant or the Drawing Room, where menus offer instant appeal.
Open: 11-3 5-11 **Bar Meals:** L served all week 12-2.30 D served all week 7-9.30 Av main course £8.50 **Restaurant Meals:** L served all week 12-2.30 D served Mon-Sat 7-9.30 Av 3 course alc £23.50 **Brewery/Company:** Free House 🍺: Wadworth 6X, Buttcombe, Ringwood, Hidden Brewery 🍷: 14 **Children's Facilities:** Menu/Portions Cutlery Highchair Food warming **Notes:** Dogs allowed in bar, in garden Water, Biscuits **Garden:** Paved courtyard with garden furniture **Parking:** 20

HORTON
The Bridge Inn ♀
Horton Road Devizes SN10 2JS
☎ 01380 860273 📠 01380 860273
Email: manager@thebridgeinnhorton.fsnet.co.uk
Dir: *A361 from Devizes, right at 3rd rdbt*
The buildings that are now the Bridge Inn were originally a family-run farm, built around 1800, and then a flour mill and bakery. One of the grinding wheels is now a part of the patio. It makes a perfect place for gongoozling (idly spectating), as narrowboats cruise past on the Kennet and Avon Canal. The menu takes in snacks, pub grub (sausage/fish and chips), grills, a vegetarian selection, and mains such as rustic chicken, and slow roast shoulder of lamb.
Open: 11.30-3 6.30-11 (Sun 12-3 Sun 7-10.30) **Bar**

Meals: L served all week 12-2.15 D served all week 7-9.15 (Sun 12-2.15, 7-9) Av main course £5 **Restaurant Meals:** L served all week 12-2.15 D served all week 7-9.15 (Sun 12-2.15, 7-9) **Brewery/Company:** Wadworth
🍺: Wadworth Henry's original IPA, 6X, Old Father Timer
♀: 8 **Children's Facilities:** Menu/Portions Cutlery Highchair Food warming **Nearby:** Longleat, Bristol Zoo, Train Museum **Notes:** Dogs allowed in bar, in garden, Water Garden: Large garden on canal-side **Parking:** 50

LACOCK
Red Lion Inn ♀
1 High Street SN15 2LQ
☎ 01249 730456 📠 01249 730766
Email: redlion.chippenham.wb@freshnet.co.uk
Web: www.redlionlacock.co.uk
Dir: *Just off A350 between Chippenham & Melksham*
The Red Lion dates back over 200 years - and, with its large open fireplace, flagstone floors and Georgian interior, it looks the part. Now, this historic inn offers Wadworth ales and a varied wine list to accompany the home-cooked meals and daily specials. Fresh lunchtime sandwiches come with a portion of chips, whilst more substantial dishes include broccoli, stilton and potato bake; breaded plaice with crunchy chips; and a range of traditional grills.

Open: 11.30-3 6-11 (May -31 Aug, Sat 11-11 Sun 11-10.30) **Bar Meals:** L served all week 12-2.30 D served all week 6-9 Av main course £8.50 **Restaurant Meals:** L served all week 12-2.30 D served all week 6-9
Brewery/Company: Wadworth 🍺: Wadworth Henry's IPA & 6X, JCB, plus guests ♀: 8 **Children's Facilities:** Menu/Portions Highchair Food warming **Nearby:** Lacock Abbey, Bowood House, Longleat **Notes:** Dogs allowed in bar Garden: Gravel laid with shrub borders **Parking:** 70

LACOCK
The George Inn ♀
4 West Street Nr Chippenham SN15 2LH
☎ 01249 730263 📠 01249 730186
Dir: *M4 junct 17 take A350, S*
Steeped in history and much used as a film and television location, this beautiful National Trust village includes an atmospheric inn. The George dates from 1361 and boasts a medieval fireplace, a low-beamed ceiling, mullioned windows, flagstone floors and an old tread wheel by which a dog would drive the spit. Wide selection of steaks and tasty pies, and fish options include specials in summer; finish with the home-made bread and butter pud.
Open: 10-2.30 5-11 (Sat-Sun all day) **Bar Meals:** L served all week 12-2 D served all week 6-9.30

Restaurant Meals: L served all week 12-2 D served all week 6-9.30 **Brewery/Company:** Wadworth
🍺: Wadworth 6X, Henrys IPA, J.C.B & Henrys Smooth
♀: 13 **Children's Facilities:** Play area Menu/Portions Highchair Food warming **Notes:** Dogs allowed in bar Garden: Large patio, grass area, swings, see-saw
Parking: 40

WILTSHIRE

WILTSHIRE

LIMPLEY STOKE
The Hop Pole Inn 🍷
Woods Hill Lower Limpley Stoke Bath BA2 7FS
☎ 01225 723134 📠 01225 723199
Email: latonahop@aol.com
Web: www.latonahotels.co.uk
Set in the beautiful Limpley Stoke Valley, the Hop Pole dates from 1580 and takes its name from the hop plant that still grows outside the pub. Eagle-eyed film fans may recognise it as the hostelry in the 1992 film *Remains of the Day*. A hearty menu includes Thai vegetable curry; home-made pies; fresh local trout; and steaks. Giant filled baps and other light bites are available too.
Open: 11-2.30 6-11 Closed: 25 Dec **Bar Meals:** L served all week 12-2 D served all week 6.30-9 Av main course £8.50 **Restaurant Meals:** L served all week 12-2.15 D served all week 6.30-9.15 (Sun 7-9) Av 3 course alc £17 **Brewery/Company:** Free House 🍺: Scottish Courage Courage Best, Butcombe Bitter, Marstons Pedigree, Guest Beers 🍷: 8 **Children's Facilities:** Fam room Menu/Portions Food warming **Nearby:** Longleat, Norwood Farm, Canal boating **Notes:** Dogs allowed in bar **Garden:** Large private garden, patio, 15 benches **Parking:** 20

LITTLE CHEVERELL
The Owl 🍷
Low Road nr Devizes SN10 4JS
☎ 01380 812263 📠 01380 812263
Email: jamie@theowl.info
Web: www.theowl.com
Dir: *A344 from Stonehenge, then A360, after 10m left onto B3098, right after 0.5m, Owl signposted*
A 19th-century local situated in a tiny hamlet surrounded by farmland, with views of Salisbury Plain and plenty of good walks. The pretty split-level garden runs down to the Cheverell Brook. There's a quiz on the first Wednesday of the month in aid of a local charity, as well as three beer festivals during the year, with one in August also hosting a soap-box derby. Typical dishes include battered calamari, lasagne, tomato and cheese pasta bake, Thai green chicken curry, sizzling beef Szechwan, and Stilton and mushroom pork.
Open: 11-3 6.30-11 (Sat 11-11, Apr-Sep 11-11) **Bar Meals:** L served all week 12-3 D served all week 7-10.30 (Apr-Sep all day) Av main course £7 **Restaurant Meals:** L served all week 12-3 D served all week 7-10.30 (Sun 12-4, 7-9.30) **Brewery/Company:** Free House 🍺: Wadworth 6X, Hook Norton Best, Cotleigh Tawney Owl, Scottish Courage Courage Directors, Greene King IPA 🍷: 23 **Children's Facilities:** Licence Play area (Swings) Menu/Portions Cutlery Games Highchair Food warming **Nearby:** Longleat, Bowood House **Notes:** Dogs allowed in bar, in garden, Water **Garden:** Decked area, brook, benches, seats 40 **Parking:** 28

LOWER CHICKSGROVE
Compasses Inn ★★★ INN 🏵 🍷
Nr Tisbury SP3 6NB
☎ 01722 714318 📠 01722 714318
Email: thecompasses@aol.com
Web: www.thecompassesinn.com
Dir: *Take 3rd right 1.5m W of Fouant on A30 to Chicksgrove. After 1.5m turn left onto Lagpond Ln, pub 1m on left.*
A 14th-century thatched inn of immense character set in a tiny hamlet amid beautiful rolling countryside, the inn offers real ale, fine wines and freshly prepared food made from seasonally available produce.
Open: 12-3 6-11 (Winter Sun eve 6-8.30) Closed: 25-26 Dec **Bar Meals:** L served Tue-Sun 12-2 D served Tue-Sat 7-9 Av main course £12.95 **Restaurant Meals:** L served Tue-Sun 12-2 D served Tue-Sat 7-9 Av 3 course alc £22 🍺: Interbrew Bass, Wadworth 6X, Ringwood Best, Chicksgrove Churl, The Hidden Pint 🍷: 7 **Children's Facilities:** Menu/Portions Cutlery Games Highchair Food warming **Nearby:** Longleat, Farmer Giles Homestead, Wilton House **Notes:** Dogs allowed in bar, **Garden:** Large grass area, seats 40 **Parking:** 30

MALMESBURY

The Smoking Dog ♀

62 The High Street SN16 9AT

☎ 01666 825823 📠 01666 826513

Email: smokindog@sabrain.com

Log fires, solid wooden floors and a relaxed atmosphere greet visitors to this refined 18th-century stone-built pub, right in the heart of Malmesbury. There's an expanding range of real ales that features continually changing guest beers, and the pub has a good reputation for interesting, freshly-cooked food. Each May the thirsty and hungry can enjoy a beer and sausage festival.
Open: 12-11 (Sun 12-10.30, Fri & Sat 12-12) **Bar Meals:** L served all week 12-2.30 D served all week 7-9.30 (Sun12-2.30, 7-9) **Restaurant Meals:** L served all week 12-2.30 D served all week 7-9.30 (Sun 12-2.30,

7-9) **Brewery/Company:** S A Brain 🍺: Archers Best, Buckleys Best, Reverend James plus 2 guest bitters
♀: 9 **Children's Facilities:** Menu/Portions Games Highchair Food warming **Nearby:** Westonbirt Aboretum, Longleat **Notes:** Dogs allowed in bar, Water, Biscuits Garden: Large suntrap with landscaped lawns

MARDEN

The Millstream ♀

Devizes SN10 3RH

☎ 01380 848308 📠 01380 848337

Email: mail@the-millstream.co.uk

Web: www.the-millstream.co.uk

Dir: *Signed from A342*

Formerly the New Inn, the Millstream reopened in July 2003 after tasteful refurbishment. Once seated in the stone and wooden floored restaurant, start perhaps with a traditional Greek salad, then try pan-fried scallops with spiced aubergine and crispy pancetta.
Open: 12-11.30 **Bar Meals:** L served all week 12-2.30 D served all week 6.30-9.30 (Sun 12-5) Av main course £11.75 **Restaurant Meals:** L served all week 12-2.30 D served all week (Sun 12-5) Av 3 course alc £25

Brewery/Company: Wadworth 🍺: 6X, Henry's IPA, JCB, Bishops Tipple, Malt & Hops, Summersault ♀: 16
Children's Facilities: Licence Fam room Play area (Rope swing in garden) Menu/Portions Games Food warming **Nearby:** Lacock Abbey, Play Farm **Notes:** Dogs allowed in bar, Water, biscuits Garden: Open lawn with stream, terrace, herb garden **Parking:** 25

MERE

The George Inn ★★★ INN

The Square BA12 6DR

☎ 01747 860427 📠 01747 861978

Email: rob.binstead@btconnect.com

Web: www.thegeorgeinnmere.co.uk

Dir: *Follow signs from A303 into village, pub opposite clock tower.*

Extensively but carefully refurbished 16th-century inn, where fugitive Charles II dined en route to Shoreham and ultimately France. Today's diners can relax and enjoy lime and chilli chicken breast, chilli con carne, beef lasagne, and tortellini pasta filled with Stilton and walnut. Salad platters and jacket potatoes are also an option.
Open: 11-3 6-11 (Sun 12-3, 7-10.30) **Bar Meals:** L served all week 12-2 D served all week 6.30-9 (Sun

12-2, 6-9) **Restaurant Meals:** L served all week 12-2 D served all week 6.30-9 **Brewery/Company:** Hall & Woodhouse 🍺: Badger Best, Sussex, Festive Pheasant, Fursty Ferret **Children's Facilities:** Fam room Menu/Portions Cutlery Highchair **Nearby:** Longleat, Paultons Park, The Rapids at Romsey **Notes:** Garden: Patio area **Parking:** 20

WILTSHIRE

WILTSHIRE

NEWTON TONEY
The Malet Arms

SP4 0HF

☎ 01980 629279 ▤ 01980 629459

Email: maletarms@hotmail.com

Dir: *8 miles north of Salisbury on A338, 2 miles from A303.*

A 17th-century inn in a quiet village through which runs the River Bourne. It was originally built as a dwelling house, much later becoming The Three Horseshoes, named after a nearby smithy. An earlier Malet Arms, owned by lord of the manor Sir Henry Malet, closed in the 1890s and its name was transferred. It's not just the village that's quiet: the pub is too, as fruit machines and piped music are banned. All food on the ever-changing blackboard menus is home cooked. Game is plentiful in season, often courtesy of the landlord who shoots pheasant and deer. Other choices might include roasted duck legs and Toulouse sausages on puy lentils braised in white wine; and chargrilled pork chop with scrumpy-soused shallots and grain mustard. Cross the road and the river to some outside tables.

Open: 11-3 6-11 (Sun 12-3, 7-10.30) Closed: 25-26 Dec, 1 Jan **Bar Meals:** L served all week 12-2.30 D served all week 6.30-10 (Sun 7-9.30) Av main course £9 **Restaurant Meals:** Av 3 course alc £25 **Brewery/Company:** Free House ◪: Ramsbury, Stonehenge, Tripple XXX, Palmers & Archers **Children's Facilities:** Play area Menu/Portions Cutlery Highchair Food warming **Nearby:** Stonehenge, Cholderton Rare Breeds Centre & The Hawk Conservancy **Notes:** Dogs allowed in bar Garden: Walled patio **Parking:** 20

NUNTON
The Radnor Arms ♀

Nr Salisbury SP5 4HS

☎ 01722 329722

Dir: *From Salisbury ring road take A338 to Ringwood. Nunton signed on right*

A popular pub in the centre of the village dating from around 1750. Bar snacks are supplemented by an extensive fish choice and daily specials, which might include braised lamb shank, wild mushroom risotto, tuna with noodles, turbot with spinach or Scotch rib-eye fillet, all freshly prepared. Fine summer garden with rural views. Hosts an annual local pumpkin competition.

Open: 11-3 6-11 (Sun 12-3, Sun 7-10.30) **Bar Meals:** L served all week 12-2.30 D served Mon-Sat 7-9.30 **Restaurant Meals:** L served all week 12-2.30 D served all week 7-9.30 **Brewery/Company:** Hall & Woodhouse ◪: Badger Tanglefoot, Best & Golden Champion **Children's Facilities:** Fam room Play area (Swings, slide, swinging tyre) Menu/Portions Highchair Food warming **Nearby:** Salisbury Cathedral, River Avon, New Forest **Notes:** Dogs allowed in bar Garden: Food served outside in large garden **Parking:** 40

PEWSEY
The Seven Stars ♀

Bottlesford SN9 6LU

☎ 01672 851325 ▤ 01672 851583

Email: sevenstarsinn@hotmail.com

Dir: *Off A345*

This thatched, creeper-clad 16th-century pub is tucked away in a hamlet in the heart of the Vale of Pewsey. Like many pubs it has a large garden, but few can match the seven splendid acres here. The front door opens straight on to the low-beamed, oak-panelled bar, with dining areas to either side, though new licensees plan some refurbishments. The weekly changing menus offer interesting starters and a comprehensive selection of main courses. Snacks and light meals are also available.

Open: 11.30-3 6-11 **Bar Meals:** L served all week 12-2.30 D served all week 6-9.30 **Restaurant Meals:** L served all week 12-2.30 D served all week 6-9.30 **Brewery/Company:** Free House ◪: Wadworth 6X, Badger Dorset Best, London Pride & Guest Ales ♀: 9 **Children's Facilities:** Menu/Portions Cutlery Highchair Food warming **Notes:** Dogs allowed in bar Garden: Lawned with terrace at front of pub **Parking:** 50

SEEND

Bell Inn

Bell Hill nr Melksham SN12 6SA

☎ 01380 828338

Email: bellseend@aol.com

Web: www.thebellinnatseend.co.uk

According to local tradition, Oliver Cromwell and his troops enjoyed breakfast at this inn, quite possibly on 18 September 1645 when he was advancing from Trowbridge to attack Devizes Castle. The extensive menu runs to poached salmon with a prawn and cream sauce; spicy bean burgers; and barbecue pork ribs, while the specials board highlights liver and bacon casserole; chicken balti; and Highland sausages in whisky. The two-door restaurant has lovely valley views.

Open: 11.15-3 6-midnight **Bar Meals:** L served all week 11.45-2.15 D served all week 6.15-9.30 (Sun 12-2.15) Av main course £7.50 **Restaurant Meals:** L served all week 11.45-2.15 D served all week 6.15-9.30 (Sun 12-2.15) **Brewery/Company:** Wadworth 🍺: Wadworth 6X, Henry's IPA & Henrys Smooth **Children's Facilities:** Play area Menu/Portions Highchair Food warming **Nearby:** Longleat, Bowood, Brockerswood **Notes:** Dogs allowed in bar, in garden, Water Garden: Large, seating for 60 people, beautiful views **Parking:** 30

SEEND

The Barge Inn 🍷

Seend Cleeve nr Melksham SN12 6QB

☎ 01380 828230 📠 01380 828972

Dir: Off A365 between Melksham & Devizes

This Victorian barge-style pub, converted from a wharf house, is situated on the Kennet and Avon Canal between Bath and Devizes. Delicately painted Victorian flowers adorn ceilings and walls. In addition to a lunchtime menu of snacks and hot dishes - tapas, baked field mushroom, goujons of Cornish cod - there's a seasonal carte supported by an extensive list of blackboard specials.

Open: 11-3 6-11 (All day Sat-Sun) **Bar Meals:** L served all week 12-2 D served all week 7-9.30 (Sat, Sun & BH lunch 12-2.30) Av main course £10 **Restaurant Meals:** L served all week 12-2 D served all week 7-9.30 (Sat, Sun & BH lunch 12-2.30) Av 3 course alc £20 **Brewery/Company:** Wadworth 🍺: Wadworth 6X & Henry's IPA, Bishops Tipple, Butcombe Bitter 🍷: 10 **Children's Facilities:** Menu/Portions Games Highchair Food warming **Nearby:** Soft Play Centre, Longleat Safari Park **Notes:** Dogs allowed in bar, Water Garden: Large canal side garden **Parking:** 50

SHERSTON

Carpenters Arms

SN16 0LS

☎ 01666 840665

Dir: On the B4040 W of Malmesbury

A 17th-century traditional village inn offering a warm welcome to families, dogs and walkers in wellies. The inn has four interconnecting rooms, with low, beamed ceilings, a wood-burner and a cosy old-world atmosphere. The sunny conservatory restaurant overlooks a beautiful garden. The menu offers a choice of starters like home-made soup, then a selection of meat dishes, curries, fish dishes, vegetarian options and blackboard specials. BBQs and hog roasts in summer.

Open: 12-3 5.30-12 (All day wknds) **Bar Meals:** L served all week 12-2 D served all week 7-9 (Fri/Sat 6.30-9.30) **Restaurant Meals:** L served all week 12-2 D served all week 7-9 (Fri/Sat 6.30-9.30) **Brewery/Company:** Enterprise Inns 🍺: Whitbread Best, Bath Gem, Wickwar Bob & Guest Ale **Children's Facilities:** Play area (Swings, slide, climbing frame) Menu/Portions Cutlery Games Highchair Food warming **Notes:** Dogs allowed in bar Garden: Plantsman's garden, array of plants **Parking:** 12

WILTSHIRE

WILTSHIRE

SWINDON
The Sun Inn ♛

Lydiard Millicent SN5 3LU
☎ 01793 770425 📄 01793 778287
Email: thesuninnlm@yahoo.co.uk
Web: www.geocities.com/thesuninnlm
Dir: *3 miles to the W of Swindon, 1.5 miles from junct 16 of M4*

This 18th-century free house is in a conservation area, near Lydiard House and Park. The walls display an eclectic mix of artwork from local artists and work by a local potter. There's an emphasis on real ale, and a huge choice of menus from bar snacks to a grill menu and house specialities like Jamaican chicken or choices from the sweet chilli sizzle platters. Daily specials might include exotic options like pan-fried fillet of kangaroo.

Open: 11.30-3 5.30-11 (Sun 6.30-10.30, Mar-Sep all day Sun) **Bar Meals:** L served all week 12-2.30 D served all week 6.30-9.30 (Sun 12-2.30, 6.30-9) **Restaurant Meals:** L served all week 12-2.30 D served all week 6.30-9.30 (Sun 12-2.30, 6.30-9) **Brewery/Company:** Free House 🍺: Sharp's Doom Bar, Interbrew Flowers Original, Wadsworth 6X, Wye Valley Brewery, West Berkshire Brewery ♛: 8 **Children's Facilities:** Menu/Portions Games Highchair Food warming Baby changing **Nearby:** Cotswolds, Lydiard Country Park, Cotswold Water Park **Notes:** Dogs allowed in bar, in garden, Water **Garden:** Large area, BBQ, suntrap **Parking:** 50

TOLLARD ROYAL
King John Inn

Salisbury SP5 5PS
☎ 01725 516207
Dir: *On B3081 (7m E of Shaftesbury)*

Named after one of King John's hunting lodges, this Victorian building was opened in 1859. A friendly and relaxing place, it is today perhaps better known as Madonna's local after she and husband Guy Ritchie moved in close by. Also nearby is a 13th-century church, and the area is excellent rambling country. A typical menu offers old English favourites like bangers and apple mash; bacon, liver and kidney casserole; Dorset lamb cutlets; and Wiltshire gammon with peaches.
Open: 11-3 6-12 (Sun 12-10.30) **Bar Meals:** L served all week 12-2 D served all week 7-9 (All day Sun summer) **Restaurant Meals:** L served all week 12-2 D served all week 7-9 (Sun 12-2.30) **Brewery/Company:** Free House 🍺: Courage Best, John Smith's, Wadworth 6X, Ringwood **Children's Facilities:** Menu/Portions Cutlery Highchair Food warming **Notes:** Dogs allowed in bar, Water **Garden:** Terrace, food served outside **Parking:** 18

UPTON LOVELL
Prince Leopold Inn ♛

nr Warminster BA12 0JP
☎ 01985 850460 📄 01985 850737
Email: Princeleopold@Lineone.net
Web: www.princeleopoldinn.co.uk
Dir: *From Warminster take A36 after 4.5m turn left into Upper Lovell*

Built in 1887 as the local shop, post office and general store, the inn was named after Prince Leopold, Queen Victoria's youngest son, who lived nearby. The restaurant has a Mediterranean feel, and the menu covers a lot of gastronomic ground, ranging from Balti curry dishes to Wiltshire gammon with fries, tomato and egg.
Open: 12-3 7-11 **Bar Meals:** L served all week 12-2.30 D served all week 7-10 Av main course £7 **Restaurant Meals:** L served all week 12-2.30 D served all week 7-10 Av 3 course alc £19 **Brewery/Company:** Free House 🍺: Ringwood Best, Scottish Courage John Smith's & San Miguel ♛: 8 **Children's Facilities:** Menu/Portions Games Food warming Baby changing **Nearby:** Longleat & Stonehenge **Notes:** Garden: Riverside garden, spectacular valley views **Parking:** 20

WARMINSTER
The Bath Arms ♟
Clay Street Crockerton BA12 8AJ
☎ 01985 212262 📠 01985 218670
Email: batharms@hotmail.co.uk

Well-known free house on the Longleat Estate, where villagers are joined by walkers and tourists and regularly returning visitors from Bath, Salisbury and Shaftsbury. In recent years the kitchen and restaurant have been remodelled by chef proprietor Dean Carr, and the garden, formerly a wasteland, has been landscaped to provide a pleasant spot for outdoor dining. Dishes take in favourite snacks and grills, with specials like roast loin of pork. **Open:** 11-3 6-11 (open all day in Summer) **Bar Meals:** L served all week 12-2.30 D served all week 6-9.30 Av main course £14 **Restaurant Meals:** L served all week 12-2.30 D served all week 6-9.30 **Brewery/Company:** Free House 🍺: Crockerton Classic, Naughty Ferrit & Guest Ales ♟: 10 **Children's Facilities:** Play area Menu/Portions Games Highchair Food warming **Nearby:** Longleat, Shearwater & Centre Parks **Notes:** Dogs allowed in bar, in garden, Water bowls **Garden:** Stone walled, lawned garden, 19 tables & BBQ **Parking:** 45

WARMINSTER
The George Inn ★★★★ INN ♟
Longbridge Deverill BA12 7DG
☎ 01985 840396 📠 01985 841333
Web: www.thegeorgeinnlongbridgedeverill.co.uk

A 17th-century coaching inn at the heart of the pretty village of Longbridge Deverill. Customers can enjoy a pint of real ale by the fire in the oak-beamed Longbridge Bar, or sit outside in the two-acre garden on the banks of the River Wylye. Food is served in a choice of two no-smoking restaurants, and there is a Sunday carvery in the Wylye Suite. **Open:** 11-11 (Sun 12pm-10.30pm, Fri 11am-12pm) **Closed:** 25 Dec from 3pm **Bar Meals:** L served all week 12-2.30 D served all week 6-9.30 (Sun 6-9) **Restaurant Meals:** L served all week 12-2.30 D served all week 6-9.30 (Sun 6-9) **Brewery/Company:** Free House 🍺: Scottish Courage John Smith's, Wadworth 6X, Hobdens Doverills Advocat ♟: 11 **Children's Facilities:** Play area (Outdoor children's play area) Highchair Baby changing **Nearby:** Longleat, Cheddar Caves, Wookey Hole **Notes:** Garden: Large, riverside setting **Parking:** 70

WHITLEY
The Pear Tree Inn ♟
Top Lane Melksham SN12 8QX
☎ 01225 709131 📠 01225 702276
Email: enquries@thepeartreeinn.com
Web: www.thepeartreeinn.com

Dir: *A365 from Melksham toward Bath, at Shaw right on B3353 into Whitley, 1st left in lane, pub is at end of lane.*

The Pear Tree, dating from 1750, is a delightful country pub and restaurant in an attractive setting overlooking wooded parkland. It has a garden, patio area and boules piste. The same food is available throughout from an extensive carte, a set lunch menu priced for two or three courses, and a choice of toasted sandwiches. **Open:** 11-3 6-11 Closed: 25/26 Dec, 1 Jan **Bar Meals:** L served all week 12-2.30 D served all week 6.30-9.30 **Restaurant Meals:** L served all week 12-2.30 D served all week 6.30-9.30 **Brewery/Company:** Free House 🍺: Wadworth 6X, Bath Ales Gem, Stonehenge Ales, Pigswill, Tunnel Vision, Doom Bar ♟: 10 **Children's Facilities:** Menu/Portions Cutlery Games Highchair Food warming **Notes:** Garden: Cottage garden with views over parkland **Parking:** 60

WILTSHIRE

WILTSHIRE

WOODFALLS

The Woodfalls Inn ★★★ INN ♟
The Ridge SP5 2LN
☎ 01725 513222 📠 01725 513220
Email: woodfallsi@aol.com
Web: www.woodfallsinn.co.uk
Dir: *B3080 to Woodfalls*
Located on an old coaching route on the northern edge of the New Forest, the Woodfalls Inn has provided hospitality to travellers since the early Victorian era. A more recent extension accommodates a purpose built function suite, in addition to the bar areas, conservatory, lounge and restaurant. Home-made dishes include chicken curry, beef or vegetable lasagne, and steak and ale pie. There is also a comprehensive selection of grills.
Open: 11-11 **Bar Meals:** L served all week 12-2.15 D served all week 6.30-9.30 Av main course £6.95 **Restaurant Meals:** L served all week 12-2.15 D served all week 6.30-9 Av 3 course alc £20 **Brewery/Company:** Free House ◖: Courage Directors & Best, Hopback's GFB, John Smiths, Ringwood 49er ♟: 9 **Children's Facilities:** Menu/Portions Games Highchair Food warming Baby changing **Nearby:** Paultons Park, Romsey Rapids, Marwell Zoo **Notes:** Dogs allowed in bar, in garden, in bedrooms, Toys & Water **Garden:** Enclosed terraced area **Parking:** 26

WOOTTON RIVERS

Royal Oak ♟
Marlborough SN8 4NQ
☎ 01672 810322 📠 01672 811168
Email: royaloak35@hotmail.com
Web: www.wiltshire-pubs.co.uk
Dir: *3m S from Marlborough*
A 16th-century thatched and timbered inn just 100 yards from the Kennet and Avon Canal and very handy for walking in the delightful Savernake Forest. Stonehenge, Salisbury, Marlborough and Hungerford are also within easy reach. Menus tend to be flexible with innumerable starters, main courses and fish dishes.
Open: 10.30-3.30 6-11 (Close Sun 10.30) **Bar Meals:** L served all week 11.30-2.30 D served all week 6-9.30 (Sun 12-3, 6-11) Av main course £10 **Restaurant Meals:** L served all week 11.30-2.30 D served all week 6-9.30 Av 3 course alc £20 **Brewery/Company:** Free House ◖: Wadworth 6X, guest ales ♟: 7 **Children's Facilities:** Fam room Menu/Portions Food warming **Notes:** Dogs allowed in bar, in garden **Garden:** Large lawn area, raised terrace with seating **Parking:** 20

WYLYE

The Bell Inn ♟
High Street Wylye nr Warminster BA12 0QP
☎ 01985 248338 📠 01985 248491
Email: thebellatwyle@hotmail.co.uk
Web: www.thebellatwylye.com
There's a wealth of old oak beams, log fires and an inglenook fireplace at this 14th-century coaching inn, situated in the pretty Wylye valley. In 2005 the Bell was taken over by the Hidden Brewery (located just two miles away in Dinton). Lunch and dinner menus feature mainly local ingredients.
Open: 11.30-2.30 6-11 (Sun 12-3, 6-10.30) **Bar Meals:** L served all week 12-2.30 D served all week 6.30-9.30 (Sun 12-2.30, 7-9) Av main course £9 **Restaurant Meals:** L served all week 12-2 D served all week 6-9.30 Av 3 course alc £19 **Brewery/Company:** Free House ◖: Hidden Pint, Hidden Quest, Hidden Oldsarum, Hidden Fantasy, Hidden Treasure & Hidden Pleasure ♟: 10 **Children's Facilities:** Menu/Portions Cutlery Games Highchair Food warming Baby changing **Nearby:** Stone Henge, Farmer Giles Farmstead **Notes:** Dogs allowed bar & garden **Garden:** Walled **Parking:** 20

St Germans Viaduct in the Tamer Valley

Scotland

Loch an Eilean

ABERDEEN

Old Blackfriars 🍷

52 Castle Street AB11 5BB

☎ 01224 581922 📠 01224 582153

Stunning stained glass and a warm, welcoming atmosphere are features of this traditional city centre pub, situated in Aberdeen's historic Castlegate. It is built on the site of property owned by the Black Friars - Dominican monks, hence the name. The varied menu runs from sandwiches and filled potatoes through to hearty dishes such as bangers and mash; chicken tikka masala; and beef au poivre. Finish with sticky toffee pudding or pancakes in maple syrup.

Open: 11-12 (Sun 12.30-11, Fri-Sat 10-1am) Closed: Dec 25 **Bar Meals:** L/D served all week 12-8.45 (Sun 12.30-8.45, Fri-Sat 12-7.45) **Brewery/Company:** Belhaven Brewery : Abbot Ale, Deuchars IPA, Caledonian 80/-, Inveralmond, Ossian and guest ales 🍷: 12 **Children's Facilities:** Licence Menu/Portions Highchair Baby changing **Nearby:** Maritime Museum, Satrosphere & Puthie Park **Notes:**

BALMEDIE

The Cock and Bull Bar and Restaurant 🍷

Ellon Road Blairton AB23 8XY

☎ 01358 743249 📠 01358 742466

Email: info@thecockandbull.co.uk

Web: www.thecockandbull.co.uk

Dir: *11m N of city centre, located on main A90 between Balmedie junct & Foveran*

Originally a coaching inn, now a cosy gastropub. The bar area is warmed by a cast-iron range. The menu, based extensively on local produce, includes dishes like salmon and chestnut noisettes with leek and onion risotto.

Open: 10-1 **Bar Meals:** L served all week 11.30-11 D served all week 6-9.30 Av main course £12.95 **Restaurant Meals:** L served all week 11.30-11 D served all week 5-9.30 Av 3 course alc £27 **Brewery/Company:** Free House : Directors Ale, Guinness, McEwans 80/, Tennants, Stella Artois 🍷: 8 **Children's Facilities:** Licence Fam room Play area (Tree house, play house) Menu/Portions Cutlery Games Highchair Food warming Baby changing **Nearby:** Nature reserve, Amusment park, beaches **Notes:** Garden: Paved area with grass **Parking:** 70

MARYCULTER

Old Mill Inn

South Deeside Road AB12 5FX

☎ 01224 733212 📠 01224 732884

Email: Info@oldmillinn.co.uk

Web: www.oldmillinn.co.uk

Dir: *5m W of Aberdeen on B9077*

This delightful family-run country inn stands on the edge of the River Dee, just over five miles from Aberdeen city centre. A former mill house, the 18th-century granite building has been tastefully modernised to include a restaurant where the finest Scottish ingredients feature on the menu: dishes like venison stovies, peppered carpaccio of beef, cullen skink, and chicken and venison terrine are typical.

Open: 11-11 **Bar Meals:** L served all week 12-2 D served all week 5.30-9.30 **Restaurant Meals:** L served all week 12-2 D served all week 5.30-9.30 **Brewery/Company:** Free House : Interbrew Bass, Caledonian Deuchers IPA, Timothy Taylor, Landlord **Children's Facilities:** Menu/Portions Highchair Food warming Baby changing **Nearby:** Storybook Glen, Crathes Castle, Fun Fair at Aberdeen beach **Notes:** Garden: Food served outdoors, patio **Parking:** 100

OLDMELDRUM

The Redgarth ☕

Kirk Brae Inverurie AB51 0DJ

☎ 01651 872353 📠 01651 873763

Email: redgarth@aol.com

Web: www.redgarth.com

Dir: *On A947*

Built as a house in 1928, this is a family-run inn with an attractive garden offering magnificent views of Bennachie and the surrounding countryside. Cask-conditioned ales and fine wines are served along with dishes prepared on the premises using fresh local produce. A typical menu offers the likes of sirloin steak garni, deep fried fillet of haddock, chicken Maryland, rack of lamb with herb stuffing, venison MacDuff, and cashew nut roast. Delicious choice of puddings.

Open: 11-3 5-11 (Fri-Sat -11.45) Closed: Dec 25-26 Jan 1-3 **Bar Meals:** L served all week 12-2 D served all week 5-9 (Fri-Sat 9.30) Av main course £7.50 **Restaurant Meals:** L served all week 12-2 D served all week 5-9 (Fri-Sat 5-9.30) Av 3 course alc £13.50 **Brewery/Company:** Free House ☕: Inveralmond Thrappledouser, Caledonian Deuchers IPA, Taylor Landlord, Isle of Skye Red Cullin, Misty Law (Kelburn) ☕: 6 **Children's Facilities:** Licence Menu/Portions Games Highchair Food warming **Nearby:** Haddo House, Fyvie Castle, Archeolink **Notes:** Garden: Beer garden, outdoor eating **Parking:** 60

ARDUAINE

Loch Melfort Hotel ★★★ HL ◉◉

PA34 4XG

☎ 01852 200233 📠 01852 200214

Email: reception@lochmelfort.co.uk

Web: www.lochmelfort.co.uk

Dir: *On the A816 20m south of Oban*

One of the finest locations on the west coast of Scotland awaits visitors to this award-winning hotel and restaurant - the perfect place for a relaxing holiday or short break at any time of the year. The hotel stands in 26 acres of grounds next to the National Trust's Arduaine Gardens, and its loch-side location gives spectacular views across Asknish Bay and the Sound of Jura. To the rear, the hotel is framed by woodlands and the magnificent mountains of Argyll. The restaurant offers superb dining with fresh local produce including meats, cheeses and locally caught fish and seafood. Meanwhile, the Skerry Bar/Bistro is very popular with both guests and locals for light lunches, teas and suppers. Here, the menu ranges from sandwiches, baguettes and toasties to dishes like warm Cajun chicken salad.

Open: 10.30-10.30 (Fri-Sat 10.30-11) Closed: Early Jan & Feb **Bar Meals:** L served all week 12-2.30 D served all week 6-9 Av main course £7.50 **Restaurant Meals:** D served all week 7-9 Av 3 course alc £25 **Brewery/Company:** Free House ☕: 80/-, Theakstons, Guinness, Miller, Kronenbourg **Children's Facilities:** Menu/Portions Cutlery Highchair Food warming **Nearby:** Oban Rare Breeds Park, Oban Sealife Centre, Kilmartin Glen & Museum **Notes:** Dogs allowed, Water Garden: Overlooking the Loch, spectacular views **Parking:** 50

CLACHAN-SEIL

Tigh an Truish Inn

Oban PA34 4QZ

☎ 01852 300242

Dir: *14m S of Oban, take A816, 12m turn off B844 toward Atlantic Bridge*

Following the Battle of Culloden in 1746, kilts were outlawed on pain of death. In defiance of this edict the islanders wore their kilts at home; but, on excursions to the mainland, they would stop at the Tigh an Truish - the 'house of trousers' - and change into the hated trews. The inn offers an appetising menu based on the best local produce, with a range of starters like sweet pickled herring with brown bread and salad; and main course dishes such as home-made vegetable lasagne.

Open: 11-3 5-11 (May-Sept all day) Closed: 25 Dec & Jan 1 **Bar Meals:** L served all week 12-2 D served all week 6-8.30 **Restaurant Meals:** L served all week 12-2 D served all week 6-8.30 **Brewery/Company:** Free House ☕: Local guest ales changing regularly **Children's Facilities:** Fam room Highchair Food warming **Notes:** Dogs allowed in bar, in garden Garden: Tables beside the sea in garden with lawn **Parking:** 35

ARGYLL & BUTE

CRINAN
Crinan Hotel
PA31 8SR
☎ 01546 830261 📄 01546 830292
Email: nryan@crinanhotel.com
Web: www.crinanhotel.com
Dir: *From M8, at end of bridge take A82, at Tarbert bear left onto A83. At Inverary follow Campbeltown signs to Lochgilphead, follow signs for A816 to Oban. 2m turn left to Crinan on B841.*
From its location at the northern end of the Crinan Canal, the hotel enjoys fabulous views across the Sound of Jura. You can be sure of the freshest seafood - landed daily just 50 metres from the hotel!
Open: 11-11 (May-Oct Mon-Sat 11-12, Sun 11-12) Closed: Xmas **Bar Meals:** L served all week 12-2.30 D served all week 6.30-8.30 Av main course £11.95
Restaurant Meals: D served all week 7-9 🍺: Belhaven, Interbrew Worthington Bitter, Tennants Velvet, Stella Artois, Guinness, Loch Fyne Ales **Children's Facilities:** Licence Menu/Portions Cutlery Games Highchair Food warming Baby changing **Nearby:** Beach, Gemini Cruises **Notes:** Dogs allowed in bar Garden: Patio **Parking:** 30

PORT APPIN
The Pierhouse Hotel & Seafood Restaurant
PA38 4DE
☎ 01631 730302 📄 01631 730400
Email: pierhouseads@btconnect.com
Web: www.pierhousehotel.co.uk
A superb setting on Loch Linnhe on Scotland's West coast with views of Lismore and the Morvern Hills makes The Pierhouse a memorable spot for a meal. The food is sourced locally, with the lobster, langoustine, prawns, scallops, salmon, oysters and mussels all taken from local waters.
Open: 11.30-11.30 (Sun 12-11.30) Closed: Dec 25 **Bar Meals:** L served all week 12.30-2.30 D served all week 6.30-9.30 Av main course £13.50 **Restaurant Meals:** L served all week 12.30-2.30 D served all week 6.30-9.30 Av 3 course alc £26.45 **Brewery/Company:** Free House 🍺: Calders Cream, Calders 70/-, Carlsberg-Tetley Tetley Bitter **Children's Facilities:** Licence Fam room Menu/Portions Cutlery Games Highchair Food warming Baby changing **Nearby:** Scottish Sealife Sanctuary, Oban Breeds Farm Park, Local Beaches **Notes:** Dogs allowed Garden: Terrace with good views, lawn **Parking:** 20

STRACHUR
Creggans Inn ★★★ HL 🌐 🍷
PA27 8BX
☎ 01369 860279 📄 01369 860637
Email: info@creggans-inn.co.uk
Web: www.creggans-inn.co.uk
Dir: *A82 from Glasgow, at Tarbet take A83 to Cairndow, then A815 down coast to Strachur*
From the hills above this comfortable free house on the very edge of Loch Fyne, you can gaze across the Mull of Kintyre to the Western Isles beyond. The hotel, which has been a coaching inn since Mary Queen of Scots' day, has 14 en suite bedrooms, together with facilities suitable for all the family. There's also a formal terraced garden and patio for alfresco summer drinking, with a good range of ales and malt whiskies to imbibe there. Local produce plays a key role in preparing the hotel's seasonal menus. A typical dinner might start with cullen skink or Loch Fyne smoked salmon, before moving on to chicken breast with garlic roasted new potatoes; or tagliatelle with pesto, toasted pine nuts and cherry tomatoes. There's a selection of home-made puddings and Scottish cheeses to finish.
Open: 11-11 **Bar Meals:** L served all week 12-2.45 D served all week 6-8.45 Av main course £8 **Restaurant Meals:** D served all week 7-9 **Brewery/Company:** Free House 🍺: Coniston Bluebird Bitter, Fyne Ales Highlander, Atlas Latitude, Deuchars IPA, Harvieston Bitter & Twisted 🍷: 7 **Children's Facilities:** Highchair Food warming Baby changing **Notes:** Garden: Formal, terraced, occasional seating **Parking:** 36

TAYVALLICH

Tayvallich Inn

By Lochgilphead PA31 8PL

☎ 01546 870282 📠 01546 870333

Email: rfhanderson@aol.com

Web: www.tayvallich-inn.com

Dir: *From Lochgilphead take A816 then B841/B8025*

This 'house in the pass', as it translates, was converted from an old bus garage in 1976 and stands by a natural harbour at the head of Loch Sween with stunning views over the anchorage, especially from the picnic tables that front the inn in summer. The cosy bar with its yachting theme and the more formal dining-room feature original works by local artists and large picture windows from which to gaze out over the village and Tayvallich Bay. Those interested in the works of 19th-century engineer Thomas Telford will find plenty of bridges and piers in the area. Expect a lot of seafood, including Loch Etive mussels steamed in white wine, garlic and cream; seared scallops on pea purée and black pudding; and the Tayvallich Seafood Platter. Other options could include prime Scottish rib-eye with onion rings and tomatoes; and beer-battered haddock and chips.

Open: 11-2.30 5.30-12 (Fri -Sat 5-1am, Sun 5-12) Closed: 25 Dec **Bar Meals:** L served all week 12-2 D served all week 6-9 Av main course £12 **Restaurant Meals:** L served all week 12-2 D served all week 6-9 **Brewery/Company:** Free House ◀: Tennants, Guinness, Loch Fyne Ales **Children's Facilities:** Menu/Portions Games Highchair Food warming **Notes:** Dogs allowed in bar, No dogs at meal times **Garden:** Patio area **Parking:** 20

RATHO

The Bridge Inn

27 Baird Road Edinburgh EH28 8RA

☎ 0131 3331320 📠 0131 333 3480

Email: info@bridgeinn.com

Dir: *From Newbridge B7030 junction, follow signs for Ratho*

This old canalside inn was rescued from decay in 1971. Now the informal Pop Inn Lounge serves snacks and bar meals all day, while the award-winning restaurant offers dishes like Ratho haggis fillet steak with Drambuie, cream and mushroom sauce; and grilled Scottish sirloin with a choice of sauces.

Open: 12-11 (Sat 11-12, Sun 12.30-11) Closed: 26 Dec, 1-2 Jan **Bar Meals:** L served all week 12-9 D served all week 12-9 (Sun 12.30-9) Av main course £8 **Restaurant Meals:** L served all week 12-2.30 D served all week 6.30-9 (Sun 12.30-9) Av 3 course alc £20 **Brewery/Company:** Free House ◀: Belhaven, Deuchars IPA, Tennants, Stella Artois, Peroni 🍷: 6 **Children's Facilities:** Licence Fam room Menu/Portions Cutlery Highchair Food warming Baby changing **Notes:** Garden: Landscaped, goose/duck reserve, patio **Parking:** 40

GLASGOW

Ubiquitous Chip 🏆🏆 🍷

12 Ashton Lane G12 8SJ

☎ 0141 334 5007 📠 0141 337 1302

Email: mail@ubiquitouschip.co.uk

Web: www.ubiquitouschip.co.uk

Dir: *In the west end of Glasgow, off Byres Road*

Offering a contemporary slant on traditional Scottish cooking, the Chip has been a Glaswegian institution for more than 35 years. The main restaurant is actually a glass-covered mews in the west end of the city with cobbled floor, water fountains and enough flora to grace an arboretum. Traditional draught beers, over a hundred malt whiskies and first class wines by the glass are served from a bar that is reputed to be the smallest in Scotland. Today's menus continue the founding philosophy of using wholesome ingredients, imaginatively prepared and presented. A typical lunch might start with oak-smoked mackerel pâté with kiwi compote, followed by pan-fried Scotch lamb's liver with Ayrshire bacon, mashed potatoes and onions in Caledonian 80/- sauce; or walnut-dipped goats' cheese fritter with aubergine caviar, white wine and orange sauce.

Open: 11-12 (12.30-12 Sun) Closed: 25 Dec, 1 Jan **Bar Meals:** L served all week 12-4 D served all week 4-11 (Sun 12.30-4) **Restaurant Meals:** L served all week 12-2.30 D served all week 5.30-11 (Sun 12.30-2.30, 6.30-11) Av 3 course alc £20 **Brewery/Company:** Free House ◀: Caledonian 80/- & Deuchars IPA 🍷: 21 **Children's Facilities:** Menu/Portions Games Highchair Food warming **Nearby:** Hunterian Museum, Science Centre, art galleries

DUMFRIES & GALLOWAY

ISLE OF WHITHORN
The Steam Packet Inn
Harbour Row Newton Stewart DG8 8LL
☎ 01988 500334 📄 01988 500627
Email: steampacketinn@btconnect.com
Web: www.steampacketinn.com
Dir: *From Newton Stewart take A714, then A746 to Whithorn, then Isle of Whithorn*
Although not an island as such, there is water in most directions around this lively quayside pub at the tip of the Machars peninsula. Menus spoil you for choice: maybe steak and kidney casserole at lunchtime or wild boar with sage derby cheese and port and honey jus for dinner.
Open: 11-11 (Winter closed 2.30-6pm) Closed: Dec 25
Bar Meals: L served all week 12-2 D served all week 6.30-9 Av main course £6 **Restaurant Meals:** L served all week 12-2 D served all week 6.30-9 🍺: Scottish Courage Theakston XB, Caledonian Deuchars IPA, Black Sheep Best Bitter, Houston Killellan **Children's Facilities:** Licence Menu/Portions Games Highchair Food warming Baby changing **Nearby:** Montreith Beach, Creams of Galloway, Whithorn Dig **Notes:** Dogs allowed in bar, in garden **Parking:** 4

KIRKCUDBRIGHT
Selkirk Arms Hotel 🍷
Old High Street DG6 4JG
☎ 01557 330402 📄 01557 331639
Email: reception@selkirkarmshotel.co.uk
Web: www.selkirkarmshotel.co.uk
A traditional white-painted pub on the street corner, with nice gardens to the rear. It has associations with the Scottish poet Robert Burns, and T. E. Lawrence (of Arabia), who lived nearby. Good choice of beers, including Youngers Tartan. Typical menu offers lamb or vegetable Madras, fresh Scottish haddock in crispy beer batter, steak and mushroom pie, spinach and cream cheese roulade, and haggis, neeps and tatties.
Open: 11-12 **Bar Meals:** L served all week 12-2 D served all week 6-9.30 **Restaurant Meals:** L served all week 12-2 D served all week 7-9.30 🍺: Youngers Tartan, John Smiths Bitter, Criffel, Old Speckled Hen 🍷: 8
Children's Facilities: Licence Menu/Portions Highchair Food warming Baby changing **Nearby:** Kirkcudbright Wildlife Park **Notes:** Dogs allowed in bar, in garden, Dog bones/biscuits **Garden:** Beautiful **Parking:** 50

MOFFAT
Black Bull Hotel 🍷
Churchgate DG10 9EG
☎ 01683 220206 📄 01683 220483
Email: hotel@blackbullmoffat.co.uk
Web: www.blackbullmoffat.co.uk
This historic pub was the headquarters of Graham of Claverhouse during the Scottish rebellion in the 17th century, and Scottish bard Robert Burns was a frequent visitor around 1790. Nowadays, it serves a varied, good value menu. Starters include mussels in white wine and garlic sauce; and battered black pudding in a creamy whisky mustard sauce. Follow with Moffat ram pie; poached Solway salmon in Cointreau, orange and ginger sauce; or hot chilli tacos.
Open: 11-11 (Thu-Sat 11-12) **Bar Meals:** L served all week 11.30-9.15 D served all week 11.30-9.15 Av main course £6.95 **Restaurant Meals:** L served all week 11.30-3 D served all week 6-9.15 Av 3 course alc £12 **Brewery/Company:** Free House 🍺: McEwans, Scottish Courage Theakston 80/- 🍷: 10 **Children's Facilities:** Menu/Portions Games Highchair Food warming **Nearby:** Station Park, Waterside Walk & Moffatasia **Notes:** Garden: Courtyard with eight tables **Parking:** 4

NEW ABBEY
Criffel Inn
The Square DG2 8BX
☎ 01387 850305 & 850244 📠 01387 850305
mail: enquiries@criffelinn.com
Web: www.criffelinn.com
Dir: *M/A74 leave at Gretna, A75 to Dumfries, A710 S to New Abbey*

A former 18th-century coaching inn set on the Solway coast in the historic conservation village of New Abbey close to the ruins of the 13th-century Sweetheart Abbey. The Graham family ensures a warm welcome and excellent home-cooked food using local produce. Dishes include chicken wrapped in smoked Ayrshire bacon served with Loch Arthur mature creamy cheese sauce; fish dishes feature sea trout and sea bass among several others. Lawned beer garden overlooking corn-mill and square; ideal for touring Dumfries and Galloway.
Open: 12-2.30 5-11 (Sat 12-12, Sun 12-11) **Bar Meals:** L served all week 12-2 D served all week 5.30-8 (Sun 12-8) Av main course £7 **Restaurant Meals:** L served all week 12-2 D served all week 5-8 (Sun 12-8) Av 3 course alc £14 **Brewery/Company:** Free House 🍺: Belhaven Best, McEwans 60- **Children's Facilities:** Fam room Menu/Portions Games Highchair Food warming **Nearby:** Never Never Land, swimming pool **Notes:** Dogs allowed in bar, in garden, Water **Garden:** Garden overlooking historic Cornmill & Square **Parking:** 8

NEW GALLOWAY
Cross Keys Hotel
High Street DG7 3RN
☎ 01644 420494 📠 01644 420672
mail: enquiries@crosskeys-newgalloway.co.uk
Web: www.crosskeys-newgalloway.co.uk
Dir: *At N end of Loch Ken, 10m from Castle Douglas*

An 18th-century coaching inn with a beamed period bar, where food is served in restored, stone-walled cells (part of the hotel was once the police station). The à la carte restaurant offers hearty food with a Scottish accent. Real ales are a speciality, and there's a good choice of malts.
Open: 12-11 (Apr-Oct 12-12 all wk) **Bar Meals:** L served all week 12-2 D served all week 6-8 (Nov-Mar no food Mon-Tue. Sun 5.30-7.30) Av main course £7 **Restaurant Meals:** L served Sunday12-2 D served Apr-Oct, Tue-Sun 6.30-8.30 (Sun 5.30-7.30) Av 3 course alc £17.50 🍺: Houston real ales, guest real ales 🍷: 6 **Children's Facilities:** Fam room Menu/Portions Cutlery Highchair Food warming Baby changing **Nearby:** Red Deer Park, Cream of Galloway Fun Park, Loch Ken Watersports & Red Kite Trail **Notes:** Garden: Small enclosed garden, good views **Parking:** 6

NEWTON STEWART
Creebridge House Hotel
Minnigaff DG8 6NP
☎ 01671 402121 📠 01671 403258
mail: info@creebridge.co.uk
Web: www.creebridge.co.uk
Dir: *From A75 into Newton Stewart, turn right over river bridge, hotel 200yds on left.*

Named after the nearby River Cree and set in three acres of gardens and woodland at the foot of Kirroughtree Forest, this country house hotel is a listed building dating from 1760. Bridge's bar and brasserie offers malt whiskies, real ales and an interesting menu with an emphasis on fresh Scottish produce. Typical starters are assiette of locally smoked, home-cured Scottish salmon; Dunsyre blue cheese soufflé; Thai pork salad; and terrine of venison, pigeon and puy lentil. The main list could offer pan-fried breast and confit leg of Barbary duck; filo tart of goat's cheese with tomatoes and onion marmalade; and pan-roasted loin of lamb.
Open: 12-2.30 6-11 (Sun, all day) Closed: 3 Jan for 3 wks **Bar Meals:** L served all week 12-2 D served all week 6-8.45 Av main course £8.50 **Restaurant Meals:** L served all week 12-2 D served all week 6-8.45 Av 3 course alc £22 **Brewery/Company:** Free House 🍺: Fuller's London Pride, Tennants, Deuchers & Guinness **Children's Facilities:** Licence Menu/Portions Games Highchair Food warming Baby changing **Nearby:** Gem Rock Museum, Scallywags Play Centre & Cream o' Galloway **Notes:** Dogs allowed in bar, in garden, Water **Garden:** Rose beds, fish pond, lawns & wooded area **Parking:** 40

PORTPATRICK
Crown Hotel
9 North Crescent DG9 8SX
☎ 01776 810261 📠 01776 810551
Email: crownhotel@supanet.com
Web: www.crownportpatrick.com
Dir: *Situated on water front, 7m from Stranraer*
Just a few yards from the water's edge in one of the region's most picturesque villages, The Crown Hotel has striking views across the Irish Sea. Naturally, seafood is a speciality, from a lunchtime seafood pancake to an evening meal of lobster thermidor. Other choices include pan-fried venison in a rich Port and redcurrant game jus.
Open: 11-12 **Bar Meals:** L served all week 12-6 D served all week 6-9.30 Av main course £7.95
Restaurant Meals: L served all week 12-2.30 D served

all week 6-9.30 Av 3 course alc £22
Brewery/Company: Free House 🍺: John Smith's, McEwans 80/-, McEwans 70/-, Guinness **Children's Facilities:** Licence Cutlery Games Highchair Food warming Baby changing **Nearby:** Leisure centre, Starnraer, Putting and bowling greens & Beach **Notes:** Dogs allowed in bar Garden: Harbour & Irish Sea views

BROUGHTY FERRY
Fisherman's Tavern 🍷
10-16 Fort Street Dundee DD5 2AD
☎ 01382 775941 📠 01382 477466
Email: bookings@fishermans-tavern-hotel.co.uk
Web: www.fishermans-tavern-hotel.co.uk
Dir: *From Dundee city centre follow A930 to Broughty Ferry, right at sign for hotel*
A terrace of three pastel-washed cottages in a side street off the waterfront in this seaside town on Dundee's eastern outskirts. There's a good selection of snacks and lighter meals that won't impede a post-prandial beach walk, while those preferring to get the walk out of the way first might try venison casserole with red wine, or one of the several seafood specialities such as grilled swordfish steak, smoked haddock

kedgeree, or breaded Norwegian scampi.
Open: 11-12 (Sat-Sun 11am-1am) **Bar Meals:** L served all week 11.30-2.30 D served all week 5.30-7.30 Av main course £6.75 **Brewery/Company:** Free House 🍺: Belhaven, Inveralmond Ossian's Ale, Caledonain Deuchers IPA,Timothy Taylor Landlord, Fullers London Pride 🍷: 26 **Children's Facilities:** Licence Fam room Play area Menu/Portions Highchair Food warming Baby changing **Nearby:** Broughty Castle, Castle Green, Discovery Point & Science Centre **Notes:** Dogs allowed in bar, in garden, Water, Biscuits Garden: Walled garden seating for 40

SORN
The Sorn Inn 🍷
35 Main Street KA5 6HU
☎ 01290 551305 📠 01290 553470
Email: craig@sorninn.com
Web: www.sorninn.com
This late 18th-century coaching inn is located in the heart of Ayrshire. It has two dining options: the chop house, which offers steaks, burgers, baguettes and simple meals such as cod and chips or goats' cheese tart; and the smart, award winning restaurant where the modern British fare could include pan-fried halibut with baby spinach and curried mussel chowder; and roast Ayrshire partridge with root vegetables and fondant potatoes.
Open: 12-2.30 6-11 (Sat 12-12, Sun 12.30-11, Fri 12-

2.30, 6-12) **Bar Meals:** L served Tue-Sun 12-2.30 D served Tue-Sun 6-9 (Sat 12-7, Sun 12.30-7) Av main course £8 **Restaurant Meals:** L served Wed-Sun 12-2.30 D served Tue-Sun 6-9 (Sun 12.30-6.30) Av 3 course alc £21.95 🍺: John Smiths, McEwans 60/-
🍷: 12 **Children's Facilities:** Licence Menu/Portions Cutlery Highchair Food warming Baby changing **Nearby:** Loudon Castle Theme Park **Parking:** 8

CASTLECARY

Castlecary House Hotel ★★ HL ☺
Castlecary Road Cumbernauld G68 0HD
☎ 01324 840233 ▤ 01324 841608
Email: enquiries@castlecaryhotel.com
Web: www.castlecaryhotel.com
Dir: *Off A80 between Glasgow and Stirling onto B816*

A friendly hotel close to the historic Antonine Wall and Forth and Clyde Canal. Serves home-cooked fare with bar meals like rustic chicken and vegetable cassoulet. Dinner menu in the restaurant offers chargrilled collops of beef in horseradish mash among other dishes.
Open: 11-11 **Bar Meals:** L/D served all week 12-9 (all day Sat-Sun) Av main course £7 **Restaurant Meals:** L served Sun 12-2 D served Mon-Sat 7-10 Av 3 course alc £19.95 **Brewery/Company:** Free House ▣: Arran

Blonde, Harviestoun Brooker's Bitter & Twisted, Inveralmond Ossian's Ale, Housten Peter's Well, Caledonian Deuchars IPA ☺: 10 **Children's Facilities:** Licence (Baby changing Unit) Menu/Portions Cutlery Games Highchair Food warming Baby changing **Nearby:** Stirling Castle, Wallace Monument, Falkirk Wheel **Notes:** Garden: Beer garden **Parking:** 100

ANSTRUTHER

The Dreel Tavern
16 High Street West KY10 3DL
☎ 01333 310727 ▤ 01333 310577
Email: dreeltavern@aol.com

Complete with a local legend concerning an amorous encounter between James V and a local gypsy woman, the 16th-century Dreel Tavern has plenty of atmosphere. Home-cooked food and cask-conditioned ales are served to hungry visitors of the present. Plenty of local fish dishes including smoked fish pie, and local crab.
Open: 11-12 (Sun 12.30-12) **Bar Meals:** L served all week 12-2 D served all week 5.30-9 (Sun 12.30-2) Av main course £6.50 **Restaurant Meals:** L served all week 12-2 D served all week 5.30-9
Brewery/Company: Free House ▣: Tetley's Bitter,

Harviestoun Bitter & Twisted, Greene King IPA, London Pride, Speckled Hen (beers changed weekly) **Children's Facilities:** Fam room Menu/Portions Highchair Food warming **Nearby:** Fisheries Museum, St Andrews Sealife Centre, Secret Bunker **Notes:** Dogs allowed in bar, Water, biscuits Garden: Enclosed area, seats approx 20 **Parking:** 3

BURNTISLAND

Burntisland Sands Hotel
Lochies Road KY3 9JX
☎ 01592 872230 ▤ 01592 872230
Email: clarkelinton@hotmail.com
Web: www.burntislandsands.co.uk
Dir: *Heading towards Kirkcaldy, Burntisland is on A921. Located on right before reaching Kinghorn.*

This small, family-run hotel, just 50 yards from an award-winning sandy beach, was once a highly regarded girls' boarding school. Reasonably priced breakfasts, snacks, lunches and evening meals are always available, with a good selection of specials. Try breaded haddock and tartare sauce; gammon steak Hawaii; or crispy shredded beef. Desserts include hot naughty fudge cake, and banana boat. There is also an excellent choice of hot

and cold filled rolls, and a children's menu.
Open: 12-12 **Bar Meals:** L served all week 12-2.30 D served all week 6-8.30 (Sat-Sun 12-8.30) Av main course £5.95 **Restaurant Meals:** L served all week 12-2.30 D served all week 5-8.30 (Sat-Sun all Day) Av 3 course alc £15 **Brewery/Company:** Free House ▣: Scottish Courage Beers, Guinness, Carling & guest ales **Children's Facilities:** Licence Play area (Swings and slides, rabbits & guinea pigs) Menu/Portions Cutlery Games Highchair Food warming Baby changing **Nearby:** Links Beach & Craigencalt Ecology Centre **Notes:** Garden: Patio/terrace, BBQ, tables & benches **Parking:** 20

FIFE

CRAIL
The Golf Hotel
4 High Street KY10 3TD
☎ 01333 450206 📄 01333 450795
Email: enquiries@thegolfhotelcrail.com
Web: www.thegolfhotelcrail.com
Dir: *On corner of High St*
The present Grade I-listed building is early 18th century, although the first inn on the site opened its doors 400 years earlier. In 1786, the Crail Golfing Society was established here, although the pub's present name appeared only in the mid-1800s. The golf club's minutes contain such gems as "Ample justice was done to Mother Duff's punch". Prepare then to do ample justice to fried fillet of Pittenweem haddock; home-made lasagne; or haggis and tatties with Drambuie cream.

Open: 11-12 **Bar Meals:** L served all week 12-7 D served all week 7-9 Av main course £8 **Restaurant Meals:** L served all week 12-7 D served all week 7-9 Av 3 course alc £15 **Brewery/Company:** Free House ☐: Scottish Courage McEwans 60/-, 80/-, 70/-, Belhaven Best & Real ale **Children's Facilities:** Menu/Portions Highchair Food warming Baby changing **Nearby:** Coastal walk, Park & Beach **Notes:** Dogs allowed in bar, in garden **Parking:** 10

ELIE
The Ship Inn 🍷
The Toft KY9 1DT
☎ 01333 330246 📄 01333 330864
Email: info@ship-elie.com
Web: www.ship-elie.co.uk
Dir: *Follow A915 & A917 to Elie. From High St follow signs to Watersport Centre and The Toft*
Run by the enthusiastic Philip family for over two decades, this lively free house stands right on the water-front at Elie Bay. The Ship has been a pub since 1838, and there's still plenty going on. The cricket team plays regular fixtures on the beach; there's also live music, and a programme of summer Sunday barbeques. Local bakers, butchers and fishmongers featured in the pub's colourful brochure provide many of the ingredients for featured dishes. Home-made soup or chicken liver pâté might precede fresh local haddock and chips; steak and ale pie; or a vegetarian burger with mozzarella, guacamole, salad and home-made chips. In summer, you might just catch an alfresco seafood lunch in the beer garden. Children's options include home-made meatballs in spaghetti; and Elie Bay fishcakes.
Open: 11-11 Closed: 25 Dec **Bar Meals:** L served all week 12-2 D served all week 6-9 **Restaurant Meals:** L served all week 12-2 D served all week 6-9 **Brewery/Company:** Free House ☐: Caledonian Deuchars IPA, Belhaven Best, Tetleys Xtra Cold, Caledonian 801, Tartan Special 🍷: 7 **Children's Facilities:** Fam room Play area **Notes:** Dogs allowed, Water, biscuits Garden: Beer garden, food served outdoors, patio,

KINCARDINE
The Unicorn 🍷
15 Excise Street Alloa FK10 4LN
☎ 01259 739129
Email: info@theunicorn.co.uk
Web: www.theunicorn.co.uk
Dir: *Exit M9 at Kincardine bridge, turn off across the bridge then bear left. Take 1st left then second left.*
This 17th-century inn in the heart of historic Kincardine was also the birthplace of Sir James Dewar, inventor of the vacuum flask. The link with innovative ideas continues with the imaginative refurbishment of this old building into a cool, contemporary pub-restaurant. The leather sofas and modern decor blend in well with the older parts of the building. There is a comfortable lounge bar, a grill room, and a more formal dining room upstairs.

This is reserved for private functions, when a special menu is served. Wherever possible the food is sourced from the best local suppliers, with the beef coming from the Buccleuch estate. Seafood is a speciality, with swordfish, salmon, lemon sole, sea bass and scallops being regularly available. When the weather allows, it is enjoyable to sit in the walled garden with its old well.
Open: 12-2 5.30-12 Closed: 1st wk in Jan, 3rd wk in July **Bar Meals:** L served Tue-Sat 12-2 D served Tue-Sat 5.30-9 Av main course £9.95 **Restaurant Meals:** D served Fri-Sat 7-9 Av 3 course alc £19.95 ☐: Stella Extra Cold, Guinness, Belhaven Best, Bitter & Twisted, Schiallion 🍷: 8 **Children's Facilities:** Menu/Portions Cutlery Games Highchair Food warming Baby changing **Nearby:** Falkirk Wheel, Stirling Castle, Knockhill Racing Circuit **Parking:** 4

ALTNAHARRA

Altnaharra Hotel

y Lairg IV27 4UE

☎ 01549 411222 📠 01549 411222

Email: office@altnaharra.co.uk

Web: www.altnaharra.com

Dir: *A9 to Bonar Bridge, A836 to Lairg & Tongue*

Originally a drover's inn understood to date back to the late 17th century, the Altnaharra is located in the beautiful Flow Country of Scotland, with endless views over timeless moorland. Interesting items of fishing memorabilia decorate the walls, including some fine historical prints and fishing records. The imaginative menu features the best of Scottish produce and options might include scallops in a brandy and cream sauce, Aberdeen Angus roast rib of beef, whole baked sea bass, Kyle of Tongue oysters, and Scottish rack of lamb. **Open:** 11-12.45 **Bar Meals:** L served all week 12-10 D served all week 12-10 Av main course £7 **Restaurant Meals:** D served all week 7-10 Av 3 course alc £32.50 **Brewery/Company:** Scottish & Newcastle 🍺: No real ale **Children's Facilities:** Play area Cutlery Highchair Baby changing **Notes:** Dogs allowed in bar, in garden **Garden:** Large lawn area, Loch views, seating **Parking:** 60

APPLECROSS

Applecross Inn

Shore Street Wester Ross IV54 8LR

☎ 01520 744262 📠 01520 744400

Email: applecrossinn@globalnet.co.uk

Web: www.applecross.uk.com

Dir: *From Lochcarron to Kishorn then L onto unclassified d to Applecross over 'Bealach Na Ba'*

Owner Judith Fish has recently refurbished the Applecross Inn to provide the best modern hospitality, whilst retaining the inn's original character and charm. Head chef Clare Mansfield aims to source three-quarters of her ingredients from top quality local producers. **Open:** 11-11 (Sun 12.30-11) Closed: 25 Dec, 1 Jan **Bar Meals:** L/D served all week 12-9 Av main course £8.95 **Restaurant Meals:** L served By appointment D served all week 6-9 Av 3 course alc £35 🍺: Isle of Skye Cask Ales, Guinness, Fosters, McEwans 80 & Kronenbourg 🍷: 6 **Children's Facilities:** Licence Play area (Beach) Menu/Portions Cutlery Games Highchair Food warming Baby changing **Nearby:** Beach **Notes:** Dogs allowed in bar, in garden, Water **Garden:** Grassed area on the beach, 6 tables **Parking:** 30

AVIEMORE

The Old Bridge Inn 🍷

Dalfaber Road PH22 1PU

☎ 01479 811137 📠 01479 810270

Email: nigel@oldbridgeinn.co.uk

Web: www.oldbridgeinn.co.uk

Dir: *Exit A9 to Aviemore, 1st left to 'Ski road', then 1st left again - 200mtrs*

Cosy and friendly Highland pub overlooking the River Spey. Dine in the relaxing bars, the comfortable restaurant, or in the attractive riverside garden. A tasty chargrill menu includes lamb chops in redcurrant jelly, Aberdeen Angus sirloin or rib-eye steaks, and butterflied breast of chicken marinated in yoghurt, lime and coriander. Seafood specials include monkfish pan fried chilli butter, mussels poached in white wine, and seafood crumble. Large selection of malt whiskies. **Open:** 11-11 **Bar Meals:** L served all week 12-2 D served all week 6-9 **Restaurant Meals:** L served all week 12-2 D served all week 6-9 **Brewery/Company:** Free House 🍺: Caledonian 80/-, Cairngorm Highland IPA 🍷: 18 **Children's Facilities:** Licence Fam room Play area Games Highchair Food warming **Nearby:** Coyumbridge Fun House & Highland Wildlife Park **Parking:** 24

HIGHLAND

HIGHLAND

BADACHRO
The Badachro Inn 🍷
Gairloch IV21 2AA
☎ 01445 741255 📠 01445 741319
Email: Lesley@badachroinn.com
Web: www.badachroinn.com
Dir: *Off A832 onto B8056, right onto Badachro after 3.25m, towards quay.*
Sheltered by Badachro Bay, one of Scotland's finest anchorages, this atmospheric local in the north Highlands is very popular in summer with yachting folk. Log fires burn cheerily in the bar in winter as the sea laps against the windows in high tides. Seals and otters can also be seen from the pub. Local seafood is a speciality, and includes oven-baked salmon, smoked haddock topped with Welsh rarebit, and dressed local crab. Extensive snack and specials menus.
Open: 12-12 (Reduced hours from 5 Jan-Mid Mar)
Closed: 25 Dec **Bar Meals:** L served all week 12-3 D served all week 6-9 (Sun 12.30-3, 6-9) Av main course £9.45 **Restaurant Meals:** L served all week 12-3 D served all week 6-9 (Sun 12.30-3, 6-9) 🍺: Red Cullen, Anceallach, Blaven, 80/-, Guinness 🍷: 11 **Children's Facilities:** Licence Menu/Portions Cutlery Highchair Food warming **Notes:** Dogs allowed in bar **Garden:** Garden overlooking Badachro Bay **Parking:** 12

CARBOST
The Old Inn
Isle of Skye IV47 8SR
☎ 01478 640205 📠 01478 640325
Email: reservations@oldinn.info
Web: www.oldinn.info
Two-hundred-year-old free house on the edge of Loch Harport with wonderful views of the Cuillin Hills from the waterside patio. Not surprisingly, the inn is popular with walkers and climbers. Open fires welcome winter visitors, and live music is a regular feature. The menu includes daily home-cooked specials, with numerous fresh fish dishes, including local prawns and oysters and mackerel from the loch.
Open: 11-1 **Bar Meals:** L served all week 12-3 D served all week 6-9 Av main course £7.95 **Restaurant Meals:** L served all week 12-3 D served all week 6-9
Brewery/Company: Free House 🍺: Red Cuillin, Black Cuillin, Hebridean Beer & Cuillin Skye Ale **Children's Facilities:** Licence Fam room Menu/Portions Cutlery Games Highchair Food warming **Nearby:** Talisker Distillery, Cuillin Hills, Talisker Bay **Notes:** Dogs allowed in bar **Garden:** Lochside **Parking:** 20

CAWDOR
Cawdor Tavern 🍷
The Lane IV12 5XP
☎ 01667 404777 📠 01667 404777
Email: cawdortavern@btopenworld.com
Dir: *From A96 (Inverness-Aberdeen) take B9006 & follow Cawdor Castle signs. Tavern in village centre.*
The Tavern was formerly a joinery workshop for the Cawdor Estate. The pub's reputation for seafood draws diners from some distance.
Open: 11-3 5-11 (May-Oct 11-11) **Closed:** 25 Dec, 1 Jan **Bar Meals:** L served all week 12-2 D served all week 5.30-9 (Sun 12.30-3, 5.30-9) Av main course £6.95 **Restaurant Meals:** L served all week (prior arrangement) 12-2 D served all week 6.30-9 (Sun 12.30-3, 5.30-9) **Brewery/Company:** Free House 🍺: Tennants 80/-, Cairngorm, Tradewinds & Stag 🍷: 8 **Children's Facilities:** Licence Fam room (Games & Books) Menu/Portions Cutlery Games Highchair Food warming Baby changing **Nearby:** Cawdor Castle, Gardens & Maze, Nairn Beach, Cawdor Pitch & Put **Notes:** Dogs allowed in bar, Water provided **Garden:** Patio area at front of tavern **Parking:** 60

DUNDONNELL
Dundonnell Hotel ★★★ HL
Little Loch Broom nr Ullapool IV23 2QR
☎ 01854 633204 📄 01854 633366
Email: trish@dundonnellhotel.co.uk
Web: www.dundonnellhotel.com
Dir: *From Inverness W on the A835, at Braemore junct take A382 for Gairloch*
The Dundonnell is one of the leading hotels in the Northern Highlands. Sheltered beneath the massive An Teallach range (one of 21 Munros in the area), the views down Little Loch Broom are superb. An Teallach is also the name of the local brewery which supplies five real ales for the Broom Beg bar. This is the 'local', where casual dining ranges from sandwiches and salads to pizzas and lasagne. The Cocktail Bar is the place for a quiet aperitif while mulling over what to eat in the spacious restaurant. Expect soup or sautéed field mushrooms to start, followed by steak and ale pie, venison pie, or succulent steaks cooked to your liking.
Open: 11-11 (Part time opening 1 Dec-28 Feb) **Bar Meals:** L served all week 12-2 D served all week 6-8.30 (Sun 12-2.30, 6-8) Av main course £5 **Restaurant Meals:** D served all week 7-8.30 Av 3 course alc £22.50 **Brewery/Company:** Free House 🍺: Beamish, Kronenbourg, McEwans, An Teallach Ale Company (5 different varieties) **Children's Facilities:** Licence Menu/Portions Highchair Food warming **Nearby:** Ullapool Leisure Centre, Gairloch pony trekking, beaches **Notes:** Dogs allowed in bar, No dogs in eating area Garden: Overlooking Little Loch Broom, seating **Parking:** 60

FORT WILLIAM
Moorings Hotel ★★★ HL ◉
Banavie PH33 7LY
☎ 01397 772797 📄 01397 772441
Email: reservations@moorings-fortwilliam.co.uk
Web: www.moorings-fortwilliam.co.uk
Dir: *From A82 in Fort William follow signs for Mallaig, then left onto A830 for 1m. Cross canal bridge then 1st right signed Banavie*
This modern hotel lies alongside Neptune's Staircase, on the coast-to-coast Caledonian Canal. The canal is a historic monument, its eight locks able to raise even sea-going craft a total of 64 feet. A range of eating options includes Mariners cellar bar, based on a nautical theme. The Caledonian is a split-level lounge bar overlooking the canal, and there is also the fine-dining Jacobean Restaurant. The bar menu includes a 'quick fix' sandwich menu, children's menu, fish, meat, vegetarian and pizza options, and dishes like five bean chilli with nachos and sour cream. The sophisticated restaurant carte offers tempting choices like fillet medallions of Aberdeenshire beef with fondant potatoes, red wine shallots, wild mushrooms and a red wine sauce.
Open: 12-11.45 (Thu-Sat til 1am) **Bar Meals:** L/D served all week 12-9.30 Av main course £9 **Restaurant Meals:** D served all week 7-9.30 Av 3 course alc £26 **Brewery/Company:** Free House 🍺: Calders 70/-, Tetley Bitter, Guinness **Children's Facilities:** Licence Menu/Portions Games Highchair Food warming **Nearby:** Nevis Range, Jacobite Steam Train, Nevis Centre **Notes:** Dogs allowed in bar, Water Garden: Small patio, food served outdoors **Parking:** 80

GAIRLOCH
The Old Inn ♦♦♦♦ ♈
Highland IV21 2BD
☎ 01445 712006 📄 01445 712044
Email: info@theoldinn.net
Web: www.theoldinn.net
Dir: *Just off main A832, near harbour at S end of village*
This attractive inn has a lovely setting at the foot of the Flowerdale Valley, looking out across Gairloch Harbour. Seafood is the main draw in an area where Loch Ewe scallops, Gairloch lobsters, Minch langoustines, brown crab, mussels and fresh fish are regularly landed.
Open: 11-12 (Winter open eve & wkends only) **Bar Meals:** L served all week 12-2.30 D served all week 5-9.30 Av main course £8 **Restaurant Meals:** L served all week 12-5 D served all week 5-9.30 Av 3 course alc £22.50 🍺: Adnams Broadside, Isle of Skye Red Cullin, Blind Piper, Houston, Peters Well, London Pride ♈: 8 **Children's Facilities:** Licence Fam room Play area Menu/Portions Games Highchair Food warming Baby changing **Nearby:** Pony treking centre, Sandy beaches **Notes:** Dogs allowed in bar, in garden Garden: Large grassy area with picnic tables **Parking:** 20

ISLE ORNSAY
Hotel Eilean Iarmain ★★ HL ◉◉

Sleat Isle of Skye IV43 8QR

☎ 01471 833332 📄 01471 833275

Email: hotel@eileaniarmain.co.uk

Web: www.eileaniarmain.co.uk

Dir: *A851, A852 right to Isle Ornsay harbour front*

This award-winning Hebridean hotel, with its own pier, overlooks the Isle of Ornsay harbour and Sleat Sound. More a small private hotel than a pub, the bar and restaurant ensure that the standards of food and wine are exacting: "we never accept second best, it shines through in the standard of food served in our restaurant".

Open: 11-1am **Bar Meals:** L served all week 12-2.30 D served all week 6-9.30 Av main course £8.50 **Restaurant Meals:** L served all week (pre booked only)

12-2 D served all week 6.30-9 **Brewery/Company:** Free House 🍺: McEwans 80/-, Guinness & Isle of Skye real ale **Children's Facilities:** Fam room Menu/Portions Cutlery Games Highchair Food warming Baby changing **Nearby:** Clan Donald Museum & gardens, Seafari & Skye Serpentarium **Notes:** Dogs allowed in bar **Garden:** At front beside pier with breathtaking views **Parking:** 30

KYLESKU
Kylesku Hotel

by Lairg IV27 4HW

☎ 01971 502231 📄 01971 502313

Email: info@kyleskuhotel.co.uk

Web: www.kyleskuhotel.co.uk

Dir: *35m N of Ullapool on A835, then A837 and A894 into Kylesku, Hotel at end of road at Old Ferry Pier.*

Old coaching inn by the ferry slipway between Loch Glencoul and Loch Glendhu in the Highlands of Sutherland. The menus specialise in locally caught seafood, plus salmon and venison in season.

Open: 11-11 (Sun 12.30-11) Closed: 1 Nov-28 Feb **Bar Meals:** L served all week 12-2.30 D served all week 6-9 (Sun 12.15-2.30, 6-9) Av main course £10 **Restaurant Meals:** D served Tue-Sun 7-8.30

Brewery/Company: Free House 🍺: Tennants Ember 89/-, Selection of Black Isle Brewery and Skye Cuillin Bottled Beers. **Children's Facilities:** Licence Menu/Portions Cutlery Highchair Food warming **Nearby:** Boat trips with seal sighting and bird colonies, Achmelvich beach **Notes:** Dogs allowed in garden **Garden:** Stunning views of sea loch

LYBSTER
Swallow Portland Arms

Caithness KW3 6BS

☎ 01593 721721 📄 01593 721722

Email: swallow.lybster@swallowhotels.com

Web: www.swallowhotels.com

Dir: *Exit A9 signed Latheron, take A99 to Wick (90m from Inverness). Lybster is 12m south of Wick.*

Newly decorated in inviting colours, this 19th-century coaching inn has evolved into a comfortable modern hotel. The bar and dining areas feature the best of fresh Scottish produce in settings that range from farmhouse to formal. The extensive menus cater for all tastes, with everything from a simple cheese ploughman's to chargrilled haunch of venison with haggis and black pudding. There's a children's menu too, and the home-made puddings include a tempting oat-baked fruit crumble.

Open: 7.30-11 Closed: Dec 31-Jan 3 **Bar Meals:** L served all week 12-3 D served all week 5-9 (Sat-Sun 12-9) Av main course £8.50 **Restaurant Meals:** L served all week 12-3 D served all week 5-9 (Sat-Sun 12-9) Av 3 course alc £20 **Brewery/Company:** Free House 🍺: McEwans 70/-, Tennants Lager, Guinness & Stella Artois **Children's Facilities:** Licence (Changing room, toys, dining area) Menu/Portions Cutlery Games Highchair Food warming Baby changing **Nearby:** Beaches, Waterlines Heritage Centre **Notes:** Garden: Food served outside **Parking:** 20

NORTH BALLACHULISH
Loch Leven Hotel
Old Ferry Road PH33 6SA
☎ 01855 821236 📠 01855 821550
Email: reception@lochlevenhotel.co.uk
Web: www.lochlevenhotel.co.uk
Dir: Off A82, N of Ballachulish Bridge
The original part of the hotel was built over 300 years ago. It stands on the northern shore of Loch Leven in an area that is very beautiful and steeped in history. Freshly prepared food is served in a friendly atmosphere.
Open: 11-12 (Sun 12.30-11.45, Closed afternoons in winter) **Bar Meals:** L served all week 12-3 D served all week 6-9 Av main course £7.95 **Restaurant Meals:** L served all week 12-3 D served all week 6-9 (Sun 12.30-3, 6-9) Av 3 course alc £16.50 **Brewery/Company:**

Free House 🍺: John Smith's Extra Smooth, McEwan's 80/-, Guinness, Tennant's Lager, Kronenbourg 1674 **Children's Facilities:** Fam room Menu/Portions Cutlery Games Highchair Food warming **Nearby:** The Hogwarts Express, Seafari adventures, Sea Life Sanctuary **Notes:** Dogs allowed in bar, Water & chews **Garden:** Wooden decking, trees & shrubs **Parking:** 25

PLOCKTON
Plockton Inn & Seafood Restaurant
Innes Street IV52 8TW
☎ 01599 544222 📠 01599 544487
Email: stay@plocktoninn.co.uk
Web: www.plocktoninn.co.uk
Dir: On A87 to Kyle of Lochalsh take turn at Balmacara. Plockton 7m N
An attractive stone-built free house standing in the village where the Hamish Macbeth TV series was filmed. Taking pride of place on the menus are fresh West Coast fish and shellfish, West Highland beef, lamb and game.
Open: 11-1 (Sun 12.30-11pm) **Bar Meals:** L served all week 12-2.30 D served all week 5.30-9.30 (Winter hrs 8.30-9pm) Av main course £9.50 **Restaurant Meals:** L served all week 12-2.30 D served all week 5.30-9.30

(Winter hrs 8.30-9pm) Av 3 course alc £17 **Children's Facilities:** Licence Play area Menu/Portions Cutlery Games Highchair Food warming Baby changing **Nearby:** Rare Animal Farm, Seal Boat Trips, Rowing Boats & Swimming Pool **Notes:** Dogs allowed in bar, in garden, **Garden:** 2 gardens, sloping grass space at rear, trees **Parking:** 10

PLOCKTON
The Plockton Hotel ★★ HL
Harbour Street IV52 8TN
☎ 01599 544274 📠 01599 544475
Email: info@plocktonhotel.co.uk
Web: www.plocktonhotel.co.uk
Dir: On A87 to Kyle of Lochalsh take turn at Balmacara. Plockton 7m N
Surrounded by a bowl of hills, the attractive stone-built Plockton Hotel is the only waterfront hostelry in this lovely National Trust village. It stands metres from the gently lapping waters of Loch Carron, fringed with palm trees! Menus are based on the freshest local produce, traditionally cooked and simply presented.
Open: 11-11.45 (Sun 12.30-11) **Bar Meals:** L served all week 12-2.15 D served all week 6-9.15 (Sun 12.30-

2.15) **Restaurant Meals:** L served all week 12-2.15 D served all week 6-9.15 **Brewery/Company:** Free House 🍺: Caledonian Deuchars IPA **Children's Facilities:** Fam room (Beside the sea-shore) Menu/Portions Highchair Food warming Baby changing **Nearby:** Eileen Dongnan Castle, Calums Seal Trips, Reptile Centre **Notes: Garden:** Beer garden, summer house, amazing views

SHIELDAIG
Shieldaig Bar ★★ SHL ◎◎ ♟

IV54 8XN

☎ 01520 755251 📄 01520 755321

Email: tighaneileanhotel@shieldaig.fsnet.co.uk

Dir: *5m S of Torridon off A896 on to village road signed Shieldaig, bar on Loch front*

The Shieldaig is a popular loch-front bar in a charming fishing village. The pub has a fine reputation for its bar snacks - sandwiches, home-made soups, burgers and bangers and mash - and for its daily-changing specials, such as Shieldaig crab cakes with tarragon mayonnaise. All the seafood is caught locally.

Open: 11-11 Closed: 25 Dec, 1 Jan **Bar Meals:** L served all week 12-2.30 D served all week 6-8.30 Av main course £8.50 **Restaurant Meals:** D served all

week 7-8.30 **Brewery/Company:** Free House 🍺: Isle of Skye Brewery Ales, Tennants Superior Ale, Black Isle Ales ♟: 12 **Children's Facilities:** Licence Menu/Portions Cutlery Games Highchair Food warming Baby changing **Notes:** Dogs allowed in garden, Water provided Garden: Open courtyard on Lochside with umbrellas **Parking:** 12

STEIN
Stein Inn ♟

Macleod's Terrace Waternish Isle of Skye IV55 8GA

☎ 01470 592362

Email: angus.teresa@steininn.co.uk

Web: www.steininn.co.uk

Set in a lovely hamlet right next to the sea, this 18th-century inn is everything that you would expect of traditional Scottish hospitality: a warm welcome, fine food, and a Highland bar offering over a hundred malt whiskies! The lunchtime bar menu features local crab sandwiches and haggis toasties, whilst evening dinner brings Scottish salmon with vermouth and tarragon sauce; Highland venison pie; and bean and nut patties with Angus' plum chutney.

Open: 11-12 (Sun 12.30-11 Winter 4-11) **Bar Meals:**

L served all week 12-4 D served all week 6-9 (Sun 12.30-4) Av main course £6.50 **Restaurant Meals:** L served none D served all week 6-9 Av 3 course alc £14.50 **Brewery/Company:** Free House 🍺: Red Cuillin, Trade Winds, Reeling Deck, Deuchars IPA, Dark Island ♟: 8 **Children's Facilities:** Licence Fam room Menu/Portions Games Highchair Food warming Baby changing **Nearby:** Beaches, Dunvegan Castle, Museum of Childhood **Notes:** Dogs allowed in bar, Dogs on lead Garden: Picnic tables overlooking the sea **Parking:** 5

TORRIDON
Ben Damph Inn ♟

By Achnasheen IV22 2EY

☎ 01445 791242 📄 01445 712253

Email: bendamph@lochtorridonhotel.com

Web: www.bendamph.lochtorridonhotel.com

Dir: *From Inverness take A9 N, then signs to Ullapool. Take A335 then A832. In Kinlochelne take A896 to Annat Village. Pub is 200 yds on right after village.*

Set on the shores of Loch Torridon at the foot of the Torridon mountains, the Ben Damph Inn is the ideal base for exploring the local area.

Open: 11-11 (3-11 Mar, Apr, Oct) Closed: Nov-Mar **Bar Meals:** L served all week (May-Sep) 12-2 D served all week 6-8.45 **Restaurant Meals:** D served all week 6-8.45 Av 3 course alc £18 🍺: Isle of Skye Red

Cullen, Cairngorm Brewery Stag & Tradewinds ♟: 8 **Children's Facilities:** Licence Play area (Toys, seats, bricks, books) Menu/Portions Cutlery Games Highchair Food warming Baby changing **Nearby:** Marine Wildlife Cruise, Pony Trekking, Deer Centre **Notes:** Dogs allowed in bar Garden: Drink only in garden Small gravelled area **Parking:** 30

PENICUIK
The Howgate Restaurant
Howgate EH26 8PY
☎ 01968 670000 📠 01968 670000
Email: peter@howgate.com
Web: www.howgate.com
Dir: *On A6094, 3m SE of Penicuik*

A long, low building originally racehorse stables, then a dairy. Now refurbished, the warm and welcoming bar and restaurant offer regularly changing menus featuring traditional and modern dishes, with starters ranging from warming soups to Shetland mussels and filled ciabattas. Good use is made of the charcoal grill for fish, meats and venison. Among the desserts are popular favourites such as banoffee pie, Luca's ice cream from Musselburgh, and its very own Howgate cheeses.

Open: 12-2 6-11 Closed: Dec 25-26, 1 Jan **Bar Meals:** L served all week 12-2 D served all week 6-9.30 Av main course £10 **Restaurant Meals:** L served all week 12-2 D served all week 6-9.30 Av 3 course alc £23.50 **Brewery/Company:** Free House 🍺: Belhaven Best, Hoegaarden, Wheat Biere & Tennants Lager 🍷: 12 **Children's Facilities:** Licence Menu/Portions Highchair Food warming **Nearby:** Glentress Forest, Roslin Chapel & Hillend Ski School **Notes:** Garden: Patio and tables adjacent to bistro **Parking:** 45

FOCHABERS
Gordon Arms Hotel
80 High Street IV32 7DH
☎ 01343 820508 📠 01343 820300
Email: info@gordonarms.co.uk
Web: www.gordonarms.co.uk
Dir: *A96 approx halfway between Aberdeen and Inverness, 9m from Elgin*

This 200-year old former coaching inn, close to the River Spey and within easy reach of Speyside's whisky distilleries, is understandably popular with salmon fishers, golfers and walkers. Its public rooms have been carefully refurbished, and the hotel makes an ideal base from which to explore this scenic corner of Scotland. The cuisine makes full use of local produce: venison, lamb and game from the uplands, fish and seafood from the Moray coast, beef from Aberdeenshire and salmon from the Spey - barely a stone's throw from the kitchen!

Open: 11-3 5-11 (Sun 12-3, 6-10.30) **Bar Meals:** L served all week 12-2 D served all week 5-6.45 **Restaurant Meals:** L served all week 12-2 D served all week 7-9 **Brewery/Company:** Free House 🍺: Caledonian Deuchars IPA, Scottish Courage John Smith's Smooth, Marstons Pedigree **Children's Facilities:** Licence Menu/Portions Cutlery Games Highchair Food warming **Nearby:** Wildlife centre, Spey Bay, Boxsters Visitor Centre **Notes:** Dogs allowed in bar **Parking:** 40

GLENDEVON
The Tormaukin Country Inn and Restaurant
By Dollar FK14 7JY
☎ 01259 781252 📠 01259 781526
Email: enquiries@tormaukin.co.uk
Web: www.tormaukin.co.uk
Dir: *N from Edinburgh, leave M90 junct 6 and take A977 to Kincardine, follow signs to Stirling, turning off at Yelts of Muckhard onto A823 Crieff.*

This attractive whitewashed free house was built in 1720 as a drovers' inn, at a time when Glendevon was frequented by cattlemen making their way from the tryst of Crieff to the market place at Falkirk. The name Tormaukin, which in Gaelic means hill of the mountain hare, reflects the inn's serene, romantic location in the midst of the Ochil Hills. The inn has been sympathetically refurbished throughout, but still bristles with real Scottish character and charm.

Open: 11-11 Closed: 25 Dec **Bar Meals:** L served all week 12-2.30 D served all week 5.30-9.30 (Open all day wknds) Av main course £9.95 **Restaurant Meals:** L served all week 2.30 D served all week 5.30-9.30 (Food served all Day wknds) Av 3 course alc £27.50 **Brewery/Company:** Free House 🍺: Harviestoun Bitter & Twisted, Timothy Taylor Landlord, Calders Cream, Guinness, Carlsberg-Tetley Tetley's Bitter & Guest Ales 🍷: 12 **Children's Facilities:** Fam room Menu/Portions Cutlery Games Highchair Food warming Baby changing **Nearby:** National Wallace Monument, Stirling Old Town Jail, Stirling Castle & Noah's Ark **Notes:** Dogs allowed in bar Garden: Patio, food served outside **Parking:** 50

KILLIECRANKIE

Killiecrankie House Hotel ◉◉ ♟
Nr Pitlochry PH16 5LG
☎ 01796 473220 📠 01796 472451
Email: enquiries@killiecrankiehotel.co.uk
Web: www.killiecrankiehotel.co.uk
Dir: *Take B8079 N out of Pitlochry. Located 3m along this road after NT Visitor Centre.*
This hotel is set in four acres of wooded grounds at the northern end of the historic Killiecrankie Pass, near the site of the Battle of Killiecrankie and overlooking the intriguingly named Soldier's Leap. The menu offers the best local produce.
Open: 12-2.30 6-11 Closed: Jan, Feb **Bar Meals:** L served all week 12.30-2 D served all week 6.30-9 Av main course £9 **Restaurant Meals:** D served all week 7-8.30 Av 3 course alc £28 🍺: Calders Cream Ale, Red McGregor, Becks, Deuchers IPA, Brooker's Bitter & Twisted ♟: 8 **Children's Facilities:** Licence Menu/Portions Highchair Food warming **Nearby:** Killiecrankie Visitor Centre, Pitlochy Park & Blair Castle **Notes:** Dogs allowed in garden Garden: 1 acre of lawns, 2 acres of woodland, formal **Parking:** 20

KINNESSWOOD

Lomond Country Inn ♟
KY13 9HN
☎ 01592 840253 📠 01592 840693
Email: info@lomondcountryinn.co.uk
Web: www.lomondcountryinn.co.uk
Dir: *M90 junct 5, follow signs for Glenrothes then Scotlandwell, Kinnesswood next village*
A privately owned hotel on the slopes of the Lomond Hills. It is the only hostelry in the area with uninterrupted views over Loch Leven to the island on which Mary, Queen of Scots was imprisoned.
Open: 11-11 (Fri-Sat 11-12.45, Sun 12.30-11) Closed: Dec 25 **Bar Meals:** L served all week 12.30-2 D served all week 6-9 Av main course £7 **Restaurant Meals:** L served all week 12-2.30 D served all week 6-9.30 (food served all Day Sun) Av 3 course alc £25 **Brewery/Company:** Free House 🍺: Deuchers IPA, Calders Cream, Tetleys, Orkney Dark Island, Bitter & Twisted ♟: 6 **Children's Facilities:** Play area (toys, chute) Baby changing **Notes:** Dogs allowed Kennels Garden: Lawn & landscaping decking overlooking Loch **Parking:** 50

PITLOCHRY

Moulin Hotel ★★ HL ♟
11-13 Kirkmichael Road Moulin PH16 5EH
☎ 01796 472196 📠 01796 474098
Email: enquiries@moulinhotel.co.uk
Web: www.moulinhotel.co.uk
Dir: *From A924 at Pitlochry take A923. Moulin 0.75m*
Situated at the foot of Ben-y-Vrackie (the speckled mountain), and just outside Pitlochry, this 312-year-old inn is surrounded by good walks and historical features. It offers good food and traditional Highland hospitality. The courtyard garden is lovely in summer, while blazing log fires warm the place through in winter. The hotel's own micro-brewery, standing adjacent, produces Braveheart, named during the filming of Mel Gibson's movie.
Open: 12-11 (Fri-Sat 12-11.45) **Bar Meals:** L/D served all week 12-9.30 Av main course £6.95 **Restaurant Meals:** D served all week 6-9 **Brewery/Company:** Free House 🍺: Moulin Braveheart, Old Remedial, Ale of Atholl & Moulin Light ♟: 20 **Children's Facilities:** Cutlery Games Highchair Food warming Baby changing **Nearby:** Noah's Ark, Perth, Beatrix Potter & Dunkeld **Notes:** Garden: Behind hotel, next to stream **Parking:** 40

ETTRICK

Tushielaw Inn

Ettrick Valley TD7 5HT

☎ 01750 62205 🖹 01750 62205

Email: robin@tushielaw.fsnet.co.uk

Web: www.tushielaw-inn.co.uk

Dir: *At junction of B709 & B711(W of Hawick)*

18th-century former toll house and drover's halt on the banks of Ettrick water. Good base for trout fishing and those tackling the Southern Upland Way. An extensive menu is always available with daily changing specials. Fresh produce is used according to season, with local lamb and Aberdeen Angus beef regular specialities. Gluten-free and vegetarian meals are always available. Home-made steak and stout pie and sticky toffee pudding rate among other popular dishes.

Open: 12-2.30 6.30-11 **Bar Meals:** L served all week 12-2 D served all week 7-9 **Restaurant Meals:** L served all week 12-2 D served all week 7-9 **Brewery/Company:** Free House **Children's Facilities:** Licence (High chair, toys, colouring) Menu/Portions Cutlery Games Highchair Food warming **Notes:** Dogs allowed in bar, in garden, Water bowls & biscuits Garden: Area with picnic tables **Parking:** 8

GALASHIELS

Kingsknowes Hotel ★★★ HL

1 Selkirk Road TD1 3HY

☎ 01896 758375 🖹 01896 750377

Email: enquiries@kingsknowes.co.uk

Web: www.kingsknowes.co.uk

Dir: *Off A7 at Galashiels/Selkirk rdbt*

In over three acres of grounds on the banks of the Tweed, a splendid baronial mansion built in 1869 for a textile magnate. There are lovely views of the Eildon Hills and Abbotsford House, Sir Walter Scott's ancestral home. Meals are served in two restaurants and the Courtyard Bar, where fresh local or regional produce is used as much as possible.

Open: 12-12 **Bar Meals:** L served all week 11.45-2 D served all week 5.45-9.30 Av main course £8.50

Restaurant Meals: L served all week 11.45-2 D served all week 5.45-9.30 **Brewery/Company:** Free House ▥: McEwans 80/-, Scottish Courage John Smith's **Children's Facilities:** Play area Menu/Portions Games Highchair Food warming Baby changing **Nearby:** Play park, skateboard park **Notes:** Dogs allowed in garden Garden: 35 acres, lawn, rockery **Parking:** 60

LAUDER

The Black Bull Hotel ★★★★ INN ♇

Market Place TD2 6SR

☎ 01578 722208 🖹 01578 722419

Email: enquiries@blackbull-lauder.com

Web: www.blackbull-lauder.com

Dir: *Located in Market Place in centre of Lauder on A68*

Dazzlingly white in the sun, a three-storey coaching inn dating from 1750. The large dining room was once a chapel, and the church spire remains in the roof! Proprietor Maureen Rennie bought the hotel in a decrepit state but has transformed it into a cosy, characterful hotel with lots of interesting pictures and artefacts. She uses only the best quality local beef, lamb, fish and seasonal game, all, of course, prepared to order. **Open:** 12-2.30 5-9 (Winter 12-2, 5.30-9) Closed: 1st 3 wks in Feb **Bar**

Meals: L served all week 12-2.30 D served all week 5-9 Av main course £8.50 ▥: Broughton Ales, Carling Lager, Guinness, Worthington & Caffreys ♇: 16 **Children's Facilities:** Licence Menu/Portions Cutlery Games Highchair Food warming Baby changing **Nearby:** Thirlestone Castle, Deer Park Fedburgh & Floors Castle **Notes:** Dogs allowed in bar **Parking:** 10

ST BOSWELLS
Buccleuch Arms Hotel ★★ HL ▾
The Green TD6 0EW
☎ 01835 822243 📄 01835 823965
Email: info@buccleucharmshotel.co.uk
Web: www.buccleucharmshotel.co.uk
Dir: *On A68, 10m N of Jedburgh. Located on village green*
The Buccleuch Arms in the heart of the Scottish Borders prides itself on being the perfect place to relax and unwind. It's a 16th-century inn with a spacious garden and children's play area. Lunchtime brings sandwiches, baguettes and baked potatoes, while the main menu might offer gourmet sausages, chargrilled local beef steak, breaded haddock fillet, and a vegetarian goats' cheese and leek tart. There's a separate children's menu, or smaller portions on request.
Open: 7.30-11 Closed: 25 Dec **Bar Meals:** L served all week 12-2 D served all week 6-9 Av main course £8 **Restaurant Meals:** L served all week 12-2 D served all week 6-9 **Brewery/Company:** Free House 🍺: Calders 70/-, 80/-, Calders Cream Ale, Broughton, Guest Beers ▾: 6 **Children's Facilities:** Licence Play area (Swings etc in enclosed garden) Menu/Portions Cutlery Games Highchair Food warming Baby changing **Nearby:** Bowhill Adventure Playground, Harestanes Visitor Centre **Notes:** Dogs allowed in bar, in garden, in bedrooms Garden: Quiet, spacious & peaceful garden **Parking:** 80

TIBBIE SHIELS INN
Tibbie Shiels Inn
St Mary's Loch Selkirk TD7 5LH
☎ 01750 42231 📄 01750 42302
Web: www.tibbieshielsinn.com
Dir: *From Moffat take A708. Inn is 14m on right*
On the isthmus between St Mary's Loch and the Loch of the Lowes, this waterside inn is named after the woman who first opened it in 1826 and expanded the inn from a small cottage to a hostelry capable of sleeping around 35 people, many of them on the floor! Famous visitors during her time included Walter Scott, Thomas Carlyle and Robert L. Stevenson. Tibbie Shiels herself is rumoured to keep watch over the bar, where the selection of over 50 malt whiskys will sustain you for ghost watching! Meals can be enjoyed either in the bar or the non-smoking dining room; the Inn also offers packed lunches for your walking, windsurfing or fishing expedition (residents fish free of charge). The menu offers a wide range of vegetarian options as well as local fish and game: highlights include Yarrow trout and Tibbies mixed grill.
Open: 11-11 (Sun 12.30-11) **Bar Meals:** L served all week 12.30-8 D served all week 12.30-8 Av main course £6.50 **Restaurant Meals:** L served all week 12.30-8 D served all week 12.30-8 Av 3 course alc £11.25 **Brewery/Company:** Free House 🍺: Broughton Greenmantle Ale, Belhaven 80/- **Children's Facilities:** Licence Menu/Portions Cutlery Highchair Food warming Baby changing **Notes:** Garden: 6 acres of Lochside **Parking:** 50

TWEEDSMUIR
The Crook Inn ▾
Scottish Borders ML12 6QN
☎ 01899 880272 📄 01899 880294
Email: thecrookinn@btinternet.com
Web: www.crookinn.co.uk
Dir: *Situated 18m N of Moffat on A701 to Edinburgh. 35m S of Edinburgh.*
The oldest licensed inn in Scotland, the Crook was transformed in the 1930s into the then fashionable art deco style. Fresh local produce is used in the extensive range of dishes on the menu.
Open: 9-11 Closed: 25 Dec, 3rd wk in Jan **Bar Meals:** L served all week 12-2.30 D served all week 5.30-8.30 Av main course £8 **Restaurant Meals:** L served all week 12-2.30 D served all week 6-9 Av 3 course alc £15 **Brewery/Company:** Free House 🍺: Broughton Greenmantle & Best, Scottish Courage John Smith's, 80/-, Guinness ▾: 9 **Children's Facilities:** Fam room Menu/Portions Highchair Food warming Baby changing **Nearby:** Dawyck Gardens, New Lanark Visitor Centre, Traquair House **Notes:** Dogs allowed in bar Garden: Large grass area surrounded by trees **Parking:** 60

SYMINGTON
Wheatsheaf Inn

Main Street Kilmarnock KA1 5QB

☎ 01563 830307 📄 01563 830307

Web: www.wheatsheafsymington.co.uk

Dir: *Telephone for directions*

This 17th-century inn lies in a lovely village setting close to the Royal Troon Golf Course, and there has been a hostelry here since the 1500s. Log fires burn in every room and the work of local artists adorns the walls. Seafood highlights the menu - maybe pan-fried scallops in lemon and chives - and alternatives include honey roasted lamb shank; haggis, tatties and neeps in Drambuie and onion cream, and the renowned steak pie. **Open:** 11-12 (Sun 11-11) Closed: 25 Dec, 1 Jan **Bar Meals:** L/D served all week 12-9.30 Av main course £8

Restaurant Meals: D served all week 12-9.30 **Brewery/Company:** Belhaven ◀: Belhaven Best, St Andrews Ale, Tennants & Stella **Children's Facilities:** Play area (Highchairs available) Baby changing **Parking:** 20

CALLANDER
The Lade Inn ♟

Kilmahog FK17 8HD

☎ 01877 330152

Email: info@theladeinn.com / frank@theladeinn.com

Web: www.theladeinn.com

Built in 1935 as a tearoom serving the Trossachs National Park area, the Lade Inn was licensed in the 1960s, taking its name from the river that feeds the local wollen mills. New owners retain the traditional charm of the popular restaurant/pub with high quality locally sourced produce (Trossachs trout and locally caught mussels) and real ales from the Trossachs Craft Brewery, their on-site microbrewery. There's folk music every Saturday night and monthly jam sessions for upcoming amateurs.

Open: 12-11 (Sat 12pm -1am, Sun 12.30-10.30) **Bar Meals:** L served all week 12-9 D served all week 12-9 (Sat 12-9, Sun 12.30-9) Av main course £4.50 **Restaurant Meals:** L served all week 12-9 D served all week 12-9 (Sat 12-9, Sun 12.30-9) Av 3 course alc £14 **Brewery/Company:** Free House ◀: Local ales: Waylade, Lade Back, Lade Out, Guinness, Stella & Guest Ales ♟: 7 **Children's Facilities:** Licence Fam room Play area Menu/Portions Cutlery Games Highchair Food warming Baby changing **Nearby:** Blair Drummond Safari Park, David Marshall Visitor Centre & Rob Roy Visitor Centre **Notes:** Dogs allowed in bar, Water & Dog Biscuits Garden: Seating area overlooking ponds **Parking:** 40

KIPPEN
Cross Keys Hotel

Main Street FK8 3DN

☎ 01786 870293

Email: crosskeys@kippen70.fsnet.co.uk

Dir: *10m from Stirling, 20m from Loch Lomand*

The village of Kippen in the Fintry Hills overlooking the Forth Valley has strong associations with Rob Roy. The pub dates from 1703. Nearby Burnside Wood is perfect for walking and nature trails. An excellent range of home-made dishes includes Scottish smoked salmon platter; smoked haddock omelette; and steak and mushroom pie. **Open:** 12-2.30 5.30-11 (Fri 5.30-12, Sat 12-12, Sun 12.30-11) Closed: 25 Dec, 1 Jan **Bar Meals:** L served all week 12-2 D served all week 5.30-9 (Sun 12.30-9) **Restaurant Meals:** L served all week 12-2 D served all

week 5.30-9 (Sun 12.30-9) **Brewery/Company:** Free House ◀: Belhaven Best, IPA, 80/-, Harviestoun Bitter & Twisted **Children's Facilities:** Licence Fam room Menu/Portions Games Highchair Food warming Baby changing **Notes:** Dogs allowed in bar, Water, Biscuits Garden: Small garden with good views of Trossachs **Parking:** 5

SOUTH AYRSHIRE / STIRLING

Wales

Fishguard Old Harbour

KENFIG
Prince of Wales Inn 🍷
CF33 4PR
☎ 01656 740356
Email: prince-of-wales@bt.connect.com
Dir: *M4 junct 37 into North Cornelly. Take left at x-roads and follow signs for Kenfig and Porthcawe. Pub is 600yds on right.*

Dating from the 16th century, this stone-built inn has been many things in its time including a school, guildhall and courtroom. Why not sup some real cask ale in the bar by an inviting log fire? Typical menu includes steak and onion pie, lasagne, chicken and mushroom pie, and a variety of fish dishes. Look out for today's specials on the blackboard. The current landlords are only the sixth in 230 years!

Open: 11-11 **Bar Meals:** L served Tue-Sun 12-3 D served Tue-Sun 6-9 (Sun 12-3) **Restaurant Meals:** L served all week 12-9 D served Tue-Sun 7-9 (Sun 12-3) **Brewery/Company:** Free House 🍺: Bass Triangle, Worthington Best, Guest Ales 🍷: 20 **Children's Facilities:** Menu/Portions Cutlery Highchair Food warming **Notes:** Dogs allowed in bar, Water, toys Garden: Food served outside **Parking:** 40

ABERGORLECH
The Black Lion
Nr Carmarthen SA32 7SN
☎ 01558 685271
Email: michelle.r@btinternet.com
Dir: *A40 E from Carmarthen, then B4310 signed Brechfa & Abergorlech*

A 17th-century coaching inn in the Brechfa Forest, with a beer garden overlooking the Cothi River, and an old pack-horse bridge. Flagstone floors, settles and a grandfather clock grace the antique-furnished bar, while the modern dining room is welcoming in pink and white. Try home-made chicken and leek pie, home-made curry of the day, or a fresh salmon steak. Miles of forest and riverside walks are easily reached from the pub.
Open: 12-3.30 7-11 (Sat 12-11pm, Sun 12-10pm)

Bar Meals: L served Tue-Sun 12-2 D served Tue-Sun 7-9 (Sun 7-8.30) Av main course £6.50 **Restaurant Meals:** L served Sun 12-2 D served Sat 7-9 Av 3 course alc £12 **Brewery/Company:** Free House 🍺: Brains SA, Buckley's Best, Spitfire, Young's Bitter **Children's Facilities:** Menu/Portions Cutlery Highchair Food warming **Notes:** Dogs allowed, Water Garden: 6 large tables & umbrellas **Parking:** 20

LLANDEILO
The Castle Hotel
113 Rhosmaen Street SA19 6EN
☎ 01558 823446 📠 01558 822290

A 19th-century Edwardian-style hotel within easy reach of Dinefwr Castle and wonderful walks through classic parkland. A charming, tiled and partly green-painted back bar attracts plenty of locals, while the front bar and side area offer smart furnishings and the chance to relax in comfort over a drink. A good range of Tomas Watkins ales is available, and quality bar and restaurant food is prepared with the finest of fresh local ingredients. Under new management.
Open: 12-11 (Sun 12-10.30) **Bar Meals:** L served Wed-Sun 12-2.30 D served Wed-Sun 6.30-9 Av main course £6.95 **Restaurant Meals:** L served all week 12-2.30 D served Mon-Sat 6.30-9 **Brewery/Company:** Celtic Inns 🍺: Tomas Watkins, Hancoats Bitter, Archers Golden, London Pride, Bombardier **Children's Facilities:** Fam room (High chairs) Menu/Portions Cutlery Highchair Food warming **Nearby:** Dinefwr Castle & Park, Gold mines **Notes:** Garden: Slabbed area inside internal buildings

PONT-AR-GOTHI
The Salutation Inn ♀
Nantgaredig SA32 7NH
☎ 01267 290336 🖹 01267 290111
Email: salutation.inn@virgin.net
Dir: *5m from Carmarthen on A40*

The 'Sal', as it is affectionately known to the locals, has long been pulling them in from as far away as Swansea and Llanelli. The Salutation has long had a reputation for food that continues under the stewardship of landlords Aurwen Mills and Mark Williams. Generous blackboards offer a wide selection of dishes based on the abundant local produce.
Open: 11-3 5-11 (All day Jun-Sep) **Bar Meals:** L served all week 12-2.30 D served all week 6-10 **Restaurant Meals:** L served all week 12-2.30 D served all week

6-10 **Brewery/Company:** Felinfoel 🍺: Felinfoel - Double Dragon, Dragon Bitter, Fosters, Stowford Press, Guinness ♀: 12 **Children's Facilities:** Play area Menu/Portions Cutlery Games Highchair Food warming Baby changing **Nearby:** Oakwood Park, Folley Farm, Gower Beaches **Notes:** Dogs allowed in bar **Garden:** Food served outside **Parking:** 15

RHANDIRMWYN
The Royal Oak Inn ★★★ INN
Llandovery SA20 0NY
☎ 01550 760201 🖹 01550 760332
Email: royaloak@rhandirmwyn.com
Web: www.rhandirmwyn.com

This comfortable inn with its stone floors and log fires was originally built as a hunting lodge in 1850. Local brews from Wye Valley and Evan Evans supplement better-known beers like Wadworth and Greene King, whilst whisky drinkers can sample from around fifty single malts. In summer, far-reaching views make the garden ideal for al fresco dining. Expect lunchtime sandwiches, as well as hot dishes like black beef curry, vegetable goulash, or grilled trout.
Open: 11.30-3 6-11 (Sun 7-10.30) **Bar Meals:** L served all week 12-2 D served all week 6-9.30 **Restaurant Meals:** L served all week 12-2 D served all week 6.30-9.30 (Sun lunch 12-2, Dinner 7-9.30) **Brewery/Company:** Free House 🍺: Greene King Abbot Ale, Wadworth 6X, Burtons,Wye Valley, Evan Evans **Children's Facilities:** Licence Menu/Portions Cutlery Highchair Food warming **Nearby:** Dolaucothi Gold Mines, Carreg Cennen Castle **Notes:** Dogs allowed in bar **Garden:** Lawn, food served outside **Parking:** 20

CARDIGAN
Webley Hotel
Poppit Sands SA43 3LN
☎ 01239 612085
Dir: *A484 from Carmarthen to Cardigan, then to St Dogmaels, turn right in village centre to Poppit Sands*

Located on the coastal path, and within walking distance of Poppit Sands, this hotel overlooks the Teifi Estuary and Cardigan Island. Children's facilities have been improved since the new owners took over a year ago, and dogs are welcome by prior arrangement. Readers' reports welcome.
Open: 9-11 **Bar Meals:** L served all week 12-3 D served all week 6-9 Av main course £6.50 **Restaurant Meals:** L served all week D served all week Av 3 course alc £9 **Brewery/Company:** Free House 🍺: Bass, Brains Buckleys Bitter, Carling, Worthington, guest beers **Children's Facilities:** Licence Menu/Portions Cutlery Games Highchair Food warming **Notes:** Dogs allowed garden only **Garden:** garden overlooks the estuary **Parking:** 60

CARMARTHENSHIRE / CEREDIGION

LLWYNDAFYDD
The Crown Inn & Restaurant
New Quay Llandysul SA44 6BU
☎ 01545 560396 📄 01545 560857
Web: www.thecrowninnandrestaurant.co.uk
Dir: *Off A487 NE of Cardigan*
A traditional Welsh longhouse dating from 1799, with
original beams, open fireplaces, and a pretty restaurant.
A varied menu offers a good selection of dishes, including
sautéed ballottine of chicken supreme; roast monkfish
wrapped in Parma ham; and warm spiced couscous.
Blackboard specials and bar meals are available
lunchtimes and evenings. Outside is a delightful, award-
winning garden. An easy walk down the lane leads to a
cove with caves and National Trust-owned cliffs.
Open: 12-3 6-11 (all day Fri/Sat (Etr-Sep) Closed Sun

eve (winter)) **Bar Meals:** L served all week 12-2 D
served all week 6-9 Av main course £8 **Restaurant
Meals:** D served all week 6.30-9 Av 3 course alc £30
Brewery/Company: Free House 🍺: Interbrew Flowers
Original & Flowers IPA , Greene King Old Speckled Hen,
Honey Beers Envill Ale, Fullers London Pride, guest beer
Children's Facilities: Licence Fam room Play area
(Climbing frames, slides, swings) Menu/Portions Games
Highchair Food warming **Nearby:** Beaches **Notes:** Dogs
allowed in bar, in garden, Water bowls **Garden:** Large
terraces, pond, lawns **Parking:** 80

BETWS-Y-COED
Ty Gwyn Hotel ★★★ INN
LL24 0SG
☎ 01690 710383 & 710787 📄 01690 710383
Email: mratcl1050@aol.com
Web: www.tygwynhotel.co.uk
Dir: *At Junction of A5/A470, 100 yards S of Waterloo
Bridge.*
Once a main watering hole for travellers on the London to
Holyhead road, this 16th-century former coaching inn is
set in the heart of Snowdonia National Park overlooking
the Conwy River. The building still retains its old world
features with low beamed ceilings and open fires. Serves
good, home-cooked food.
Open: 12-3 6-11 **Bar Meals:** L served all week 12-2
D served all week 6.30-9 Av main course £8.95

Restaurant Meals: L served all week 12-2 D served
all week 6.30-9 **Brewery/Company:** Free House
🍺: Adnams Broadside, Reverend James Old Speckled
Hen, Bombardier & IPA **Children's Facilities:** Menu/
Portions Games Highchair Food warming **Nearby:** Welsh
Mountain Zoo, Butterfly Museum, Mini Steam Railway
Parking: 12

BETWS-YN-RHOS
The Wheatsheaf Inn
LL22 8AW
☎ 01492 680218 📄 01492 680666
Email: perry@jonnyp.fsnet.co.uk
Dir: *A55 to Abergele, take A548 to Llanrwst from the
High St. 2m turn right B5381, 1m to Betws-yn-Rhos*
This 13th-century alehouse was licensed as a coaching
inn in 1640. Splendid oak beams, old stone pillars and an
original hayloft ladder combine to make this an ideal spot
to enjoy a pint of Greene King or one of the Wheatsheaf's
special malt whiskies. A single menu serves the lounge
bar and restaurant with dishes that may include grilled
halibut with prawns; royal game pie and madeira sauce;
or mushroom stroganoff.
Open: 12-3 6-11 **Bar Meals:** L served all week 12-2 D

served all week 6-9 (Sun 12-3) Av main course £8
Restaurant Meals: L served all week 12-2 D served all
week 6-9.30 (Sun 12-3) Av 3 course alc £16
Brewery/Company: Enterprise Inns 🍺: Greene King
IPA, Courage Directors, & John Smiths **Children's
Facilities:** Play area (Wendy house in the beer garden)
Menu/Portions Cutlery Games Highchair Food warming
Nearby: Castle & Marina at Conwy, Ryhl Sun Centre&
Llandudno Happy Valley **Notes:** Garden: Paved beer
garden with BBQ **Parking:** 30

CAPEL CURIG

Cobdens Hotel ★★ SHL

Snowdonia LL24 0EE

☎ 01690 720243 📠 01690 720354

Email: info@cobdens.co.uk

Web: www.cobdens.co.uk

Situated in a beautiful mountain village in the heart of Snowdonia, this 250-year-old inn offers wholesome, locally sourced food and real ales. Start with local rabbit and pancetta carbonara; or leek and potato terrine. Mains include roasted Welsh lamb with garlic and thyme mash; Welsh beef steaks; and pasta with roasted courgette, blue cheese and chestnut. Try bara brith parfait for pudding! Snacks and sandwiches also available.

Open: 11-11 **Closed:** 6-26 Jan **Bar Meals:** L served all week 12-2.30 D served all week 6-9 Av main course £10 **Restaurant Meals:** L served all week 12-2 D served all week 6-9 Av 3 course alc £22 **Brewery/Company:** Free House 🍺: Conwy Castle Beer, Cobdens Ale & Guest Ale **Children's Facilities:** Licence Menu/Portions Cutlery Games Food warming **Nearby:** Betws-y-Coed, Dry slope skiing, Snowdown Railway **Notes:** Dogs allowed in bar, in garden, in bedrooms, Water bowls & food **Garden:** By river, part of Snowdonia National Park **Parking:** 35

PRESTATYN

Nant Hall Restaurant & Bar 🍷

Nant Hall Road LL19 9LD

☎ 01745 886766 📠 01745 886998

Email: mail@nanthall.com

Web: www.nanthall.com

The team at Conwy's Castle Hotel have been inundated with customers since taking over the business at Nant Hall. The Grade II listed Victorian country house, with style and ambience to match, is set in around 7 acres of grounds with a large outdoor seating area for alfresco summer dining. The extensive menu includes roasted Welsh lamb over bubble and squeak with fennel; pan-fried salmon with soft herb crust; and vegetarian Mexican fajitas.

Open: 11-12 **Bar Meals:** L served all week 12 D served all week 6-9.30 (Sun 12-6) Av main course £10 **Brewery/Company:** Free House 🍺: Stella Artois, 4X, Boddingtons, Welsh Smooth Bitter & Conwy Bitter 🍷: 14 **Children's Facilities:** Fam room Play area Menu/Portions Games Highchair Food warming Baby changing **Nearby:** Prestatyn Nova Centre, Talacre Beach & Rhye Sun Centre **Notes:** **Garden:** Large seated area, grass & hard surfaces **Parking:** 150

RHEWL

The Drovers Arms, Rhewl

Denbigh Road Ruthin LL15 2UD

☎ 01824 703163 📠 01824 703163

Email: Allen_Given@hotmail.com

Dir: 1.3m from Ruthin on the A525

A small village pub whose name recalls a past written up and illustrated on storyboards displayed inside. Main courses are divided on the menu into poultry, traditional meat, fish, grills and vegetarian; examples, one from each section, are chicken tarragon; Welsh lamb's liver and onions; Vale of Clwyd sirloin steak; home-made fish pie; and fresh mushroom Stroganoff. Desserts include treacle sponge pudding, and Black Forest gâteau.

Open: 12-3 5-11 (Times vary ring for details) **Bar Meals:** L served all week 12-2 D served all week 6-8.45 (Sun 12-2.30) **Restaurant Meals:** L served all week 12-2 D served Mon-Sat 6-9 (Sun 12-2.30) 🍺: London Pride, Youngs, Tetley Smooth **Children's Facilities:** Licence Play area (Bouncy castle, playhouse) Games Highchair Food warming **Notes:** **Garden:** Large garden with tables **Parking:** 20

RUTHIN
White Horse Inn 🍷
Hendrerwydd LL16 4LL
☎ 01824 790218
Email: vintr74@hotmail.com
Web: www.white-horse-inn.co.uk
A beautiful setting, the cosy atmosphere and good food and drink make the White Horse Inn a magnet for those travelling in the Vale of Clwyd. The bar menu includes a choice of hot dishes, as well as sandwiches and salads. The restaurant is a large, bright room with superb views of Moel Fammau and Moel Arther and the à la carte menu has many tempting dishes.
Open: 12-2.30 6-11 **Bar Meals:** L served all week 12-2.30 D served all week 6-9.15 (Sun 12-2.30) Av main course £15 **Restaurant Meals:** L served all week 12-2.30 D served all week 6-9.15 (Sun 6-8.30) Av 3 course alc £25 **Brewery/Company:** Free House 🍺: Regular changing guest ales 🍷: 7 **Children's Facilities:** Fam room Menu/Portions Highchair Food warming **Nearby:** Moel Famau Country Park, Chester Walled City, Bodelwyddan Castle **Notes:** Dogs allowed in bar, Water **Garden:** Front & back, trees **Parking:** 35

RUTHIN
Ye Olde Anchor Inn
Rhos Street LL15 1DY
☎ 01824 702813 📠 01824 703050
Email: hotel@anchorinn.co.uk
Web: www.anchorinn.co.uk
Dir: *At junction of A525 and A494*
Built in 1742, this impressive-looking inn has 16 windows at the front alone - all with award-winning window boxes. Choose starters of chicken satay; or mushrooms with spinach and cream cheese. Follow with breast of chicken stuffed with a herbed cream cheese; or a classic French Châteaubriand steak. Home-baked bread comes with the meal. A varied selection of freshly prepared desserts is available.
Open: 11-11 **Bar Meals:** L served all week 12-2 D served all week 6-9.30 (Sun 12-3) Av main course £7 **Restaurant Meals:** L served all week 12-2 D served all week 6-9.30 Av 3 course alc £13 **Brewery/Company:** Free House 🍺: Timothy Taylor, Worthington, Carling, guest ales **Children's Facilities:** Menu/Portions Highchair Food warming **Notes:** Dogs allowed in bar **Parking:** 20

BABELL
Black Lion Inn
Nr Holywell CH8 8PZ
☎ 01352 720239
Dir: *From Holywell take B5121 towards A541 (Mold to Denbigh road) & take 2nd right to Babell*
The paved patio at the front of this listed 13th-century free house is the ideal place to enjoy a meal or a quiet pint. Since taking over in 2005, the team at the Black Lion has developed a mix of traditional food, modern service and the finest local meat and game. Expect braised steak in red wine and mustard; shortcrust country pie; and grilled Dover sole. Home-made puds include profiteroles and fresh cream.
Open: 6-11 (open all day Sat & Sun) **Bar Meals:** L served Sat & Sun D served Thu-Mon 6-9 **Restaurant Meals:** L served Sat & Sun 12-2 D served Thu-Mon 6.30-9 **Brewery/Company:** Free House 🍺: Thwaites Lancaster Bomber, Thwaites Smooth Bitter, Guest Cask, Bragdyr Bryn, George Wright Brewery & Facers Beers **Children's Facilities:** Menu/Portions Cutlery Highchair **Parking:** 80

HALKYN

Britannia Inn

Pentre Road CH8 8BS

☎ 01352 780272

Email: sarah.pollitt@tesco.net

Dir: *Off A55 on B5123*

On the old coach route between Chester and Holyhead, a 500-year-old stone pub with lovely views over the Dee estuary and the Wirral. It features a family farm with chickens, ducks and donkeys, and the large patio is ideal for alfresco eating and drinking on warm days. Typical dishes range from rump steak sandwich to pork escalope in pepper sauce, chicken tikka masala, three bean bake, and stuffed salmon roast.
Open: 11-11 **Bar Meals:** L served all week 12-2.30 D served all week 6.30-9 **Restaurant Meals:** L served all week 12-2.30 D served all week 6.30-9 **Brewery/Company:** J W Lees ◖: J W Lees Bitter, GB Mild, Golden Original **Children's Facilities:** Play area (Petting farm) Menu/Portions Cutlery Games Highchair Food warming **Nearby:** Chester Zoo, Conwy Castle & Beaches **Notes:** Garden: Large patio area **Parking:** 40

NORTHOP

Stables Bar Restaurant ♟

Nr Mold CH7 6AB

☎ 01352 840577 🗎 01352 840382

Email: info@soughtonhall.co.uk

Web: www.soughtonhall.co.uk

Dir: *From A55, take A119 through Northop village*

In the magnificent setting of the 17th-century Soughton Hall stables, this destination pub has kept many of its original features, including the cobbled floors, stalls and roof timbers. The tables are named after famous racecourses and their winners. The menu continues the racing theme, listing deep-fried cod and monkfish with mushy peas and chips, and roast lamb cutlets, with steaks from the chargrill. Seasonal specials and vegetarian choices increase the choice.
Open: 11-11.30 **Bar Meals:** L served all week 12-3 D served all week 7-9.30 (Sun 4-9.30) Av main course £7.50 **Restaurant Meals:** L served all week 12-3 D served all week 7-10 (Sun 1-3, 7-10) Av 3 course alc £20 **Brewery/Company:** Free House ◖: Shepherds Neame Spitfire, Shepherd Neame Bishops Finger, Coach House Honeypot, Dick Turpin, Plassey Bitter, Stables Bitter ♟: 6 **Children's Facilities:** Fam room Menu/Portions Highchair **Notes:** Garden: Food served outdoors, patio, **Parking:** 150

BLAENAU FFESTINIOG

The Miners Arms

Llechwedd Slate Caverns LL41 3NB

☎ 01766 830306 🗎 01766 831260

Email: quarrytours@aol.com

Web: www.llechwedd-slate-caverns.co.uk

Dir: *Blaenau Ffestiniog is 25 m from Llandudno on the N Wales coast, situated on the A470 to main N-S Trunk Rd*

Slate floors, open fires and staff in Victorian costume emphasise the heritage theme of this welcoming pub nestling in the centre of a Welsh village. On the site of Llechwedd Slate Caverns, one of the country's leading tourist attractions, it caters for all comers and tastes: expect steak and ale casserole, pork pie and salad, various ploughman's lunches, and hot apple pie, as well as afternoon tea with scones and cream.
Open: 11-5.30 Closed: Oct-Easter **Bar Meals:** L served all week 11-5 **Brewery/Company:** Free House ◖: **Children's Facilities:** Fam room Play area Highchair Baby changing **Notes:** Dogs allowed **Parking:** 200

GWYNEDD

LLANBEDR
Victoria Inn ★★★★ INN ♟
LL45 2LD
☎ 01341 241213 📄 01341 241644
Email: junevicinn@aol.com
Dir: *Telephone for directions*

Heavily beamed and wonderfully atmospheric, the Victoria is perfect for the pub connoisseur seeking authentic features such as flagged floors, an unusual circular wooden settle, an ancient stove and a grandfather clock. Good food in the bars and restaurant includes honey roast ham, sausage in onion gravy, Japanese torpedo prawns served with a lemon mayonnaise dip, and Welsh dragon tart. Relax with a leisurely drink in the pub's well-kept garden.

Open: 12-11 (Sun 12-10.30, Fri & Sat 12-12) **Bar**

Meals: L served all week 12-9 D served all week 6-9 **Restaurant Meals:** L served all week 12-3 D served all week 6-9 **Brewery/Company:** Frederic Robinson ◖: Robinson's Best Bitter, Hartleys XB ♟: 10 **Children's Facilities:** Play area (Climbing frame and slide) Menu/Portions Cutlery Highchair Food warming Baby changing **Notes:** Dogs allowed in bar, in garden Garden: Riverside garden, pond, trees & plants **Parking:** 50

LLANBERIS
Pen-Y-Gwryd Hotel
Nantgwynant LL55 4NT
☎ 01286 870211
Web: www.pyg.co.uk
Dir: *A5 to Capel Curig, left on A4086 to T-junct.*

This slate-roofed climbers' pub and rescue post in the heart of Snowdonia has long been the home of British mountaineering. The 1953 Everest team used it as their training base, and etched their signatures on the ceiling. The appetising and inexpensive menus make good use of Welsh lamb and local pork; other options include home-made pâté with pickles, salad and crusty bread; or ham and cannellini bean spaghetti with home-made olive and herb flatbread.

Open: 11-11 Closed: Nov to New Year, mid-week Jan-Feb **Bar Meals:** L served all week 12-2 D served all week **Restaurant Meals:** L served all week D served all week 7.30-8 **Brewery/Company:** Free House ◖: Interbrew Bass & Boddingtons Bitter **Children's Facilities:** Fam room Play area (Large room with table tennis, pool) Menu/Portions Highchair Food warming **Nearby:** Snowdon, Angelsey Sea Zoo, Ffestiniog Railway **Notes:** Dogs allowed in bar Garden: Mountain garden with lake and sauna **Parking:** 25

LLANDWROG
The Harp Inn ♟
Tyn'llan Nr Caernarvon LL54 5SY
☎ 01286 831071 📄 01286 830239
Email: management@theharp.globalnet.co.uk
Web: www.theharphotel.co.uk
Dir: *A55 from Chester bypass, signed off A487 Pwllheli rd*

This characterful old in stands in the centre of a lovely village. There used to be a secret passage to the ancient churchyard across the road, and the building is said to be haunted. Nowadays you'll find real ale, a non-smoking restaurant and a peaceful garden. It offers a varied menu.

Open: 12-3 6-11 (Times vary ring for details, Sat 12-11) Closed: 1 Jan **Bar Meals:** L served Tue-Sun 12-2 D served Tue-Sun 6.30-8.30 Av main course £7.95

Restaurant Meals: L served Tue-Sun 12-2 D served Tue-Sun 6.30-8.30 **Brewery/Company:** Free House ◖: Guest Welsh Ales ♟: 8 **Children's Facilities:** Fam room (Games for all ages) Menu/Portions Cutlery Games Highchair Food warming **Nearby:** Caernarfon Castle Snowdon Railway **Notes:** Dogs allowed in bar, in garden Garden 6 tables **Parking:** 20

GWYNEDD

MALLWYD

The Brigands Inn ★★★★ INN

SY20 9HJ

☎ 01650 511999 📠 01650 531208

Web: www.brigandsinn.com

Dir: On A487 between Dolgellau and Machynlleth.

At the heart of the Cambrian Mountains, on the upper banks of the gin-clear River Dovey, lies the Brigands Inn, a renowned 15th-century coaching establishment. The pub's impressive setting makes it a popular base for exploring this scenic, spectacular corner of Wales. The chef sources the finest local produce to create a fusion of contemporary and classic Welsh cuisine. The menus reflect the changing seasons with a good selection of fish, meat and game. **Open:** 10-11 **Bar Meals:** L served all week 12-2.30 D

served all week 6-9 Av main course £7.95 **Restaurant Meals:** L served all week 12-2.30 D served all week 6-9 🍺: Worthington Cream, Worthington Cask, Archers Guest Ale **Children's Facilities:** Menu/Portions Highchair Food warming Baby changing **Nearby:** Centre for Alternative Technology, Celtica, King Arthurs Labyrinth **Notes:** Garden: Large, landscaped garden **Parking:** 80

TUDWEILIOG

Lion Hotel

Pwllheli LL53 8ND

☎ 01758 770244 📠 01758 770546

Dir: A499 from Caernarfon, B4417 Tudweiliog

The Lee family have run this friendly, 300-year-old village inn on the Lleyn Peninsula for over 30 years. The large garden and children's play area makes the pub especially popular with cyclists, walkers and families, with a beach just one mile away. The bar features an extensive list of over 80 malt whiskies. There is a non-smoking family dining room but food is served throughout, from lunchtime baguettes to traditional favourites such as home-made lasagne gammon steak. There is a good children's and vegetarian menu. **Open:** 11.30-11 (Sun 12-2, Winter 12-2, 7-11 all day

Sat, Jan) **Bar Meals:** L served all week 12-2 D served all week 6-9 Av main course £7 **Restaurant Meals:** L served all week 12-2 D served all week 6-9 Av 3 course alc £12 **Brewery/Company:** Free House 🍺: Interbrew Boddingtons, Purple Moose Brewery Ales **Children's Facilities:** Fam room Play area (Climbing frame, swing, slide) Highchair Food warming Baby changing **Nearby:** Beaches, Horseriding **Notes:** Garden: Food served outside, play area **Parking:** 40

WAUNFAWR

Snowdonia Parc Brewpub & Campsite

Caernarfon LL55 4AQ

☎ 01286 650409 & 650218 📠 01286 650409

Email: karen@snowdonia-park.co.uk

Web: www.snowdonia-park.co.uk

This pub stands 400 feet above sea level at Waunfawr station on the Welsh Highland Railway, and there are steam trains on site. All around is pleasant mountain scenery. Expect standard pub food. Children and dogs are welcome, and a children's playground is provided. **Open:** 11-11 (Sun 11-10.30) **Bar Meals:** L served all week 11-8.30 D served all week 5-8.30 **Restaurant Meals:** L served all week 11-8.30 D served all week 11-8.30 🍺: Marston's Bitter & Pedigree, Welsh Highand Bitter (ownbrew), Mansfield Dark Mild, Stella, Kronenburg

Children's Facilities: Fam room Play area (Swings, Roundabout, Bouncy Castle Apr-Sep) Menu/Portions Cutlery Games Highchair Food warming Baby changing **Nearby:** Welsh Highland Railway, Gypsy Wood Park & The Greenwood Centre **Notes:** Dogs allowed in bar, in garden, Water bowls Garden: Views towards Snowdonia Mountains **Parking:** 100

ISLE OF ANGLESEY / MONMOUTHSHIRE

RED WHARF BAY
The Ship Inn 🍷
LL75 8RJ
☎ 01248 852568   📠 01248 851013
Web: www.shipinnredwharfbay.co.uk
Large numbers of wading birds flock to feed on the extensive sands of Red Wharf Bay, making the Ship's waterside beer garden a birdwatcher's paradise on warm days. Before the age of steam, sailing ships landed cargoes from all over the world; now, the boats bring fresh Conwy Bay fish and seafood to the kitchens of this traditional free house. A single menu is served to diners in the bars and non-smoking restaurant, where seafood dishes are a mainstay of the daily menu. Start, perhaps, with soused herrings, rocket and tomato salad; or roast quail, apricot stuffing and pesto. Main course choices might include local seafood platter with sauté potatoes and ratatouille; poached local skate on chive mash; or tomato and Parmesan tart with artichokes and wild mushrooms. Home-made desserts like dark chocolate and Welsh liqueur cup round things off nicely.
Open: 11-11   **Bar Meals:** L served all week 12-2.30 D served all week 6-9 (Sun 12-9)   **Restaurant Meals:** L served Sun 12-2.30 D served Fri-Sat 7-9.30 **Brewery/Company:** Free House 🍺: Brains SA, Adnams, Guest Beers 🍷: 16   **Children's Facilities:** Fam room Play area Menu/Portions Highchair Food warming   **Nearby:** Red Wharf Bay   **Notes:** Garden: On water's edge, food served outside   **Parking:** 45

ABERGAVENNY
Clytha Arms 🍷
Clytha NP7 9BW
☎ 01873 840206   📠 01873 840206
Email: info@clytha-arms.com
Web: www.clytha-arms.com
Dir: *From A449/A40 junction (E of Abergavenny) follow signs for 'Old Road Abergavenny/Clytha'*
A converted dower house surrounded by two acres of lawns and gardens, this family-run free house functions successfully as both informal pub and outstanding restaurant. A truly extensive list of bar snacks includes tapas; bacon, laverbread and cockles; faggots and peas; and charcuterie with Catalan tomato bread. Fish and shellfish are plentiful, including whole crab from Pembroke and Cornwall, grilled mackerel, salmon and prawn pie, eel pie, Cajun-spiced black bream, and brodetto, Italy's version of bouillabaisse. Apart from fish in the restaurant, there may be Caerphilly cheese- and walnut-stuffed aubergine; Caribbean fruit curry; fillet of teriyaki beef; and venison in Rioja with chorizo and ceps.
Open: 12-3 6-12 (Sat 12-12) Closed: 25 Dec   **Bar Meals:** L served Tue-Sun 12.30-2.15 D served Tue-Sun 7-9.30 Av main course £8   **Restaurant Meals:** L served all week 12.30-2.30 D served Tue-Sun 7-9.30 Av 3 course alc £28 🍺: Bass, Felinfoel Double Dragon, Hook Norton, 3 Guest beers (300+ per year) 🍷: 10   **Children's Facilities:** Play area (Paddock with swing, large garden boules) Menu/Portions Cutlery Games Highchair Food warming Baby changing   **Nearby:** Castles, Raglan Garden Centre   **Notes:** Garden: 2 acres with paddock, fountain & lawns   **Parking:** 100

LLANTRISANT
The Greyhound Inn 🍷
Usk NP15 1LE
☎ 01291 672505 & 673447   📠 01291 673255
Email: enquiry@greyhound-inn.com
Web: www.greyhound-inn.com
Dir: *From M4 take A449 towards Monmouth, 1st junct to Usk, left onto Usk Sq. Take 2nd left signed Llantrisant, 2.5m to inn*
During the 17th century this Welsh longhouse, or farm-house, oversaw a 400-acre estate, then in 1845 the milk parlour was converted into an inn. The regular menu and specials blackboards offer a variety of dishes.
Open: 11-11 (Sun 12-4, 7-11) Closed: 25, 31 Dec, 1 Jan   **Bar Meals:** L served all week 12-2.15 D served Mon-Sat 6-10 (Sun 12-2.15) Av main course £8   **Restaurant Meals:** L served all week 12-2.15 D served Mon-Sat 6-10.30   **Brewery/Company:** Free House 🍺: Interbrew Flowers Original & Bass, Greene King Abbot Ale & Guest Beer 🍷: 10   **Children's Facilities:** Fam room Highchair Food warming   **Nearby:** Walking in Wentwood Forest, Raglan Castle, Usk Valley Walks   **Notes:** Garden: Pond with fountain, gardens & flowers   **Parking:** 60

LLANVAIR DISCOED
The Woodland Restaurant & Bar ♥
NP16 6LX

☎ 01633 400313 🖷 01633 400313

Email: lausnik@aol.co.uk

This old inn has been extended to accommodate a growing number of diners, but remains at heart a friendly, family-run village local serving a good range of beers. The pub is located close to the Roman fortress town of Caerwent and Wentworth's forest and reservoir. Its nickname, the war office recalls the fact that Irish navvies building the reservoir used to hold bare-knuckle fights here. A varied menu of freshly prepared dishes caters for all tastes from ciabatta bread with various toppings to loin of cod on king prawn risotto with beurre blanc, or lemon sole with lemon parsley butter. Meat is sourced from a local butcher who slaughters all his own meat, and the fish is mostly from Cornwall. Outside there's a large, well-equipped garden with plenty of bench seating. **Open:** 11-3 6-11 (Sun 12-3, closed Sun eve) **Bar Meals:** L served Tue-Sun 12-2 D served Tue-Sat 6-10 (Sun 12-2) Av main course £10 **Restaurant Meals:** L served Tue-Sun 12-2 D served Tue-Sat 6-9.30 (Sun 12-3) Av 3 course alc £20 **Brewery/Company:** Free House 🍺: Reverend James, Brains, Felinfoel Double Dragon, Bass & Tomas Watkins OSB ♥: 8 **Children's Facilities:** Play area (Swings & slide) Menu/Portions Highchair Food warming **Nearby:** Tintern Abbey, Wentwood Forest, Tredegar House & Country Park **Notes:** Dogs allowed in bar, in garden, Water Garden: Plenty of bench seating **Parking:** 30

SHIRENEWTON
The Carpenters Arms
Usk Road Nr Chepstow NP16 6BU

☎ 01291 641231 🖷 01291 641231

Web: www.chepstow.co.uk/carps

Dir: *M48 junct 2 take A48 to Chepstow then A4661, B4235. Village 3m on left*

A 400-year-old hostelry, formerly a carpenter's shop and smithy, with flagstone floors, open fires and antiques. It's set in a pleasant wooded location in the valley of the Mounton Brook which lies between the bigger valleys of the Wye and Usk. Straightforward bar food is typified by chicken in leek and stilton sauce, steak and mushroom pie, smoked haddock and potato pie, guinea fowl in orange sauce, and lamb rogan josh. New owners. **Open:** 11-11 **Bar Meals:** L served all week 12-2 D served all week 7-9.30 Av main course £6.95 **Restaurant Meals:** L served all week 12-9.30 D served all week 12-9.30 Av 3 course alc £12 **Brewery/Company:** Punch Taverns 🍺: Fuller's London Pride, Wadworth 6X, Marston's Pedigree,Theakston Old Peculier **Children's Facilities:** Licence Fam room Menu/Portions Cutlery Highchair Food warming **Notes:** Dogs allowed in bar Garden: Patio at front of pub with benches **Parking:** 20

TINTERN PARVA
Fountain Inn ◆◆◆
Trellech Grange NP16 6QW

☎ 01291 689303 🖷 01291 689303

Email: thefountaininn@msn.com

Web: www.fountaininn-tintern.com

Dir: *From M48 junct 2 follow Chepstow then Tintern signs. In Tintern turn by the George Hotel for Raglan. Stay on this lane always bearing to the right, The inn is situated at the top of the hill*

A fire nearly destroyed this fine old inn, but the thick 17th-century walls survived the flames, and its character remains unspoilt. It enjoys views of the Wye Valley from the garden, and is close to Tintern Abbey. Home-cooked food includes grilled sardines with balsamic vinegar and cherry tomatoes; leek and Caerphilly sausages with onion gravy; and beef and Guinness pie. Also a good selection of steaks, omelettes, and seafood choices. Recent change of licensee. **Open:** 12-3 6.30-11 **Bar Meals:** L served all week 12-2.30 D served all week 7-9.15 Av main course £10 **Restaurant Meals:** L served all week 12-2.30 D served all week 7-9.15 Av 3 course alc £20 **Brewery/Company:** Free House 🍺: Hook Norton, Spinning Dog, Ring of Bells, Interbrew Bass, Hobgoblin, Rev James, Kingstone Classic & Cats Wiskers ♥: 10 **Children's Facilities:** Fam room Menu/Portions Cutlery Games Highchair Food warming **Notes:** Dogs allowed in bar, in garden, in bedrooms, Water, open fields for walks Garden: Views of Wye Valley with stream **Parking:** 30

MONMOUTHSHIRE

TRELLECK
The Lion Inn
Monmouth NP25 4PA
☎ 01600 860322 📄 01600 860060
Email: debs@globalnet.co.uk
Web: www.lioninn.co.uk
Dir: *From A40 S of Monmouth take B4293, follow signs for Trellech. From M8 junct 2, straight across rdbt, 2nd left at 2nd rdbt, B4293 to Trellech.*
Built in the late 16th century, the multi-award-winning Lion has been a coaching inn, a brewhouse and a pig farm. It serves traditional pub grub, but also authentic Hungarian dishes.
Open: 12-3 6-11 (All day summer Sat, Thu-Sat 6-12, Mon 7-11) **Bar Meals:** L served all week 12-2 D served Mon-Sat 6-9.30 (Sat-Sun 12-2.30) Av main course £8 **Restaurant Meals:** L served all week 12-2 D served Mon-Sat 6-9.30 (Sat-Sun 12-2.30) Av 3 course alc £20 🍺: Bath Ales, Wadworth 6X, Wye Valley Butty Bach, Sharps Cornish Coaster **Children's Facilities:** Cutlery Games Food warming Baby changing **Nearby:** Wye Valley, Chepstow Castle, Tintern Abbey **Notes:** Dogs allowed in bar, in garden **Parking:** 40

USK
The Nags Head Inn 🍷
Twyn Square NP15 1BH
☎ 01291 672820 📄 01291 672720
Web: www.nagshead-usk.co.uk
Dir: *On A472*
This 15th-century coaching inn overlooks the square just a short stroll from the River Usk, and boasts magnificent hanging flower baskets. The traditional bar is furnished with polished tables and chairs, and decorated with collections of horse brasses, farming tools and lanterns hanging from exposed oak beams. Game in season figures strongly among the speciality dishes, including whole stuffed partridge (one of the hardest birds to shoot), pheasant in port, and wild boar steak with apricot and brandy sauce. There is a good choice for vegetarians, too, such as Glamorgan sausage filled with cheese and leek and served with a chilli relish.
Open: 10-3 5.30-11 Closed: 25 Dec **Bar Meals:** L served all week 10-2 D served all week 5.30-10.30 (Sun 12-2, 6-9.30) Av main course £8 **Restaurant Meals:** L served all week 11.30-2 D served all week 5.30-10.30 **Brewery/Company:** Free House 🍺: Brains Bitter, Dark, Buckleys Best, Reverend James & Bread of Heaven 🍷: 8 **Children's Facilities:** Menu/Portions Cutlery Games Highchair Food warming

AMROTH
The New Inn
Narberth SA67 8NW
☎ 01834 812368
Dir: *A48 to Carmarthen, A40 to St Clears, A477 to Llanteg then left*
A 400-year-old inn, originally a farmhouse, belonging to Amroth Castle Estate. It has old world charm with beamed ceilings, a Flemish chimney, a flagstone floor and an inglenook fireplace. It is close to the beach, and local lobster and crab are a feature, along with a popular choice of home-made dishes including steak and kidney pie, soup and curry. Enjoy food or drink outside on the large lawn complete with picnic benches.
Open: 11.30-3 5.30-11 Closed: Nov-Mar **Bar Meals:** L served all week 12-2 D served all week 6-9 **Restaurant Meals:** L served all week 12-2 D served all week 6-9 **Brewery/Company:** Free House 🍺: Burton, Carlsberg-Tetley Tetley Bitter, Speckled Hen & Guest ales **Children's Facilities:** Fam room Menu/Portions Highchair Food warming **Notes:** Dogs allowed in bar Garden: Large lawn with picnic benches **Parking:** 100

CAREW
Carew Inn
Tenby SA70 8SL
☎ 01646 651267
Email: mandy@carewinn.co.uk
Web: www.carewinn.co.uk
Dir: *From A477 take A4075. Inn 400yds opp castle & Celtic cross*

A traditional stone-built country inn situated opposite the Carew Celtic cross and Norman castle. Enjoy the one-mile circular walk around the castle and millpond. A good range of bar meals includes Welsh black steak and kidney pie; chilli con carne; Thai red chicken curry; and seafood pancakes. Fruit crumble and old favourite jam roly poly feature among the puddings. Live music every Thursday night under the marquee.

Open: 11-11 Closed: Dec 25 **Bar Meals:** L served all week 11.30-2 D served all week 5.30-9 Av main course £8.50 **Restaurant Meals:** L served all week 11.30-2 D served all week 5.30-9 Av 3 course alc £15 **Brewery/Company:** Free House ▥: Worthington Best, SA Brains Reverend James & Guest Ales **Children's Facilities:** Play area (small climbing frame, slide, see-saw) Menu/Portions Cutlery Games Highchair Food warming Baby changing **Notes:** Dogs allowed in bar, in garden, Water provided Garden: overlooks Carew Castle **Parking:** 20

CILGERRAN
Pendre Inn
Pendre nr Cardigan SA43 2SL
☎ 01239 614223
Web: www.pendreinn.co.uk
Dir: *Off A478 south of Cardigan*

Dating back to the 14th century, this is a pub full of memorabilia and featuring exposed interior walls, old beams, slate floors and an inglenook fireplace. An ancient ash tree grows through the pavement in front of the white stone, thick-walled building. Typical menu includes lamb steaks with red wine and cherries, rump and sirloin steaks, pork loin with honey and mustard glaze, and salmon with hollandaise sauce.
Open: 12-11 **Bar Meals:** L served Wed-Sun 12-2 D served Wed-Sun 6-8.30 Av main course £6 **Restaurant**

Meals: L served Wed-Sun 12-2 D served Wed-Sun 6-8 Av 3 course alc £12 **Brewery/Company:** Free House ▥: Tomos Watkins, OSB, Murphys, Worthington **Children's Facilities:** Menu/Portions Games Highchair Food warming **Nearby:** Cardigan Farm Park, Dyffed Shire Horse Centre, Cilgerran Nature Reserve **Notes:** Garden: Lawn/patio with large trees and water feature **Parking:** 4

LAMPHEY
The Dial Inn ♥
Ridegway Road nr Pembroke SA71 5NU
☎ 01646 672426 🖶 01646 672426
Dir: *Just off A4139 (Tenby to Pembroke rd)*

The Dial started life around 1830 as the Dower House for nearby Lamphey Court, and was converted into a pub in 1966. It immediately established itself as a popular village local, and in recent years the owners have extended the dining areas. Food is a real strength, and Pembrokeshire farm products are used whenever possible. You can choose from traditional bar food, the imaginative restaurant menu, or the daily blackboard.
Open: 11-3 6-12 **Bar Meals:** L served all week 12-3 D served all week 6.30-9.30 **Restaurant Meals:** L served all week 12-3 D served all week 6.30-9.30

Brewery/Company: Free House ▥: Coors Beer, Runmey Bitter ♥: 8 **Children's Facilities:** Licence Fam room (games (darts/pool)) Menu/Portions Cutlery Games Highchair Food warming **Nearby:** Folly Farm, Oakwood, Manor Park **Notes:** Garden: Patio area **Parking:** 50

PEMBROKE DOCK
Ferry Inn
Pembroke Ferry SA72 6UD
☎ 01646 682947
Email: ferryinn@aol.com
Dir: *A477, off A48, right at garage, signs for Cleddau Bridge, left at rdbt*
There are fine views across the Cleddau estuary from the terrace of this 16th-century free house. Once the haunt of smugglers, the riverside inn has a nautical-themed bar with a 'great disaster' corner highlighting pictures of local catastrophes! The pub is also said to be haunted. Fresh fish features strongly on the menu: favourites include locally caught trout; salmon fillet with dill butter; and brill with cherry tomatoes and crème frâiche.
Open: 11.30-2.45 7-11 (Summer hols open all day)

Closed: 25-26 Dec **Bar Meals:** L served all week 12-2 D served all week 7-9.30 (Sun 12-1.30, 7-9) Av main course £10 **Restaurant Meals:** L served all week 12-2 D served all week 7-9.30 (Sun 12-1.30, 7-9) **Brewery/Company:** Free House 🍺: Worthington, Bass, Felinfoel Double Dragon, Weekly Guest Ale **Children's Facilities:** Menu/Portions Highchair Food warming **Nearby:** Oakwood Park, Folly Farm, Dinosaur Park **Notes:** Garden: Beer terrace on edge of river, amazing views **Parking:** 12

PORTHGAIN
The Sloop Inn 🍷
Haverfordwest SA62 5BN
☎ 01348 831449 📠 01348 831388
Email: matthew@sloop-inn.freeserve.co.uk
Web: www.sloop.co.uk
From the outside this family-friendly harbourside pub doesn't look particularly large, but appearances are deceptive. 'Basic' is the owners' word for the brick, slate, quarry tile and part-carpeted interior, but the seating's comfy.The bar menu has sandwiches, baguettes, light snacks and main meals. From the specials board, updated twice daily, come lemon pepper haddock fillets with a trio of flavoured butters; and rib-eye steak topped with red onion marmalade and stilton.
Open: 9.30-11 (Sun 9.30-10.30) **Bar Meals:** L served

all week 12-2.30 D served all week 6-9.30 Av main course £7 **Restaurant Meals:** L served all week 12-2.30 D served all week 6-9.30 Av 3 course alc £22 **Brewery/Company:** Free House 🍺: Reverend James, Brains Draught & Felinfoel 🍷: 8 **Children's Facilities:** Licence Games Highchair Food warming Baby changing **Nearby:** Harbour, beach & ancient buildings **Notes:** Garden: Raised patio area, sun trap & safe **Parking:** 50

STACKPOLE
The Stackpole Inn 🍷
nr Pembroke SA71 5DF
☎ 01646 672324 📠 01646 672716
Email: info@stackpoleinn.co.uk
Dir: *From Pembroke take B4319 & follow signs for Stackpole, approx 4m.*
This 17th-century inn stands close to the coastal path, in gardens at the heart of the National Trust's Stackpole Estate. Produce from the Welsh countryside and fish from the nearby coast feature in the home-cooked menu.
Open: 12-2.30 6-11 (Summer 12-3, 5.30-11) **Bar Meals:** L served all week 12-2 D served all week 6.30-9 (Summer Sat/Sun 12-3, 5.30-9) Av main course £9 **Restaurant Meals:** L served all week 12-2 D served all week (apart from Sun Winter) 6.30-9 (Summer Sat/Sun

12-3, 5.30-9) Av 3 course alc £19 🍺: Brains Reverend James, Felinfoel, Double Dragon, Best Bitter & Variable Guest Ale 🍷: 12 **Children's Facilities:** Licence Menu/Portions Highchair Food warming **Nearby:** Blue flag beach, Pembroke Castle, Folly Farm & Oakland **Notes:** Dogs allowed in bar, in garden Garden: Landscaped garden, picturesque **Parking:** 25

WOLF'S CASTLE
The Wolfe Inn ▼
Nr Haverfordwest SA62 5LS
☎ 01437 741662 📠 01437 741676
Dir: *On A40 between Haverfordwest & Fishguard, (7m from both towns)*

The Wolfe is an oak-beamed, stone-built property in a lovely village setting. The bar-brasserie and restaurant comprise four interconnecting but distinctly different rooms: the Victorian Parlour, Hunters' Lodge, the Brasserie and a conservatory. The inn uses mainly local produce in its 'robust, real food'. Example dishes are fillet of beef Bordelaise, lamb all'aglio e Menta, chicken piccante, salmon fillet with cream and Pernod sauce, and mussels in garlic, white wine and cream. Award-winning local cheeses and scrumptious home-made desserts follow.

Open: 12-2 6-11 **Bar Meals:** L served all week 12-2 D served all week 7-9 Av main course £12 **Restaurant Meals:** L served all week 12-2 D served all week 7-9 Av 3 course alc £25 **Brewery/Company:** Free House 🍺: Interbrew Worthington Bitter, Monthly Guest Beer ▼: 11 **Children's Facilities:** Menu/Portions Cutlery Highchair Food warming Baby changing **Nearby:** Dinosaur Park, Folly Farm, Tenby **Notes:** Garden: Enclosed garden, secluded, patio area **Parking:** 20

BERRIEW
The Lion Hotel
Nr Welshpool SY21 8PQ
☎ 01686 640452 📠 01686 640604
Email: patrick@okeeffe.demon.co.uk
Web: www.thelionhotelberriew.co.uk
Dir: *5m from Welshpool on A483, right to Berriew. Centre of village next to church.*

Behind the black and white timbered grid of this 17th-century coaching inn lie bars and dining areas where yet more old timbers testify to its age. Menus include loin of venison with pan-fried wild mushrooms and redcurrant jus; slow-roasted Welsh lamb shoulder with red wine mint gravy; leek and mozzarella-filled crêpe with spiced tomato sauce; and a fish board with sea bream, halibut, red snapper and salmon based dishes.

Open: 12-3.30 6-11 (Fri 5.30-11, Sat 12-11, Sun 7-10.30) **Bar Meals:** L served all week 12-2 D served all week 7-9 **Restaurant Meals:** L served all week 12-2 D served all week 7-9 🍺: Banks Bitter/Mild, Pedigree, Old Empire **Children's Facilities:** Licence Fam room Menu/Portions Games Highchair Food warming Baby changing **Nearby:** Powys Castle, River Rhew, Welshpool-Llanfair Light Railway **Notes:** Dogs allowed in bar, in garden, in bedrooms, Water **Garden:** Patio area surrounded by plants **Parking:** 6

BRECON
White Swan Inn ◉▼
Llanfrynach LD3 7BZ
☎ 01874 665276 📠 01874 665362
Web: www.the-white-swan.com
Dir: *3m E of Brecon off the A40, take the B4558 and follow the signs to Llanfrynach*

The long, white-painted stone frontage of the White Swan overlooks St Brynach's churchyard in the heart of the Brecon Beacons National Park. With its exposed oak beams, stone walls and inglenook fireplace, the stamp of character and atmosphere is everywhere. The theme here is unpretentious gastro-pub food with the emphasis on fish and modern dishes characterised by a distinct European flavour. Expect venison with port and cranberry sauce, or, perhaps, lamb with sweet potato. Other options include trio of mullet, sea bass and salmon; Caesar salad; Gressingham duck breast; and asparagus mousse gateau with crepes. Traditional afternoon tea with clotted cream is a perennial favourite.

Open: 12-2 6.30-11 Closed: 25-26 Dec, 1 Jan **Bar Meals:** L served Tue-Sun 12-2 D served Tue-Sun 7-9.30 (Sun 12-2.30, 7-9) Av main course £13 **Restaurant Meals:** L served Tue-Sun 12-2 D served Tue-Sun 7-9.30 (Sun 12-2.30, 7-9) Av 3 course alc £25 **Brewery/Company:** Free House 🍺: HB, Worthington Cream Flow, Worthington Cask ▼: 8 **Children's Facilities:** Menu/Portions Cutlery Games Highchair Food warming Baby changing **Nearby:** Upper Cantref Trekking Centre & Rare Breed Farm, Llangorse Lake, Brecon Promenade **Notes:** Garden: Vine & spectacular views **Parking:** 35

PEMBROKESHIRE / POWYS

POWYS

COEDWAY
The Old Hand and Diamond
nr Shrewsbury SY5 9AR
☎ 01743 884379 📠 01743 872305
Email: moz123@aol.com
Web: www.oldhandanddiamond.co.uk
Dir: *9m from Shrewsbury*
A 17th-century inn located close to the Powys/Shropshire border and the River Severn amid open countryside. It retains much of its original character and has open log fires in cooler weather. Food options include a popular lunchtime carvery, a daily curry, steaks, Greek salad, and home-made fish cakes.
Open: 11-11 **Bar Meals:** L served all week 12-2 D served all week 6-9.30 (Fri/Sat/Sun 12-9.30) Av main course £9 **Restaurant Meals:** L served all week 12-2 D served all week 6-9.30 (Fri/Sat/Sun-12-9.30) Av 3 course alc £17 **Brewery/Company:** Free House
🍺: Bass, Worthington, Shropshire Lad & Guest beers
Children's Facilities: Play area (Swings, climbing frame) Menu/Portions Cutlery Games Highchair Food warming Baby changing **Notes:** Garden: Food served outside
Parking: 90

CRICKHOWELL
Nantyffin Cider Mill ◎ ♟
Brecon Road NP8 1SG
☎ 01873 810775 📠 01873 810986
Email: info@cidermill.co.uk
Web: www.cidermill.co.uk
Dir: *At junct of A40 & A479, 1.5m west of Crickhowell*
Located at the foot of the Black Mountains between Crickhowell and Brecon, the Nantyffin is renowned for its successful pairing of traditional pub values with acclaimed French bistro-style food. Originally a drovers' inn dating from the 16th century, it became well-known for the cider it produced in the 19th century. The original cider press, fully working until the 1960s, has been incorporated into the main dining room. Menus are based on carefully sourced local produce, including organically reared, free-range meat and poultry from the proprietor's farm in Llangynidr. Dishes using home-reared meat include roast loin of old spot pork with bubble and squeak, red wine sauce and onion rings; and half a roast duck with parsnip purée, caramelized apples and port wine sauce.
Open: 12-2.30 6-9.30 Closed: 1wk Jan **Bar Meals:** L served Tue-Sun 12-2.30 D served Tue-Sun 6.30-9.30 **Restaurant Meals:** L served Tue-Sun 12-2.30 D served Tue-Sun 7-9.30 **Brewery/Company:** Free House
🍺: Uleys Old Spot, Felinfoel Best Bitter, Marston's Pedigree, Hancocks HB, Brains Buckley IPA ♟: 8
Children's Facilities: Menu/Portions Highchair Food warming Games **Nearby:** Big Pit Mining Museum, Brecon Beacons National Park **Notes:** Dogs allowed in garden Garden: Overlooking River Usk **Parking:** 40

HAY-ON-WYE
Kilverts Hotel ♟
The Bullring HR3 5AG
☎ 01497 821042 📠 01497 821580
Email: info@kilverts.co.uk
Web: www.kilverts.co.uk
Dir: *From A50 take A49, then L onto B4348 into Hay-on-Wye. In town centre near Butter Market*
A timber-framed, olde worlde style bar, offering local beers and Black Fox organic cider. The gardens have lawns and flower beds with a pond and fountain, as well as a pavement terrace at the front. Pizza and pasta menus are supplemented by daily specials offering fresh fish and local lamb dishes, as well as the carte.
Open: 9-11 (Sun 12-10.30) Closed: 25 Dec **Bar Meals:** L served all week 12-2 D served all week 7-9.30 Av main course £9.75 **Restaurant Meals:** D served all week 7-9.30 **Brewery/Company:** Free House 🍺: Wye Valley Butty Bach, Brains Cream Flow & Hancock's HB, The Reverend James ♟: 10 **Children's Facilities:** Fam room Menu/Portions Cutlery Highchair Food warming **Nearby:** Kington Small Breeds Farm, Shortwood Farm **Notes:** Dogs allowed in bar Garden: Lawns **Parking:** 13

LLANDRINDOD WELLS
The Gold Bell Country Inn 🍷
Llanyre Powys LD1 6DY
☎ 01597 823959
Web: www.goldbellcountryinn.co.uk
Dir: *1.5m NW of Llandrindod Wells on the A4081*
Now under new ownership, this free house has recently changed its name from the Bell Country Inn to the Gold Bell Country Inn. It's a former drovers' inn set in the hills above Llandrindod Wells, right at the centre of Wales with most attractions within an hour's drive. Food is served in the dining room, lounge bar and restaurant, including local specialities and traditional dishes. In summer meals are also served outside on the patio area.
Open: 7-1.30 **Bar Meals:** L served all week 12-2.15 D served Mon-Sat 6.30-9.30 Av main course £10

Restaurant Meals: L served all week 12-2 D served Mon-Sat 6.30-9.30 **Brewery/Company:** Free House 🍺: Brain's, Hancock's, guest ales 🍷: 12 **Children's Facilities:** Play area (Swings) Menu/Portions Cutlery Games Highchair Food warming Baby changing **Nearby:** Quackers Indoor Play Centre **Notes:** Garden: Food served outside Patio area **Parking:** 20

LLANFYLLIN
Cain Valley Hotel ★★ HL
High Street SY22 5AQ
☎ 01691 648366 📠 01691 648307
Email: info@cainvalleyhotel.co.uk
Web: www.cainvalleyhotel.co.uk
Dir: *from Shrewsbury & Oswestry follow signs for Lake Vyrnwy & onto A490 to Llanfyllin.Hotel on R*
Family-run coaching inn dating from the 17th century, with a stunning Jacobean staircase, oak-panelled lounge bar and a heavily beamed restaurant with exposed hand-made bricks. A full bar menu is available at lunchtime and in the evening. Local lamb steak with red wine and rosemary sauce, vegetable risotto, prime steak braised in real ale, or salmon fillet in a dill butter and lemon sauce may be on the menu.

Open: 11.30-12 (Sun 12-10) Closed: 25 Dec **Bar Meals:** L served all week 12-2 D served all week 7-9 Av main course £7.50 **Restaurant Meals:** L served all week 12-2 D served all week 7-9 **Brewery/Company:** Free House 🍺: Worthingtons, Ansells Mild, Guinness, Carling & Tetleys **Children's Facilities:** Play area Menu/Portions Cutlery Highchair Food warming **Nearby:** Lake Vyrnwy, Llechwedd Slate Caverns **Parking:** 12

LLANFYLLIN
The Stumble Inn
Bwlch-y-Cibau SY22 5LL
☎ 01691 648860 📠 01691 648955
Web: www.stumbleinn.co.uk
Dir: *A458 to Welshpool, B4393 to Four Crosses and Llansantffraid, A495 Melford, A490 to Bwlch-y-Cibau*
Located opposite the church in a peaceful farming community in unspoilt mid-Wales countryside close to Lake Vyrnwy, this popular stone-built 18th-century inn offers a traditional pub atmosphere. Ideal base for walkers and cyclists. The menu changes frequently and might feature duck with orange sauce, lamb shank, whole Dover sole, pork with lemon and mustard sauce, sizzling Chinese steak, mushroom Stroganoff, and Mediterranean risotto.

Open: 11-11 **Bar Meals:** L served all week from 12 D served all week 6-9 Av main course £5.95 **Restaurant Meals:** L served all week 12-2 D served all week 6-10 **Brewery/Company:** Free House 🍺: Coors Worthington's, Hook Norton, guest ales **Children's Facilities:** Games Highchair Food warming **Nearby:** Park Hill Farm, Lake Vyrnwy, Powys Castle **Parking:** 20

POWYS

LLANGATTOCK
The Vine Tree Inn
The Legar Crickhowell NP8 1HG
☎ 01873 810514 📄 01873 811299
Web: www.vinetreeinn.co.uk
Dir: *Take A40 W from Abergavenny then A4077 from Crickhowell*
A pretty pink pub located on the banks of the River Usk, at the edge of the National Park and within walking distance of Crickhowell. It is predominantly a dining pub serving a comprehensive menu from rabbit in a wine and celery sauce to monkfish in leek and Pernod sauce. Among the other choices on the menu you may find gammon in a parsley sauce, pork loin stuffed with marinated apricots, or a 16oz T-bone steak. The large garden overlooks the river, bridge and Table Mountain.

Open: 12-3 6-11 (Sun 12-3, 6.30-9) **Bar Meals:** L served all week 12-3 D served all week 6-10 (Sun 12-3, 6.30-9) Av main course £7.50 **Restaurant Meals:** L served all week 12-3 D served all week 6-10 Av 3 course alc £15 **Brewery/Company:** Free House
🍺: Fuller's London Pride, Coors Worthington's, Golden Valley **Children's Facilities:** Menu/Portions Highchair Food warming **Notes:** Garden: Large private garden, stunning views **Parking:** 27

MONTGOMERY
Dragon Hotel ★★ HL ⊛
SY15 6PA
☎ 01686 668359 📄 0870 011 8227
Email: reception@dragonhotel.com
Web: www.dragonhotel.com
Dir: *A483 toward Welshpool, right onto B4386 then B4385 & behind the town hall*
This strikingly attractive, black-and-white-timbered old coaching inn has an interior that dates in parts back to the mid-1600s. The bar, lounge and most bedrooms contain beams and masonry reputed to have been removed from the ruins of the castle destroyed by Oliver Cromwell in 1649. Today the hotel prides itself on the quality of its kitchen where fresh local produce is prepared to a high standard, and recognised by the AA with a Rosette for fine food. The bar menu features sandwiches, baked potatoes and jumbo Welsh rarebit specials with various garnishes. Restaurant starters might include leek-laced Welsh cakes with Tintern cheese sauce, or chicken liver terrine. Follow with pan-fried duck breast with a blackcurrant and cassis sauce, or local fillet of beef with rösti potato, celeriac puree and a rich port sauce.
Open: 11-11 **Bar Meals:** L served all week 12-2 D served all week 7-9 Av main course £8 **Restaurant Meals:** L served bookings only 12-2 D served bookings only 7-9 Av 3 course alc £27 **Brewery/Company:** Free House 🍺: Wood Special, Interbrew Bass & Guest **Children's Facilities:** Licence Menu/Portions Highchair Food warming Baby changing **Notes:** Garden: Patio area at the front **Parking:** 20

NEW RADNOR
Red Lion Inn
Llanfihangel-nant-Melan Presteigne LD8 2TN
☎ 01544 350220 📄 01544 350220
Email: theredlioninn@yahoo.co.uk
Web: www.theredlioninn.net
Dir: *A483 to Crossgates then right onto A44*
Old habits die hard here this ancient drover's inn still provides water - for hosing down the bike. Next door is one of four churches named after St Michael that encircle the burial place of the last Welsh dragon. According to legend, should anything happen to them the dragon will rise again. The inn has a lounge and a locals' bar, two small restaurants and a sun-trap garden. A broad menu draws extensively on local produce, including herbs from the garden. Mussels, usually served as a starter in white wine, garlic and cream, come from the River Conwy up north. Main courses might include game terrine with Cognac and grape preserve; Welsh Black beef fillet with béarnaise sauce; organic salmon fish cakes; and leek, wild mushroom and chestnut gateau. Round off with Welsh cheeses and home-made walnut bread.
Open: 12-2.30 6-11 (Open all day summer) **Bar Meals:** L served Wed-Mon 12-2 D served Wed-Mon 6-9 Av main course £7 **Restaurant Meals:** L served Wed-Mon 12-2 D served Wed-Mon 6-9 Av 3 course alc £16 **Brewery/Company:** Free House 🍺: Parish (Woods), Springer (Spinning Dog Brewery) **Children's Facilities:** Fam room Menu/Portions Cutlery Games Highchair Food warming **Nearby:** Small Animals Farm, Red Kite Feeding Station, Elan Valley **Notes:** Dogs allowed in bar Garden: Country garden overlooking mid Wales Hills **Parking:** 30

TRECASTLE
The Castle Coaching Inn
nr Brecon LD3 8UH

☎ 01874 636354 🖹 01874 636457

Email: guest@castle-coaching-inn.co.uk
Web: www.castle-coaching-inn.co.uk
Dir: *On A40 W of Brecon*

A Georgian coaching inn on the old London to Carmarthen coaching route, now the main A40 trunk road. Family-owned and run, the hotel has been carefully restored in recent years, and has lovely old fireplaces and a remarkable bow-fronted bar window. The inn also offers a peaceful terrace and garden. Food is served in the bar or more formally in the restaurant, and landlord John Porter continues to maintain high standards.
Open: 12-3 6-11 **Bar Meals:** L served Mon-Sun 12-2 D served Mon-Sat 6.30-9 (Sun 7-9) Av main course £10 **Restaurant Meals:** L served Mon-Sun 12-2 D served Mon-Sat 6.30-9 (Sun 7-9) Av 3 course alc £16 🍺: Fuller's London Pride, Breconshire Brewery Red Dragon, Taylor Landlords **Children's Facilities:** Licence Menu/Portions Cutlery Highchair Food warming Baby changing **Notes:** Garden: Paved terrace **Parking:** 25

UPPER CWMTWRCH
Lowther's Gourmet Restaurant and Bar
SA9 2XH

☎ 01639 830938

Web: www.lowthers.org.uk
Dir: *2m from Ystalyfera rdbt at Upper Cwmtwrch, next to the river*

A traditional family-owned pub and restaurant, which occupies a scenic riverside location at the foot of the Black Mountains. Relax by the cosy wood-burner on a cold winter's day or, in summer, make use of the colourful garden and patio for alfresco dining. The pub brews its own beers and offers wholesome fare made from Welsh produce wherever possible. Traditional roasts, sizzling bass in garlic, and Welsh black beef feature on the extensive menu.
Open: 12-4 6-11 (Sun 12-3, 6-10.30) Closed: 26 Dec **Bar Meals:** L served 11.30-2.30 D served 6-10 Av main course £13 **Restaurant Meals:** L served all week 12-3 D served all week 6-9 Av 3 course alc £25 **Brewery/Company:** Free House **Children's Facilities:** Play area (Swings, Slide, See-saw) Menu/Portions Highchair Food warming **Notes:** Garden: Food served outside **Parking:** 40

REYNOLDSTON
King Arthur Hotel 🍷
Higher Green Swansea SA3 1AD

☎ 01792 390775 🖹 01792 391075

Email: info@kingarthurhotel.co.uk
Web: www.kingarthurhotel.co.uk
Dir: *Just N of A4118 SW of Swansea*

Traditionally styled with real log fires and excellent ales, the King Arthur is an atmospheric base from which to explore Gower, Britain's first designated Area of Outstanding Natural Beauty. Food ranges from bar snacks (jacket potatoes, freshly baked baguettes) to hearty pub food including pies; home-made curries; and sausages and mash. Typical specials include Welsh Black fillet steak with roasted vegetables and red wine jus; and halibut steak with a panaché of vegetables.
Open: 11-11 Closed: 25 Dec **Bar Meals:** L served all week 12-6 D served all week 6-9 Av main course £8 **Restaurant Meals:** L served all week 12-2.30 D served all week 6-9 **Brewery/Company:** Free House 🍺: Felinfoel Double Dragon, Worthington Bitter & Bass & Tomos Watkins OSB 🍷: 9 **Children's Facilities:** Fam room Highchair Food warming Baby changing **Nearby:** Gower Heritage Museum, Parkmill, Wetlands Centre, Llanelli & Beaches **Notes:** Garden: 20 tables on grass area at front of pub **Parking:** 80

POWYS / SWANSEA

1001 Great Family Pubs

ST HILARY
The Bush Inn ♀
nr Cowbridge CF71 7DP
☎ 01446 772745
Dir: *S of A48, E of Cowbridge*

This is a thatched pub in a picturesque village in the Vale of Glamorgan, with seating at the front overlooking the 14th-century church. It has been a meeting place for people for over two hundred years, and one of the earlier ones remains in the form of a resident ghost, a highwayman who was caught close to the pub and hanged on the downs. His presence notwithstanding, The Bush is a warm, friendly and happy pub with enthusiastic new owners. An inglenook fireplace, flagstone floors and a spiral staircase are features of the cosy interior, and the pretty restaurant has French windows leading out to the garden. There is a separate bar and restaurant menu which, between them, will give you choices like light bites, sandwiches and salads, chargrilled steaks, the fresh fish special of the day, and vegetarian options. There is a selection of desserts on the blackboard menu.
Open: 11.30-11 (Sun 12-10.30) **Bar Meals:** L served all week 12-2.30 D served Mon-Sat 6.45-9.30 (Sun 12.15-3.30) Av main course £12 **Restaurant Meals:** L served all week 12-2.30 D served Mon-Sat 6.45-9.30 (Sun 12.15-3.30) Av 3 course alc £25
Brewery/Company: Punch Taverns ◼: Hancock's HB, Greene King Old Speckled Hen, Interbrew Worthington Bitter & Bass, Guest Beer ♀: 10 **Children's Facilities:** Licence Menu/Portions Cutlery Games Highchair Food warming **Notes:** Dogs allowed in bar, Water **Garden:** Bar tables on grass **Parking:** 60

LLANARMON DYFFRYN CEIRIOG
The West Arms Hotel ★★★ HL ☺☺ ♀
nr Llangollen LL20 7LD
☎ 01691 600665 📠 01691 600622
Email: gowestarms@aol.com
Web: www.thewestarms.co.uk
Dir: *Leave A483 at Chirk, follow signs for Ceiriog Valley B4500, hotel is 11m from Chirk*

Period features keep the past alive at this 17th-century drovers' inn. Award-winning chef Grant Williams has worked in kitchens around the world, appeared on TV cookery programmes, and even cooked for Prince Charles. Substantial meals are available lunchtimes and evenings from the bar menu and specials board.
Open: 8-11pm **Bar Meals:** L served all week 12-2 D served all week 7-9 **Restaurant Meals:** L served Sun 12-2 D served all week 7-9 **Brewery/Company:** Free House ◼: Interbrew Flowers IPA, Jennings Cumberland Ale ♀: 10 **Children's Facilities:** Play area (Swing, climbing frame) Menu/Portions Cutlery Games Highchair Food warming Baby changing **Nearby:** Chirk Castle, Llangollen Railway, Oswestry **Notes:** Dogs allowed in bar, in garden **Garden:** Large lawn **Parking:** 30

MARFORD
Trevor Arms Hotel ♀
nr Wrexham LL12 8TA
☎ 01244 570436 📠 01244 570273
Email: info@trevorarmsmarford.fsnet.co.uk
Web: www.trevorarmshotel.com
Dir: *Off A483 onto B5102 then R onto B5445 into Marford*

This reputedly haunted early 19th-century coaching inn takes its name from Lord Trevor of Trevallin, who was killed in a duel. Despite its grisly past, the Trevallin is a charming inn, offering a varied menu.
Open: 11-11.30 (Fri/Sat 11-12) **Bar Meals:** L served all week 11-10 D served all week 6-10 (Sun 12-8.30) Av main course £7.50 **Restaurant Meals:** L served all week 11-10 D served all week 11-10 (Sun 12-8.30) Av 3 course alc £16 ◼: Greenalls, Scottish Courage, Bombardier & John Smiths, Morland Old Speckled Hen & 2 Guest beers ♀: 12 **Children's Facilities:** Fam room Play area (Swings and a pets' corner) Menu/Portions Highchair Food warming Baby changing **Nearby:** Chester Zoo, Ellesmere Port, Blue Planet Aquarium **Notes:** Wooded area, nature reserve **Parking:** 70